Grosset's UNIVERSAL Library

THE WORLD OF
Aldous Huxley

AN OMNIBUS OF HIS FICTION

AND NON-FICTION OVER

THREE DECADES

EDITED AND WITH AN INTRODUCTION

BY CHARLES J. ROLO

Grosset's UNIVERSAL *Library*

NEW YORK, N. Y.

Contents

Introduction

By Charles J. Rolo

I

SOME time ago, a little book called *Modern Man Is Obsolete* created a considerable stir. Has man's power outstripped his wisdom? It is essentially the question that Aldous Huxley has been investigating for a quarter of a century—investigating with fabulous erudition and a dazzling style, with the varied gifts of a great comic artist who is, always and inescapably, a passionately serious thinker. Few living writers have more important things to say, and none says them more entertainingly.

This volume assembles a large collection of Mr. Huxley's best fiction, some of it out of print, and endeavors to reflect his adventures in negation and belief, in the course of which all the values of our lunatic civilization are submitted to a scathing and informed assessment. Huxley surveys a nightmare world with "multiplicity of eyes"—scientific, economic, artistic, philosophic; the amused eyes of a man of sense and the religious eyes of a modern mystic. "Literature," he says, "is also philosophy, is also science. In terms of beauty it enunciates truths." Whether or not the reader agrees with Mr. Huxley's conclusions, he cannot fail to find, in his sardonic scrutiny of the *condition humaine*, a profusion of particular truths. One by one Huxley punctures the "highly inflated balloons" of human stupidity —the out-of-date beliefs and the up-to-date substitutes for belief, the shams, prejudices and pretensions of homo *soi-disant* sapiens. In an essay on Ben Jonson, he wrote: "A little ruthless laughter clears the air as nothing else can do; it is good for us, every now and then, to see our ideals laughed at, our conception of nobility caricatured; it is good for human pomposity to be made to look mean and ridiculous . . . it is very good for most of us to be made uncomfortable." Turning a page in Huxley, you say, "There but for the grace of God. . . ."—and suddenly you wonder whether Divine Grace has intervened in time.

In *Crome Yellow*, there is this description of the imaginary Tales of Knockespotch:

> Fabulous characters shoot across its pages like gaily dressed performers on the trapeze. There are extraordinary adventures and still

vii

more extraordinary speculations. Intelligences and emotions . . .
move in intricate and subtle dances. . . . An immense erudition
and an immense fancy go hand in hand. All the ideas of the present
and past, on every possible subject, bob up among the Tales, smile
gravely or grimace a caricature of themselves, then disappear to make
place for something new. The verbal surface of his writing is rich
and fantastically diversified. The wit is incessant.

With omission of the "extraordinary adventures"—Huxley has written
superb narrative passages but he is not primarily a storyteller—the Tales
of Knockespotch sound like a bantering description of Huxley's own work.
"*Extraordinary speculations.*" Philip Quarles, the author-hero of *Point
Counter Point,* into whose notebook Huxley has packed a treatise on the
novel, observes: "Everything's incredible, if you can skin off the crust of
obviousness our habits put on it." Huxley does this by showing that the
everyday object, the commonplace event, is a lens through which the
meditative eye can look, as through a telescope, beyond the quotidian
view to unfamiliar horizons. "One sentence," says Quarles, "and I am
already involved in history, art and all the sciences. The whole story of
the universe is implicit in any part of it. Make the smell of roast duck
in an old kitchen diaphanous and you will have a glimpse of everything,
from the spiral nebulae to Mozart's music and the stigmata of St. Francis
of Assisi. Question: can this be achieved without pedantry?"
    Romain Rolland once said, improving Buffon's dictum: "*Le style
c'est l'âme.*" There is no pedantry in the soul of a writer whose daemon
pokes fun at his gifts as frequently as Huxley's does. Philip Quarles's wife
says to him: "Ah, if you were a little less of an overman, Phil, what good
novels you'd write." Francis Chelifer mockingly writes in *Those Barren
Leaves:* "Style pours from my fountain pen. . . . I apologize." Culture,
Huxley remarks, is really a classy form of "family gossip," and he adds,
"I enjoy writing that kind of gossip myself."
    "*An immense erudition and an immense fancy go hand in hand.*" Hux-
ley's command of learned fact endows him with a perfect grasp of the
striking analogy, the significant relationship: "A cow's pituitary will make
frogs breed out of season. Urine of a pregnant woman brings the mouse
on heat. Sheep's thyroid transforms the cretinous dwarf into a well-
grown and intelligent human being. Between one form of animal life and
another, patterns are interchangeable."
    His erudition is piloted by an irreverent fancy. Writing of modesty and
manners, he informs you that French kings held audience on the *chaise
percée.* Writing of mind and matter, he recalls that Mme. Guyon's

spiritual ecstasies were frequent and most spiritually significant in the fourth month of her pregnancies.

"*Ideas bob up, smile gravely or grimace.*" Into the fabric of his fiction Huxley has woven essays and paragraphs on subjects ranging from the Absolute to Zoology. Ideas "bob up" about love in crinolines, the longevity of carps, baroque style and Etruscan art; Proust in his bathtub and Dante in his Inferno; about population trends and popular songs ("the national anthems of Wombland"). The gardens of Srinagar set his mind ranging from horticulture to migrant birds, unemployment among college graduates, the categorical imperative, apophthegms and cracker mottoes, and Hindu totems. Applying past tense to present tension, he modulates on the theme, "Experientia docet. Experientia doesn't." With ruinous contempt he inveighs against nationalism, the cant of hero worship and the cult of efficiency; against the half-educated New Stupid, the degrading effects of popular entertainment, and a civilization in which man dances Petrouchka to the baleful music of the machine. "He writes," Grant Overton punned,[1] "not that he who runs may read, but he who reads may run." Where to? The condemned playground or the contemplative's oasis? You reads Mr. Huxley and you takes your choice.

II

Aldous Leonard Huxley was born on July 26, 1894, the third son (Julian, the scientist, being the eldest) of Dr. Leonard Huxley—teacher, editor and man of letters—and of Julia Arnold, niece of the poet, Matthew Arnold, and sister of the novelist, Mrs. Humphrey Ward. He is the grandson of T. H. Huxley, the scientist, and the great-grandson of Dr. Thomas Arnold, a formidable moralist.

Failing eyesight cut short Huxley's education at Eton and prevented him from becoming a doctor. Three years of almost total blindness, which spared him the conventional activities of English gentlemen, left him with a lasting bent for the reflective life. "My ambition and pleasure," he once wrote, "are to understand, not to act." He says he prefers freedom to household gods and solitude to "the agony of parties." He is more at home on the mental plane of existence than in the earthly paradise. Self-hindered by "an asceticism of the mind," he cannot surrender to "all the obviously luscious emotions" of the gregarious. When Philip Quarles reflects that his talent is not of the heart, the feelings, the sympathies, Huxley probably had in mind his own limitations. But this emotional aloofness is the source of other strengths—the sad clearness of vision, the

[1] *Cargoes and Crusaders* (Doubleday, Doran).

colossal intellectual vitality, the corrosive spirit of analysis—which give to
his talent its special character and luster. A writer should be judged by
what he has done; not by what he might have done, had he been an
altogether different sort of writer.

As soon as Huxley could see well enough to read through a magnifying
glass,[2] he went to Balliol College, Oxford, where he took First Class
Honors in English Literature. In 1916, A. L. Huxley, "young poet
unknown to fame," made his debut with *The Burning Wheel* (from
which "Mole" is reprinted here). During the last two years of the war, he
cut down trees and worked in a government office. He was married in
1919—to Maria Nys, a Belgian—and there followed years of "all-devouring
journalism": music, art and drama criticism, book reviews, articles on
house decoration and architecture.

Meanwhile Huxley had published three more volumes of poetry, *Jonah*,
The Defeat of Youth, and *Leda*, in which there is a curious alternation
between lyricism and iconoclastic verse that achieves bizarre effects with
the data and jargon of science. These early poems show the influence of
French masters, especially of Rimbaud, Corbière and Jules Laforgue, to
whose *"pierrot lunaire"*—the romantic pierrot orphaned by the moon—
Huxley was then compared by a critic. The lyrics, it seems to me, are
lacking in genuine poetic inspiration; the satiric verse (such as the Philosophers' Songs included in this volume) is clever, amusing, often startling.
"Wings . . . frail and misty" rhyme with "animal triste," "spermatozoa"
with "one poor Noah." Two lovers sit "in blissful calm/quietly sweating
palm to palm." This may be poetry of the conjuring-trick variety, but it
shows an original and accomplished hand.

Two volumes of short stories and two novels established Huxley's
reputation before he was thirty. Preferring "sunlight to literary company,"
he then settled in Italy for a number of years, and there formed a close
friendship with D. H. Lawrence during the last part of Lawrence's life.
Since the middle thirties, the Huxleys have lived in this country. Their
home is now in the California desert, some distance from Los Angeles.
Huxley's output to date totals more than thirty volumes, plus prefaces,
pamphlets, translations and innumerable contributions to periodicals. "I
never take a complete holiday," he says, "as I find that my health breaks
down as soon as I stop working. Holidays are healthful only to those who
dislike their work. I happen to find mine tolerably agreeable. My recrea-
tions are reading, painting and traveling." He seems to have read everything, seen everything, been almost everywhere.

[2] Thanks in part to the Bates method, described in *The Art of Seeing*, he can
now read without glasses.

"You are not your grandfather's *Enkel* for nothing," D. H. Lawrence once wrote to Aldous with reference to Grandfather Huxley, ally of Darwin and scourge of theologians, who rained explosives on the "buttresses of superstition." He bequeathed to his grandson's generation a disquieting scientific materialism and to Aldous what Lawrence called his "desperate courage of repulsion and repudiation," which fiercely repudiated superstitions, old and new, but was also repelled by the fruits of science and presently repudiated materialism. Grandfather abandoned an experiment in vegetarianism because it diminished his mental firepower; his *Enkel*, agreeing that butcher's meat has martial properties, prescribes for that reason the Buddhist's diet of vegetables. In place of "superstition," T. H. Huxley offered Victorian England the scientist's consolation prize: inevitable progress. Aldous affirms that technological advance is spiritual regression to the death-without-tears of *Brave New World*. To a community made safe for gadgets, he opposes a community made safe for God.

Lawrence's reference to Aldous Huxley's heredity today recalls Dr. Arnold, who struggled to inject religious principle into literature and English schoolboys; whose friends marveled, says Lytton Strachey, at his "absolute wrestling with evil." Dr. Arnold's great-grandson *has* injected religious principle into the modern novel and he too has wrestled with the problem of evil. It would seem that both ancestors have lived on and waged a fierce vendetta of ideas in the mortal coils of Aldous Huxley— sceptic, moralist and artist.

III

"Passion and reason, self-division's cause." It is a persistent Huxleyan theme and a key to his own work. His sympathies, he disclosed in an essay on Pascal, leaned even then (1927) toward the "Pascalian," the moralist and mystic. His reason, which found the positivist role "only too easy to play," was on Grandfather Huxley's side of the fence. It spoke for that "second me" of which Alphonse Daudet once said: "The second me, I have never been able to intoxicate, to make shed tears, to lull to sleep. And how it delves into things, and how it mocks!"

When Huxley came of age, human behavior, it seemed to the modernist, was entirely explicable in terms of Libido, Instinct, glandular function or conditioned reflex. Science and psychology had substituted for the Absolute the atom, for the soul the complex, for virtue and vice the inscrutable hormone. It was by a "conjuring trick," Huxley concluded (in the essay on Pascal), that man, out of his longing for certainty and justification, had deduced "all the Gods and Goods, all the Truths and

Beauties . . . of a bewildered humanity." But to the Pascalian, the materialist's picture of man and the cosmos was squalid and incomplete. While repudiating the Gods and Goods, Huxley implicitly continued to search for them, applying to the task an integrity that bit like acid through illusion, sentimentality and convention. All his work is a quest for values in the face of scepticism battening at the vitals of belief; for meaning amid the pointlessness; for freedom amid "the fact of slavery"—bondage to institutions, to time and the ego, to the limitations of a body "at the mercy of one's skin and mucus. At the mercy of those thin threads of nerve."

The rebellious sceptic is a wrecker of false idols. The Pascalian, surveying the barren altars, is a rebel against "Omnipresent Nil." This mocking, half-detached desolation is a corrosive solvent to satire. Huxley's is pitched in a variety of keys. There is a terrible farce. There is despairing buffoonery like that of the "mild and melancholy" Gumbril (*Antic Hay*), who puts on cloak and beaver to play "the Complete Man," who stifles his frustration in learned chatter about "the marriage ceremonies of octopuses." But as with Hume when he despaired of philosophy, "cheerfulness keeps breaking in." Then Huxley's wit sparkles and stings; his fancy cuts elegant capers.

Contrast being the mainspring of satire, the ideal construction for the satirist is one that holds the reader, not so much by the sequence of events in time (the story), as by the startling effects that result from viewing related events simultaneously. Music achieves these effects by its abrupt transitions. The Diabelli variations, for example, contain "the whole range of thought and feeling, yet in organic relation to a ridiculous little waltz tune." Huxley's most important innovation as a craftsman has been the partial replacement of story with music.

All the novelist needs for the abrupt transitions is "a sufficiency of characters and parallel, contrapuntal plots." In *Antic Hay*, while Shearwater the physiologist is playing guinea pig in an absurd experiment, his neglected wife plays Madame Bovary on Mercaptan's Crébillon-haunted sofa and in the terrifying embrace of Coleman, the bearded Diabolist. While Gumbril Senior, the architect, translates his dreams into models of grandiose cities, Gumbril Junior dreams up ads for his pneumatic trousers.

Another musical form Huxley has used as effectively as counterpoint is modulation, achieved in prose by showing "several people falling in love, or dying or praying in different ways—dissimilars solving the same problem. Or vice versa." *Those Barren Leaves* modulates between the parallel amours of a middle-aged romanticist, an elderly cynic and a moron, two ingenuous twenty-year-olds and three self-conscious intellectuals. Another way of modulating is to consider the events of the story in their various aspects—emotional, scientific, religious, metaphysical, etc. Juxtapose, for example, acoustics and the music of Bach—as in the simultaneously esthetic and scientific account of a concert in *Point Counter Point*; juxtapose spiritual pretensions and economic facts—as when Burlap (in the same novel) interrupts his apostrophes to "Lady Poverty" to advise, expertly, on gramophone shares; juxtapose sex and philosophy—as when Calamy (*Those Barren Leaves*), in an *entr'acte* between love-making, discourses on the different modes in which his hand exists. Thus seen, reality looks exceedingly queer. Hence the pervading quality of irony in Huxley's work.

"I have a literary theory," he says, "that I must have a two-angled vision of all my characters. Either I try to show them as they feel themselves to be; or else I try to give two rather similar characters who throw light on each other." This double vision produces a brand of irony that cuts both ways. Usually the ironist intends the opposite of what he states. Huxley often intends both what he states and the opposite, distilling a sharper flavor from the simultaneity. In the restaurant conversation in the fourth chapter of *Antic Hay*, Lypiatt talks of ideals, Shearwater of kidneys, Mercaptan of the civilized middle way between "Homo au *naturel*" and "Homo à la H. G. Wells." Each punctures the other with arguments which, even when they reflect the author's opinions, have a sly rebound that heightens the speaker's grotesquerie.

From the neat antithesis to the odd and laughter-provoking word or phrase, the suggestive name, the satiric portrait—Huxley commands every device of the comic artist. "*Vivre—nos valets le feront pour nous.*" To the romantics, living was a coarse affair which Villiers de L'Isle-Adam relegated to footmen. In the essay on "Vulgarity in Literature" the odd quotation, insistently repeated like the humorous phrase of scherzo, builds a richly comic effect. It is a stylistic device that Huxley continually employs, with delightful results.

You can almost guess, from the sound of their names, the bombast of Casimir Lypiatt, the would-be Titan; the stoatishness of Mr. Stoyte; the Wildean propensities of Beppo Bowles; the foibles of Lady Giblet and Baron Badgery. And Pasteur Mercaptan, the mannered esthete with the rococo boudoir and the perfumed style—how appropriate that he should bear the name of a group of colorless fluids having (says Webster) "a strong, repulsive garlic odor."

Perhaps the most accomplished caricaturist in English prose of our time, Huxley puts human flummery and pretentiousness on parade in a crowded gallery of portraits, drawn with atrocious raillery or polite malice. Mrs. Wimbush dabbles in New Thought, the Occult and hypo-chondria: "I have the Infinite to keep in tune with. And then there's the next world and one's Aura, and Mrs. Eddy and saying you're not ill. . . . One's never dull for a moment." She casts horoscopes of race horses and football teams and places her bets at the bidding of the stars. Mr. Barbecue-Smith—best-selling author of *Pipelines to the Infinite*—is the *reductio ad absurdum* of the journalistic charlatan. Commanding trances at will, he lets the "Niagara of the Infinite" pump inspiration into his pen—cascades of "uplifting aphorisms." At thirty-eight he was a struggling journalist. Now . . . Proudly he exhibits himself, "like the two cats in the advertisement of Nestlé's milk. One black and thin, the other white, sleek and fat. Before Inspiration and After."

Often the portrait is achieved in a single epigrammatic phrase, the absurdity of a personage is compressed into a mannerism or physical peculiarity. Molly d'Exergillod—"A professional athlete of the tongue"; Grace Peddley—"She was almost too hospitable—she kept open bed, you know"; Spandrell—"When he smiles, it's like an appendicitis opera-tion with ironical corners." Jeremy Pordage "flutes." Beppo Bowles "fiz-zles." Miss Penny's brassy laugh makes her long earrings swing and rattle, like "corpses hanging in chains." Mr. Quarles Senior pronounces his *a*'s "as though a flock of sheep had broken loose in his vocabulary."

"Everyone's a walking tragedy and a walking farce at the same time. The man who slips on a banana skin and fractures his skull describes against the sky, as he falls, the most richly comic arabesque." Huxley has an extraordinary capacity to distill vials of wrathful humor out of things which he also regards as horrible. Modern man, modern civilization, frac-turing their skulls on the banana skins of stupidity, success worship and lust for power, describe, against Huxley's skyline, a richly comic arabesque.

IV

"The chief defeat of the novel of ideas," says Philip Quarles, "is that you must write about people who have ideas to express—which excludes all but about .01 percent of the human race." Huxley's characters, though individualized by satiric detail, are essentially embodiments of an attitude, mouthpieces for a set of ideas. The central figure is almost invariably a writer, a Hamletlike intellectual, who articulates Huxley's opinions and dilemmas. His foil is the sentimentalist in reverse (Spandrell, Chelifer, Mark Staithes), at once hypnotized and sickened by everyday reality, who, like today's Existentialist hero, makes a cult of his nausea. Other recurring types are: the disenchanted siren, forever confronted with "steppes of ennui" and the certainty that "tomorrow will be as awful as today" (Myra Viveash, Lucy Tantamount, etc.); the Victorian materialist (Mr. Scogan, Gumbril Senior, Mr. Cardan), a genial figure for whom Huxley seems to have once had a nostalgic sympathy; the elderly pedant (Quarles Senior, Beavis Senior, Jeremy Pordage), whom his creator detests; the (surprisingly) ethereal mother figure, who evokes the scent of lavender and the rustle of long skirts; and Huxley's *bête noire*, the type whose personality is simply an inflation of a single idea—life for passion's sake (Lillian Aldwinkle) or for wit's sake (Molly d'Exergillod)—theatrical romanticists like Casimir Lypiatt, or slimy hypocrites like Burlap. One more must be added: the man of wisdom (Mark Rampion, Dr. Miller, Mr. Propter, Bruno Rontini), who carries Huxley's positive message. Huxley himself has said that "People who can reel off neatly formulated notions aren't quite real. They're slightly monstrous." The admirable man in Huxley's novels is always slightly monstrous. Since his virtue is shown mainly by his ideas—he is only marginally involved in the action —he tends to remain *vox et praeterea nihil*.

Each of the previous types represents a set of ideas which are debunked and are used to debunk others. Huxley's idol smashing begins at home: the values of the intellectual and the artist are those he most systematically disparages. The so-called "higher life" of scholarship is simply "idea-mongering . . . a more complete escape from the responsibilities of living than alcohol or morphia. . . . Books are opium." When Denis, the young poet of *Crome Yellow*, holds forth on the beauty of words, Mr. Scogan suggests "a mental carminative." Art is "the last and silliest of the idols . . . the sweetest of the inebriants. . . . Art for Art's sake—halma for halma's sake."

If you would worship at the shrine of Reason, Huxley will marshal precedents to show that "the madman not the philosopher appeals to what is fundamental, the passion and the instincts." As for the notion that Revolution, Marxist or technological, brings liberty—"There was never," says Mr. Bojanus, "a greater swindle 'atched in the 'ole of 'istory!" Marx's dictatorship of the proletariat turned out to be Stalin's dictatorship to the proletariat. The freedom of shorter working hours has turned out to mean for most people the tyranny of imbecile distractions. Idealism, says Huxley, is usually "the noble toga that political gentlemen drape over their will to power." Fame seeking? "Compared with it pure sensuality is all but harmless." And Christianity? In America it seems to have been transformed "from a religion . . . into a system for the justification of wealth and the preachment of industrious respectability; from a system that condemned the Pharisee . . . into one that exalts the Pharisee above every other human type."

There is some justice in one critic's quip that Huxley makes the worst of both worlds. He uses science and psychology to debunk values rooted in the stubborn stupidity of custom and simultaneously he mocks at the conceits of the new gospels. "Filippo Lippi," he writes, "once had a bump of art. He is now an incestuous homo-sexualist with a bent toward anal-eroticism. . . . Fifty years from now . . . the current explanation [will be] something more fundamental even than feces and infantile incestuousness." "Dream," says one character in *Antic Hay*. "The world is inadmissible. It's altogether too late in the day. Dreams . . . they belonged to the Rostand epoch. *Le rêve*—ah! Now the word merely connotes Freud." It's also a bit late in the day for love. "If you aren't in love," says Calamy, "it's a mere experiment in applied physiology. . . . But if you are, it means that you become enslaved . . . in a way that's positively disgraceful." Love as *Liebe-Triebe, Cuore-Dolore*—to the modernist, pretty disgraceful. And love as applied physiology—at best, "twin cannibals in bedlam"; more often, merely a relief for "itch and ennui," or, as Helen Ledwidge says, "just hygiene."

Science which equates love and applied physiology, masterpieces and feces, which informs the poet that his "mind sublime [is] issued from the monkey's womb"—science itself dances a pretty pointless jig in Huxley's books. The laboratory in *Antic Hay* portrays the futility of the scientist's cosmos: "The cock into which Shearwater had engrafted an ovary came out, not knowing whether to crow or cluck. The beetles, who had had their heads cut off and replaced by the heads of other beetles, darted uncertainly about, some obeying their heads, some their genital organs." Shearwater himself, imprisoned in a Hot Box, is nightmarishly pedaling away on a stationary bicycle—to discover the effects of prolonged sweating. The data of such experiments are the only truths the modernist can accept, yet what do they tell him in terms of the Gods, the Goods, the Beauties they have displaced? "What's he to Hecuba?" chant the minstrels in a night club where Gumbril and Myra Viveash are dancing. And dolefully they answer, "Nothing at all."

Unable to pay homage to the traditional values, unable to see in the laws of science more than "stammering provisional theories" about one part of reality, Huxley has for twenty-five years grappled with the problem of the moral vacuum. It is a problem that is focal to our time, as evidenced by the popularity of such books as Liebman's *Peace of Mind*, Du Noüy's *Human Destiny*, Wylie's *Essay on Morals*—best sellers all; and by the palsy of the modern hero, a man "things are done to," as Wyndham

Lewis wrote of Hemingway's heroes. The father figure who laid down the law has been largely replaced either by the Kafkaesque son in search of a father, in search of the law, or by the escapist seeking, to quote Cyril Connolly's inspired pun, "a womb with a view." Wombland to the right, Anarchy to the left. Mr. Connolly goes on to enshrine the modernist's dilemma in the despairing aphorism: "Everything is a dangerous drug except reality, which is unendurable." How, then, should one live? Where to turn for principle?

Throughout Huxley's books one theme, which recurs crescendo, hints at the nature of the final solution. From the start, Huxley mobilized his prodigious intellectual virtuosity to puncture "the pathetic belief" in rationalism, in the values of the intellect as opposed to the animal senses and the spirit. Reason, weaker than passion, is a sorry guide to conduct —"Five words sum up every biography: *Video meliora proboque, deteriora sequor.*" Man often sees the good but needs must love the lowest. Still less can reason furnish an answer to the fundamental mysteries or explain away soul in terms of body, mind in terms of matter. "When you reflect that it's the human mind," says Calamy, "that has invented space, time and matter, picking them out of reality in a quite arbitrary fashion—can you attempt to explain a thing in terms of something it has invented itself?" God as $2+2=4$, Gumbril reflects in chapel. It just won't do. It was therefore to "Divine unreason" that Huxley looked for "the lost purpose and the vanished good." But before deciding to inhabit the mystic's oasis, he cultivated a variety of gardens.

V

The ghost of Laforgue's *"pierrot lunaire"* wanders in and out of Huxley's first novel, *Crome Yellow* (1921). There is a youthful glow in its pages, sparked by a touch of the fantastic—a tale of dwarfs, love on the parapets of Crome under the "gibbous" moon, and peacocks on the lawn. It is a charming overture that introduces one of Huxley's main themes: the inadequacy of the self-conscious intellectual. Denis, the young poet, is inept at human contacts, a failing ascribed to most of Huxley's heroes. "We are all," he reflects wistfully, "parallel straight lines." "Twenty tons of ratiocination" in books have crushed his spontaneity. What he aspires to is the joyful paganism of Anne. But then Anne was born a pagan; for the overeducated Denis to become one will be laborious, perhaps impossible. Here, lightly treated, is the basic problem of *Point Counter Point.*

Antic Hay (1923) dramatizes in terms of life the implications of scientific materialism. Nowhere else is Huxley's comic inventiveness so exuberantly sustained through overtones of desolation. Disoriented by science, like the beetles onto which Shearwater has engrafted new heads, Huxley's men and women pointlessly "dance the antic hay," trying to give Nil the slip in infantile pleasures and pursuits. "I glory in the name of earwig," says Gumbril—and stripped of his false beard behaves like one. "I wish I could recapture the deliciousness of raspberry syrup," sighs Myra Viveash. Each time the taxi drives through Piccadilly Circus on that nightmarish "Last Ride," Myra leans out to watch the flickering sky signs. "They're me," she says expiringly. "Those things are me."

Even in the early twenties, there existed in Huxley a core of mystical feeling. Gumbril becomes conscious in the night of "a crystal quiet . . . inexpressibly lovely," an interior universe in which the demon Nil is exorcised. It is this universe that Calamy, hero of *Those Barren Leaves* (1925), eventually decides to explore in solitude, hoping that he may "burrow [his] way right through the mystery [to] some kind of truth, some explanation." He had previously experimented with the life of Reason, an Epicurean cultivation of body and mind in which the day ends with "three hours' meditation about the Absolute, and then bed, not unaccompanied." But in the interval between a French chef's master-piece of maigre cooking and the night of amorous repose, the Absolute will not yield its significance. Calamy abandons the ideal of graceful compromise for the discipline of the mystics.

To the would-be mystic, Huxley opposes Francis Chelifer, a poet, whose answer to the "horrors and squalors of civilized life" is self-immola-tion in "the navel of reality"—a suburban boarding house and editorship of the *Rabbit Fanciers' Gazette*. Chelifer insists that Calamy has no right to escape from what for ninety-nine out of every hundred human beings is reality. Calamy replies: "One has a right to be six foot nine inches high. Why hasn't one the right to a mind that can't be content with the surface-life of appearances?"

In *Point Counter Point* (1928) Huxley repudiated mysticism, to which he returned eight years later, and championed a doctrine of "life-worship" inspired by the Greeks, by Blake, and the "noble savagery" of D. H. Lawrence, after whom the character of Mark Rampion is modeled. Here he achieved a novel of the same stature as (and of far greater appeal than) André Gide's masterpiece, *The Counterfeiters*, which is similar to it in structure and doctrine.

Point Counter Point, from which I have pieced into a more or less self-contained narrative some of the most striking passages, is a richer orches-tration of the themes in Huxley's earlier work. Lord Edward Tantamount epitomizes the futility of science: hatching "asymmetrical tadpoles" in a glass tank is as irrelevant to the problems of living as Shearwater's point-less pedaling. He himself is not quite human, a "fossil child." His assistant, Illidge, a militant Communist, is one of several variations on the theme of self-division: his Communism is rooted in Marxian deter-minism which, as a scientist, he knows to be fifty years out of date. Walter is another victim of "passion and reason." He is obsessively in love—"*quia turpe, quia indignum*"—with Lucy, "a bored and perfumed imita-tion of a savage," who reintroduces the "bitch" motif. She is a sadistic reincarnation of Myra Viveash, hell-bent on giving Nil the slip in pro-gressively intenser pleasures. "The deathly sort of liveliness," she says, "is the most lively, really." She craves, à la Maurice Barrès, "*du sang, de la volupté, et de la mort.*" Meanwhile, there are bullfights: "Twenty thou-sand simultaneous sadistic *frissons.*"

The trouble with Lucy and Walter and the rest—Spandrell, the "little Stavrogin," Burlap, the fake Franciscan, Webley, the strutting Fuehrer —is, says their creator, that they are not in any real sense adults. Walter is a mother's boy who sobs on the shoulder of one mistress, worships at the feet of another. Spandrell's sadism is a childish revenge on his mother for her second marriage. Webley is still playing soldiers. Lucy is still pulling legs off flies—her victims happen to be lovesick young men. Burlap enjoys nothing better than a romp in the bathtub with the frightened virgin he has seduced. They are representatives of an age that "invented Peter Pan and raised that monstrosity of arrested development to the rank of an ideal"—the ideal that caused Scott Fitzgerald to write bitterly: "There are no second acts in American lives." Arrested development (or pro-longed infantilism), which Hollywood has made epidemic, now engages the attention even of the mass magazines, which have subventioned psychiatrists to analyze the bull market in divorce and neurosis. Prolonged infantilism is becoming recognized as the *mal du siècle*, a less class-conscious palsy than the romantic spleen of an era that had not yet unearthed and contaminated the "little man."

Self-division, infantilism is the harsh "point" to which the "wholeness" of Mark Rampion provides the answering counterpoint. The Good Life he preaches is a Blakean synthesis of reason, feeling and instinct, which harmonizes and includes the claims of body and heart as well as of intellect and spirit.

This remains the official Huxleyan doctrine until *Eyeless in Gaza.* Huxley himself expressed doubts as to whether taste and instinct did not make him "congenitally incapable" of giving the Lawrencean emphasis to heart and blood. Although he wrote at this time a caustic essay about Swift's hatred of the body—"the harmless necessary tripes"—Huxley's books suggest that he himself is easily repelled by physical phenomena. There is a strong element of shame and *Schaudern* in most of his sex scenes. Illness in its mildest forms fills him with nausea. And when he quotes Odo of Cluny's reference to the body as "a bag of muck," one suspects that he does not entirely disagree with the fastidious Bishop.

During the next four years Huxley published two volumes of essays, *Do What You Will* (1929) and *Music at Night* (1931), represented here by "Fashions in Love," "Meditation on El Greco," "Sermons in Cats" and three sections from "Vulgarity in Literature"; *The Cicadas and Other Poems* (1929), of which four are included; and a volume of stories, *Brief Candles* (1930), from which I have chosen the short novel, *After the Fireworks*, one of the most attractive things Huxley has written.

Brave New World (1932) was not so much a book of prophecy as a fable which satirically dramatized the choice between a return to primitivism (advocated by Lawrence) and a forward march toward the scientific and industrialized Utopia. The Savage, a child of the Brave New World who, through an accident, grew up among the Pueblo Indians, is restored to a civilization where babies are decanted from bottles, happiness is mass-produced by sleep-hypnosis and sustained by Feelies, Scent Organs and soma, the perfect drug ("All the advantages of Christianity and alcohol; none of their defects"). He finds chemically pure contentment detestable, the absence of morality, danger and beauty a privation. For in the Brave New World, God and Good have been abolished—they are unnecessary since "everybody's happy nowadays." Reading and solitude have been abolished—they reduce gadget consumption. Truth-seeking is taboo and pure science muzzled—they are a menace to Stability. Stability is all of the Ten Commandments and "Our Ford" is its prophet.

The Savage is clearly speaking for Huxley when he fiercely repudiates the Brave New World. But the conclusion shows that it's too late in the day for noble savagery. The Savage, his native *Penitente*-ism inflamed by the unzipped charms of the pneumatic new woman, is driven to maniacal self-torture and suicide.

A visit to Central America (*Beyond the Mexique Bay*, 1934) confirmed Huxley's doubts about the animal innocence of primitive man. He found the noble savage ignoble, Lawrence's faith in blood too costly in terms of spirit, and his *Plumed Serpent* a testament to "the hopeless psychological squalor of human beings who have not yet reached the spiritual and mental stage of consciousness." "The advance from primitivism to civilization," Huxley wrote, "is a progress whose price is fixed. . . . I thought once that it was possible to make very nearly the best of both worlds. But this, I believe, was a delusion." For Lawrence, the animal purpose sufficed. But Lawrence had never looked through a microscope at "the awful unconsciousness" of primal biological energy. Not content with "mere energy . . . that for all its mysterious divineness was yet beneath good and evil," Huxley turned back to the interior universe which Calamy had set out to explore.

Eyeless in Gaza (1936) is Huxley's first statement of a personal religion, arrived at by direct experience and therefore immune to sceptical erosion. The title refers to Samson, blind and a slave, who with God's strength tore down the house of the Philistines. In brief, Huxley preaches "nonattachment" as the means to union with the spiritual reality underlying the phenomenal world—"a form of life more intense . . . richer and of finer quality than ordinary life." "Good," Anthony Beavis reflects, "is what makes for unity. . . . Evil is the accentuation of division. Pride, hatred, anger—the essentially evil sentiments . . . because they are all intensifications of separateness." Huxley's credo is therefore also pacifist. Since separateness is the condition of individual life, evil is inherent in reality on the human level. But there is a way—that of the contemplatives—of transcending separateness, which is rooted in selfhood. Huxley warns, however, that "The contemplative life can be made a kind of high-brow substitute for Marlene Dietrich; a subject for erotic musings in the twilight. Meditation—valuable only as a means for effecting desirable changes in the mode of existence. To live contemplatively is to live in London, but to live there in noncockney style."

Paradoxically, the discovery of a faith leads Huxley to cultivate what Gide called "the art of being disagreeable." "To disturb," Gide once said, "That is my role," and it is doubtless Huxley's intent. The satire is hereafter more bitter; each of the characters, with few exceptions, achieves a detestable perfection in his particular brand of rottenness. The harsh point of *Eyeless in Gaza* is the gruesome description of Helen's abortion, the tragic suicide of Brian Foxe, the hideous amputation performed on Mark Staithes, the symbolism of a dog that falls from a passing plane, drenching in its blood two naked lovers on a rooftop. Such events belong, says Huxley elsewhere, "to the very essence of the world in which we elect to live." By intensifying the harshness of the point, he points up the nemesis that waits on wrongdoing.

"Mysticism?" Huxley quotes a certain Eminence as saying, "What you mean is misty schism." The prelate was doubtless concerned with dogma, but the pun has its point in reference to literature. For mistiness is inescapable when what the writer wishes to express is inexpressible. "The only vocabulary at our disposal," says Mr. Propter in Huxley's next novel, "is a vocabulary primarily intended for thinking strictly human thoughts about strictly human concerns. What we want to talk about are non-human realities." The writer seeking to convey mystical experience to the nonmystic is in the position of someone trying to describe music to a man born deaf. And that is only one half of Mr. Huxley's dilemma. The other half is the problem of integrating message and story, of devising a dramatic interplay between the mystic, whose characteristics are serenity and nonattachment, and unregenerate men and women, whose characteristics are excitement and craving—which, as Huxley pointed out in *Brave New World*, constitute the raw material of nine tenths of all art. From the writer's point of view, mystic and nonmystic are almost as fire and water. They may meet but they cannot easily be made to mix, and it seems unlikely that they would be inclined to mate. Huxley has stated the problem with candor; he has not, for all his command of ways and means, solved it. The contemplative sage in the last two novels plays a marginal role. The novel, qua work of art, suffers from marginalia.

The fifth section of this volume contains extracts from five of Huxley's six most recent books. These selections summarize his views on human freedom and divine Reality, the changes desirable in the structure of government and industry, the relationship between politics and religion, the responsibilities of science—in short, the means to ends saner than atomic extinction. It was not possible in a single volume, without heavy sacrifice of the fiction, to assemble this picture of Huxley's views on the world today in the form of five complete chapters. I therefore had no choice but to employ scissors on an author whose work is generally beyond addition or subtraction. In the cutting and piecing together, great care has been taken to preserve the continuity of Mr. Huxley's ideas. Should there be, notwithstanding, any uneasy transitions, the fault is entirely mine.

VI

Huxley's mystical-pacifist credo and its social implications are first set forth in detail in *Ends and Means* (1937), which is also "a kind of practical cookery book of reform." Huxley defines the ideal man as one who is "nonattached to his bodily sensations [and] exclusive loves. Non-attached to wealth, fame, social position. Nonattached even to science, art, speculation, philanthropy. For, like patriotism, in Nurse Cavell's phrase, 'they are not enough.'" The social context most congenial to this ideal is, Huxley argues, decentralization and self-government in politics and industry—genuine democracy as opposed to State Socialism or Capitalism, which concentrate power in the hands of political and economic bosses.

After Many a Summer Dies the Swan (1940) is a lively story about man's age-old wish to live forever, with digressions on time and the ego as a moral reading on the text. The setting is the Hollywood-Gothic castle of a California millionaire, with chromium-plated drawbridge, Second Empire bar, soda fountain in the Louis Quinze boudoir, thirteenth-century stained-glass windows in the lavatories, and a replica of the Grotto of Lourdes by the tennis court. Huxley casts a searing eye at the batty flora and fauna of Los Angeles, then spins a fantastic plot around the brutish tycoon who hires a scientist to prolong his life—and discovers he can live to be an ape.

The commentary is supplied by Mr. Propter, who brings into clearer focus the ideas of Anthony Beavis. Good, he explains, exists below the human level, as proper functioning of the animal organism (roughly Lawrence's credo); and above it on the level of spirit, as the experience of eternity, the knowledge of God—"a being"—Huxley quotes Tauler's definition—"withdrawn from creatures, a free power, a pure working." Good lies outside of time, which is the very "raw material of evil"; outside of personality, which, as Spinoza held, is "human bondage." Ideals are "merely the projection, on an enormously enlarged scale, of some aspect of personality"—the sacrifice of one set of personal passions for another set—and therefore the work of the devil. "It's a matter of experience and observation," says Mr. Propter, "that most idealism leads to war, persecution and mass insanity."

This theme Huxley exemplifies in the life of Father Joseph, Cardinal Richelieu's *Grey Eminence* (1940). Patriotism was perhaps the only passion not mastered by the almost saintly Capuchin, who rose daily at four to spend two hours in meditation, went about barefoot, scorned wealth and honors. Patriotism made him the most baleful figure in Europe, the architect of a vast Gestapo and the Machiavellian foreign minister who used every underhand stratagem to prolong the horrors of the Thirty Years War—one of the most fatally important links in the chain of disaster leading to August 1914 and September 1939.

In *Time Must Have a Stop* (1944), the story commutes between London, Florence and eternity. The harsh point is "disaster following on the heels of good intention." The answering counterpoint: "There's only one corner of the universe you can be sure of improving, and that's your own self . . . [by] the sacrifice of self-will to make room for knowledge of God."

Huxley's hero, Sebastian Barnack, an adolescent poet with the looks of a "Della Robbia angel," spends a holiday in Italy with his Uncle Eustace, discovers the *estasi dell'amore*, and in his efforts to obtain a dinner jacket brings disaster on a saintly old man, Bruno Rontini. Meanwhile Uncle Eustace dies, because he lived too well, and floating in eternity supplies a God's-eye view of the human comedy. Convulsed with sardonic mirth at the grotesquerie of mankind, he nevertheless fights against surrendering his human identity to the divine light; keeps that ridiculous identity alive with the memory of fragrant cigars, limericks, Proust and the *poses intimes* of an Italian tart. In the Epilogue, Sebastian, maimed by the war and spiritually awakened by the dying Rontini, expounds in his notebook the basic tenets of a modern mystic's religion.

For the reader willing to grapple with first sources, Huxley published, in 1945, *The Perennial Philosophy*: an anthology of the teachings of the mystics with explanatory comments. *Philosophia Perennis*—the phrase was coined by Leibniz—is "the metaphysic that recognizes a divine Reality substantial to the world of things and lives and minds; the psychology that finds in the soul something similar to, even identical with, divine Reality; the ethic that places man's final end in the knowledge of the immanent and transcendent Ground of all being." It is universal and immemorial, the "Highest Common Factor" of all religions.

Fifty years ago Tolstoy wrote: "If the arrangement of society is bad (as ours is), and a small number of people have power over the majority and oppress it, every victory over Nature will inevitably serve only to increase that power and oppression." That, says Huxley in *Science, Liberty and Peace* (1946), is what has been happening ever since Tolstoy's day. The discoveries of pure science have been applied in the interests of private banking, mass-producing industry and centralized government; in the interests of nationalism, and therefore of war. The result has been concentration of power in the hands of the few, economic insecurity and decline of liberty for the many. Man as a moral, social and political being has been sacrificed to *homo faber*, man the forger of new gadgets. What Huxley prescribes is, broadly speaking, a restatement of the Emersonian doctrine of self-reliance. His specific recommendations are set forth in the last extract in this volume (What Can the Scientist Do?).

VII

It is not uncommon to hear Aldous Huxley spoken of, even by *aficionados*, as a sophisticated debunker who, having plumbed the depths of nihilism, made a jet-propelled take-off into the mystical stratosphere. This opinion is, I think, partly due to the fact that fashion, which so rap-

turously press-agented Huxley's early novels, has in the long run done
him an injustice. The shadow of the Pascalian was not reflected in the
portrait of the enfant terrible which fashion, in the twenties, painted
in its own image. The "unshakable sophistication" which delighted
Mencken and Scott Fitzgerald still gives glitter to Huxley's thought. But
"unshakable sophistication" coupled with "amateur in garbage," "cynic
in ragtime," "fastidious sensualist" (I quote from early reviews) conjures
up a Michael Arlen, a Carl Van Vechten—an elegant trifler engaged,
like Paul Morand, in compiling a Baedeker of the boudoir and cosmopolitan vice. That was Mr. Huxley's reward for being, despite his essential
seriousness, so unfailingly entertaining. As he notes in Music at Night:
"Because we all know how to read, we imagine that we know what we
read. Enormous fallacy!"

This review of Huxley's adventures in negation and belief has shown
that he was never satisfied with garbage collecting and the smashing of
idols; that early in his career he "chased the absolute in remote strange
regions" and seemed on the point of embracing mysticism at the conclusion of Those Barren Leaves. The sceptical esthete of the twenties
faced God and detected a "conjuring trick"; but he failed to outface man's
need for a God. Sceptic, esthete, satirist, stylistic virtuoso, encyclopedia of
scientific fact, columnist of the family gossip known as Culture, amateur
of the fantastic and expert in human folly—Huxley has been all of these
things. But his energizing impulse has always been, as it is now, preoccupation with the spirit of man.

The two Huxley brothers stand—as did their eminent ancestors—
at two extreme destinations which the intellectual can reach in an age
allergic to belief and uneasy in doubt. For Julian, "Freud in combination
with Darwin suffices." For Aldous, without divine Reality, life is "a tale
told by an idiot." The tale his books tell is a twentieth-century Pilgrim's
Progress, in which Darwin, Freud and their colleagues patrol the frontier
between the realm of ape men and the free state of God-men. He describes,
in richly comic arabesques, the antics of a generation which thought itself
to be the ape's offspring, a monkey on a string agitated by animal instinct.
He echoes our frustrations, articulates our dilemmas, chronicles our
struggle with the Janus-headed monster that has Time on one face and
Ego on the other. He has come close to writing a biography of the ideas
of modern man.

THE WORLD OF ALDOUS HUXLEY

I
NOVELS

ANTIC HAY

My men like satyrs grazing on the lawns
Shall with their goat-feet dance the antic hay.

MARLOWE

Chapter I

GUMBRIL, Theodore Gumbril Junior, B.A. Oxon, sat in his oaken stall on the north side of the School Chapel and wondered, as he listened through the uneasy silence of half a thousand schoolboys to the First Lesson, pondered, as he looked up at the vast window opposite, all blue and jaundiced and bloody with nineteenth-century glass, speculated in his rapid and rambling way about the existence and the nature of God.

Standing in front of the spread brass eagle and fortified in his convictions by the sixth chapter of Deuteronomy (for this first Sunday of term was the fifth after Easter), the Reverend Pelvey could speak of these things with an enviable certainty. "Hear, O Israel," he was booming out over the top of the portentous Book: "the Lord our God is one Lord."

One Lord; Mr. Pelvey knew; he had studied theology. But if theology and theosophy, then why not theography and theometry, why not theognomy, theotrophy, theotomy, theogamy? Why not theophysics and theochemistry? Why not that ingenious toy, the theotrope or wheel of gods? Why not a monumental theodrome?

In the great window opposite, young David stood like a cock, crowing on the dunghill of a tumbled giant. From the middle of Goliath's forehead there issued, like a narwhal's budding horn, a curious excrescence. Was it the embedded pebble? Or perhaps the giant's married life.

". . . . with all thine heart," declaimed the Reverend Pelvey, "and with all thy soul, and with all thy might."

No, but seriously, Gumbril reminded himself, the problem was very

3

troublesome indeed. God as a sense of warmth about the heart, God as exultation, God as tears in the eyes, God as a rush of power or thought —that was all right. But God as truth, God as 2+2=4—that wasn't so clearly all right. Was there any chance of their being the same? Were there bridges to join the two worlds? And could it be that the Reverend Pelvey, M.A., foghorning away from behind the imperial bird, could it be that he had an answer and a clue? That was hardly believable. Particularly if one knew Mr. Pelvey personally. And Gumbril did.

"And these words which I command thee this day," retorted Mr. Pelvey, "shall be in thine heart."

Or in the heart, or in the head? Reply, Mr. Pelvey, reply. Gumbril jumped between the horns of the dilemma and voted for other organs.

"And thou shalt teach them diligently to thy children, and shalt talk of them when thou sittest in thine house, and when thou walkest by the way, and when thou liest down, and when thou risest up."

Diligently to thy children . . . Gumbril remembered his own childhood; they had not been very diligently taught to him. "Beetles, black beetles"—his father had a really passionate feeling about the clergy. Mumbo-jumbery was another of his favorite words. An atheist and an anticlerical of the strict old school he was. Not that in any case he gave himself much time to think about these things; he was too busy being an unsuccessful architect. As for Gumbril's mother her diligence had not been dogmatic. She had just been diligently good, that was all. Good; good? It was a word people only used nowadays with a kind of deprecating humorousness. Good. Beyond good and evil? We are all that nowadays. Or merely below them, like earwigs? I glory in the name of earwig. Gumbril made a mental gesture and inwardly declaimed. But good in any case, there was no getting out of that, good she had been. Not nice, not merely *molto simpatica*—how charmingly and effectively these foreign tags assist one in the great task of calling a spade by some other name! —but good. You felt the active radiance of her goodness when you were near her . . . And that feeling, was that less real and valid than two plus two?

The Reverend Pelvey had nothing to reply. He was reading with a holy gusto of "houses full of all good things which thou fillest not, and wells digged, which thou diggedst not, vineyards and olive trees, which thou plantedst not."

She had been good and she had died when he was still a boy; died— but he hadn't been told that till much later—of creeping and devouring pain. Malignant disease—oh, *caro nome!*

"Thou shalt fear the Lord thy God," said Mr. Pelvey.

Even when the ulcers are benign; thou shalt fear. He had traveled up from school to see her, just before she died. He hadn't known that she was going to die, but when he entered her room, when he saw her lying so weakly in the bed, he had suddenly began to cry, uncontrollably. All the fortitude, the laughter even, had been hers. And she had spoken to him. A few words only; but they had contained all the wisdom he needed to live by. She had told him what he was, and what he should try to be, and how to be it. And crying, still crying, he had promised that he would try.

"And the Lord commanded us to do all these statutes," said Mr. Pelvey, "for our good always, that he might preserve us alive as it is at this day."

And had he kept his promise, Gumbril wondered, had he preserved himself alive?

"Here endeth the First Lesson." Mr. Pelvey retreated from the eagle and the organ presaged the coming Te Deum.

Gumbril hoisted himself to his feet; the folds of his B.A. gown billowed nobly about him as he rose. He sighed and shook his head with the gesture of one who tries to shake off a fly or an importunate thought. When the time came for singing, he sang. On the opposite side of the chapel two boys were grinning and whispering to one another behind their lifted Prayer Books. Gumbril frowned at them ferociously. The two boys caught his eye and their faces at once took on an expression of sickly piety; they began to sing with unction. They were two ugly, stupid-looking louts, who ought to have been apprenticed years ago to some useful trade. Instead of which they were wasting their own and their teachers' and their more intelligent comrades' time in trying, quite vainly, to acquire an elegant literary education. The minds of dogs, Gumbril reflected, do not benefit by being treated as though they were the minds of men.

"Oh Lord, have mercy upon us: have mercy upon us."

Gumbril shrugged his shoulders and looked round the chapel at the faces of the boys. Lord indeed have mercy upon us. He was disturbed to find the sentiment echoed on a somewhat different note in the Second Lesson which was drawn from the twenty-third chapter of St. Luke. "Father, forgive them," said Mr. Pelvey in his unvaryingly juicy voice; "for they know not what they do." Ah, but suppose one did know what one was doing? Suppose one knew only too well? And of course one always did know. One was not a fool.

But this was all nonsense, all nonsense. One must think of something better than this. What a comfort it would be, for example, if one could bring air cushions into chapel! These polished oaken stalls were devilishly hard; they were meant for stout and lusty pedagogues not for bony starvelings like himself. An air cushion, a delicious pneu.

"Here endeth," boomed Mr. Pelvey, closing his book on the back of the German eagle.

As if by magic, Dr. Jolly was ready at the organ with the *Benedictus*. It was positively a relief to stand again; this oak was adamantine. But air cushions, alas, would be too bad an example for the boys. Hardy young Spartans! it was an essential part of their education that they should listen to the word of revelation without pneumatic easement. No, air cushions wouldn't do. The real remedy, it suddenly flashed across his mind, would be trousers with pneumatic seats. For all occasions; not merely for churchgoing.

The organ blew a thin Puritan-preacher's note through one of its hundred nostrils. "I believe . . ." With a noise like the breaking of a wave, five hundred turned toward the East. The view of David and Goliath was exchanged for a Crucifixion in the grand manner of eighteen hundred and sixty. "Father forgive them; for they know not what they do." No, no, Gumbril preferred to look at the grooved stonework rushing smoothly up on either side of the great East window toward the vaulted roof; preferred to reflect, like the dutiful son of an architect he was, that Perpendicular at its best—and its best is its largest—is the finest sort of English Gothic. At its worst and smallest, as in most of the colleges of Oxford, it is mean, petty, and, but for a certain picturesqueness, almost wholly disgusting. He felt like a lecturer: next slide, please. "And the life everlasting. Amen." Like an oboe, Mr. Pelvey intoned: "The Lord be with you."

For prayer, Gumbril reflected, there would be Dunlop knees. Still, in the days when he had made a habit of praying, they hadn't been necessary. "Our Father . . ." The words were the same as they were in the old days; but Mr. Pelvey's method of reciting them made them sound rather different. Her dresses, when he had leaned his forehead against her knee to say those words—those words, good Lord! that Mr. Pelvey was oboeing out of existence—were always black in the evenings, and of silk, and smelled of orris root. And when she was dying, she had said to him: "Remember the Parable of the Sower, and the seeds that fell in shallow ground." No, no. Amen, decidedly. "O Lord, show thy mercy upon us," chanted oboe Pelvey, and Gumbril trombone responded, profoundly and grotesquely: "And grant us thy salvation." No, the knees were obviously less important, except for people like revivalists and housemaids, than the seat. Sedentary are commoner than genuflectory profes-

ability of glass, through breakages in general, to this particular broken vase; he practically forced his mother to repeat her question. And then, with a burst of tears, he had answered, yes. It had always been difficult for him to say things directly, point-blank. His mother had told him, when she was dying . . . No, no; not that.

In 1898 or 1899—oh, these dates!—he had made a pact with his little cousin, Molly, that she should let him see her with no clothes on, if he would do the same by her. She had fulfilled her part of the bargain; but he, overwhelmed at the last moment by a passion of modesty, had broken his promise.

Then, when he was about twelve and still at his preparatory school, in 1902 or 1903 he had done badly in his exams, on purpose; he had been frightened of Sadler, who was in the same form, and wanted to get the prize. Sadler was stronger than he was and had a genius for persecution. He had done so badly that his mother was unhappy; and it was impossible for him to explain.

In 1906 he had fallen in love for the first time—ah, much more violently than ever since—with a boy of his own age. Platonic it had been and profound. He had done badly that term, too; not on purpose, but because he had spent so much time helping young Vickers with his work. Vickers was really very stupid. The next term he had "come out" —*staphylococcus pyogenes* is a lover of growing adolescence—with spots and boils all over his face and neck. Gumbril's affection ceased as suddenly as it had begun. He finished that term, he remembered, with a second prize.

But it was time to be thinking seriously of Pio Nono. With a sigh of disgusted weariness, Gumbril looked at his papers. What had Falarope Major to say of the pontiff? "Pius IX was called Ferretti. He was a liberal before he was a Pope. A kindly man of less than average intelligence, he thought that all difficulties could be settled by a little good will, a few reforms and a political amnesty. He wrote several encyclicals and a syllabus." Gumbril admired the phrase about less than average intelligence; Falarope Major should have at least one mark for having learned it so well by heart. He turned to the next paper. Higgs was of opinion that "Pius the Ninth was a good but stupid man, who thought he could settle the Risorgimento with a few reforms and a political armistice." Beddoes was severer. "Pius IX was a bad man, who said that he was infallible which showed he had less than average intelligence." Sopwith Minor shared the general opinion about Pio's intelligence and displayed a great familiarity with the wrong dates. Clegg-Weller was voluminous and informative. "Pius IX was not so clever as his prime minister Cardinal Antonelli. When he came to the tiara he was a liberal and Metternich said he had never reckoned on a liberal pope. He then became a conservative. He was kindly, but not intelligent, and he thought Garibaldi and Cavour would be content with a few reforms and an amnesty." At the top of Garstang's paper was written: "I have had measles all the holidays, so have been unable to read more than the first thirty pages of the book. Pope Pius IX does not come into these pages, of the contents of which I will proceed to give the following précis." And the précis duly followed. Gumbril would have liked to give him full marks. But the businesslike answer of Appleyard called him back to a better sense of his duty. "Pius IX became Pope in 1846 and died in 1878. He was a kindly man but his intelligence was below the . . ."

Gumbril laid the paper down and shut his eyes. No, this was really impossible. Definitely, it couldn't go on, it could not go on. There were thirteen weeks in the summer term, there would be thirteen in the autumn and eleven or twelve in the spring; and then another summer of thirteen, and so it would go on forever. Forever. It wouldn't do. He would go away and live uncomfortably on his three hundred. Or, no, he would go away and he would make money—that was more like it—money on a large scale, easily; he would be free and he would live. For the first time, he would live. Behind his closed eyes, he saw himself living.

Over the plushy floors of some vast and ignoble Ritz slowly he walked, at ease, with confidence: over the plushy floors and there, at the end of a long vista, there was Myra Viveash, waiting, this time, for him; coming forward impatiently to meet him, his abject lover now, not the cool, free, laughing mistress who had lent herself contemptuously once to his pathetic and silent importunity and then, after a day, withdrawn the gift again. Over the plushy floors to dine. Not that he was in love with Myra any longer: but revenge is sweet.

He sat in his own house. The Chinese statues looked out from the niches; the Maillols passionately mediated, slept and were more than alive. The Goyas hung on the walls, there was a Boucher in the bathroom; and when he entered with his guests, what a Piazzetta exploded above the dining-room mantelpiece! Over the ancient wine they talked together, and he knew everything they knew and more; he gave, he inspired, it was the others who assimilated and were enriched. After dinner there were Mozart quartets; he opened his portfolios and showed his Daumiers, his Tiepolos, his Canaletto sketches, his drawings by Picasso and Lewis, and the purity of his naked Ingres. And later, talking of Odalisques, there were orgies without fatigue or disgust, and the women were pictures and lust in action, art.

Over the empty plains forty horses impelled him toward Mantua: rubadub—adubadub, with the silencer out. Toward the most romantic city in all the world.

When he spoke to women—how easily and insolently he spoke now!— they listened and laughed and looked at him sideways and dropped their eyelids over the admission, the invitation of their glance. With Phyllis once he had sat, for how long? in a warm and moonless darkness, saying nothing, risking no gesture. And in the end they had parted, reluctantly and still in silence. Phyllis now was with him once again in the summer night; but this time he spoke, now softly, now in the angry breathless whisper of desire, he reached out and took her, and she was naked in his arms. All chance encounters, all plotted opportunities recurred; he knew, now, how to live, how to take advantage of them.

Over the empty plains toward Mantua, toward Mantua, he slid along at ease, free and alone. He explored the horrors of Roman society; visited Athens and Seville. To Unamuno and Papini he conversed familiarly in their own tongues. He understood perfectly and without effort the quantum theory. To his friend Shearwater he gave half a million for physiological research. He visited Schoenberg and persuaded him to write still better music. He exhibited to the politicians the full extent of their stupidity and their wickedness; he set them working for the salvation not the destruction of humanity. Once in the past when he had been called upon to make a public speech, he had felt so nervous that he was sick; the thousands who listened to him now bent like wheat under the wind of his eloquence. But it was only by the way and occasionally that he troubled himself to move them. He found it easy now to come to terms with everyone he met, to understand all points of view, to identify himself with even the most unfamiliar spirit. And he knew how everybody lived and what it was like to be a mill girl, a dustman, an engine driver, a Jew, an Anglican bishop, a confidence trickster. Accustomed as he was to being swindled and imposed upon without protest, he now knew the art of being brutal. He was just dressing down that insolent porter at the Continental, who had complained that ten francs wasn't enough (and had got, as a matter of historic fact, another five in addition) when his land-lady gave a knock, opened the door and said: "Dinner's ready, Mr. Gumbril."

Feeling a little ashamed at having been interrupted in what was, after all, one of the ignobler and more trivial occupations of his new life, Gumbril went down to his fatty chop and green peas. It was the first meal to be eaten under the new dispensation; he ate it, for all that it was unhappily indistinguishable from the meals of the past, with elation and a certain solemnity, as though he were partaking of a sacrament. He felt buoyant with the thought that at last, at last, he was doing something about life.

When the chop was eaten, he went upstairs and, after filling two suitcases and a gladstone bag with the most valued of his possessions, addressed himself to the task of writing to the Headmaster. He might have gone away, of course, without writing. But it would be nobler, more in keeping, he felt, with his new life, to leave a justification behind— or rather not a justification, a denouncement. He picked up his pen and denounced.

Chapter II

GUMBRIL SENIOR occupied a tall, narrow-shouldered and rachitic house in a little obscure square not far from Paddington. There were five floors, and a basement with beetles, and nearly a hundred stairs, which shook when any one ran too rudely down them. It was a prematurely old and decaying house in a decaying quarter. The square in which it stood was steadily coming down in the world. The houses, which a few years ago had all been occupied by respectable families, were now split up into squalid little maisonettes, and from the neighboring slums, which along with most other unpleasant things the old bourgeois families had been able to ignore, invading bands of children came to sport on the once sacred pavements.

Mr. Gumbril was almost the last survivor of the old inhabitants. He liked his house and he liked his square. Social decadence had not affected the fourteen plane trees which adorned its little garden, and the gambols of the dirty children did not disturb the starlings who came, evening by evening in summertime, to roost in their branches.

On fine evenings he used to sit out on his balcony waiting for the coming of the birds. And just at sunset, when the sky was most golden, there would be a twittering overhead and the black, innumerable flocks of starlings would come sweeping across on the way from their daily haunts to their roosting places, chosen so capriciously among the tree-planted squares and gardens of the city and so tenaciously retained, year after year, to the exclusion of every other place. Why his fourteen plane trees should have been chosen Mr. Gumbril could never imagine. There were plenty of larger and more umbrageous gardens all round; but they remained birdless, while every evening, from the larger flocks, a faithful legion detached itself to settle clamorously among his trees. They sat and chattered till the sun went down and twilight was past, with intervals every now and then of silence that fell suddenly and inexplicably on all the birds at once, lasted through a few seconds of thrilling suspense, to end as suddenly and senselessly in an outburst of the same loud and simultaneous conversation.

The starlings were Mr. Gumbril's most affectionately cherished friends; sitting out on his balcony to watch and listen to them, he had caught at the shut of treacherous evenings many colds and chills on the liver, he had laid up for himself many painful hours of rheumatism. These little accidents did nothing, however, to damp his affection for the birds; and still on every evening that could possibly be called fine, he was always to be seen in the twilight, sitting on the balcony, gazing up, round-spectacled and rapt, at the fourteen plane trees. The breezes stirred in his gray hair, tossing it up in long, light wisps that fell across his forehead and over his spectacles; and then he would shake his head impatiently and the bony hand would be freed for a moment from its unceasing combing and clutching of the sparse gray beard to push back the strayed tendrils, to smoothe and reduce to order the whole ruffled head. The birds chattered on, the hand went back to its clutching and combing; once more the wind blew; darkness came down and the gas lamps round the square lit up the outer leaves of the plane trees, touched the privet bushes inside the railings with an emerald light; behind them was impenetrable night; instead of shorn grass and bedded geraniums there was mystery, there were endless depths. And the birds at last were silent.

Mr. Gumbril would get up from his iron chair, stretch his arms and his stiff cold legs and go in through the French window to work. The birds were his diversion; when they were silent, it was time to think of serious matters.

Tonight, however, he was not working; for always on Sunday evenings, his old friend Porteous came to dine and talk. Breaking in unexpectedly at midnight, Gumbril Junior found them sitting in front of the gas fire in his father's study.

"My dear fellow, what on earth are you doing here?" Gumbril Senior jumped up excitedly at his son's entrance. The light silky hair floated up with the movement, turned for a moment into a silver aureole, then subsided again. Mr. Porteous stayed where he was, calm, solid and undisheveled as a seated pillar box. He wore a monocle on a black ribbon, a black stock tie that revealed above its double folds a quarter of an inch of stiff white collar, a double-breasted black coat, a pair of pale checked trousers and patent-leather boots with cloth tops. Mr. Porteous was very particular about his appearance. Meeting him casually for the first time, one would not have guessed that Mr. Porteous was an expert on Late Latin poetry; and he did not mean that you should guess. Thin limbed, bent and agile in his loose, crumpled clothes, Gumbril Senior had the air, beside Mr. Porteous, of a strangely animated scarecrow.

"What on earth?" the old gentleman repeated his question.

Gumbril Junior shrugged his shoulders. "I was bored, I decided to cease being a schoolmaster." He spoke with a fine airy assumption of carelessness. "How are you, Mr. Porteous?"

"Thank you, invariably well."

"Well, well," said Gumbril Senior sitting down again, "I must say I'm not surprised. I'm only surprised that you stood it, not being a born pedagogue, for as long as you did. What ever induced you to think of turning usher I can't imagine." He looked at his son first through his spectacles, then over the top of them, the motives of the boy's conduct revealed themselves to neither vision.

"What else was there for me to do?" asked Gumbril Junior, pulling up a chair toward the fire. "You gave me a pedagogue's education and washed your hands of me. No opportunities, no openings. I had no alternative: And now you reproach me."

Mr. Gumbril made an impatient gesture. "You're talking nonsense," he said. "The only point of the kind of education you had is this, it gives a young man leisure to find out what he's interested in. You apparently weren't sufficiently interested in anything . . ."

"I am interested in everything," interrupted Gumbril Junior.

"Which comes to the same thing," said his father parenthetically, "as being interested in nothing." And he went on from the point at which he had been interrupted. "You weren't sufficiently interested in anything to want to devote yourself to it. That was why you sought the last refuge of feeble minds with classical educations, you became a schoolmaster."

"Come, come," said Porteous. "I do a little teaching myself, I must stand up for the profession."

Gumbril Senior let go his beard and brushed back the hair that the wind of his own vehemence had brought tumbling into his eyes. "I don't denigrate the profession," he said. "Not at all. It would be an excellent profession if everyone who went into it were as much interested in teaching as you are in your job, Porteous, or I in mine. It's these undecided creatures like Theodore, who ruin it by drifting in. Until all teachers are geniuses and enthusiasts, nobody will learn anything, except what they teach themselves."

"Still," said Mr. Porteous, "I wish I hadn't had to learn so much by

"Monstrous," put in Gumbril Senior, with a genuine indignation, "monstrous these medieval survivals in schools. Chapel, indeed!"

"It came," Gumbril Junior went on, "like an apocalypse, suddenly, like a divine inspiration. A grand and luminous idea came to me—the idea of Gumbril's Patent Small Clothes."

"And what are Gumbril's Patent Small Clothes?"

"A boon to those whose occupation is sedentary;" Gumbril Junior had already composed his prospectus and his first advertisements, "a comfort to all travelers, civilization's substitute for steatopygism, indispensable to first-nighters, the concertgoers' friend, the . . ."

"Lectulus Dei floridus," intoned Mr. Porteous.
"Gazopyhlacium Ecclesiæ,
Cithara benesonans Dei,
Cymbalum jubilationis Christi,
Promptuarium mysteriorum fidei, ora pro nobis.

Your small clothes sound to me very like one one of my old litanies, Theodore."

"We want scientific descriptions, not litanies," said Gumbril Senior. "What are Gumbril's Patent Small Clothes?"

"Scientifically, then," said Gumbril Junior, "my Patent Small Clothes may be described as trousers with a pneumatic seat, inflatable by means of a tube fitted with a valve; the whole constructed of stout seamless red rubber, enclosed between two layers of cloth."

"I must say," said Gumbril Senior on a tone of somewhat grudging approbation, "I have heard of worse inventions. You are too stout, Porteous, to be able to appreciate the idea. We Gumbrils are all a bony lot."

"When I have taken out a patent for my invention," his son went on, very businesslike and cool, "I shall either sell it to some capitalist, or I shall exploit it commercially myself. In either case, I shall make money, which is more, I may say, than you or any other Gumbril have ever done."

"Quite right," said Gumbril Senior, "quite right," and he laughed very cheerfully. "And nor will you. You can be grateful to your intolerable Aunt Flo for having left you that three hundred a year. You'll need it. But if you really want a capitalist," he went on, "I have exactly the man for you. He's a man who has a mania for buying Tudor houses and making them more Tudor than they are. I've pulled half a dozen of the wretched things to pieces and put them together again differently for him."

"He doesn't sound much good to me," said his son.

"Ah, but that's only his vice. Only his amusement. His business," Gumbril Senior hesitated.

"Well, what is his business?"

"Well, it seems to be everything. Patent medicine, trade newspapers, bankrupt tobacconist's stock—he's talked to me about those and heaps more. He seems to flit like a butterfly in search of honey, or rather money."

"And he makes it?"

"Well, he pays my fees and he buys more Tudor houses and he gives me luncheons at the Ritz. That's all I know."

"Well, there's no harm in trying."

"I'll write to him," said Gumbril Senior. "His name is Boldero. He'll either laugh at your idea, or take it and give you nothing for it. Still," he looked at his son over the top of his spectacles, "if by any conceivable chance you ever should become rich, if, if, if . . ." And he emphasized the remoteness of the conditional by raising his eyebrows a little higher, by throwing out his hands in a dubious gesture a little further at every repetition of the word, "if—why, then I've got exactly the thing for you. Look at this really delightful little idea I had this afternoon." He put his hand in his coat pocket and after some sorting and sifting produced a sheet of squared paper on which was roughly drawn the elevation of a house. "For anyone with eight or ten thousand to spend, this would be—this would be . . ." Gumbril Senior smoothed his hair and hesitated, searching for something strong enough to say of his little idea—"well, this would be much too good for most of the greasy devils who do have eight or ten thousand to spend."

He passed the sheet to Gumbril Junior, who held it out so that both Mr. Porteous and himself could look at it. Gumbril Senior got up from his chair and, standing behind them, leaned over to elucidate and explain.

"You see the idea," he said, anxious lest they should fail to understand. "A central block of three stories, with low wings of only one, ending in pavilions with a second floor. And the flat roofs of the wings are used as gardens—you see?—protected from the north by a wall. In the east wing there is the kitchen and the garage, with the maids' rooms in the pavilion at the end. The west is a library, and it has an arcaded loggia along the front. And instead of a solid superstructure corresponding to the maids' rooms, there's a pergola with brick piers. You see? And in the main block there's a Spanish sort of balcony along the whole length at first-floor level; that gives a good horizontal line. And you get the perpendiculars with coigns and raised panels. And the roof's hidden by a balustrade, and there are balustrades along the open sides of the roof gardens on the wings. All in brick it is. This is the garden front; the entrance front will be admirable too. Do you like it?"

Gumbril Junior nodded. "Very much," he said.

His father sighed and taking the sketch put it back in his pocket. "You must hurry up with your ten thousand," he said. "And you, Porteous, and you. I've been waiting so long to build your splendid house."

Laughing, Mr. Porteous got up from his chair. "And long, dear Gumbril," he said, "may you continue to wait. For my splendid house won't be built this side of New Jerusalem and you must go on living a long time yet. A long, long time," Mr. Porteous repeated and carefully he buttoned up his double-breasted coat, carefully, as though he were adjusting an instrument of precision, he took out and replaced his monocle. Then, very erect and neat, very soldiery and pillar-boxical, he marched toward the door. "You've kept me very late tonight," he said. "Unconscionably late."

The front door closed heavily behind Mr. Porteous's departure. Gumbril Senior came upstairs again into the big room on the first floor smoothing down his hair, which the impetuosity of his ascent had once more disarranged.

"That's a good fellow," he said of his departed guest, "a splendid fellow."

"I always admire the monocle," said Gumbril Junior irrelevantly. But his father turned the irrelevance into relevance.

"He couldn't have come through without it, I believe. It was a symbol, a proud flag. Poverty's squalid, not fine at all. The monocle made a kind of difference, you understand. I'm always so enormously thankful I had a little money. I couldn't have stuck it without. It needs strength, more strength than I've got." He clutched his beard close under the chin and remained for a moment pensively silent. "The advantage of Porteous's line of business," he went on at last, reflectively, "is that it can be carried on by oneself, without collaboration. There's no need to appeal to anyone outside oneself, or to have any dealings with other people at all, if one doesn't want to. That's so deplorable about architecture. There's no privacy, so to speak, always this horrible jostling with clients and builders and contractors and people, before one can get anything done. It's really revolting. I'm not good at people. Most of them I don't like at all, not at all," Mr. Gumbril repeated with vehemence. "I don't deal with them very well, it isn't my business. My business is architecture. But I don't often get a chance of practicing it. Not properly."

Gumbril Senior smiled rather sadly. "Still," he said. "I can do something. I have my talent; I have my imagination. They can't take those from me. Come and see what I've been doing lately."

He led the way out of the room and mounted, two steps at a time, toward a higher floor. He opened the door of what should have been, in a well-ordered house, the Best Bedroom, and slipped into the darkness.

"Don't rush in," he called back to his son, "for God's sake don't rush in. You'll smash something. Wait till I've turned on the light. It's so like these asinine electricians to have hidden the switch behind the door like this." Gumbril Junior heard him fumbling in the darkness; there was suddenly light. He stepped in.

The only furniture in the room consisted of a couple of long trestle tables. On these, on the mantelpiece and all over the floor were scattered confusedly like the elements of a jumbled city, a vast collection of architectural models. There were cathedrals, there were town halls, universities, public libraries, there were three or four elegant little skyscrapers, there were blocks of offices, huge warehouses, factories, and finally dozens of magnificent country mansions, complete with their terraced gardens, their noble flights of steps, their fountains and ornamental waters and grandly bridged canals, their little rococo pavilions and garden houses.

"Aren't they beautiful?" Gumbril Senior turned enthusiastically toward his son. His long gray hair floated wispily about his head; his spectacles flashed and behind them his eyes shone with emotion.

"Beautiful," Gumbril Junior agreed.

"When you're really rich," said his father, "I'll build you one of these." And he pointed to a little village of Chatsworths clustering, at one end of a long table, round the dome of a vaster and austerer St. Peter's. "Look at this one, for example." He picked his way nimbly across the room, seized the little electric reading lamp that stood between a railway station and a baptistry on the mantelpiece, and was back again in an instant, trailing behind him a long flex that, as it tautened out, twitched one of the crowning pinnacles off the top of a skyscraper near the fireplace. "Look," he repeated, "look." He switched on the current, moving the lamp back and forth, up and down in front of the miniature palace. "See the beauty of the light and shade," he said. "There, underneath the great, ponderous cornice, isn't that fine? And look how splendidly the pilasters carry up the vertical lines. And then the solidity of it, the size, the immense, impending bleakness of it!" He threw up his arms; he turned his eyes upward as though standing overwhelmed at the foot of some huge precipitous façade. The lights and shadows vacillated wildly through all the city of palaces and domes as he brandished the lamp in ecstasy above his head.

"And then," he had suddenly stooped down; he was peering and pointing once more into the details of his palace, "then there's the doorway

—all florid and rich with carving. How magnificently and surprisingly it flowers out of the bare walls! Like the colossal writing of Darius, like the figures graven in the bald face of the precipice over Behistun— unexpected and beautiful and human, human in the surrounding emptiness."

Gumbril Senior brushed back his hair and turned, smiling, to look at his son over the top of his spectacles.

"Very fine," Gumbril Junior nodded to him. "But isn't the wall a little too blank? You seem to allow very few windows in this vast palazzo."

"True," his father replied, "very true." He sighed. "I'm afraid this design would hardly do for England. It's meant for a place where there's some sun—where you do your best to keep the light out, instead of letting it in, as you have to do here. Windows are the curse of architecture in this country. Your walls have to be like sieves, all holes, it's heartbreaking. If you wanted me to build you this house, you'd have to live in Barbados or somewhere like that."

"There's nothing I should like better," said Gumbril Junior.

"Another great advantage of sunny countries," Gumbril Senior pursued, "is that one can really live like an aristocrat, in privacy, by oneself. No need to look out on the dirty world or to let the dirty world look in on you. Here's this great house, for example, looking out on the world through a few dark portholes and a single cavernous doorway. But look inside." He held his lamp above the courtyard that was at the heart of the palace. Gumbril Junior leaned and looked, like his father. "All the life looks inward—into a lovely courtyard, a more than Spanish patio. Look there at the treble tiers of arcades, the vaulted cloisters for your cool peripatetic meditations, the central Triton spouting white water into a marble pool, the mosaic work on the floor and flowering up the walls, brilliant against the white stucco. And there's the archway that leads out into the gardens. And now you must come and have a look at the garden front."

He walked round with his lamp to the other side of the table. There was suddenly a crash; the wire had twitched a cathedral from off the table. It lay on the floor in disastrous ruin as though shattered by some appalling cataclysm.

"Hell and death!" said Gumbril Senior in an outburst of Elizabethan fury. He put down the lamp and ran to see how irreparable the disaster had been. "They're so horribly expensive, these models," he explained, as he bent over the ruins. Tenderly he picked up the pieces and replaced them on the table. "It might have been worse," he said at last, brushing the dust off his hands. "Though I'm afraid that dome will never be quite the same again." Picking up the lamp once more he held it high above his head and stood looking out, with a melancholy satisfaction, over his creations. "And to think," he said after a pause, "that I've been spending these last days designing model cottages for workmen at Bletchley! I'm in luck to have got the job, of course, but really, that a civilized man should have to do jobs like that. It's too much. In the old days these creatures built their own hovels and very nice and suitable they were too. The architects busied themselves with architecture—which is the expression of human dignity and greatness, which is man's protest, not his miserable acquiescence. You can't do much protesting in a model cottage at seven hundred pounds a time. A little, no doubt; you can protest a little; you can give your cottage decent proportions and avoid sordidness and vulgarity. But that's all, it's really a negative process. You can only begin to protest positively and actively when you abandon the petty human scale and build for giants—when you build for the spirit and the imagination of man, not for his little body. Model cottages indeed!"

Mr. Gumbril snorted with indignation. "When I think of Alberti!" And he thought of Alberti—Alberti the noblest Roman of them all, the true and only Roman. For the Romans themselves had lived their own actual lives, sordidly and extravagantly in the middle of a vulgar empire. Alberti and his followers in the Renaissance lived the ideal Roman life. They put Plutarch into their architecture. They took the detestable real Cato, the Brutus of history and made of them Roman heroes to walk as guides and models before them. Before Alberti there were no true Romans and with Piranesi's death the race began to wither toward extinction.

"And when I think of Brunelleschi!" Gumbril Senior went on to remember with passion the architect who had suspended on eight thin flying ribs of marble the lightest of all domes and the loveliest.

"And when of Michelangelo! The grim enormous apse. . . . And of Wren and of Palladio, when I think of all these—" Gumbril Senior waved his arms and was silent. He could not put into words what he felt when he thought of them.

Gumbril Junior looked at his watch. "Half-past two," he said. "Time to go to bed."

Chapter III

"Mister Gumbril!" Surprise was mingled with delight. "This is indeed a pleasure." Delight was now the prevailing emotion expressed by the voice that advanced, as yet without a visible source, from the dark recesses of the shop.

"The pleasure, Mr. Bojanus, is mine." Gumbril closed the shop door behind him.

A very small man, dressed in a frock coat, popped out from a canyon that opened, a mere black crevice, between two stratified precipices of mid-season suitings, and advancing into the open space before the door bowed with an old-world grace, revealing a nacreous scalp thinly mantled with long damp creepers of brown hair.

"And to what, may I ask, do I owe this pleasure, sir?" Mr. Bojanus looked up archly with a sideways cock of his head that tilted the rigid points of his waxed mustache. The fingers of his right hand were thrust into the bosom of his frock coat and his toes were turned out in the dancing master's First Position. "A light spring greatcoat, is it? Or a new suit? I notice," his eye traveled professionally up and and down Gumbril's long thin form, "I notice that the garments you are wearing at present, Mr. Gumbril, look—how shall I say?—well, a trifle negleejay as the French would put it, a trifle negleejay."

Gumbril looked down at himself. He resented Mr. Bojanus's negleejay, he was pained and wounded by the aspersion. Negleejay? And he had fancied that he really looked rather elegant and distinguished (but, after all, he always looked that, even in rags); no, that he looked positively neat, like Mr. Porteous, positively soldierly in his black jacket and his musical-comedy trousers and his patent-leather shoes. And the black felt hat—didn't that just add the foreign, the Southern touch which saved the whole composition from banality? He regarded himself, trying to see his clothes—garments, Mr. Bojanus had called them, garments, good Lord!—through the tailor's expert eyes. There were sagging folds about the overloaded pockets, there was a stain on his waistcoat, the knees of his trousers were baggy and puckered like the bare knees of Hélène Fourmont in Rubens's fur-coat portrait at Vienna. Yes, it was all horribly negleejay. He felt depressed; but looking at Mr. Bojanus's studied and professional correctness, he was a little comforted. That frock coat, for example. It was like something in a very modern picture—such a smooth unwrinkled cylinder about the chest, such a sense of pure and abstract conic-ness in the sleeky rounded skirts! Nothing could have been less negleejay. He was reassured.

"I want you," he said at last, clearing his throat importantly, "to make me a pair of trousers to a novel specification of my own. It's a new idea." And he gave a brief description of Gumbril's Patent Small Clothes. Mr. Bojanus listened with attention.

"I can make them for you," he said, when the description was finished. "I can make them for you—if you *really* wish, Mr. Gumbril," he added.

"Thank you," said Gumbril.

"And do you intend, may I ask, Mr. Gumbril, to wear these . . . these garments?"

Guiltily, Gumbril denied himself. "Only to demonstrate the idea, Mr. Bojanus. I am exploiting the invention commercially, you see."

"Commercially? I see, Mr. Gumbril."

"Perhaps you would like a share," suggested Gumbril.

Mr. Bojanus shook his head. "It wouldn't do for my cleeantail, I fear, Mr. Gumbril. You could hardly expect the Best People to wear such things."

"Couldn't you?"

Mr. Bojanus went on shaking his head. "I know them," he said, "I know the Best People. Well." And he added with an irrelevance that was, perhaps, only apparent. "Between ourselves, Mr. Gumbril, I am a great admirer of Lenin. . . ."

"So am I," said Gumbril, "theoretically. But then I have so little to lose to Lenin. I can afford to admire him. But you, Mr. Bojanus, you, the prosperous bourgeois—oh, purely in the economic sense of the word, Mr. Bojanus . . ."

Mr. Bojanus accepted the explanation with one of his old-world bows.

". . . you would be among the first to suffer if an English Lenin were to start his activities here."

"There, Mr. Gumbril, if I may be allowed to say so, you are wrong." Mr. Bojanus removed his hand from his bosom and employed it to emphasize the points of his discourse. "When the revolution comes, Mr. Gumbril, the great and necessary revolution, as Alderman Beckford called it, it won't be the owning of a little money that'll get a man into trouble. It'll be his class habits, Mr. Gumbril, his class speech, his class education. It'll be Shibboleth all over again, Mr. Gumbril; mark my words. The Red Guards will stop people in the street and ask them to say some such word as 'towel.' If they call it 'towel,' like you and your friends, Mr. Gumbril, why then . . ." Mr. Bojanus went through the gestures of pointing a rifle and pulling the trigger; he clicked his tongue against his teeth to symbolize the report . . . "that'll be the end of them. But if they say 'téaul,' like the rest of us, Mr. Gumbril, it'll be: 'Pass Friend and Long Live the Proletariat.' Long live Tèaul."

"I'm afraid you may be right," said Gumbril.

"I'm convinced of it," said Mr. Bojanus. "It's my clients, Mr. Gumbril, it's the Best People that the other people resent. It's their confidence, their ease, it's the habit their money and their position give them of ordering people about, it's the way they take their place in the world for granted, it's their prestige, which the other people would like to deny but can't—it's all that, Mr. Gumbril, that's so galling."

Gumbril nodded. He himself had envied his securer friends their power of ignoring the humanity of those who were not of their class. To do that really well, one must always have lived in a large house full of clockwork servants; one must never have been short of money, never at a restaurant ordered the cheaper thing instead of the more delicious; one must never have regarded a policeman as anything but one's paid defender against the lower orders, never for a moment have doubted one's divine right to do, within the accepted limits, exactly what one liked without a further thought to anything or anyone but oneself and one's own enjoyment. Gumbril had been brought up among these blessed beings; but he was not one of them. Alas? or fortunately? He hardly knew which.

"And what good do you expect the revolution to do, Mr. Bojanus?" he asked at last.

Mr. Bojanus replaced his hand in his bosom. "None whatever, Mr. Gumbril," he said. "None whatever."

"But Liberty," Gumbril suggested, "equality and all that. What about those, Mr. Bojanus?"

Mr. Bojanus smiled up at him tolerantly and kindly, as he might have smiled at someone who had suggested, shall we say, that evening trousers should be turned up at the bottom. "Liberty, Mr. Gumbril," he said. "You don't suppose any serious-minded person imagines a revolution is going to bring liberty, do you?"

"The people who make the revolution always seem to ask for liberty."

"But do they ever get it, Mr. Gumbril?" Mr. Bojanus cocked his head playfully and smiled. "Look at history, Mr. Gumbril, look at history. First it's the French Revolution. They ask for political liberty. And they gets it. Then comes the Reform Bill, then Forty-Eight, then all the Franchise Acts and Votes for Women—always more and more political liberty. And what's the result, Mr. Gumbril? Nothing at all. Who's freer for political liberty? Not a soul, Mr. Gumbril. There was never a greater swindle hatched in the whole of history. And when you think how those poor young men like Shelley talked about it—it's pathetic," said Mr. Bojanus, shaking his head, "reely pathetic. Political liberty's a swindle because a man doesn't spend his time being political. He spends it sleeping, eating, amusing himself a little and working— mostly working. When they'd got all the political liberty they wanted —or found they didn't want—they began to understand this. And so now it's all for the industrial revolution. Mr. Gumbril. But bless you, that's as big a swindle as the other. How can there ever be liberty under any system? No amount of profit sharing or self-government by the workers, no amount of hyjeenic conditions or cocoa villages or recreation grounds can get rid of the fundamental slavery—the necessity of working. Liberty? Why it doesn't exist. There's no liberty in this world; only gilded caiges. And then, Mr. Gumbril, even suppose you could somehow get rid of the necessity of working, suppose a man's time were all leisure. Would he be free then? I say nothing of the natural slavery of eating and sleeping and all that, Mr. Gumbril; I say nothing of that, because that, if I may say so, would be too hairsplitting and metaphysical. But what I do ask you is this," and Mr. Bojanus wagged his forefinger almost menacingly at the sleeping partner in this dialogue: "would a man with unlimited leisure be free, Mr. Gumbril. I say he would not. Not unless he happened to be a man like you or me, Mr. Gumbril, a man of sense, a man of independent judgment. An ordinary man would not be free. Because he wouldn't know how to occupy his leisure except in some way that would be forced on him by other people. People don't know how to entertain themselves now; they leave it to other people to do it for them. They swallow what's given them. They have to swallow it, whether they like it or not. Cinemas, newspapers, magazines, gramophones, football matches, wireless telephones—take them or leave them, if you want to amuse yourself. The ordinary man can't leave them. He takes; and what's that but slavery? And so you see, Mr. Gumbril," Mr. Bojanus smiled with a kind of roguish triumph, "you see that even in the purely hypothetical case of a man with indefinite leisure, there still would be no freedom. And the case, as I have said, is purely hypothetical; at any rate so far as concerns the sort of people who want a revolution. And as for the sort of people who do enjoy leisure, even now—why I think, Mr. Gumbril, you and I know enough about the Best People to know that freedom, except possibly sexual freedom, is not their strongest point. And sexual freedom—what's that?" Mr. Bojanus dramatically inquired. "You and I, Mr. Gumbril," he answered confidentially, "we know. It's a horrible, hideous slavery. That's what it is. Or am I wrong, Mr. Gumbril?"

"Quite right, quite right, Mr. Bojanus," Gumbril hastened to reply.

"From all of which," continued Mr. Bojanus, "it follows that, except for a few, a very few people like you and me, Mr. Gumbril, there's no such thing as liberty. It's a hoax, Mr. Gumbril. A horrible plant. And if I may be allowed to say so," Mr. Bojanus lowered his voice, but still spoke with emphasis, "a bloody swindle."

"But in that case, Mr. Bojanus, why are you so anxious to have a revolution?" Gumbril inquired.

Thoughtfully, Mr. Bojanus twisted to a finer point his waxed mustaches. "Well," he said at last, "it would be a nice change. I was always one for change and a little excitement. And then there's the scientific interest. You never quite know how an experiment will turn out, do you, Mr. Gumbril? I remember when I was a boy, my old dad—a great gardener he was, a regular floriculturist, you might say, Mr. Gumbril— he tried the experiment of grafting a sprig of Gloire de Dijon onto a black currant bush. And, would you believe it? the roses came out black, coal black, Mr. Gumbril. Nobody would ever have guessed that if the thing had never been tried. And that's what I say about the revolution. You don't know what'll come of it till you try. Black roses, blue roses— 'oo knows, Mr. Gumbril, 'oo knows?"

"Who indeed?" Gumbril looked at his watch. "About those trousers . . ." he added.

"Those garments," corrected Mr. Bojanus. "Ah, yes. Should we say next Tuesday?"

"Let us say next Tuesday." Gumbril opened the shop door. "Good morning, Mr. Bojanus."

Mr. Bojanus bowed him out, as though he had been a prince of the blood.

The sun was shining and at the end of the street between the houses the sky was blue. Gauzily the distance faded to a soft, rich indistinctness; there were veils of golden muslin thickening down the length of every vista. On the trees in the Hanover Square gardens the young leaves were still so green that they seemed to be alight, green fire, and the sooty trunks looked blacker and dirtier than ever. It would have been a pleasant and apposite thing if a cuckoo had started calling. But though the cuckoo was silent it was a happy day. A day, Gumbril reflected, as he strolled idly along, to be in love.

From the world of tailors Gumbril passed into that of the artificial pearl merchants and with a still keener appreciation of the amorous qualities of this spring day, he began a leisured march along the perfumed pavements of Bond Street. He thought with a profound satisfaction of those sixty-three papers on the Risorgimento. How pleasant it was to waste time! And Bond Street offered so many opportunities for wasting it agreeably. He trotted round the Spring Exhibition at the Grosvenor and came out, a little regretting, he had to confess, his eighteen pence for admission. After that he pretended that he wanted to buy a grand piano. When he had finished practicing his favorite passages on the magnificent instrument to which they obsequiously introduced him, he looked in for a few moments at Sotheby's, sniffed among the ancient books and strolled on again, admiring the cigars, the lucid scent bottles, the socks, the old masters, the emerald necklaces, everything, in fact, in all the shops he passed.

FORTHCOMING EXHIBITION OF WORKS BY CASIMIR LYPIATT. The announcement caught his eye. And so poor old Lypiatt was on the warpath again, he reflected, as he pushed open the doors of the Albemarle Galleries. Poor old Lypiatt! Dear old Lypiatt, even. He liked Lypiatt. Though he had his defects. It would be fun to see him again.

Gumbril found himself in the midst of a dismal collection of etchings. He passed them in review, wondering why it was that, in these hard days when no painter can sell a picture, almost any dull fool who can scratch a conventional etcher's view of two boats, a suggested cloud and the flat sea should be able to get rid of his prints by the dozen and at guineas apiece. He was interrupted in his speculations by the approach of the assistant in charge of the gallery. He came up shyly and uncomfortably, but with the conscientious determination of one ambitious to do his duty and make good. He was a very young man with pale hair to which heavy oiling had given a curious grayish color, and a face of such childish contour and so imberb that he looked like a little boy playing at grownups. He had only been at this job a few weeks and he found it very difficult.

"This," he remarked, with a little introductory cough, pointing to one view of the two boats and the flat sea, "is an earlier state than this." And he pointed to another view, where the boats were still two and the sea seemed just as flat—though possibly, on a closer inspection, it might really have been flatter.

"Indeed," said Gumbril.

The assistant was rather pained by his coldness. He blushed, but constrained himself to go on. "Some excellent judges," he said, "prefer the earlier state, though it is less highly finished."

"Ah?"

"Beautiful atmosphere, isn't it?" The assistant put his head on one side and pursed his childish lips appreciatively.

Gumbril nodded.

With desperation, the assistant indicated the shadowed rump of one of the boats. "A wonderful feeling in this passage," he said, redder than ever.

"Very intense," said Gumbril.

The assistant smiled at him gratefully. "That's the word," he said, delighted. "Intense. That's it. Very intense." He repeated the word several times as though to make sure of remembering it when the occasion next presented itself. He was determined to make good.

"I see Mr. Lypiatt is to have a show here soon," remarked Gumbril, who had had enough of the boats.

"He is making the final arrangements with Mr. Albemarle at this very moment," said the assistant, triumphantly, with the air of one who produces at the dramatic and critical moment, a rabbit out of the empty hat.

"You don't say so?" Gumbril was duly impressed. "Then I'll wait till he comes out," he said, and sat down with his back to the boats.

The assistant returned to his desk and picked up the gold-belted fountain pen which his Aunt had given him when he first went into business, last Christmas. "Very intense," he wrote in capitals on a half sheet of notepaper. "The feeling in this passage is very intense." He studied the paper for a few moments, then folded it up carefully and put it away in his waistcoat pocket. "Always make a note of it." That was one of the business mottoes he had himself written out so laboriously in India ink and old English lettering. It hung over his bed between "The Lord is my Shepherd," which his mother had given him, and a quotation from Dr. Frank Crane, "A smiling face sells more goods than a clever tongue." Still, a clever tongue, the young assistant had often reflected, was a very useful thing, especially in this job. He wondered whether one could say that the composition of a picture was very intense. Mr. Albemarle was very keen on the composition, he noticed. But perhaps it was better to stick to plain "fine," which was a little commonplace, perhaps, but very safe. He would ask Mr. Albemarle about it. And then there was all that stuff about plastic values and pure plasticity. He sighed. It was all very difficult. A chap might be as willing and eager to make good as he liked; but when it came to this about atmosphere and intense passages and plasticity—well, really, what could a chap do? Make a note of it. It was the only thing.

In Mr. Albemarle's private room Casimir Lypiatt thumped the table. "Size, Mr. Albemarle," he was saying, "size and vehemence and spiritual significance—that's what the old fellows had and we haven't . . ." He gesticulated as he talked, his face worked and his green eyes, set in their dark, charred orbits, were full of a troubled light. The forehead was precipitous, the nose long and sharp; in the bony and almost fleshless face the lips of the wide mouth were surprisingly full.

"Precisely, precisely," said Mr. Albemarle in his juicy voice. He was a round, smooth little man with a head like an egg; he spoke, he moved with a certain pomp, a butlerish gravity, that were evidently meant to be ducal.

"That's what I've set myself to recapture," Lypiatt went on: "the size, the masterfulness of the masters." He felt a warmth running through him as he spoke, flushing his cheeks, pulsing hotly behind the eyes, as though he had drunk a draft of some heartening red wine. His own

words elated him and drunkenly gesticulating he was as though drunken.
The greatness of the masters—he felt it in him. He knew his own power,
he knew, he knew. He could do all that they had done. Nothing was
beyond his strength.

Egg-headed Albemarle confronted him, impeccably the butler, exacer-
batingly serene. Albemarle too should be fired. He struck the table once
more, he broke out again.

"It's been my mission," he shouted, "all these years."

All these years . . . Time had worn the hair from his temples; the high,
steep forehead seemed higher than it really was. He was forty now; the
turbulent young Lypiatt, who had once declared that no man could do
anything worth doing after he was thirty, was forty now. But in these
fiery moments he could forget the years, he could forget the disappointments, the unsold pictures, the bad reviews. "My mission," he repeated,
"and by God! I feel, I feel, I know I can carry it through."

Warmly the blood pulsed behind his eyes.

"Quite," said Mr. Albemarle, nodding the egg. "Quite."

"And how small the scale is nowadays," Lypiatt went on, rhapsodically.
"How trivial the conception, how limited the scope! You see no painter-
sculptor-poets, like Michelangelo; no scientist-artists, like Leonardo; no
mathematician-courtiers, like Boscovitch; no impresario-musicians, like
Händel; no geniuses of all trades, like Wren. I have set myself against
this abject specialization of ours. I stand alone, opposing it with my
example." Lypiatt raised his hand. Like the statue of Liberty, standing
colossal and alone.

"Nevertheless," began Mr. Albemarle.

"Painter, poet, musician," cried Lypiatt. "I am all three. I . . ."

". . . there is a danger of—how shall I put it—dissipating one's
energies," Mr. Albemarle went on with determination. Discreetly, he
looked at his watch. This conversation, he thought, seemed to be pro-
longing itself unnecessarily.

"There is a greater danger in letting them stagnate and atrophy,"
Lypiatt retorted. "Let me give you my experience." Vehemently, he
gave it.

Out in the gallery, among the boats, the views of the Grand Canal,
and the Firth of Forth, Gumbril placidly ruminated. Poor old Lypiatt,
he was thinking. Dear old Lypiatt, even, in spite of his fantastic egotism.
Such a bad painter, such a bombinating poet, such a loud emotional
improviser on the piano! And going on like this, year after year, pegging
away at the same old things—always badly! And always without a penny,

always living in the most hideous squalor! Magnificent and pathetic old
Lypiatt!

A door suddenly opened and a loud unsteady voice, now deep and
harsh, now breaking to shrillness, exploded into the gallery.

". . . like a Veronese," it was saying; "enormous, vehement, a great
swirling composition," ("swirling composition"—mentally, the young
assistant made a note of that), "but much more serious, of course, much
more spiritually significant, much more——"

"Lypiatt!" Gumbril had risen from his chair, had turned, had advanced, holding out his hand.

"Why it's Gumbril. Good Lord!" and Lypiatt seized the proffered
hand with an excruciating cordiality. He seemed to be in exuberantly
good spirits. "We're settling about my show, Mr. Albemarle and I," he
explained. "You know Gumbril, Mr. Albemarle?"

"Pleased to meet you," said Mr. Albemarle. "Our friend, Mr. Lypiatt,"
he added richly, "has the true artistic temp . . ."

"It's going to be magnificent." Lypiatt could not wait till Mr. Albemarle had finished speaking. He gave Gumbril a heroic blow on the
shoulder. ". . . artistic temperament, as I was saying," pursued Mr. Albemarle. "He is altogether too impatient and enthusiastic for us poor
people . . ." a ducal smile of condescension accompanied this graceful
act of self-abasement ". . . who move in the prosaic, practical, workaday
world."

Lypiatt laughed, a loud discordant peal. He didn't seem to mind being
accused of having an artistic temperament; he seemed, indeed, to enjoy
it, if anything. "Fire and water," he said aphoristically, "brought together, beget steam. Mr. Albemarle and I go driving along like a steam
engine. Psh, psh!" He worked his arms like a pair of alternate pistons.
He laughed; but Mr. Albemarle only coldly and courteously smiled. "I
was just telling Mr. Albemarle about the great Crucifixion I've just
been doing. It's as big and headlong as a Veronese, but much more
serious, more . . ."

Behind them the little assistant was expounding to a new visitor the
beauties of the etchings. "Very intense," he was saying, "the feeling in
this passage." The shadow, indeed, clung with an insistent affection
round the stern of the boat. "And what a fine, what a——" he hesitated
for an instant, and under his pale oiled hair his face became suddenly
very red—"what a swirling composition." He looked anxiously at the
visitor. The remark had been received without comment. He felt immensely relieved.

They left the galleries together. Lypiatt set the pace, striding along at a great rate and with a magnificent brutality through the elegant and leisured crowd, gesticulating and loudly talking as he went. He carried his hat in his hand, his tie was brilliantly orange. People turned to look at him as he passed and he liked it. He had, indeed, a remarkable face, a face that ought by rights to have belonged to a man of genius. Lypiatt was aware of it. The man of genius, he liked to say, bears upon his brow a kind of mark of Cain, by which men recognize him at once—"and having recognized, generally stone him," he would add with that peculiar laugh he always uttered whenever he said anything rather bitter or cynical. A laugh that was meant to show that the bitterness, the cynicism, justifiable as events might have made them, were really only a mask and that beneath it the artist was still serenely and tragically smiling. Lypiatt thought a great deal about the ideal artist. That titanic abstraction stalked within his own skin. He was it—a little too consciously, perhaps.

"This time," he kept repeating, "they'll be bowled over. This time . . . It's going to be terrific." And with the blood beating behind his eyes, with the exultant consciousness and certainty of power growing and growing in him with every word he spoke, Lypiatt began to describe the pictures there would be at his show; he talked about the preface he was writing to the catalogue, the poems that would be printed in it by way of literary complement to the pictures. He talked, he talked.

Gumbril listened, not very attentively. He was wondering how anyone could talk so loud, could boast so extravagantly. It was as though the man had to shout in order to convince himself of his own existence. Poor Lypiatt; after all these years, Gumbril supposed, he must have some doubts about it. Ah, but this time, this time he was going to bowl them all over.

"You're pleased, then, with what you've done recently," he said at the end of one of Lypiatt's long tirades.

"Pleased?" exclaimed Lypiatt. "I thould think I was."

Gumbril might have reminded him that he had been as well pleased in the past and that "they" had by no means been bowled over. He preferred, however, to say nothing. Lypiatt went on about the size and universality of the old masters. He himself, it was tacitly understood, was one of them.

They parted near the bottom of the Tottenham Court Road, Lypiatt to go northward to his studio off Maple Street, Gumbril to pay one of his secret visits to those rooms of his in Great Russell Street. He had taken them nearly a year ago now, two little rooms over a grocer's shop, promising himself goodness only knew what adventures in them. But somehow there had been no adventures. Still, it had pleased him, all the same, to be able to go there from time to time when he was in London and to think, as he sat in solitude before his gas fire, that there was literally not a soul in the universe who knew where he was. He had an almost childish affection for mysteries and secrets.

"Good-by," said Gumbril, raising his hand to the salute. "And I'll beat up some people for dinner on Friday." (For they had agreed to meet again.) He turned away, thinking that he had spoken the last words; but he was mistaken.

"Oh, by the way," said Lypiatt, who had also turned to go, but who now came stepping quickly after his companion. "Can you, by any chance, lend me five pounds? Only till after the exhibition, you know. I'm a bit short."

Poor old Lypiatt. But it was with reluctance that Gumbril parted from his Treasury notes.

Chapter IV

LYPIATT had a habit, which some of his friends found rather trying— and not only friends, for Lypiatt was ready to let the merest acquaintances, the most absolute strangers, even, into the secrets of his inspiration— a habit of reciting at every possible opportunity his own verses. He would declaim in a voice loud and tremulous with an emotion that never seemed to vary with the varying subject matter of his poems, for whole quarters of an hour at a stretch; would go on declaiming till his auditors were overwhelmed with such a confusion of embarrassment and shame that the blood rushed to their cheeks and they dared not meet one another's eyes.

He was declaiming now; not merely across the dinner table to his own friends, but to the whole restaurant. For at the first reverberating lines of his latest, "The Conquistador," there had been a startled turning of heads, a craning of necks from every corner of the room. The people who came to this Soho restaurant because it was, notoriously, so "artistic" looked at one another significantly and nodded; they were getting their money's worth, this time. And Lypiatt, with a fine air of rapt unconsciousness, went on with his recitation.

"Look down on Mexico, Conquistador"—that was the refrain.

The Conquistador, Lypiatt had made it clear, was the Artist, and the Vale of Mexico on which he looked down, the towered cities of Tlacopan

and Chalco, of Tenochtitlan and Iztapalapan, symbolized—well, it was
difficult to say precisely what. The universe, perhaps?

"Look down," cried Lypiatt, with a quivering voice.

> Look down, Conquistador!
> There on the valley's broad green floor,
> There lies the lake; the jewelled cities gleam;
> Chalco and Tlacopan
> Awaiting the coming Man.
> Look down on Mexico, Conquistador,
> Land of your golden dream.

"Not 'dream,'" said Gumbril, putting down the glass from which he
had been profoundly drinking. "You can't possibly say 'dream,' you
know."

"Why do you interrupt me?" Lypiatt turned on him angrily. His wide
mouth twitched at the corners, his whole long face worked with excitement. "Why don't you let me finish?" He allowed his hand, which had
hung awkwardly in the air above him, suspended, as it were, at the top
of a gesture, to sink slowly to the table. "Imbecile!" he said and once more
picked up his knife and fork.

"But really," Gumbril insisted, "you can't say 'dream.' Can you now,
seriously?" He had drunk the best part of a bottle of Burgundy and he
felt good-humored, obstinate and a little bellicose.

"And why not?" Lypiatt asked.

"Oh, because one simply can't." Gumbril leaned back in his chair,
smiled and caressed his drooping blond mustache. "Not in this year of
grace, nineteen twenty-two."

"But why?" Lypiatt repeated, with exasperation.

"Because it's altogether too late in the day," declared precious Mr.
Mercaptan, rushing up to his emphasis with flutes and roaring, like a
true Conquistador, to fall back, however, at the end of the sentence rather
ignominiously into a breathless confusion. He was a sleek comfortable
young man with smooth, brown hair parted in the center and conducted
in a pair of flowing curves across the temples, to be looped in damp curls
behind his ears. His face ought to have been rather more exquisite, rather
more refinedly dix-huitième than it actually was. It had a rather gross,
snouty look, which was sadly out of harmony with Mr. Mercaptan's
inimitably graceful style. For Mr. Mercaptan had a style and used it,
delightfully, in his middle articles for the literary weeklies. His most
precious work, however, was that little volume of essays, prose poems,
vignettes and paradoxes, in which he had so brilliantly illustrated his

favorite theme—the pettiness, the simian limitations, the insignificance and the absurd pretentiousness of Homo soi-distant sapiens. Those who met Mr. Mercaptan personally often came away with the feeling that perhaps, after all, he was right in judging so severely of humanity.

"Too late in the day," he repeated. "Times have changed. Sunt lacrymae rerum, nos et mutamur in illis." He laughed his own applause.

"Quot homines, tot disputandum est," said Gumbril, taking another sip of his Beaune Supérieure. At the moment, he was all for Mercaptan.

"But why is it too late?" Lypiatt insisted.

Mr. Mercaptan made a delicate gesture. "Ça se sent, mon cher ami," he said, "ça ne s'explique pas." Satan, it is said, carries hell in his heart; so it was with Mr. Mercaptan—wherever he was, it was Paris. "Dreams in nineteen twenty-two." He shrugged his shoulders.

"After you've accepted the war, swallowed the Russian famine," said Gumbril. "Dreams!"

"They belong to the Rostand epoch," said Mr. Mercaptan, with a little titter. "Le Rêve—ah!"

Lypiatt dropped his knife and fork with a clatter and leaned forward, eager for battle. "Now I have you," he said, "now I have you on the hip. You've given yourself away. You've given away the secret of your spiritual poverty, your weakness and pettiness and impotence . . ."

"Impotence? You malign me, sir," said Gumbril.

Shearwater ponderously stirred. He had been silent all this time, sitting with hunched shoulders, his elbows on the table, his big round head bent forward, absorbed, apparently, in the slow meticulous crumbling of a piece of bread. Sometimes he put a piece of crust in his mouth and under the bushy brown mustache his jaw moved slowly, ruminatively, with a sideways motion, like a cow's. He nudged Gumbril with his elbow. "Ass," he said, "be quiet."

Lypiatt went on torrentially. "You're afraid of ideals, that's what it is. You daren't admit to having dreams. Oh, I call them dreams," he added parenthetically. "I don't mind being thought a fool and old-fashioned. The word's shorter and more English. Besides, it rhymes with gleams. Ha, ha!" And Lypiatt laughed his loud Titan's laugh, the laugh of cynicism which seems to belie, but which, for those who have understanding, reveals the high, positive spirit within. "Ideals—they're not sufficiently genteel for you civilized young men. You've quite outgrown that sort of thing. No dream, no religion, no morality."

"I glory in the name of earwig," said Gumbril. He was pleased with that little invention. It was felicitous; it was well chosen. "One's an earwig in sheer self-protection," he explained.

But Mr. Mercaptan refused to accept the name of earwig at any price. "What there is to be ashamed of in being civilized, I really don't know," he said, in a voice that was now the bull's, now the piping robin's. "No, if I glory in anything, it's in my little rococo boudoir, and the conversations across the polished mahogany, and the delicate, lascivious, witty little flirtations on ample sofas inhabited by the soul of Crébillon Fils. We needn't all be Russians, I hope. These revolting Dostoevskis." Mr. Mercaptan spoke with a profound feeling. "Nor all Utopians. Homo au naturel——" Mr. Mercaptan applied his thumb and forefinger to his, alas, too snoutlike nose, "ça pue. And as for Homo à la H. G. Wells— ça ne pue pas assez. What I glory in is the civilized, middle way between stink and asepsis. Give me a little musk, a little intoxicating feminine exhalation, the bouquet of old wine and strawberries, a lavender bag under every pillow and pots pourri in the corners of the drawing room. Readable books, amusing conversation, civilized women, graceful art and dry vintage music, with a quiet life and reasonable comfort—that's all I ask for."

"Talking about comfort," Gumbril put in, before Lypiatt had time to fling his answering thunders, "I must tell you about my new invention. Pneumatic trousers," he explained. "Blow them up. Perfect comfort. You see the idea? You're a sedentary man, Mercaptan. Let me put you down for a couple of pairs."

Mr. Mercaptan shook his head. "Too Wellsian," he said. "Too horribly Utopian. They'd be ludicrously out of place in my boudoir. And besides, my sofa is well enough sprung already, thank you."

"But what about Tolstoy?" shouted Lypiatt, letting out his impatience in a violent blast.

Mr. Mercaptan waved his hand. "Russian," he said, "Russian."

"And Michelangelo?"

"Alberti," said Gumbril, very seriously, giving them all a piece of his father's mind. "Alberti was much the better architect, I assure you."

"And pretentiousness for pretentiousness," said Mr. Mercaptan, "I prefer old Borromini and the baroque."

"What about Beethoven?" went on Lypiatt. "What about Blake? Where do they come in under your scheme of things."

Mr. Mercaptan shrugged his shoulders. "They stay in the hall," he said. "I don't let them into the boudoir."

"You disgust me," said Lypiatt, with rising indignation, and making wider gestures, "you disgust me—you and your odious little sham eighteenth-century civilization; your piddling little poetry; your art for art's sake instead of for God's sake; your nauseating little copulations without love or passion; your hoggish materialism; your bestial indifference to all that's unhappy and your yelping hatred of all that's great."

"Charming, charming," murmured Mr. Mercaptan, who was pouring oil on his salad.

"How can you ever hope to achieve anything decent or solid, when you don't even believe in decency or solidity? I look about me," and Lypiatt cast his eyes wildly round the crowded room, "and I find myself alone, spiritually alone. I strive on by myself, by myself." He struck his breast, a giant, a solitary giant. "I have set myself to restore painting and poetry to their rightful position among the great moral forces. They have been amusements, they have been mere games for too long. I am giving my life for that. My life." His voice trembled a little. "People mock me, hate me, stone me, deride me. But I go on, I go on. For I know I'm right. And in the end they too will recognize that I've been right." It was a loud soliloquy. One could fancy that Lypiatt had been engaged in recognizing himself.

"All the same," said Gumbril with a cheerful stubbornness, "I persist that the word 'dream' is inadmissible."

"*Inadmissible*," repeated Mr. Mercaptan, imparting to the word an additional significance by giving it its French pronunciation. "In the age of Rostand, well and good. But now . . ."

"Now," said Gumbril, "the word merely connotes Freud."

"It's a matter of literary tact," explained Mr. Mercaptan. "Have you no literary tact?"

"No," said Lypiatt, with emphasis, "thank God, I haven't. I have no tact of any kind. I do things straightforwardly, frankly, as the spirit moves me. I don't like compromises."

He struck the table. The gesture startlingly let loose a peal of cracked and diabolic laughter. Gumbril and Lypiatt and Mr. Mercaptan looked quickly up; even Shearwater lifted his great spherical head and turned toward the sound the large disk of his face. A young man with a blond fan-shaped beard stood by the table, looking down at them through a pair of bright blue eyes and smiling equivocally and disquietingly as though his mind were full of some nameless and fantastic malice.

"*Come sta la Sua Terribiltà?*" he asked; and taking off his preposterous bowler hat, he bowed profoundly to Lypiatt. "How I recognize my Buonarotti!" he added, affectionately.

Lypiatt laughed, rather uncomfortably, and no longer on the Titanic scale. "How I recognize my Coleman!" he echoed, rather feebly.

"On the contrary," Gumbril corrected, "how almost completely I fail to recognize. This beard." He pointed to the blond fan. "Why, may I ask?"

"More Russianism," said Mr. Mercaptan and shook his head.

"Ah, why indeed?" Coleman lowered his voice to a confidential whisper. "For religious reasons," he said and made the sign of the cross.

> Christ-like in my behaviour,
> Like every good believer,
> I imitate the Saviour,
> And cultivate a beaver.

"There be beavers which have made themselves beavers for the kingdom of heaven's sake. But there are some beavers, on the other hand, which were so born from their mother's womb." He burst into a fit of outrageous laughter which stopped as suddenly and as voluntarily as it had begun.

Lypiatt shook his head. "Hideous," he said, "hideous."

"Moreover," Coleman went on, without paying any attention, "I have other and alas! less holy reasons for this change of face. It enables one to make such delightful acquaintances in the street. You hear someone saying 'Beaver,' as you pass, and you immediately have the right to rush up and get into conversation. I owe to this dear symbol," and he caressed the golden beard tenderly with the palm of his hand, "the most admirably dangerous relations."

"Magnificent," said Gumbril, drinking his own health. "I shall stop shaving at once."

Shearwater looked round the table with raised eyebrows and a wrinkled forehead. "This conversation is rather beyond me," he said gravely. Under the formidable mustache, under the thick tufted eyebrows, the mouth was small and ingenuous, the mild gray eyes full of an almost childish inquiry. "What does the word 'beaver' signify in this context? You don't refer, I suppose, to the rodent, *Castor fiber*?"

"But this is a very great man," said Coleman, raising his bowler. "Tell me who he is?"

"Our friend Shearwater," said Gumbril, "the physiologist."

Coleman bowed. "Physiological Shearwater," he said. "Accept my homage. To one who doesn't know what a beaver is, I resign all my claims to superiority. There's nothing else but beavers in all the papers. Tell me do you never read the *Daily Express*?"

"No."

"Nor the *Daily Mail*?"

Shearwater shook his head.

"Nor the *Mirror*? nor the *Sketch*? nor the *Graphic*? nor even (for I was forgetting that physiologists must surely have Liberal opinions) even the *Daily News?*"

Shearwater continued to shake his large spherical head.

"Nor any of the evening papers?"

"No."

Coleman once more lifted his hat. "O eloquent, just and mighty Death," he exclaimed and replaced it on his head. "You never read any papers at all—not even our friend Mercaptan's delicious little middles in the weeklies? How is your delicious little middle, by the way?" Coleman turned to Mr. Mercaptan and with the point of his huge stick gave him a little prod in the stomach. "*Ça marche—les tripes? Hein?*" He turned back to Shearwater. "Not even those?" he asked.

"Never," said Shearwater. "I have more serious things to think about than newspapers."

"And what serious thing may I ask?"

"Well, at the present moment," said Shearwater, "I am chiefly preoccupied with the kidneys."

"The kidneys!" In an ecstasy of delight, Coleman thumped the floor with the ferrule of his stick. "The kidneys! Tell me all about kidneys. This is of the first importance. This is really life. And I shall sit down at your table without asking permission of Buonarotti here, and in the teeth of Mercaptan, and without so much as thinking about this species of Gumbril, who might as well not be there at all, I shall sit down and . . ."

"Talking of sitting," said Gumbril, "I wish I could persuade you to order a pair of my patent pneumatic trousers. They will——"

Coleman waved him away. "Not now, not now," he said. "I shall sit down now and listen to the physiologue talking about runions, while I myself actually eat them—*sautés. Sautés*, mark my words."

Laying his hat and stick on the floor beside him, he sat down at the end of the table, between Lypiatt and Shearwater.

"Two believers," he said, laying his hand for a moment on Lypiatt's arm, "and three blackhearted unbelievers—confronted. Eh, Buonarotti? You and I are both *croyants et pratiquants*, as Mercaptan would say. I believe in one devil, father quasi-almighty, Samael and his wife, the Woman of Whoredom. Ha, ha!" He laughed his ferocious, artificial laugh.

"Here's an end to any civilized conversation," Mr. Mercaptan complained, hissing on the c, labiating lingeringly on the v of "civilized" and giving the first two i's their fullest value. The word, in his mouth, seemed to take on a special and a richer significance.

Coleman ignored him. "Tell me, you physiologue," he went on, "tell

me about the physiology of the Archetypal Man. This is most important;
Buonarotti shares my opinion about this, I know. Has the Archetypal
Man a *boyau rectum*, as Mercaptan would say again, or not? Everything
depends on this, as Voltaire realized ages ago. 'His feet,' as we know
already on inspired authority, 'were straight feet; and the sole of his feet
were like the sole of a calf's foot.' But the viscera, you must tell us something about the viscera. Mustn't he, Buonarotti? And where are my
rognons sautés?" he shouted at the waiter.

"You revolt me," said Lypiatt.

"Not mortually I 'ope?" Coleman turned with solicitude to his neighbor; then shook his head. "Mortually I fear. Kiss me, Ardy, and I die
happy." He blew a kiss into the air. "But why is the physiologue so slow?
Up, pachyderm, up. Answer. You hold the key to everything. The key,
I tell you, the key. I remember, when I used to hang about the biological
laboratories at school, eviscerating frogs—crucified with pins, they were,
belly upwards, like little green Christs.—I remember once, when I was
sitting there, quietly poring over the entrails, in came the laboratory boy
and said to the stinks usher: 'Please, sir, may I have the key of the
Absolute?' And, would you believe it, that usher calmly put his hand in
his trouser pocket and fished out a small Yale key and gave it him without a word. What a gesture! The key of the Absolute. But it was only
the absolute alcohol the urchin wanted—to pickle some loathsome fetus
in, I suppose. God rot his soul in peace! And now, Castor Fiber, out
with your key. Tell us about the Archetypal Man, tell us about the
primordial Adam. Tell us all about the *boyau rectum.*"

Ponderously, Shearwater moved his clumsy frame; leaning back in his
chair he scrutinized Coleman with a large, benevolent curiosity. The eyes
under the savage eyebrows were mild and gentle; behind the fearful
disguise of the mustache he smiled poutingly, like a baby who sees the
approaching bottle. The broad domed forehead was serene. He ran his
hand through his thick brown hair, scratched his head meditatively and
then, when he had thoroughly examined, had comprehended and duly
classified the strange phenomenon of Coleman, opened his mouth and
uttered a little good-natured laugh of amusement.

"Voltaire's question," he said at last, in his slow, deep voice, "seemed
at the time he asked it an unanswerable piece of irony. It would have
seemed almost equally ironic to his contemporaries if he had asked
whether God had a pair of kidneys. We know a little more about the
kidneys nowadays. If he had asked me, I should answer: why not? The
kidneys are so beautifully organized; they do their work of regulation
with such a miraculous—it's hard to find another word—such a posi-

tively divine precision, such knowledge and wisdom, that there's no reason why your archetypal man, whoever he is, or anyone else, for that matter, should be ashamed of owning a pair."

Coleman clapped his hands. "The key," he cried, "the key. Out of the trouser pocket of babes and sucklings it comes. The genuine, the unique Yale. How right I was to come here tonight! But, holy Sephiroth, there's my trollop."

He picked up his stick, jumped from his chair and threaded his way between the tables. A woman was standing near the door. Coleman came up to her, pointed without speaking to the table, and returned, driving her along in front of him, tapping her gently over the haunches with his stick, as one might drive a docile animal to the slaughter.

"Allow me to introduce," said Coleman, "the sharer of my joys and sorrows. *La compagne de mes nuits blanches et de mes jours plutôt sales. In a word, Zoe. Qui ne comprend pas le français, qui me déteste avec une passion égale à la mienne, et qui mangera, ma foi, des rognons pour faire honneur au physiologue.*"

"Have some Burgundy?" Gumbril proffered the bottle.

Zoe nodded and pushed forward her glass. She was dark-haired, had pale skin and eyes like round black berries. Her mouth was small and floridly curved. She was dressed, rather depressingly, like a picture by Augustus John, in blue and orange. Her expression was sullen and ferocious and she looked about her with an air of profound contempt.

"Shearwater's no better than a mystic," fluted Mr. Mercaptan. "A mystical scientist; really, one hadn't reckoned on that."

"Like a Liberal Pope," said Gumbril. "Poor Metternich, you remember? Pio Nono." And he burst into a fit of esoteric laughter. "Of less than average intelligence," he murmured, delightedly, and refilled his glass.

"It's only the deliberately blind who wouldn't reckon on the combination," Lypiatt put in, indignantly. "What are science and art, what are religion and philosophy but so many expressions in human terms of some reality more than human? Newton and Boehme and Michelangelo—what are they doing but expressing, in different ways, different aspects of the same thing?"

"Alberti, I beg you," said Gumbril. "I assure you he was the better architect."

"*Fi donc!*" said Mr. Mercaptan. "San Carlo alle Quatro Fontane—" But he got no further. Lypiatt abolished him with a gesture.

"One reality," he cried, "there is only one reality."

"One reality," Coleman reached out a hand across the table and caressed Zoe's bare white arm, "and that is callipygous." Zoe jabbed at his hand with her fork.

"We are all trying to talk about it," continued Lypiatt. "The physicists have formulated their laws, which are after all no more than stammering provisional theories about a part of it. The physiologists are penetrating into the secrets of life, psychologists into the mind. And we artists are trying to say what is revealed to us about the moral nature, the personality of that reality, which is the universe."

Mr. Mercaptan threw up his hands in affected horror. "Oh, *barbaridad barbaridad!*" Nothing less than the pure Castilian would relieve his feelings. "But all this is meaningless."

"Quite right about the chemists and physicists," said Shearwater. "They're always trying to pretend that they're nearer the truth than we are. They take their crude theories as facts and try to make us accept them when we're dealing with life. Oh, they are sacred, their theories. Laws of Nature they call them; and they talk about their known truths and our romantic biological fancies. What a fuss they make when we talk about life. Bloody fools!" said Shearwater, mild and crushing. "Nobody but a fool could talk of mechanism in face of the kidneys. And there are actually imbeciles who talk about the mechanism of heredity and reproduction."

"All the same," began Mr. Mercaptan very earnestly, anxious to deny his own life, "there are eminent authorities. I can only quote what they say, of course. I can't pretend to know anything about it myself. But——"

"Reproduction, reproduction," Coleman murmured the word to himself ecstatically. "Delightful and horrifying to think they all come to that, even the most virginal, that they were all made for that, little she-dogs, in spite of their china-blue eyes. What sort of a mandrake shall we produce, Zoe and I?" he asked, turning to Shearwater. "How I should like to have a child," he went on without waiting for an answer. "I shouldn't teach it anything; no language, nothing at all. Just a child of nature. I believe it would really be the devil. And then what fun it would be if it suddenly started to say 'Bekkos,' like the children in Herodotus. And Buonarotti here would paint an allegorical picture of it and write an epic called 'The Ignoble Savage.' And Castor Fiber would come and sound its kidneys and investigate its sexual instincts. And Mercaptan would write one of his inimitable middle articles about it. And Gumbril would make it a pair of patent trousers. And Zoe and I would look parentally on and fairly swell with pride. Shouldn't we, Zoe?" Zoe preserved her expression of sullen, unchanging contempt and did not deign to answer. "Ah, how delightful it would be! I long for posterity. I live in hopes. I stope against Stopes. I——"

Zoe threw a piece of bread, which caught him on the cheek, a little below the eye. Coleman leaned back and laughed and laughed till the tears rolled down his face.

Chapter V

ONE after another, they engaged themselves in the revolving doors of the restaurant, trotted round in the moving cage of glass and ejected themselves into the coolness and darkness of the street. Shearwater lifted up his large face and took two or three deep breaths. "Too much carbon dioxide and ammonia in there," he said. "It is unfortunate that when two or three are gathered together in God's name, or even in the more civilized name of Mercaptan of the delicious middle," Mercaptan dexterously parried the prod which Coleman aimed at him, "it is altogether deplorable that they should necessarily empest the air."

Lypiatt had turned his eyes heavenward. "What stars," he said, "and what prodigious gaps between the stars."

"A real light-opera summer night." And Mercaptan began to sing in fragmentary German the 'Barcarolle' from the *Tales of Hoffman*. "Liebe Nacht, du schöne Nacht, oh stille mein tumpty-tum. Te, tum, Te tum . . . Delicious Offenbach. Ah, if only we could have a Third Empire. Another comic Napoleon! That would make Paris look like Paris again. Tiddy, Tumpty-ti-tum."

They walked along without any particular destination, but simply for the sake of walking through this soft cool night. Coleman led the way, tapping the pavement at every step with the ferrule of his stick. "This blind leading the blind," he explained. "Ah, if only there were a ditch, a crevasse, a great hole full of stinging centipedes and dung. How gleefully I should lead you all into it!"

"I think you would do well," said Shearwater gravely, "to go and see a doctor."

Coleman gave vent to a howl of delight.

"Does it occur to you," he went on, "that at this moment, we are walking through the midst of seven million distinct and separate individuals, each with distinct and separate lives and all completely indifferent to our existence? Seven million people, each one of whom thinks himself quite as important as each of us does. Millions of them are now sleeping in an empested atmosphere. Hundreds of thousands of couples are at this moment engaged in mutually caressing one another in a manner too hideous to be thought of, but in no way differing from the manner in which each of us performs, delightfully, passionately and beautifully, his similar work of love. Thousands of women are now in the throes of parturition, and of both sexes, thousands are dying of the most diverse and appalling diseases, or simply because they have lived too long. Thousands are drunk, thousands have overeaten, thousands have not had enough to eat. And they are all alive, all unique and separate and sensitive, like you and me. It's a horrible thought. Ah, if I could lead them all into that great hole of centipedes."

He tapped and tapped on the pavement in front of him, as though searching for the crevasse. At the top of his voice he began to chant: "O all ye Beasts and Cattle, curse ye the Lord: curse him and vilify him forever."

"All this religion," sighed Mercaptan. "What with Lypiatt on one side, being a muscular Christian artist, and Coleman on the other, howling the black mass . . . Really!" He elaborated an Italianate gesture, and turned to Zoe. "What do you think of it all?" he asked. Zoe jerked her head in Coleman's direction. "I think 'e's a bloody swine," she said. They were the first words she had spoken since she had joined the party.

"Hear, hear," cried Coleman and he waved his stick.

In the warm, yellow light of the coffee stall at Hyde Park Corner loitered a little group of people. Among the peaked caps and the chauffeurs' dustcoats, among the weather-stained workmen's jackets and the knotted handkerchiefs, there emerged an alien elegance. A tall tubed hat and a silk-faced overcoat, a cloak of flame-colored satin and in bright coppery hair a great Spanish comb of carved tortoise shell.

"Well I'm damned," said Gumbril as they approached. "I believe it's Myra Viveash."

"So it is," said Lypiatt, peering in his turn. He began suddenly to walk with an affected swagger, kicking his heels at every step. Looking at himself from outside, his divining eyes pierced through the veil of cynical je-m'en-fichisme to the bruised heart beneath. Besides, he didn't want anyone to guess.

"The Viveash is it?" Coleman quickened his rapping along the pavement. "And who is the present incumbent?" He pointed at the top hat.

"Can it be Bruin Opps?" said Gumbril dubiously.

"Opps!" Coleman yelled out the name. "Opps!"

The top hat turned, revealing a shirt front, a long, gray face, a glitter of circular glass over the left eye. "Who the devil are you?" The voice was harsh and arrogantly offensive.

"I am that I am," said Coleman. "But I have with me——" he pointed to Shearwater, to Gumbril, to Zoe "—a physiologue, a pedagogue and a priapagogue; for I leave out of account mere artists and journalists whose titles do not end with the magic syllable. And finally," indicating himself, "plain Dog, which being interpreted cabalistically backwards signifies God. All at your service." He took off his hat and bowed.

The top hat turned back toward the Spanish comb. "Who is this horrible drunk?" it inquired.

Mrs. Viveash did not answer him, but stepped forward to meet the newcomers. In one hand she held a peeled hard-boiled egg and a thick slice of bread and butter in the other, and between her sentences she bit at them alternatively.

"Coleman," she exclaimed and her voice, as she spoke, seemed always on the point of expiring, as though each word were the last, uttered faintly and breakingly from the deathbed—— the last, with all the profound and nameless significance of the ultimate word. "It's a very long time since I heard you raving last. And you, Theodore darling, why do I never see you now?"

Gumbril shrugged his shoulders. "Because you don't want to, I suppose," he said.

Myra laughed and took another bite at her bread and butter . . . She laid the back of her hand—for she was still holding the butt end of her hard-boiled egg—on Lypiatt's arm. The Titan, who had been looking at the sky, seemed to be surprised to find her standing there. "You?" he said, smiling and wrinkling up his forehead interrogatively.

"It's tomorrow I'm sitting for you, Casimir, isn't it?"

"Ah, you remembered." The veil parted for a moment. Poor Lypiatt! "And happy Mercaptan? Always happy?"

Gallantly Mercaptan kissed the back of the hand which held the egg. "I might be happier," he murmured, rolling up at her from the snouty face a pair of small brown eyes. "*Puis-je espérer?*"

Mrs. Viveash laughed expiringly from her inward deathbed and turned on him without speaking her pale unwavering glance. Her eyes had a formidable capacity for looking and expressing nothing; they were like the pale blue eyes which peer out of the Siamese cat's black-velvet mask.

"Bellissima," murmured Mercaptan, flowering under their cool light.

Mrs. Viveash addressed herself to the company at large. "We have had the most appalling evening," she said. "Haven't we, Bruin?"

Bruin Opps said nothing, but only scowled. He didn't like these damned intruders. The skin of his contracted brows oozed over the rim of his monocle onto the shining glass.

"I thought it would be fun," Myra went on, "to go to that place at Hampton Court, where you have dinner on an island and dance."

"What is there about islands," put in Mercaptan, in a deliciously whimsical parenthesis, "that makes them so peculiarly voluptuous? Cythera, Monkey Island, Capri. *Je me demande.*"

"Another charming middle." Coleman pointed his stick menacingly; Mr. Mercaptan stepped quickly out of range.

"So we took a cab," Mrs. Viveash continued, "and set out. And what a cab, my God! A cab with only one gear and that the lowest. A cab as old as the century, a museum specimen, a collector's piece." They had been hours and hours on the way. And when they got there, the food they were offered to eat, the wine they were expected to drink! From her eternal deathbed Mrs. Viveash cried out in unaffected horror. Everything tasted as though it had been kept soaking for a week in the river before being served up—rather weedy, with that delicious typhoid flavor of Thames water. There was Thames even in the champagne. They had not been able to eat so much as a crust of bread. Hungry and thirsty, they had re-embarked in their antique taxi and here, at last, they were, at the first outpost of civilization, eating for dear life.

"Oh, a terrible evening," Mrs. Viveash concluded. "The only thing which kept up my spirits was the spectacle of Bruin's bad temper. You've no idea, Bruin, what an incomparable comic you can be."

Bruin ignored the remark. With an expression of painfully repressed disgust he was eating a hard-boiled egg. Myra's caprices were becoming more and more impossible. That Hampton Court business had been bad enough; but when it came to eating in the street, in the middle of a lot of filthy workmen—well, really, that was rather too much.

Mrs. Viveash looked about her. "Am I never to know who this mysterious person is?" She pointed to Shearwater who was standing a little apart from the group, his back leaning against the Park railings and staring thoughtfully at the ground.

"The physiologue," Coleman explained, "and he has the key. The key, the key!" He hammered the pavement with his stick.

Gumbril performed the introduction in more commonplace style.

"You don't seem to take much interest in us, Mr. Shearwater," Myra called expiringly. Shearwater looked up; Mrs. Viveash regarded him intently through pale, unwavering eyes, smiling as she looked that queer, downward-turning smile which gave to her face, through its mask of laughter, a peculiar expression of agony. "You don't seem to take much interest in us," she repeated.

Shearwater shook his heavy head. "No," he said, "I don't think I do."
"Why don't you?"

"Why should I? There's not time to be interested in everything. One can only be interested in what's worth while."

"And we're not worth while?"

"Not to me personally," replied Shearwater with candor. "The Great Wall of China, the political situation in Italy, the habits of Trematodes —all these are most interesting in themselves. But they aren't interesting to me; I don't permit them to be, I haven't the leisure."

"And what do you allow yourself to be interested in?"

"Shall we go?" said Bruin impatiently; he had succeeded in swallowing the last fragment of his hard-boiled egg. Mrs. Viveash did not answer, did not even look at him.

Shearwater who had hesitated before replying was about to speak. But Coleman answered for him. "Be respectful," he said to Mrs. Viveash. "This is a great man. He reads no papers, not even those in which our Mercaptan so beautifully writes. He does not know what a beaver is. And he lives for nothing but the kidneys."

Mrs. Viveash smiled her smile of agony. "Kidneys? But what a *memento mori*. There are other portions of the anatomy." She threw back her cloak, revealing an arm, a bare shoulder, a slant of pectoral muscle. She was wearing a white dress that, leaving her back and shoulders bare, came up under either arm to a point in front and was held there by a golden thread about the neck. "For example," she said. And twisted her hand several times over and over, making the slender arm turn at the elbow, as though to demonstrate the movement of the articulations and the muscular play.

"*Memento vivere*," Mr. Mercaptan aptly commented. "*Vivamus, mea Lesbia, atque amenus.*"

Mrs. Viveash dropped her arm and pulled the cloak back into place. She looked at Shearwater, who had followed all her movements with conscientious attention and who now nodded with an expression of interrogation on his face, as though to ask: what next?

"We all know that you've got beautiful arms," said Bruin angrily. "There's no need for you to make an exhibition of them in the street, at midnight. Let's get out of this." He laid his hand on her shoulder and made as if to draw her away. "We'd better be going. Goodness knows what's happening behind us." He indicated with a little movement of the head the loiterers round the coffee stall. "Some disturbance among the *canaille*."

Mrs. Viveash looked round. The cab drivers and the other consumers of midnight coffee had gathered in an interested circle, curious and sympathetic, round the figure of a woman who was sitting, like a limp bundle tied up in black cotton and mackintosh, on the stallkeeper's high stool, leaning wearily against the wall of the booth. A man stood beside her drinking tea out of a thick white cup. Everyone was talking at once.

"Mayn't the poor wretches talk?" asked Mrs. Viveash, turning back to Bruin. "I never knew anyone who had the lower classes on the brain as much as you have."

"I loathe them," said Bruin. "I hate every one poor, or ill, or old. Can't abide them; they make me positively sick."

"*Quelle âme bien-née*," piped Mr. Mercaptan. "And how well and frankly you express what we all feel and lack the courage to say."

Lypiatt gave vent to indignant laughter.

"I remember when I was a little boy," Bruin went on, "my old grandfather used to tell me stories about his childhood. He told me that when he was about five or six, just before the passing of the Reform Bill of 'thirty-two, there was a song which all right-thinking people used to sing, with a chorus that went like this: 'Rot the People, blast the People, damn the Lower Classes.' I wish I knew the rest of the words and the tune. It must have been a good song."

Coleman was enraptured with the song. He shouldered his walking stick and began marching round and round the nearest lamp-post chanting the words to a stirring march tune. "Rot the People, blast the People. . . ." He marked the rhythm with heavy stamps of his feet.

"Ah, if only they'd invent servants with internal combustion engines," said Bruin, almost pathetically. "However well trained they are, they always betray their humanity occasionally. And that is really intolerable."

"How tedious is a guilty conscience!" Gumbril murmured the quotation.

"But Mr. Shearwater," said Myra, bringing back the conversation to more congenial themes, "hasn't told us yet what he thinks of arms."

"Nothing at all," said Shearwater. "I'm occupied with the regulation of the blood at the moment."

"But is it true what he says, Theodore?" She appealed to Gumbril.

"I should think so," Gumbril's answer was rather dim and remote. He was straining to hear the talk of Bruin's *canaille* and Mrs. Viveash's question seemed a little irrelevant.

"I used to do cartin' jobs," the man with the teacup was saying. " 'Ad a van and a nold pony of me own. And didn't do so badly neither. The only trouble was me lifting furniture and 'eavy weights about the place. Because I 'ad malaria out in India, in the war. . . ."

"Nor even—you compel me to violate the laws of modesty—nor even," Mrs. Viveash went on, smiling painfully, speaking huskily, expiringly, "of legs?"

A spring of blasphemy was touched in Coleman's brain. "Neither delighteth He in any man's legs," he shouted, and with an extravagant show of affection he embraced Zoe, who caught hold of his hand and bit it.

"It comes back on you when you get tired like, malaria does." The man's face was sallow and there was an air of peculiar listlessness and hopelessness about his misery. "It comes back on you and then you go down with fever and you're as weak as a child."

Shearwater shook his head.

"Nor even of the heart?" Mrs. Viveash lifted her eyebrows. "Ah, now the inevitable word has been pronounced; the real subject of every conversation has appeared on the scene. Love, Mr. Shearwater!"

"But as I says," recapitulated the man with the teacup, "we didn't do so badly after all. We 'ad nothing to complain about. 'Ad we, Florrie?"

The black bundle made an affirmative movement with its upper extremity.

"That's one of the subjects," said Shearwater, "like the Great Wall of China and the habits of Trematodes, I don't allow myself to be interested in."

Mrs. Viveash laughed, breathed out a little "Good God!" of incredulity and astonishment and asked, "Why not?"

"No time," he explained. "You people of leisure have nothing else to do or think about. I'm busy and so naturally less interested in the subject than you; and I take care, what's more, to limit such interest as I have."

"I was goin' up Ludgate 'ill one day with a vanload of stuff for a chap in Clerkenwell. I was leadin' Jerry up the 'ill—Jerry's the name of our ole pony . . ."

"One can't have everything," Shearwater was explaining, "not all at the same time, in any case. I've arranged my life for work now. I'm quietly married, I simmer away domestically."

"*Quelle horreur!*" said Mr. Mercaptan. All the Louis Quinze Abbé in him was shocked and revolted by the thought.

"But love?" questioned Mrs. Viveash. "Love?"

"Love," Lypiatt echoed. He was looking up at the Milky Way.

"All of a sudden out jumps a copper at me. ' 'Ow old is that 'orse?' 'e says. 'It ain't fit to drawr a load; it limps in all four feet,' 'e says. 'No, it doesn't,' I says. 'None of your answerin' back,' 'e says. 'Take it outer the shafts at once.' "

"But I know all about love already. I know precious little still about kidneys."

"But, my good Shearwater, how can you know all about love before you've made it with all women?"

"Off we goes, me and the cop and the 'orse, up in front of the police court magistrate. . . ."

"Or are you one of those imbeciles," Mrs. Viveash went on, "who speak of women with a large W and pretend we're all the same? Poor Theodore here might possibly think so in his feebler moments." Gumbril smiled vaguely from a distance. He was following the man with the teacup into the magistrate's stuffy court. "And Mercaptan certainly does; because all the women who ever sat on his *dix-huitième* sofa certainly were exactly like one another. And perhaps Casimir does too; all women look like his absurd ideal. But you, Shearwater, you're intelligent. Surely you don't believe anything so stupid."

Shearwater shook his head.

"The cop, 'e gave evidence against me. 'Limping in all four feet,' 'e says. 'It wasn't,' I says, and the police court vet, 'e bore me out. 'The 'orse 'as been very well treated,' 'e says. 'But 'e's old, 'e's very old.' 'I know 'e's old,' I says. 'But where am I goin' to find the price for a young one?' "

"x^2-y^2," Shearwater was saying, "$=(x+y)$ $(x-y)$ and the equation holds good whatever the values of x and y. It's the same with your love business, Mrs. Viveash. The relation is still fundamentally the same, whatever the value of the unknown personal quantities concerned. Little individual tics and peculiarities—after all, what do they matter?"

"What indeed?" said Coleman. "Tics, mere tics. Sheep ticks, horse ticks, bed bugs, tape worms, taint worms, guinea worms, liver flukes . . ."

" 'The 'orse must be destroyed,' says the beak. ' 'E's too old for work.' 'But I'm not,' I says. 'I can't get a old-age pension at thirty-two, can I? 'Ow am I to earn my living if you take away what I earns my living by?' "

Mrs. Viveash smiled agonizingly. "Here's a man who thinks personal peculiarities are trivial and unimportant," she said. "You're not even interested in people, then?"

" 'I don't know what you can do,' 'e says. 'I'm only 'ere to administer the law.' 'Seems a queer sort of law,' I says. 'What law is it?' "

Shearwater scratched his head. Under his formidable black mustache he smiled at last his ingenuous, childish smile. "No," he said. "No, I suppose I'm not. It hadn't occurred to me, until you said it. But I suppose I'm not. No." He laughed, quite delighted, it seemed, by this discovery about himself.

" 'What law is it?' 'e says. 'The Croolty to Animals law. That's what it is,' 'e says."

The smile of mockery and suffering appeared and faded. "One of these days," said Mrs. Viveash, "you may find them more absorbing than you do now."

"Meanwhile," said Shearwater . . .

"I couldn't find a job 'ere and 'aving been workin' on my own, my own master like, couldn't get unemployment pay. So when we 'eard of jobs at Portsmouth, we thought we'd try to get one, even if it did mean walkin' there."

"Meanwhile, I have my kidneys."

" ' 'Opeless,' 'e says to me, 'quite 'opeless. More than two 'undred come for three vacancies.' So there was nothing for it but to walk back again. Took us four days it did, this time. She was very bad on the way, very bad. Being nearly six months gone. Our first it is. Things will be 'arder still, when it comes."

From the black bundle there issued a sound of quiet sobbing.

"Look here," said Gumbril, making a sudden irruption into the conversation. "This is really too awful." He was consumed with indignation and pity; he felt like a prophet in Nineveh.

"There are two wretched people here," and Gumbril told them breathlessly what he had overheard. It was terrible, terrible. "All the way to Portsmouth and back again; on foot; without proper food; and the woman's with child."

Coleman exploded with delight. "Gravid," he kept repeating, "gravid, gravid. The laws of gravity, first formulated by Newton, now recodified by the immortal Einstein. God said, Let Newstein be, and there was Light. And God said, Let there be Light; and there was darkness o'er the face of the earth." He roared with laughter.

Between them they raised five pounds. Mrs. Viveash undertook to give them to the black bundle. The cabmen made way for her as she advanced; there was an uncomfortable silence. The black bundle lifted a face that was old and worn, like the face of a statue in the portal of a cathedral; an old face, but one was aware, somehow, that it belonged to a woman still young by the reckoning of years. Her hands trembled as she took the notes, and when she opened her mouth to speak her hardly articulate whisper of gratitude, one saw that she had lost several of her teeth.

The party disintegrated. All went their ways: Mr. Mercaptan to his rococo boudoir, his sweet barocco bedroom in Sloane Street; Coleman and Zoe toward goodness only knew what scenes of intimate life in Pimlico; Lypiatt to his studio off the Tottenham Court Road, alone, silently brooding and perhaps too consciously bowed with unhappiness. But the unhappiness, poor Titan! was real enough for had he not seen Mrs. Viveash and the insufferable, the stupid and loutish Opps driving off in one taxi? "Must finish up with a little dancing," Myra had huskily uttered from that deathbed on which her restless spirit forever and wearily exerted itself. Obediently, Bruin had given an address and they had driven off. But after the dancing? Oh, was it possible that that odious, bad-blooded young cad was her lover? And that she should like him? It was no wonder that Lypiatt should have walked, bent like Atlas under the weight of a world. And when, in Piccadilly, a belated and still unsuccessful prostitute sidled out of the darkness, as he strode by unseeing in his misery, when she squeaked up at him a despairing "Cheer up, duckie," Lypiatt suddenly threw up his head and laughed titanically, with the terrible bitterness of a noble soul in pain. Even the poor drabs at the street corners were affected by the unhappiness that radiated out from him, wave after throbbing wave, like music, he liked to fancy, into the night. Even the wretched drabs. He walked on, more desperately bowed than ever; but met no further adventure on his way.

Gumbril and Shearwater both lived in Paddington; they set off in company up Park Lane, walking in silence. Gumbril gave a little skip to get himself into step with his companion. To be out of step when steps so loudly and flat-footedly flapped on empty pavements was disagreeable, he found, was embarrassing, was somehow dangerous. Stepping like this, out of time, one gave oneself away, so to speak, one made the night aware of two presences, when there might, if steps sounded in unison, be only one, heavier, more formidable, more secure than either of the separate two. In unison, then, they flapped up Park Lane. A policeman and the three poets, sulking back to back on their fountain, were the only human things besides themselves under the mauve electric moons.

"It's appalling, it's horrible," said Gumbril at last, after a long, long silence, during which he had, indeed, been relishing to the full the horror of it all. "Life, don't you know."

"What's appalling?" Shearwater inquired. He walked with his big head bowed, his hands clasped behind his back and clutching his hat; walked clumsily, with sudden lurches of his whole massive anatomy. Wherever he was, Shearwater always seemed to take up the space that two or three ordinary people would normally occupy. Cool fingers of wind passed refreshingly through his hair. He was thinking of the experiment he meant to try, in the next few days, down at the physiological laboratory. You'd put a man on an ergometer in a heated chamber and set him to work—hours at a time. He'd sweat, of course, prodigiously. You'd make arrangements for collecting the sweat, weighing it, analyzing it and so on.

The interesting thing would be to see what happened at the end of a few days. The man would have got rid of so much of his salts that the blood composition might be altered and all sorts of delightful consequences might follow. It ought to be a capital experiment. Gumbril's exclamation disturbed him. "What's appalling?" he asked rather irritably.

"Those people at the coffee stall," Gumbril answered. "It's appalling that human beings should have to live like that. Worse than dogs."

"Dogs have nothing to complain of." Shearwater went off at a tangent. "Nor guinea pigs, nor rats. It's these blasted antivivisection maniacs who make all the fuss."

"But think," cried Gumbril, "what these wretched people have had to suffer! Walking all the way to Portsmouth in search of work; and the woman with child. It's horrifying. And then, the way people of that class are habitually treated. One has no idea of it until one has actually been treated that way oneself. In the war, for example, when one went to have one's mitral murmurs listened to by the medical board—they treated one then as though one belonged to the lower orders, like all the rest of the poor wretches. It was a real eye opener. One felt like a cow being got into a train. And to think that the majority of one's fellow beings pass their whole lives being shoved about like maltreated animals!"

"H'm," said Shearwater. If you went on sweating indefinitely, he supposed, you would end by dying.

Gumbril looked through the railings at the profound darkness of the park. Vast it was and melancholy with a string, here and there, of receding lights. "Terrible," he said, and repeated the word several times. "Terrible, terrible." All the legless soldiers grinding barrel organs, all the hawkers of toys stamping their leaky boots in the gutters of the Strand; at the corner of Cursitor Street and Chancery Lane, the old woman with matches, forever holding to her left eye a handkerchief as yellow and dirty as the winter fog. What was wrong with the eye? He had never dared to look, but hurried past as though she were not there, or sometimes, when the fog was more than ordinarily cold and stifling, paused for an instant with averted eyes to drop a brown coin into her tray of matches. And then there were the murderers hanged at eight o'clock, while one was savoring, almost with voluptuous consciousness, the final dream-haunted doze. There was the phthisical charwoman who used to work at his father's house, until she got too weak and died. There were the lovers who turned on the gas and the ruined shopkeepers jumping in front of trains. Had one a right to be contented and well fed, had one a right to one's education and good taste, a right to knowledge and conversation and the leisurely complexities of love?

He looked once more through the railings at the park's impenetrable rustic night, at the lines of beaded lamps. He looked, and remembered another night, years ago, during the war, when there were no lights in the park and the electric moons above the roadway were in almost total eclipse. He had walked up this street alone, full of melancholy emotions which, though the cause of them was different, were in themselves much the same as the melancholy emotions which swelled windily up within him tonight. He had been most horribly in love.

"What did you think," he asked abruptly, "of Myra Viveash?"

"Think?" said Shearwater. "I don't know that I thought very much about her. Not a case for ratiocination exactly, is she? She seemed to me entertaining enough, as women go. I said I'd lunch with her on Thursday."

Gumbril felt, all of a sudden, the need to speak confidentially. "There was a time," he said in a tone that was quite unreally airy, offhand and disengaged, "years ago, when I totally lost my head about her. Totally." Those tear-wet patches on his pillow cold against his cheek in the darkness; and oh, the horrible pain of weeping, vainly, for something that was nothing, that was everything in the world! "Toward the end of the war it was. I remember walking up this dismal street one night, in the pitch darkness, writhing with jealousy." He was silent. Spectrally, like a dim haunting ghost, he had hung about her; dumbly, dumbly imploring, appealing. "The weak silent man," she used to call him. And once for two or three days, out of pity, out of affection, out of a mere desire, perhaps to lay the tiresome ghost, she had given him what his mournful silence implored—only to take it back, almost as soon as accorded. That other night, when he had walked up this street before, desire had eaten out his vitals and his body seemed empty, sickeningly and achingly void; jealousy was busily reminding him, with an unflagging malice, of her beauty—of her beauty and the hateful, ruffian hands which now caressed, the eyes which looked on it. That was all long ago.

"She is certainly handsome," said Shearwater, commenting, at one or two removes, on Gumbril's last remark. "I can see that she might make anyone who got involved in her decidedly uncomfortable." After a day or two's continuous sweating, it suddenly occurred to him, one might perhaps find sea water more refreshing than fresh water. That would be queer.

Gumbril burst out ferociously laughing. "But there were other times," he went on jauntily, "when other people were jealous of me." Ah, revenge, revenge. In the better world of the imagination it was possible to get one's own back. What fiendish vendettas were there carried to successful ends! "I remember once writing her a quatrain in French." (He had written it years after the whole thing was over; he had never sent it to anyone at

all; but that was all one.) "How did it go? Ah, yes." And he recited with
suitable gestures:

> Puisque nous sommes là, je dois,
> Vous avertir, sans trop de honte,
> Que je n'égale pas le Comte,
> Casanovesque de Sixfois.

"Rather prettily turned, I flatter myself. Rather elegantly gross."

Gumbril's laughter went hooting past the Marble Arch. It stopped
rather suddenly, however, at the corner of the Edgeware Road. He had suddenly remembered Mr. Mercaptan, and the thought depressed him.

Chapter VI

IT WAS between Whitefield Street and the Tottenham Court Road, in
a "heavenly Mews," as he liked to call it (for he had a characteristic weakness for philosophical paronomasia), that Casimir Lypiatt lived and
worked. You passed under an archway of bald and sooty brick—and at
night, when the green gas lamp underneath the arch threw vivid lights
and enormous architectural shadows, you could fancy yourself at the
entrance of one of Piranesi's prisons—and you found yourself in a long
cul-de-sac, flanked on either side by low buildings, having stabling for
horses below and, less commodiously, stabling for human beings in the
attics above. An old-fashioned smell of animals mingled with the more
progressive stink of burned oil. The air was a little thicker here, it
seemed, than in the streets outside; looking down the mews on even
the clearest day, you could see the forms of things dimming and sof-
tening, the colors growing richer and deeper with every yard of distance.
It was the best place in the world, Lypiatt used to say, for studying
aerial perspective; that was why he lived there. But you always felt about
poor Lypiatt that he was facing misfortune with a jest a little too self-
consciously.

Mrs. Viveash's taxi drove in under the Piranesian arch, drove in
slowly and as though with a gingerly reluctance to soil its white wheels
on pavements so sordid. The cabman looked round inquiringly.

"This right?" he asked.

With a white-gloved finger Mrs. Viveash prodded the air two or three
times, indicating that he was to drive straight on. Halfway down the
mews she rapped the glass; the man drew up.

"Never been down 'ere before," he said, for the sake of making a little conversation, while Mrs. Viveash fumbled for her money. He looked at her with a polite and slightly ironic curiosity that was frankly mingled with admiration.

"You're lucky," said Mrs. Viveash. "We poor decayed gentlewomen— you see what we're reduced to." And she handed him a florin.

Slowly the taxi man unbuttoned his coat and put the coin away in an inner pocket. He watched her as she crossed the dirty street, placing her feet with a meticulous precision one after the other in the same straight line, as though she were treading a knife edge between goodness only knew what invisible gulfs. Floating she seemed to go, with a little spring at every step and the skirt of her summery dress—white it was, with a florid pattern printed in black all over it—blowing airily out round her swaying march. "Decayed gentlewomen" indeed! The driver started his machine with an unnecessary violence; he felt, for some reason, positively indignant.

Between the broad double doors through which the horses passed to their fodder and repose were little narrow human doors—for the Yahoos, Lypiatt used to say in his large allusive way; and when he said it he laughed with the loud and bell-mouthed cynicism of one who sees himself as a misunderstood and embittered Prometheus. At one of these little Yahoo doors Mrs. Viveash halted and rapped as loudly as a small and stiff-hinged knocker would permit. Patiently she waited; several small and dirty children collected to stare at her. She knocked again and again waited. More children came running up from the further end of the mews; two young girls of fifteen or sixteen appeared at a neighboring doorway and immediately gave tongue in whoops of mirthless hyena-like laughter.

"Have you ever read about the pied piper of Hamelin?" Mrs. Viveash asked the nearest child. Terrified, it shrank away. "I thought not," she said and knocked again.

There was a sound, at last, of heavy feet slowly descending steep stairs; the door opened.

"Welcome to the palazzo!" It was Lypiatt's heroic formula of hospitality.

"Welcome at last," Mrs. Viveash corrected, and followed him up a narrow dark staircase that was as steep as a ladder. He was dressed in a velveteen jacket and linen trousers that should have been white, but needed washing. He was disheveled and his hands were dirty.

"Did you knock more than once?" he asked, looking back over his shoulder.

"More than twenty times," Mrs. Viveash justifiably exaggerated.

"I'm infinitely sorry," protested Lypiatt. "I get so deeply absorbed in my work, you know. Did you wait long?"

"The children enjoyed it, at any rate." Mrs. Viveash was irritated by a suspicion, which was probably, after all, quite unjustified, that Casimir had been rather consciously absorbed in his work; that he had heard her first knock and plunged the more profoundly into those depths of absorption where the true artist always dwells, or at any rate ought to dwell; to rise at her third appeal with a slow, pained reluctance, cursing, perhaps, at the importunity of a world which thus noisily interrupted the flow of his inspiration. "Queer, the way they stare at one," she went on with a note in her dying voice of a petulance that the children had not inspired. "Does one look such a guy?"

Lypiatt threw open the door at the head of the stairs and stood there on the threshold, waiting for her. "Queer?" he repeated. "Not a bit." And as she moved past him into the room, he laid his hand on her shoulder and fell into step with her, leaving the door to slam behind them. "Merely an example of the mob's instinctive dislike of the aristocratic individual. That's all. 'Oh, why was I born with a different face?' Thank God I was, though. And so were you. But the difference has its disadvantages; the children throw stones."

"They didn't throw stones." Mrs. Viveash was too truthful, this time.

They halted in the middle of the studio. It was not a very large room and there were too many things in it. The easel stood near the center of the studio; round it Lypiatt kept a space permanently cleared. There was a broad fairway leading to the door, and another, narrower and tortuously winding between boxes and piled-up furniture and tumbled books, gave access to his bed. There was a piano and a table permanently set with dirty plates and strewed with the relics of two or three meals. Bookshelves stood on either side of the fireplace, and lying on the floor were still more books, piles on dusty piles. Mrs. Viveash stood looking at the picture on the easel (abstract again—she didn't like it) and Lypiatt, who had dropped his hand from her shoulder, had stepped back the better to see her, stood earnestly looking at Mrs. Viveash.

"May I kiss you?" he asked after a silence.

Mrs. Viveash turned toward him, smiling agonizingly, her eyebrows ironically lifted, her eyes steady and calm and palely, brightly inexpressive. "If it really gives you any pleasure," she said. "It won't, I may say, to me."

"You make me suffer a great deal," said Lypiatt, and said it so quietly and unaffectedly that Myra was almost startled; she was accustomed, with Casimir, to noisier and more magniloquent protestations.

"I'm very sorry," she said; and, really, she felt sorry. "But I can't help it, can I?"

"I suppose you can't," he said. "You can't," he repeated and his voice had now become the voice of Prometheus in his bitterness. "Nor can tigresses." He had begun to pace up and down the unobstructed fairway between his easel and the door; Lypiatt liked pacing while he talked. "You like playing with the victim," he went on; "he must die slowly."

Reassured, Mrs. Viveash faintly smiled. This was the familiar Casimir. So long as he could talk like this, could talk like an old-fashioned French novel, it was all right; he couldn't really be so very unhappy. She sat down on the nearest unencumbered chair. Lypiatt continued to walk back and forth, waving his arms as he walked.

"But perhaps it's good for one to suffer," he went on, "perhaps it's unavoidable and necessary. Perhaps I ought to thank you. Can an artist do anything if he's happy? Would he ever want to do anything? What is art, after all, but a protest against the horrible inclemency of life?" He halted in front of her, with arms extended in a questioning gesture. Mrs. Viveash slightly shrugged her shoulders. She really didn't know; she couldn't answer. "Ah, but that's all nonsense," he burst out again, "all rot. I want to be happy and contented and successful; and of course I should work better if I were. And I want, oh, above everything, everything, I want you: to possess you completely and exclusively and jealously and forever. And the desire is like rust corroding my heart, it's like moth-eating holes in the fabric of my mind. And you merely laugh." He threw up his hands and let them limply fall again.

"But I don't laugh," said Mrs. Viveash. On the contrary, she was very sorry for him; and, what was more, he rather bored her. For a few days, once, she had thought she might be in love with him. His impetuosity had seemed a torrent strong enough to carry her away. She had found out her mistake very soon. After that he had rather amused her: and now he rather bored her. No, decidedly, she never laughed. She wondered why she still went on seeing him. Simply because one must see someone? or why? "Are you going to go on with my portrait?" she asked.

Lypiatt sighed. "Yes," he said, "I suppose I'd better be getting on with my work. Work—it's the only thing. 'Portrait of a Tigress.' " The cynical Titan spoke again. "Or shall I call it, 'Portrait of a Woman Who Has Never Been in Love'?"

"That would be a very stupid title," said Mrs. Viveash.

"Or, 'Portrait of the Artist's Heart Disease'? That would be good;

that would be damned good." Lypiatt laughed very loudly and slapped his thighs. He looked, Mrs. Viveash thought, peculiarly ugly when he laughed. His face seemed to go all to pieces; not a corner of it but was wrinkled and distorted by the violent grimace of mirth. Even the forehead was ruined when he laughed. Foreheads are generally the human part of people's faces. Let the nose twitch and the mouth grin and the eyes twinkle monkeyishly as you like; the forehead can still be calm and serene, the forehead still knows how to be human. But when Casimir laughed, his forehead joined in the general distorting grimace. And sometimes even when he wasn't laughing, when he was just vivaciously talking, his forehead seemed to lose its calm and would twitch and wrinkle itself in a dreadful kind of agitation. "Portrait of the Artist's Heart Disease"—she didn't find it so very funny.

"The critics would think it was a problem picture," Lypiatt went on. "And so it would be, by God; so it would be. You are a problem. You're the Sphinx. I wish I were Oedipus and could kill you."

All this mythology! Mrs. Viveash shook her head.

He made his way through the intervening litter and picked up a canvas that was leaning with averted face against the wall near the window. He held it out at arm's length and examined it, his head critically cocked on one side. "Oh, it's good," he said softly. "It's good. Look at it." And stepping out once more into the open, he propped it up against the table so that Mrs. Viveash could see it without moving from her chair.

It was a stormy vision of her, it was Myra seen, so to speak, through a tornado. He had distorted her in the portrait, had made her longer and thinner than she really was, had turned her arms into sleek tubes and put a bright metallic polish on the curve of her cheek. The figure in the portrait seemed to be leaning backward a little from the surface of the canvas, leaning sideways too, with the twist of an ivory statuette carved out of the curving tip of a great tusk. Only somehow in Lypiatt's portrait the curve seemed to lack grace, it was without point; it had no sense.

"You've made me look," said Mrs. Viveash at last, "as though I were being blown out of shape by the wind." All this show of violence—what was the point of it? She didn't like it; she didn't like it at all. But Casimir was delighted with her comment. He slapped his thighs and once more laughed his restless sharp-featured face to pieces.

"Yes, by God," he shouted, "by God! that's right. Blown out of shape by the wind. That's it: you've said it." He began stamping up and down the room again, gesticulating. "The wind, the great wind that's in me."

He struck his forehead. "The wind of life, the wild west wind. I feel it inside me, blowing, blowing. It carries me along with it; for though it's inside me, it's more than I am, it's force that comes from somewhere else, it's Life itself, it's God. It blows me along in the teeth of opposing fate; it makes me work on, fight on." He was like a man who walks along a sinister road at night and sings to keep up his own spirits, to emphasize and magnify his own existence. "And when I paint, when I write or improvise my music, it bends the things I have in my mind, it pushes them in one direction, so that everything I do has the look of a tree that streams northeast with all its branches and all its trunk from the root upward, as though it were trying to run from before the Atlantic gale."

Lypiatt stretched out his two hands and, with fingers splayed out to the widest and trembling in the excessive tension of the muscles, moved them slowly upward and sideways, as though he were running his palms up the stem of a little wind-wizened tree on a hilltop above the ocean.

Mrs. Viveash continued to look at the unfinished portrait. It was as noisy and easy and immediately effective as a vermouth advertisement in the streets of Padua. Cinzano, Bonomelli, Campari—illustrious names. Giotto and Mantegna moldered meanwhile in their respective chapels.

"And look at this," Lypiatt went on. He took down the canvas that was clamped to the easel and held it out for her inspection. It was one of Casimir's abstract paintings: a procession of machinelike forms rushing up diagonally from right to left across the canvas, with, as it were, a spray of energy blowing back from the crest of the wave toward the top right-hand corner. "In this painting," he said, "I symbolize the Artist's conquering spirit—rushing on the universe, making it its own." He began to declaim:

> Look down, Conquistador,
> There on the valley's broad green floor,
> There lies the lake, the jeweled cities gleam,
> Chalco and Tlacopan
> Awaiting the coming Man;
> Look down on Mexico, Conquistador,
> Land of your golden dream.

"Or the same idea in terms of music——" and Lypiatt dashed to the piano and evoked a distorted ghost of Scriabine. "You see?" he asked feverishly, when the ghost was laid down again and the sad cheap jangling had faded again into silence. "You *feel?* The artist rushes on the world, conquers it, gives it beauty, imposes a moral significance." He returned to the picture. "This will be fine when it's finished," he said. "Tremendous. You feel the wind blowing there, too." And with a pointing finger he followed up the onrush of the forms. "The great southwester driving them on. 'Like leaves from an enchanter fleeing.' Only not chaotically, not in disorder. They're blown, so to speak, in column of four—by a conscious wind." He leaned the canvas against the table and was free again to march and brandish his conquering fists.

"Life," he said, "life—that's the great, essential thing. You've got to get life into your art; otherwise it's nothing. And life only comes out of life, out of passion and feeling; it can't come out of theories. That's the stupidity of all this chatter about art for art's sake and the esthetic emotions and purely formal values and all that. It's only the formal relations that matter; one subject is just as good as another—that's the theory. You've only got to look at the pictures of the people who put it into practice to see that it won't do. Life comes out of life. You must paint with passion and the passion will stimulate your intellect to create the right formal relations. And to paint with passion, you must paint things that passionately interest you, moving things, human things. Nobody, except a mystical pantheist, like Van Gogh, can seriously be as much interested in napkins, apples and bottles as in his lover's face, or the resurrection, or the destiny of man. Could Mantegna have devised his splendid compositions if he had painted arrangements of Chianti flasks and cheeses instead of Crucifixions, martyrs and triumphs of great men? Nobody but a fool could believe it. And could I have painted that portrait if I hadn't loved you, if you weren't killing me?"

Ah, Bonomelli and illustrious Cinzano!

"Passionately I paint passion. I draw life out of life. And I wish them joy of their bottles and their Canadian apples and their muddy table napkins with the beastly folds in them that look like loops of tripe." Once more Lypiatt disintegrated himself with laughter; then was silent.

Mrs. Viveash nodded, slowly and reflectively. "I think you're right," she said. Yes, he was surely right; there must be life, life was the important thing. That was precisely why his paintings were so bad—she saw now; there was no life in them. Plenty of noise there was, and gesticulation and a violent galvanized twitching; but no life, only the theatrical show of it. There was a flaw in the conduit; somewhere between the man and his work life leaked out. He protested too much. But it was no good; there was no disguising the deadness. Her portrait was a dancing mummy. He bored her now. Did she even positively dislike him? Behind her unchanging pale eyes Mrs. Viveash wondered. But in any case, she reflected, one needn't always like the people with whom one associates.

There are music halls as well as confidential boudoirs; some people are admitted to the tea party and the tête-à-tête; others, on a stage invisible, poor things! to themselves, do their little song-and-dance, roll out their characteristic patter, and having provided you with your entertainment are dismissed with their due share of applause. But then, what if they become boring?

"Well," said Lypiatt at last—he had stood there, motionless, for a long time, biting his nails, "I suppose we'd better begin our sitting." He picked up the unfinished portrait and adjusted it on the easel. "I've wasted a lot of time," he said, "and there isn't, after all, so much of it to waste." He spoke gloomily and his whole person had become, all of a sudden, curiously shrunken and deflated. "There isn't so much of it," he repeated, and sighed. "I still think of myself as a young man, young and promising, don't you know. Casimir Lypiatt—it's a young, promising sort of name, isn't it? But I'm not young, I've passed the age of promise. Every now and then I realize it, and it's painful; it's depressing."

Mrs. Viveash stepped up on to the model's dais and took her seat. "Is that right?" she asked.

Lypiatt looked first at her, then at his picture. Her beauty, his passion —were they only to meet on the canvas? Opps was her lover. Time was passing; he felt tired. "That'll do," he said and began painting. "How young are you?" he asked after a moment.

"Twenty-five, I should imagine," said Mrs. Viveash.

"Twenty-five? Good Lord, it's nearly fifteen years since I was twenty-five. Fifteen years, fighting all the time. God, how I hate people sometimes! Everybody. It's not their malignity I mind; I can give them back as good as they give me. It's their power of silence and indifference, it's their capacity for making themselves deaf. Here am I with something to say to them, something important and essential. And I've been saying it for more than fifteen years, I've been shouting it. They pay no attention. I bring them my head and heart on a charger and they don't even notice that the things are there. I sometimes wonder how much longer I can manage to go on." His voice had become very low and it trembled. "One's nearly forty, you know. . . ." The voice faded huskily away into silence. Languidly and as though the business exhausted him, he began mixing colors on his palette.

Mrs. Viveash looked at him. No, he wasn't young; at the moment, indeed, he seemed to have become much older than he really was. An old man was standing there, peaked and sharp and worn. He had failed, he was unhappy. But the world would have been unjuster, less discriminating if it had given him success.

blood behind his eyes. He laughed aloud; he was a laughing lion. He
stretched out his arms; he was enormous; his arms reached out like the
branches of a cedar. The Artist walked across the world and the mangy
dogs ran yelping and snapping behind him. The great wind blew and
blew, driving him on; it lifted him and he began to fly.

Mrs. Viveash listened. It didn't look as though he would get much
further with the portrait.

Chapter VII

IT WAS Press Day. The critics had begun to arrive. Mr. Albemarle
circulated among them with a ducal amiability. The young assistant
hovered vaguely about, straining to hear what the great men had to say
and trying to pretend that he wasn't eavesdropping. Lypiatt's pictures
hung on the walls and Lypiatt's catalogue, thick with its preface and its
explanatory notes, was in all hands.

"Very strong," Mr. Albemarle kept repeating, "very strong indeed." It
was his password for the day.

Little Mr. Clew, who represented the *Daily Post*, was inclined to be
enthusiastic. "How well he writes!" he said to Mr. Albemarle, looking up
from the catalogue. "And how well he paints! What *impasto*."

Impasto, impasto—the young assistant sidled off unobtrusively to the
desk and made a note of it. He would look the word up in Grubb's
Dictionary of Art and Artists, later on. He made his way back, circuitously
and as though by accident, into Mr. Clew's neighborhood.

Mr. Clew was one of those rare people who have a real passion for art.
He loved painting, all painting, indiscriminately. In a picture gallery he
was like a Turk in a harem; he adored them all. He loved Memling as
much as Raphael; he loved Grünewald and Michelangelo, Holman Hunt
and Manet, Romney and Tintoretto; how happy he could be with all of
them! Sometimes, it is true, he hated; but that was only when familiarity
had not yet bred love. At the first Post-Impressionist Exhibition, for
example, in 1911, he had taken a very firm stand. "This is an obscene
farce," he had written then. Now, however, there was no more passionate
admirer of Matisse's genius. As a connoisseur and *kunstforscher* Mr.
Clew was much esteemed. People would bring him dirty old pictures to
look at and he would exclaim at once: Why, it's an El Greco, a Piazzetta,
or some other suitable name. Asked how he knew, he would shrug his
shoulders and say: But it's signed all over. His certainty and his enthusiasm were infectious. Since the coming of El Greco into fashion, he had

discovered dozens of early works by that great artist. For Lord Petersfield's collection alone he had found four early El Grecos, all by pupils of Bassano. Lord Petersfield's confidence in Mr. Clew was unbounded; not even that affair of the Primitives had shaken it. It was a sad affair: Lord Petersfield's Duccio had shown signs of cracking; the estate carpenter was sent for to take a look at the panel; he had looked. "A worse seasoned piece of Illinois hickory," he said, "I've never seen." After that he looked at the Simone Martini; for that, on the contrary, he was full of praise. Smooth grained, well seasoned—it wouldn't crack, no, not in a hundred years. "A nicer slice of board never came out of America." He had a hyperbolical way of speaking. Lord Petersfield was extremely angry; he dismissed the estate carpenter on the spot. After that he told Mr. Clew that he wanted a Giorgione, and Mr. Clew went out and found him one which was signed all over.

"I like this very much," said Mr. Clew, pointing to one of the thoughts with which Lypiatt had prefaced his catalogue. " 'Genius,' " he adjusted his spectacles and began to read aloud, " 'is life. Genius is a force of nature. In art, nothing else counts. The modern impotents, who are afraid of genius and who are envious of it, have invented in self-defense the notion of the Artist. The Artist with his sense of form, his style, his devotion to pure beauty, et cetera, et cetera. But Genius includes the Artist: every Genius has, among very many others, the qualities attributed by the impotents to the Artist. The Artist without genius is a carver of fountains through which no water flows.' Very true," said Mr. Clew, "very true indeed." He marked the passage with his pencil.

Mr. Albemarle produced the password. "Very strongly put," he said.

"I have always felt that myself," said Mr. Clew. "El Greco, for example. . . ."

"Good morning, what about El Greco?" said a voice, all in one breath. The thin, long, skin-covered skeleton of Mr. Mallard hung over them like a guilty conscience. Mr. Mallard wrote every week in the *Hebdomadal Digest*. He had an immense knowledge of art and a sincere dislike of all that was beautiful. The only modern painter whom he really admired was Hodler. All others were treated by him with a merciless savagery; he tore them to pieces in his weekly articles with all the holy gusto of a Calvinist iconoclast smashing images of the Virgin.

"What about El Greco?" he repeated. He had a peculiarly passionate loathing of El Greco.

Mr. Clew smiled up at him propitiatingly; he was afraid of Mr. Mallard. His enthusiasms were no match for Mr. Mallard's erudite and logical disgusts. "I was merely quoting him as an example," he said.

"An example, I hope, of incompetent drawing, baroque composition, disgusting forms, garish coloring and hysterical subject matter." Mr. Mallard showed his old ivory teeth in a menacing smile. "Those are the only things which El Greco's work exemplifies."

Mr. Clew gave a nervous little laugh. "What do you think of these?" he asked, pointing to Lypiatt's canvases.

"They look to me very ordinarily bad," answered Mr. Mallard.

The young assistant listened appalled. In a business like this, how was it possible to make good?

"All the same," said Mr. Clew courageously, "I like that bowl of roses in the window with the landscape behind. Number twenty-nine." He looked in the catalogue. "And there's a really charming little verse about it:

> O beauty of the rose,
> Goodness as well as perfume exhaling!
> Who gazes on these flowers,
> On this blue hill and ripening field—he knows
> Where duty leads and that the nameless Powers
> In a rose can speak their will.

Really charming!" Mr. Clew made another mark with his pencil.

"But commonplace, commonplace;" Mr. Mallard shook his head. "And in any case a verse can't justify a bad picture. What an unsubtle harmony of color! And how uninteresting the composition is! That receding diagonal—it's been worked to death." He too made a mark in his cata- logue—a cross and a little circle, arranged like the skull and crossbones on a pirate's flag. Mr. Mallard's catalogues were always covered with these little marks; they were his symbols of condemnation.

Mr. Albemarle, meanwhile, had moved away to greet the new arrivals. To the critic of the Daily Cinema he had to explain that there were no portraits of celebrities. The reporter from the Evening Planet had to be told which were the best pictures.

"Mr. Lypiatt," he dictated, "is a poet and philosopher as well as a painter. His catalogue is a—h'm—declaration of faith."

The reporter took it down in shorthand. "And very nice too," he said. "I'm most grateful to you, sir, most grateful." And he hurried away, to get to the Cattle Show before the King should arrive. Mr. Albemarle affably addressed himself to the critic of the Morning Globe.

"I always regard this gallery," said a loud and cheerful voice, full of bulls and canaries in chorus, "as positively a mauvais lieu. Such exhibi- tions!" And Mr. Mercaptan shrugged his shoulders expressively. He halted to wait for his companion.

Mrs. Viveash had lagged behind, reading the catalogue as she slowly
walked along. "It's a complete book," she said, "full of poems and essays
and short stories even, so far as I can see."

"Oh, the usual cracker mottoes." Mr. Mercaptan laughed. "I know the
sort of thing. 'Look after the past and the future will look after itself.'
'God squared minus Man squared equals Art-plus-life times Art-minus-
Life.' 'The Higher the Art the fewer the morals'—only that's too nearly
good sense to have been invented by Lypiatt. But I know the sort of
thing. I could go on like that forever." Mr. Mercaptan was delighted with
himself.

"I'll read you one of them," said Mrs. Viveash. " 'A picture is a
chemical combination of plastic form and spiritual significance.' "

"Crikey," said Mr. Mercaptan.

" 'Those who think that a picture is a matter of nothing but plastic
form are like those who imagine that water is made of nothing but
hydrogen.' "

Mr. Mercaptan made a grimace. "What writing!" he exclaimed, "*le
style c'est l'homme.* Lypiatt hasn't got a style. Argal—inexorable conclusion—Lypiatt doesn't exist. My word, though. Look at those horrible great
nudes there. Like Carracis with cubical muscles."

"Samson and Delilah," said Mrs. Viveash. "Would you like me to
read about them?"

"Certainly not."

Mrs. Viveash did not press the matter. Casimir, she thought, must have
been thinking of her when he wrote this little poem about Poets and
Women, crossed genius, torments, the sweating of masterpieces. She
sighed. "Those leopards are rather nice," she said, and looked at the
catalogue again. " 'An animal is a symbol and its form is significant. In
the long process of adaptation, evolution has refined and simplified and
shaped, till every part of the animal expresses one desire, a single idea.
Man, who has become what he is, not by specialization but by generalization, symbolizes with his body no one thing. He is a symbol of everything from the most hideous and ferocious bestiality to godhead.' "

"Dear me," said Mr. Mercaptan.

A canvas of mountains and enormous clouds like nascent sculptures
presented itself.

" 'Aerial Alps' " Mrs. Viveash began to read.

Aerial Alps of amber and of snow,
Junonian flesh, and bosomy alabaster
Carved by the wind's uncertain hands . . .

Mr. Mercaptan stopped his ears. "Please, please," he begged.

"Number seventeen," said Mrs. Viveash, "is called 'Woman on a Cosmic Background.'" A female figure stood leaning against a pillar on a hilltop and beyond was a blue night with stars. "Underneath is written. 'For one at least; she is more than the starry universe.'" Mrs. Viveash remembered that Lypiatt had once said very much that sort of thing to her. "So many of Casimir's things remind me," she said, "of those Italian vermouth advertisements. You know—Cinzano, Bonomelli and all those. I wish they didn't. This woman in white with her head in the Great Bear. . . ." She shook her head. "Poor Casimir."

Mr. Mercaptan roared and squealed with laughter. "Bonomelli," he said, "that's precisely it. What a critic, Myra! I take off my hat." They moved on. "And what's this grand transformation scene?" he asked.

Mrs. Viveash looked at the catalogue. "It's called 'The Sermon on the Mount,'" she said. "And really, do you know, I rather like it. All that crowd of figures slanting up the hill and the single figure at the top—it seems to me very dramatic."

"My dear," protested Mr. Mercaptan.

"And in spite of everything," said Mrs. Viveash, feeling suddenly and uncomfortably that she had somehow been betraying the man, "he's really very nice, you know. Very nice, indeed." Her expiring voice sounded very decidedly.

"Ah, ces femmes," exclaimed Mr. Mercaptan, "ces femmes! They're all Pasiphaes and Ledas. They all in their hearts prefer beasts to men, savages to civilized beings. Even you, Myra, I really believe." He shook his head.

Mrs. Viveash ignored the outburst. "Very nice," she repeated, thoughtfully. "Only rather a bore. . . ." Her voice expired altogether.

They continued their round of the gallery.

Chapter VIII

CRITICALLY, in the glasses of Mr. Bojanus's fitting room, Gumbril examined his profile, his back view. Inflated, the Patent Small Clothes bulged, bulged decidedly, though with a certain gracious opulence that might, in a person of the other sex, have seemed only deliciously natural. In him, however, Gumbril had to admit, the opulence seemed a little misplaced and paradoxical. Still, if one has to suffer in order to be beautiful, one must also expect to be ugly in order not to suffer. Practically, the trousers were a tremendous success. He sat down heavily on the hard wooden bench of the fitting room and was received as though on a lap of bounding resiliency; the Patent Small Clothes, there was no doubt, would be proof even against marble. And the coat, he comforted himself, would mask with its skirts the too decided bulge. Or if it didn't, well, there was no help for it. One must resign oneself to bulging; that was all.

"Very nice," he declared at last.

Mr. Bojanus, who had been watching his client in silence and with a polite but also, Gumbril could not help feeling, a somewhat ironical smile, coughed. "It depends," he said, "precisely what you mean by 'nice.'" He cocked his head on one side, and the fine waxed end of his mustache was like a pointer aimed up at some remote star.

Gumbril said nothing, but catching sight once more of his own side view nodded a dubious agreement.

"If by nice," continued Mr. Bojanus, "you mean comfortable, well and good. If, however, you mean elegant, then, Mr. Gumbril, I fear I must disagree."

"But elegance," said Gumbril, feebly playing the philosopher, "is only relative, Mr. Bojanus. There are certain African Negroes, among whom it is considered elegant to pierce the lips and distend them with wooden plates, until the mouth looks like a pelican's beak."

Mr. Bojanus placed his hand in his bosom and slightly bowed. "Very possibly, Mr. Gumbril," he replied. "But if you'll pardon my saying so, we are not African Negroes."

Gumbril was crushed, deservedly. He looked at himself again in the mirrors. "Do you object," he asked after a pause, "to all eccentricities in dress, Mr. Bojanus? Would you put us all into your elegant uniform?"

"Certainly not," replied Mr. Bojanus. "There are certain walks of life in which eccentricity in appearance is positively a *sine qua non*, Mr. Gumbril, and I might say *de rigueur*."

"And which walks of life, Mr. Bojanus, may I ask? You refer perhaps to the artistic walks? Sombreros and Byronic collars and possibly velveteen trousers? Though all that sort of thing is surely a little out of date, nowadays."

Enigmatically Mr. Bojanus smiled, a playful Sphinx. He thrust his right hand deeper into his bosom and with his left twisted to a finer needle the point of his mustache. "Not artists, Mr. Gumbril." He shook his head. "In practice they may show themselves a little eccentric and negleejay. But they have no need to look unusual on principle. It's only the politicians who need do it on principle. It's only *de rigueur*, as one might say, in the political walks, Mr. Gumbril."

"You surprise me," said Gumbril. "I should have thought that it was to the politician's interest to look respectable and normal."

"But it is still more to his interest as a leader of men to look distinguished," Mr. Bojanus replied. "Well, not precisely distinguished," he corrected himself, "because that implies that politicians look *distangay*, which I regret to say, Mr. Gumbril, they very often don't. Distinguishable is more what I mean."

"Eccentricity is their badge of office?" suggested Gumbril. He sat down luxuriously on the Patent Small Clothes.

"That's more like it," said Mr. Bojanus, tilting his mustaches. "The leader has got to look different from the other ones. In the good old days they always wore their official badges. The leader had his livery, like everyone else, to show who he was. That was sensible, Mr. Gumbril. Nowadays he has no badge—at least not for ordinary occasions—for I don't count Privy Counselors' uniforms and all that sort of once-a-year fancy dress. He's reduced to dressing in some eccentric way or making the most of the peculiarities of his personal appearance. A very haphazard method of doing things, Mr. Gumbril, very haphazard."

Gumbril agreed.

Mr. Bojanus went on, making small, neat gestures as he spoke. "Some of them," he said, "wear huge collars like Mr. Gladstone. Some wear orchids and eyeglasses, like Joe Chamberlain. Some let their hair grow, like Lloyd George. Some wear curious hats, like Winston Churchill. Some put on black shirts, like this Mussolini, and some put on red ones, like Garibaldi. Some turn up their mustaches, like the German Emperor. Some turn them down, like Clemenceau. Some grow whiskers, like Tirpitz. I don't speak of all the uniforms, orders, ornaments, headdresses, feathers, crowns, buttons, tattooings, earrings, sashes, swords, trains, tiaras, urims, thummims and what not, Mr. Gumbril, that have been used in the past and in other parts of the world to distinguish the leader. We, 'oo know our history, Mr. Gumbril, we know all about that."

Gumbril made a deprecating gesture. "You speak for yourself, Mr. Bojanus," he said.

Mr. Bojanus bowed.

"Pray continue," said Gumbril.

Mr. Bojanus bowed again. "Well, Mr. Gumbril," he said, "the point of all these things, as I've already remarked, is to make the leader look different, so that he can be recognized at the first *coop d'oil*, as you might say, by the herd he happens to be leading. For the human herd, Mr. Gumbril, is a herd which can't do without a leader. Sheep, for example: I never noticed that they had a leader; nor rooks. Bees, on the other hand, I take it, have. At least when they're swarming. Correct me, Mr. Gumbril, if I'm wrong. Natural history was never, as you might say, my forty."

"Nor mine," protested Gumbril.

"As for elephants and wolves, Mr. Gumbril, I can't pretend to speak of them with first-'and knowledge. Nor llamas, nor locusts, nor squab pigeons, nor lemmings. But human beings, Mr. Gumbril, those I can claim to talk of with authority, if I may say so in all modesty, and not as the scribes. I have made a special study of them, Mr. Gumbril. And my profession has brought me into contact with very numerous specimens."

Gumbril could not help wondering where precisely in Mr. Bojanus's museum he himself had his place.

"The human herd," Mr. Bojanus went on, "must have a leader. And a leader must have something to distinguish him from the herd. It's important for his interests that he should be recognized easily. See a baby reaching out of a bath and you immediately think of Pears' Soap; see the white hair waving out behind and think of Lloyd George. That's the secret. But in my opinion, Mr. Gumbril, the old system was much more sensible, give them regular uniforms and badges, I say; make cabinet ministers wear feathers in their hair. Then the people will be looking to a real fixed symbol of leadership, not to the peculiarities of the mere individuals. Beards and hair and funny collars change; but a good uniform is always the same. Give them feathers; that's what I say, Mr. Gumbril. Feathers will increase the dignity of the state and lessen the importance of the individual. And that," concluded Mr. Bojanus with emphasis, "that, Mr. Gumbril, will be all to the good."

"But you don't mean to tell me," said Gumbril, "that if I chose to show myself to the multitude in my inflated trousers, I could become a leader—do you?"

"Ah, no," said Mr. Bojanus. "You'd have to have the talent for talking and ordering people about, to begin with. Feathers wouldn't give the genius, but they'd magnify the effect of what there was."

Gumbril got up and began to divest himself of the Small Clothes. He unscrewed the valve and the air whistled out, dyingly. He too sighed. "Curious," he said pensively, "that I've never felt the need for a leader. I've never met anyone I felt I could wholeheartedly admire or believe in, never anyone I wanted to follow. It must be pleasant, I should think, to hand oneself over to somebody else. It must give you a warm, splendid, comfortable feeling."

Mr. Bojanus smiled and shook his head. "You and I, Mr. Gumbril," he said, "we're not the sort of people to be impressed with feathers or even

by talking and ordering about. We may not be leaders ourselves. But at
any rate we aren't the herd."

"Not the main herd, perhaps."

"Not any herd," Mr. Bojanus insisted proudly.

Gumbril shook his head dubiously and buttoned up his trousers. He
was not sure, now he came to think of it, that he didn't belong to all the
herds—by a sort of honorary membership and temporarily, as occasion
offered, as one belongs to the Union at the sister university or the Naval
and Military Club while one's own is having its annual clean-out. Shearwater's herd, Lypiatt's herd, Mr. Mercaptan's herd, Mrs. Viveash's herd,
the architectural herd of his father, the educational herd (but that, thank
God! was now bleating on distant pastures), the herd of Mr. Bojanus—
he belonged to them all a little, to none of them completely. Nobody
belonged to his herd. How could they? No chameleon can live with comfort on a tartan. He put on his coat.

"I'll send the garments this evening," said Mr. Bojanus.

Gumbril left the shop. At the theatrical wigmaker's in Leicester Square
he ordered a blond fan-shaped beard to match his own hair and mustache.
He would, at any rate, be his own leader; he would wear a badge, a symbol
of authority. And Coleman had said that there were dangerous relations
to be entered into by the symbol's aid.

Ah, now he was provisionally a member of Coleman's herd. It was all
very depressing.

Chapter IX

FAN shaped, blond, mounted on gauze and guaranteed undetectable, it
arrived from the wigmaker, preciously packed in a stout cardboard box
six times too large for it and accompanied by a quarter of a pint of the
choicest spirit gum. In the privacy of his bedroom Gumbril uncoffined
it, held it out for his own admiration, caressed its silkiness and finally
tried it on, holding it provisionally to his chin, in front of the looking
glass. The effect, he decided immediately, was stunning, was grandiose.
From melancholy and all too mild he saw himself transformed on the
instant into a sort of jovial Henry the Eighth, into a massive Rabelaisian
man, broad and powerful and exuberant with vitality and hair.

The proportions of his face were startlingly altered. The podium, below
the mouth, had been insufficiently massive to carry the stately order of the
nose, and the ratiocinative attic of the forehead, noble enough, no doubt,

in itself, had been disproportionately high. The beard now supplied the deficiencies in the stylobate, and planted now on a firm basement of will, the order of the senses, the aerial attic of ideas reared themselves with a more classical harmoniousness of proportion. It only remained for him to order from Mr. Bojanus an American coat, padded out at the shoulders as squarely and heroically as a doublet of the cinquecento, and he would look the complete Rabelaisian man. Great eater, deep drinker, stout fighter, prodigious lover; clear thinker, creator of beauty, seeker of truth and prophet of heroic grandeurs. Fitted out with coat and beard, he could qualify for the next vacancy among the cenobites of Thélème.

He removed his beard—"put his beaver up," as they used to say in the fine old days of chivalry; he would have to remember that little joke for Coleman's benefit. He put his beaver up—ha, ha—and stared ruefully at the far from Rabelaisian figure which now confronted him. The mustache —that was genuine enough—which had looked, in conjunction with the splendid work of art below, so fierce and manly, served by itself, he now perceived, only droopily to emphasize his native mildness and melancholy.

It was a dismal affair which might have belonged to Maurice Barrès in youth; a slanting, flagging, sagging thing, such as could only grow on the lip of an assiduous Cultivator of the Me and would become, as one grew older, ludicrously out of place on the visage of a roaring Nationalist. If it weren't that it fitted in so splendidly with the beard, if it weren't that it became so marvelously different in the new context he had now discovered for it, he would have shaved it off then and there.

Mournful appendage. But now he would transform it; he would add to it its better half. Zadig's quatrain to his mistress, when the tablet on which it was written was broken in two, became a treasonable libel on the king. So this mustache, thought Gumbril, as gingerly he applied the spirit gum to his cheeks and chin, this mustache which by itself serves only to betray me becomes, as soon as it is joined to its missing context, an amorous arm for the conquest of the fair sex.

A little farfetched, he decided; a little ponderous. And besides, as so few people had read Zadig, not much use in conversation. Cautiously and with neat meticulous finger tips he adjusted the transformation to his gummed face, pressed it firmly, held it while it stuck fast. The portals of Thélème opened before him; he was free of those rich orchards, those halls and courts, those broad staircases winding in noble spirals within the flanks of each of the fair round towers. And it was Coleman who had pointed out the way; he felt duly grateful. One last look at the Complete Man, one final and definitive constatation that the Mild and Melancholy One was, for the time at least, no more, and he was ready in all confidence

to set out. He selected a loose, light greatcoat—not that he needed a coat
at all, for the day was bright and warm; but until Mr. Bojanus had done
his labor of padding he would have to broaden himself out in this way,
even if it did mean that he might be uncomfortably hot. To fall short of
Complete Manhood for fear of a little inconvenience would be absurd.
He slipped, therefore, into his light coat—a toga, Mr. Bojanus called it, a
very neat toga in real West Country whipcord. He put on his broadest and
blackest felt hat, for breadth above everything was what he needed to give
him completeness, breadth of stature, breadth of mind, breadth of human
sympathy, breadth of smile, breadth of humor, breadth of everything.
The final touch was a massive and antique Malacca cane belonging to his
father. If he had possessed a bulldog, he would have taken it out on a
leash. But he did not. He issued into the sunshine, unaccompanied.

But unaccompanied he did not mean to remain for long. These warm
bright May days were wonderful days for being in love on. And to be alone
on such days was like a malady. It was a malady from which the Mild
and Melancholy Man suffered all too frequently. And yet there were
millions of superfluous women in the country; millions of them. Every
day, in the streets, one saw thousands of them passing; and some were
exquisite, were ravishing, the only possible soul mates. Thousands of
unique soul mates every day. The Mild and Melancholy One allowed them
to pass—forever. But today—today he was the complete and Rabelaisian
man; he was bearded to the teeth; the imbecile game was at its height;
there would be opportunities and the Complete Man would know how
to take them. No, he would not be unaccompanied for long.

Outside in the square the fourteen plane trees glowed in their young,
unsullied green. At the end of every street the golden muslin of the haze
hung in an unwrinkled curtain that thinned away above the sky's gauzy
horizon to transparent nothing against the intenser blue. The dim conch-
like murmur that in a city is silence seemed hazily to identify itself with
the golden mistiness of summer and against this dim wide background
the yells of the playing children detached themselves distinct and piercing.
"Beaver," they shouted, "beaver!" and, "Is it cold up there?" Full of playful menace, the Complete Man shook at them his borrowed Malacca.
He accepted their prompt hail as the most favorable of omens.

At the first tobacconist's Gumbril bought the longest cigar he could
find and trailing behind him expiring blue wreaths of Cuban smoke he
made his way slowly and with an ample swagger toward the Park. It was
there, under the elms, on the shores of the ornamental waters, that he
expected to find his opportunity, that he intended—how confidently
behind his Gargantuan mask!—to take it.

The opportunity offered itself sooner than he expected.

He had just turned into the Queen's Road and was sauntering past Whiteley's with the air of one who knows that he has a right to a good place, to two or three good places even, in the sun, when he noticed just in front of him, peering intently at the New Season's Models, a young woman whom, in his mild and melancholy days, he would have only hopelessly admired, but who now, to the Complete Man, seemed a destined and accessible prey. She was fairly tall, but seemed taller than she actually was by reason of her remarkable slenderness. Not that she looked disagreeably thin, far from it. It was a rounded slenderness. The Complete Man decided to consider her as tubular—flexible and tubular, like a section of boa constrictor, should one say? She was dressed in clothes that emphasized this serpentine slimness, in a close-fitting gray jacket that buttoned up to the neck and a long, narrow gray skirt that came down to her ankles. On her head was a small, sleek black hat that looked almost as though it were made of metal. It was trimmed on one side with a bunch of dull golden foliage.

Those golden leaves were the only touch of ornament in all the severe smoothness and unbroken tubularity of her person. As for her face, that was neither strictly beautiful, nor strictly ugly, but combined elements of both beauty and ugliness into a whole that was unexpected, that was oddly and somehow unnaturally attractive.

Pretending he too, to take an interest in the New Season's Models, Gumbril made, squinting sideways over the burning tip of his cigar, an inventory of her features. The forehead, that was mostly hidden by her hat; it might be pensively and serenely high, it might be of that degree of lowness which in men is villainous, but in women is only another —a rather rustic one perhaps, rather *canaille* even—but definitely another attraction. There was no telling. As for her eyes, they were green, and limpid; set wide apart in her head they looked out from under heavy lids and through openings that slanted up toward the outer corners. Her nose was slightly aquiline. Her mouth was full lipped, but straight and unexpectedly wide. Her chin was small, round and firm. She had a pale skin, a little flushed over the cheekbones, which were prominent.

On the left cheek, close under the corner of the slanting eye, she had a brown mole. Such hair as Gumbril could see beneath her hat was pale and inconspicuously blond. When she had finished looking at the New Season's Models she moved slowly on, halting for a moment before the traveling trunks and the fitted picnic baskets; dwelling for a full minute over the corsets, passing the hats, for some reason, rather contemptuously, but pausing, which seemed strange, for a long pensive look at the cigars and wine. As for the tennis rackets and cricket bats, the school outfits and the gentleman's hosiery—she hadn't so much as a look for one of them. But how lovingly she lingered before the boots and shoes! Her own feet, the Complete Man noticed with satisfaction, had an elegance of florid curves. And while other folk walked on neat's leather she was content to be shod with nothing coarser than mottled serpent's skin.

Slowly they drifted up Queen's Road, lingering before every jeweler's, every antiquarian's, every milliner's on the way. The stranger gave him no opportunity, and indeed, Gumbril reflected, how should she? For the imbecile game on which he was relying is a traveling piquet for two players, not a game of patience. No sane human being could play it in solitude. He would have to make the opportunity himself.

All that was mild in him, all that was melancholy, shrank with a sickened reluctance from the task of breaking—with what consequences delicious and perilous in the future or, in the case of the deserved snub, immediately humiliating?—a silence which, by the tenth or twelfth shop window, had become quite unbearably significant. The Mild and Melancholy One would have drifted to the top of the road, sharing, with that community of tastes which is the basis of every happy union, her enthusiasm for brass candlesticks and toasting forks, imitation Chippendale furniture, gold watch bracelets and low-waisted summer frocks; would have drifted to the top of the road and watched her, dumbly, disappearing forever into the green Park or along the blank pavements of the Bayswater Road. Would have watched her forever disappear and then if the pubs had happened to be open, would have gone and ordered a glass of port, and sitting at the Bar would have savored, still dumbly, among the other drinkers, the muddy grapes of the Douro and his own unique loneliness.

That was what the Mild and Melancholy One would have done. But the sight, as he gazed earnestly into an antiquary's window, of his own powerful bearded face, reflected in a sham Hepplewhite mirror, reminded him that the Mild and Melancholy One was temporarily extinct and that it was the Complete Man who now dawdled, smoking his long cigar, up the Queen's Road toward the Abbey of Thélème.

He squared his shoulders; in that loose toga of Mr. Bojanus's he looked as copious as François Premier. The time, he decided, had come.

It was at this moment that the reflection of the stranger's face joined itself in the little mirror, as she made a little movement away from the Old Welsh dresser in the corner, to that of his own. She looked at the spurious Hepplewhite. Their eyes met in the hospitable glass. Gumbril smiled. The corners of the stranger's wide mouth seemed faintly to move;

like petals of the magnolia, her eyelids came slowly down over her slanting eyes. Gumbril turned from the reflection to the reality.

"If you want to say Beaver," he said, "you may."

The Complete Man had made his first speech.

"I want to say nothing," said the stranger. She spoke with a charming precision and distinctness, lingering with a pretty emphasis on the n of nothing. "N-n-nothing"—it sounded rather final. She turned away, she moved on.

But the Complete Man was not one to be put off by a mere ultimatum. "There," he said, falling into step with her, "now I've had it—the deserved snub. Honor is saved, prestige duly upheld. Now we can get on with our conversation."

The Mild and Melancholy One stood by, gasping with astonished admiration.

"You are v-very impertinent," said the stranger, smiling and looking up from under the magnolia petals.

"It is in my character," said the Complete Man. "You mustn't blame me. One cannot escape from one's heredity; that's one's share of original sin."

"There is always grace," said the stranger.

Gumbril caressed his beard. "True," he replied.

"I advise you to pr-ray for it."

His prayer, the Mild and Melancholy One reflected, had already been answered. The original sin in him had been self-corrected.

"Here is another antique shop," said Gumbril, "shall we stop and have a look at it?"

The stranger glanced at him doubtfully. But he looked quite serious. They stopped.

"How revolting this sham cottage furniture is," Gumbril remarked. The shop he noticed, was called "Ye Olde Farme House."

The stranger, who had been on the point of saying how much she liked those lovely old Welsh dressers, gave him her heartiest agreement. "So v-vulgar."

"So horribly refined. So refined and artistic."

She laughed on a descending chromatic scale. This was excitingly new. Poor Aunt Aggie with her Arts and Crafts, and her old English furniture. And to think she had taken them so seriously! She saw in a flash the fastidious lady that she now was—with Louis whatever-it-was furniture at home, and jewels, and young poets to tea, and real artists. In the past, when she had imagined herself entertaining real artists, it had always been among really artistic furniture. Aunt Aggie's furniture. But now—no, oh no. This man was probably an artist. His beard; and that big black hat. But not poor; very well dressed.

"Yes it's funny to think that there are people who call that sort of thing artistic. One's quite s-sorry for them," she added, with a little hiss.

"You have a kind heart," said Gumbril. "I'm glad to see that."

"Not v-very kind, I'm af-fraid." She looked at him sideways, and significantly, as the fastidious lady would have looked at one of the poets.

"Well, kind enough, I hope," said the Complete Man; he was delighted with his new acquaintance.

Together they disembogued into the Bayswater Road. It was here, Gumbril reflected, that the Mild and Melancholy One would dumbly have slunk away to his glass of port and his loneliness among the alien topers at the bar. But the Complete Man took his new friend by the elbow, and steered her into the traffic. Together they crossed the road, together entered the park.

"I still think you are v-very impertinent," said the lady. "What induced you to follow me?"

With a single comprehensive gesture, Gumbril indicated the sun, the sky, the green trees airily glittering, the grass, the emerald lights and violet shadows of the rustic distance. "On a day like this," he said, "how could I help it?"

"Original sin?"

"Oh," the Complete Man modestly shook his head, "I lay no claim to originality in this."

The stranger laughed. This was nearly as good as a young poet at the tea table. She was very glad that she'd decided, after all, to put on her best suit this afternoon, even if it was a little stuffy for the warmth of the day. He, too, she noticed, was wearing a greatcoat; which seemed rather odd.

"Is it original," he went on, "to go and tumble stupidly like an elephant into a pitfall, head over ears, at first sight . . . ?"

She looked at him sideways, then closed down the magnolia petals, and smiled. This was going to be the real thing—one of those long, those interminable, or at any rate indefinitely renewable, conversations about love; witty, subtle, penetrating and bold, like the conversations in books, like the conversations across the tea table between brilliant young poets and ladies of quality, grown fastidious through an excessive experience, fastidious and a little weary, but still, in their subtle way, insatiably curious.

"Suppose we sit down," suggested Gumbril, and he pointed to a couple of green iron chairs standing isolated in the middle of the grass close together and with their fronts slanting inward a little toward one another in a position that suggested a confidential intimacy. At the prospect of the conversation that, inevitably, was about to unroll itself, he felt decidedly less elated than did his new friend. If there was anything he disliked it was conversations about love. It bored him, oh, it bored him most horribly, this minute analysis of the passion that young women always seemed to expect one, at some point or other in one's relation with them, to make. How love alters the character for both good and bad; how physical passion need not be incompatible with the spiritual; how a hateful and tyrannous possessiveness can be allied in love with the most unselfish solicitude for the other party—oh, he knew all this and much more, so well, so well. And whether one can be in love with more than one person at a time, whether love can exist without jealousy, whether pity, affection, desire can in any way replace the full and genuine passion—how often he had had to thrash out these dreary questions!

And all the philosophic speculations were equally familiar, all the physiological and anthropological and psychological facts. In the theory of the subject he had ceased to take any interest. Unhappily, a discussion of the theory always seemed to be an essential preliminary to the practice of it. He sighed a little wearily as he took his seat on the green iron chair. But then, recollecting that he was now the Complete Man, and that the Complete Man must do everything with a flourish and a high hand, he leaned forward and, smiling with a charming insolence through his beard, began:

"Tiresias, you may remember, was granted the singular privilege of living both as a man and a woman."

Ah, this was the genuine young poet. Supporting an elbow on the back of her chair and leaning her cheek against her hand, she disposed herself to listen and, where necessary, brilliantly to interpellate; it was through half-closed eyes that she looked at him, and she smiled faintly in a manner which she knew, from experience, to be enigmatic and, though a shade haughty, though a tiny bit mocking and ironical, exceedingly attractive.

An hour and a half later they were driving toward an address in Bloxam Gardens, Maida Vale. The name seemed vaguely familiar to Gumbril. Bloxam Gardens—perhaps one of his aunts had lived there once?

"It's a dr-dreadful little maisonette," she explained. "Full of awful things. We had to take it furnished. It's so impossible to find anything now."

Gumbril leaned back in his corner, wondering as he studied that

averted profile, who or what this young woman could be. She seemed
to be in the obvious moment, to like the sort of things one would expect
people to like; she seemed to be as highly civilized, in Mr. Mercaptan's
rather technical sense of the term, as free of all prejudices as the great
exponent of civilization himself.

She seemed, from her coolly dropped hints, to possess all the dangerous
experience, all the assurance and easy ruthlessness, of a great lady whose
whole life is occupied in the interminable affairs of the heart, the senses
and the head. But, by a strange contradiction, she seemed to find her life
narrow and uninteresting. She had complained in so many words that
her husband misunderstood and neglected her, had complained, by implication, that she knew very few interesting people.

The maisonette in Bloxam Gardens was certainly not very splendid—
six rooms on the second and third floors of a peeling stucco house. And
the furniture—decidedly Hire Purchase. And the curtains and cretonnes
—brightly "modern," positively "futurist."

"What one has to put up with in furnished flats!" The lady made a
grimace as she ushered him into the sitting room. And while she spoke
the words she really managed to persuade herself that the furniture wasn't
theirs, that they had found all this sordid stuff cluttering up the rooms,
not chosen it, oh with pains! themselves, not doggedly paid for it, month
by month.

"Our own things," she murmured vaguely, "are stored. In the Riviera."
It was there, under the palms, among the gaudy melon flowers and the
croupiers, that the fastidious lady had last held her salon of young poets.
In the Riviera—that would explain, now she came to think of it, a lot
of things, if explanation ever became necessary.

The Complete Man nodded sympathetically. "Other people's taste,"
he held up his hands, they both laughed. "But why do we think of other
people?" he added. And coming forward with a conquering impulsive-
ness he took both her long, fine hands in his and raised them to his
bearded mouth.

She looked at him for a second, then dropped her eyelids, took back
her hands. "I must go and make the tea," she said. "The servants——"
the plural was a pardonable exaggeration—"are out."

Gallantly, the Complete Man offered to come and help her. These
scenes of intimate life had a charm all their own. But she would not
allow it. "No, no," she was very firm, "I simply forbid you. You must
stay here. I won't be a moment," and she was gone, closing the door carefully behind her.

Left to himself, Gumbril sat down and filed his nails.

As for the young lady, she hurried along to her dingy little kitchen, lit the gas, put the kettle on, set out the teapot and the cups on a tray and from the biscuit box where it was stored, took out the remains of a chocolate cake, which had already seen service at the day-before-yesterday's tea party. When all was ready here, she tiptoed across to her bedroom and sitting down at her dressing table, began with hands that trembled a little with excitement to powder her nose and heighten the color of her cheeks. Even after the last touch had been given, she still sat there, looking at her image in the glass.

The lady and the poet, she was thinking, the *grande dame* and the brilliant young man of genius. She liked young men with beards. But he was not an artist, in spite of the beard, in spite of the hat. He was a writer of sorts. So she gathered; but he was reticent, he was delightfully mysterious. She too, for that matter. The great lady slips out, masked, into the street; touches the young man's sleeve; Come with me. She chooses, does not let herself passively be chosen. The young poet falls at her feet; she lifts him up. One is accustomed to this sort of thing.

She opened her jewel box, took out all her rings—there were not many of them, alas—and put them on. Two or three of them; on second thought, she took off again; they were a little, she suspected with a sudden qualm, in other people's taste.

He was very clever, very artistic—only that seemed to be the wrong word to use; he seemed to know all the new things, all the interesting people. Perhaps he would introduce her to some of them. And he was so much at ease behind his knowledge, so well assured. But for her part, she felt pretty certain, she had made no stupid mistakes. She too had been, had looked at any rate—which was the important thing—very much at ease.

She liked young men with beards. They looked like Russians. Catherine of Russia had been one of the great ladies with caprices. Masked in the streets. Young poet, come with me. Or even, Young butcher's boy. But that, no, that was going too far, too low. Still, life, life—it was there to be lived—life—to be enjoyed. And now, and now? She was still wondering what would happen next, when the kettle, which was one of those funny ones which whistle when they come to the boil, began, fitfully, at first, then under full steam, unflaggingly, to sound its mournful, other-worldly note. She sighed and bestirred herself to attend to it.

"Let me help you," Gumbril jumped up as she came into the room. "What can I do?" He hovered rather ineptly round her.

The lady put down her tray on the little table. "N-nothing," she said.

"N-nothing?" he imitated her with a playful mockery. "Am I good for n-nothing at all?" He took one of her hands and kissed it.

"Nothing that's of the l-least importance." She sat down and began to pour out the tea.

The Complete Man also sat down. "So to adore at first sight," he asked, "is not of the l-least importance?"

She shook her head, smiled, raised and lowered her eyelids. One was so well accustomed to this sort of thing; it had no importance. "Sugar?" she asked. The young poet was safely there, sparkling across the tea table. He offered love and she, with the easy heartlessness of one who is so well accustomed to this sort of thing, offered him sugar.

He nodded, "Please. But if it's of no importance to you," he went on, "then I'll go away at once."

The lady laughed her section of a descending chromatic scale. "Oh no you won't," she said. "You can't." And she felt that the grande dame had made a very fine stroke.

"Quite right," the Complete Man replied. "I couldn't." He stirred his tea. "But who are you," he looked up at her suddenly, "you devilish female?" He was genuinely anxious to know; and besides, he was paying her a very pretty compliment. "What do you do with your dangerous existence?"

"I enjoy life," she said. "I think one ought to enjoy life. Don't you? I think it's one's first duty." She became quite grave. "One ought to enjoy every moment of it," she said. "Oh, passionately, adventurously, newly, excitingly, uniquely."

The Complete Man laughed. "A conscientious hedonist. I see."

She felt uncomfortably that the fastidious lady had not quite lived up to her character. She had spoken more like a young woman who finds life too dull and daily, and would like to get on to the cinema. "I am very conscientious," she said, making significant play with the magnolia petals and smiling her riddling smile. She must retrieve the Great Catherine's reputation.

"I could see that from the first," mocked the Complete Man with a triumphant insolence. "Conscience doth make cowards of us all."

The fastidious lady only contemptuously smiled. "Have a little chocolate cake," she suggested. Her heart was beating. She wondered, she wondered.

There was a long silence. Gumbril finished his chocolate cake, gloomily drank his tea and did not speak. He found, all at once, that he had nothing to say. His jovial confidence seemed for the moment to have deserted him. He was only the Mild and Melancholy One foolishly disguised as a Complete Man; a sheep in beaver's clothing. He entrenched himself behind his formidable silence and waited; waited, at first, sitting

in his chair, then, when this total inactivity became unbearable, striding
about the room.

She looked at him, for all her air of serene composure, with a certain
disquiet. What on earth was he up to now? What could he be thinking
about? Frowning like that, he looked like a young Jupiter, bearded and
burly (though not, she noticed, quite so burly as he had appeared in his
overcoat) making ready to throw a thunderbolt. Perhaps he was thinking
of her—suspecting her, seeing through the fastidious lady and feeling
angry at her attempted deception. Or perhaps he was bored with her; perhaps he was wanting to go away. Well, let him go; she didn't mind.
Or perhaps he was just made like that—a moody young poet; that
seemed, on the whole, the most likely explanation; it was also the
most pleasing and romantic. She waited. They both waited.

Gumbril looked at her and was put to shame by the spectacle of her
quiet serenity. He must do something, he told himself; he must recover
the Complete Man's lost *morale*. Desperately he came to a halt in front
of the one decent picture hanging on the walls. It was an eighteenth-
century engraving of Raphael's "Transfiguration"—better, he always
thought, in black and white than in its bleakly colored original.

"That's a nice engraving," he said. "Very nice." The mere fact of
having uttered at all was a great comfort to him, a real relief.

"Yes," she said. "That belongs to me. I found it in a secondhand shop,
not far from here."

"Photography," he pronounced, with that temporary earnestness which
made him seem an enthusiast about everything, "is a mixed blessing.
It has made it possible to reproduce pictures so easily and cheaply that
all the bad artists who were well occupied in the past, making engravings
of good men's paintings, are now free to do bad original work of their
own." All this was terribly impersonal, he told himself, terribly off the
point. He was losing ground. He must do something drastic to win it
back. But what?

She came to his rescue. "I bought another at the same time," she
said. " 'The Last Communion of St. Jerome,' by—who is it? I forget."

"Ah, you mean Domenichino's 'St. Jerome'?" The Complete Man was
afloat again. "Poussin's favorite picture. Mine too, very nearly. I'd like
to see that."

"It's in my room, I'm afraid. But if you don't mind."

He bowed. "If you don't."

She smiled graciously to him and got up. "This way," she said, and
opened the door.

"It's a lovely picture," Gumbril went on, loquaciously now, behind her, as they walked down the dark corridor. "And besides, I have a sentimental attachment to it. There used to be a copy of an engraving of it at home, when I was a child. And I remember wondering and wondering— oh, it went on for years—every time I saw the picture; wondering why on earth that old bishop (for I did know it was a bishop) should be handing the naked old man a five-shilling piece."

She opened a door; they were in her very pink room. Grave in its solemn and subtly harmonious beauty, the picture hung over the mantelpiece, hung there, among the photographs of the little friends of her own age, like some strange object from another world. From within that chipped gilt frame all the beauty, all the grandeur of religion looked darkly out upon the pink room. The little friends of her own age, all deliciously nubile, sweetly smiled, turned up their eyes, clasped Persian cats or stood jauntily, feet apart, hand in the breeches pocket of the land girl's uniform; the pink roses on the wallpaper, the pink and white curtains, the pink bed, the strawberry-colored carpet, filled all the air with the rosy reflections of nakedness and life.

And utterly remote, absorbed in their grave solemn ecstasy, the robed and mitered priest held out, the dying saint yearningly received the body of the Son of God. The ministrants looked gravely on, the little angels looped in the air above a gravely triumphant festoon, the lion slept at the saint's feet, and through the arch beyond, the eye traveled out over a quiet country of dark trees and hills.

"There it is," she waved toward the mantelpiece.

But Gumbril had taken it all in long ago. "You see what I mean by the five-shilling piece." And stepping up to the picture, he pointed to the round bright wafer which the priest holds in his hand and whose averted disk is like the essential sun at the center of the picture's harmonious universe. "Those were the days of five-shilling pieces," he went on. "You're probably too young to remember those large lovely things. They came my way occasionally and consecrated wafers didn't. So you can understand how much the picture puzzled me. A bishop giving a naked old man five shillings in a church, with angels fluttering overhead, and a lion sleeping in the foreground. It was obscure; it was horribly obscure." He turned away from the picture and confronted his hostess, who was standing a little way behind him smiling enigmatically and invitingly.

"Obscure," he repeated. "But so is everything. So is life in general. And you," he stepped toward her, "you in particular."

"Am I"? she lifted her limpid eyes at him. Oh, how her heart was beating; how hard it was to be the fastidious lady, calmly satisfying her caprice. How difficult it was to be accustomed to this sort of thing. What was going to happen next?

What happened next was that the Complete Man came still closer, put his arm round her, as though he were inviting her to the fox trot, and began kissing her with a startling violence. His beard tickled her neck; shivering a little, she brought down the magnolia petals across her eyes. The Complete Man lifted her up, walked across the room carrying the fastidious lady in his arms and deposited her on the rosy catafalque of the bed. Lying there with her eyes shut she did her best to pretend she was dead.

Gumbril had looked at his wrist watch and found that it was six o'clock. Already? He prepared himself to take his departure. Wrapped in a pink kimono, she came out into the hall to wish him farewell.

"When shall I see you again, Rosie?" He had learned that her name was Rosie.

She had recovered her great lady's equanimity and detachment and was able to shrug her shoulders and smile. "How should I know?" she asked, implying that she could not foresee what her caprice might be an hour hence.

"May I write then, and ask one of these days if you do know?"

She put her head on one side and raised her eyebrows, doubtfully. At last she nodded. "Yes, you can write," she permitted.

"Good," said the Complete Man, and picked up his wide hat. She held out her hand to him with stateliness and with a formal gallantry he kissed it. He was just closing the front door behind him when he remembered something. He turned round. "I say," he called after the retreating pink kimono, "It's rather absurd. But how can I write? I don't know your name. I can't just address it Rosie."

The great lady laughed delightedly. This had the real capriccio flavor. "Wait," she said and she ran into the sitting room. She was back again in a moment with an oblong of pasteboard. "There," she said and dropped it into his greatcoat pocket. Then blowing a kiss she was gone.

The Complete Man closed the door and descended the stairs. Well, well, he said to himself; well, well. He put his hand in his coat pocket and took out the card. In the dim light of the staircase he read the name on it with some difficulty. Mrs. James—but no, but no. He read again, straining his eyes; there was no question of it. Mrs. James Shearwater.

Mrs. James Shearwater.

That was why he had vaguely known the name of Bloxam Gardens.

Mrs. James Shear——. Step after step he descended, ponderously. "Good Lord," he said out loud. "Good Lord."

But why had he never seen her? Why did Shearwater never produce her? Now he came to think of it, he hardly ever spoke of her.

Why had she said the flat wasn't theirs? It was; he had heard Shearwater talk about it.

Did she make a habit of this sort of thing?

Could Shearwater be wholly unaware of what she was really like?

But, for that matter, what was she really like?

He was half way down the last flight, when with a rattle and a squeak of hinges the door of the house, which was only separated by a short lobby from the foot of the stairs, opened, revealing, on the doorstep, Shearwater and a friend, eagerly talking.

". . . I take my rabbit," the friend was saying—he was a young man with dark protruding eyes and staring, doggy nostrils, very eager, lively and loud. "I take my rabbit and I inject into it the solution of eyes, pulped eyes of another dead rabbit. You see?"

Gumbril's first instinct was to rush up the stairs and hide in the first likely-looking corner. But he pulled himself together at once. He was a Complete Man and Complete Men do not hide; moreover, he was sufficiently disguised to be quite unrecognizable. He stood where he was and listened to the conversation.

"The rabbit," continued the young man, and with his bright eyes and staring, sniffing nose, he looked like a poacher's terrier ready to go barking after the first white tail that passed his way; "the rabbit naturally develops the appropriate resistance, develops a specific anti-eye to protect itself. I then take some of its anti-eye serum and inject it into my female rabbit, I then immediately breed from her." He paused.

"Well?" asked Shearwater, in his slow, ponderous way. He lifted his great round head inquiringly and looked at the doggy young man from under his bushy eyebrows.

The doggy young man smiled triumphantly. "The young ones," he said emphasizing his words by striking his right fist against the extended palm of his left hand, "the young ones are born with defective sight."

Thoughtfully Shearwater pulled at his formidable mustache. "Hm," he said slowly. "Very remarkable."

"You realize the full significance of it?" asked the young man. "We seem to be affecting the germ plasm directly. We have found a way of making acquired characteristics . . ."

"Pardon me," said Gumbril. He had decided that it was time to be gone. He ran down the stairs and across the tiled hall; he pushed his way firmly but politely between the talkers.

". . . heritable," continued the young man, imperturbably eager, speaking through and over and round the obstacle.

"Damn," said Shearwater. The Complete Man had trodden on his toe. "Sorry," he added, absent-mindedly apologizing for the injury he had received.

Gumbril hurried off along the street. "If we really have found out a technique for influencing the germ plasm directly . . ." he heard the doggy young man saying; but he was already too far away to catch the rest of the sentence. There are many ways, he reflected, of spending an afternoon.

The doggy young man refused to come in; he had to get in his game of tennis before dinner. Shearwater climbed the stairs alone. He was taking off his hat in the little hall of his own apartment when Rosie came out of the sitting room with a trayful of tea things.

"Well?" he asked, kissing her affectionately on the forehead. "Well? People to tea?"

"Only one," Rosie replied. "I'll go and make you a fresh cup."

She glided off, rustling in her pink kimono toward the kitchen.

Shearwater sat down in the sitting room. He had brought home with him from the library the fifteenth volume of the *Biochemical Journal*. There was something in it he wanted to look up. He turned over the pages. Ah, here it was. He began reading. Rosie came back again.

"Here's your tea," she said.

He thanked her without looking up. The tea grew cold on the little table at his side.

Lying on the sofa, Rosie pondered and remembered. Had the events of the afternoon, she asked herself, really happened? They seemed very improbable and remote, now, in this studious silence. She couldn't help feeling a little disappointed. Was it only this? So simple and obvious? She tried to work herself up into a more exalted mood. She even tried to feel guilty; but there she failed completely. She tried to feel rapturous; but without much more success. Still, he certainly had been a most extraordinary man. Such impudence, and at the same time such delicacy and tact.

It was a pity she couldn't afford to change the furniture. She saw now that it wouldn't do at all. She would go and tell Aunt Aggie about the dreadful middle classness of her Art and Craftiness.

She ought to have an Empire *chaise longue*. Like Madame Récamier. She could see herself lying there, dispensing tea. "Like a delicious pink snake." He had called her that.

Well, really now she came to think of it all again, it had been too queer, too queer.

"What's a hedonist?" she suddenly asked.

Shearwater looked up from the *Journal of Biochemistry*. "What?" he said.

"A hedonist."

"A man who holds that the end of life is pleasure."

A "conscientious hedonist"—ah, that was good.

"This tea is cold," Shearwater remarked.

"You should have drunk it before," she said. The silence renewed and prolonged itself.

Rosie was getting much better, Shearwater reflected, as he washed his hands before supper, about not interrupting him when he was busy. This evening she had really not disturbed him at all, or at most only once, and that not seriously. There had been times in the past when the child had really made life almost impossible. There were those months at the beginning of their married life when she had thought she would like to study physiology herself and be a help to him. He remembered the hours he had spent trying to teach her elementary facts about the chromosomes. It had been a great relief when she abandoned the attempt. He had suggested she should go in for stenciling patterns on Government linen. Such pretty curtains and things one could make like that. But she hadn't taken very kindly to the idea. There had followed a long period when she seemed to have nothing to do but prevent him from doing anything. Ringing him up at the laboratory, invading his study, sitting on his knee, or throwing her arms round his neck, or pulling his hair, or asking ridiculous questions when he was trying to work.

Shearwater flattered himself that he had been extremely patient. He had never got cross. He had just gone on as though she weren't there. As though she weren't there.

"Hurry up," he heard her calling. "The soup's getting cold."

"Coming," he shouted back and began to dry his large, blunt hands.

She seemed to have been improving lately. And tonight, tonight she had been a model of nonexistence.

He came striding heavily into the dining room. Rosie was sitting at the head of the table, ladling out the soup. With her left hand she held back the flowing pink sleeve of her kimono so that it should not trail in the plates or the tureen. Her bare arm showed white and pearly through the steam of lentils.

How pretty she was! He could not resist the temptation, but coming up behind her bent down and kissed her, rather clumsily, on the back of her neck.

Rosie drew away from him. "Really, Jim," she said disapprovingly. "At meal times!" The fastidious lady had to draw the line at these ill-timed, fumbling familiarities.

"And what about work times?" Shearwater asked laughing. "Still, you were wonderful this evening, Rosie, quite wonderful." He sat down and began eating his soup. "Not a sound all the time I was reading; or at any rate, only one sound, so far as I remember."

The great lady said nothing, but only smiled—a little contemptuously and with a touch of pity. She pushed away the plate of soup unfinished and planted her elbows on the table. Slipping her hands under the sleeves of her kimono, she began, lightly, delicately, with the tips of her fingers, to caress her own arms.

How smooth they were, how soft and warm and how secret under the sleeves. And all her body was as smooth and warm, was as soft and secret, still more secret beneath the pink folds. Like a warm serpent hidden away, secretly, secretly.

Chapter X

MR. BOLDERO liked the idea of the Patent Small Clothes. He liked it immensely, he said, immensely.

"There's money in it," he said.

Mr. Boldero was a small dark man of about forty-five, active as a bird and with a bird's brown beady eyes, a bird's sharp nose. He was always busy, always had twenty different irons in the fire at once, was always fresh, clear-headed, never tired. He was also always unpunctual, always untidy. He had no sense of time or of order. But he got away with it, as he liked to say. He delivered the goods—or rather the goods, in the convenient form of cash, delivered themselves, almost miraculously it always seemed, to him.

He was like a bird in appearance. But in mind, Gumbril found, after having seen him once or twice, he was like a caterpillar: he ate all that was put before him, he consumed a hundred times his own mental weight every day. Other people's ideas, other people's knowledge—they were his food. He devoured them and they were at once his own. All that belonged to other people he annexed without a scruple or a second thought, quite naturally, as though it were already his own. And he absorbed it so rapidly and completely, he laid public claim to it so promptly that he sometimes deceived people into believing that he had really anticipated them in their ideas, that he had known for years and years the things they had just been telling him and which he would at once airily repeat to them with the perfect assurance of one who knows—knows by instinct, as it were, by inheritance.

At their first luncheon he had asked Gumbril to tell him all about modern painting. Gumbril had given him a brief lecture; before the savory had appeared on the table, Mr. Boldero was talking with perfect familiarity of Picasso and Derain. He almost made it understood that he had a fine collection of their works in his drawing room at home. Being a trifle deaf, however, he was not very good at names and Gumbril's all too tactful corrections were lost on him. He could not be induced to abandon his Bacosso in favor of any other version of the Spaniard's name. Bacosso —why, he had known all about Bacosso since he was a schoolboy! Bacosso was an old master, already.

Mr. Boldero was very severe with the waiters and knew so well how things ought to be done at a good restaurant that Gumbril felt sure he must recently have lunched with some meticulous gormandizer of the old school. And when the waiter made as though to serve them with brandy in small glasses, Mr. Boldero was so passionately indignant that he sent for the manager.

"Do you mean to tell me," he shouted in a perfect frenzy of righteous anger, "that you don't yet know how brandy ought to be drunk?"

Perhaps it was only last week that he himself, Gumbril reflected, had learned to aerate his cognac in Gargantuan beakers.

Meanwhile, of course, the Patent Small Clothes were not neglected. As soon as he had been told about the things, Mr. Boldero began speaking of them with a perfect and practiced familiarity. They were already his, mentally his. And it was only Mr. Boldero's generosity that prevented him from making the Small Clothes more effectively his own.

"If it weren't for the friendship and respect which I feel for your father, Mr. Gumbril," he said, twinkling genially over the brandy, "I'd just annex your Small Clothes. Bag and baggage. Just annex them."

"Ah, but they're my patent," said Gumbril. "Or at least they're in process of being patented. The agents are at work."

Mr. Boldero laughed. "Do you suppose that would trouble me if I wanted to be unscrupulous? I'd just take the idea and manufacture the article. You'd bring an action. I'd have it defended with all the professional erudition that could be bought. You'd find yourself let in for a case that might cost thousands. And how would you pay for it? You'd be forced to come to an agreement out of court, Mr. Gumbril. That's what you'd have to do. And a damned bad agreement it would be for you, I can tell you." Mr. Boldero laughed very cheerfully at the thought of the badness of this agreement. "But don't be alarmed," he said. "I shan't do it, you know."

Gumbril was not wholly reassured. Tactfully, he tried to find out what terms Mr. Boldero was prepared to offer. Mr. Boldero was nebulously vague.

They met again in Gumbril's rooms. The contemporary drawings on the walls reminded Mr. Boldero that he was now an art expert. He told Gumbril all about it—in Gumbril's own words. Every now and then, it was true, Mr. Boldero made a little slip. Bacosso, for example, remained unshakably Bacosso. But on the whole the performance was most impressive. It made Gumbril feel very uncomfortable, however, while it lasted. For he recognized in this characteristic of Mr. Boldero a horrible caricature of himself. He too was an assimilator; more discriminating, no doubt, more tactful, knowing better than Mr. Boldero how to turn the assimilated experience into something new and truly his own; but still a caterpillar, definitely a caterpillar. He began studying Mr. Boldero with a close and disgustful attention, as one might pore over some repulsive *memento mori*.

It was a relief when Mr. Boldero stopped talking art and consented to get down to business. Gumbril was wearing for the occasion the sample pair of Small Clothes which Mr. Bojanus had made for him. For Mr. Boldero's benefit he put them, so to speak, through their paces. He allowed himself to drop with a bump onto the floor—arriving there bruiseless and unjarred. He sat in complete comfort for minutes at a stretch on the edge of the ornamental iron fender. In the intervals he paraded up and down before Mr. Boldero like a mannequin. "A trifle bulgy," said Mr. Boldero. "But still . . ." He was, taking it all round, favorably impressed. It was time, he said, to begin thinking of details. They would have to begin by making experiments with the bladders to discover a model, combining, as Mr. Boldero put it, "maximum efficiency with minimum bulge." When they had found the right thing, they would have it made in suitable quantities by any good rubber firm. As for the trousers themselves, they could rely for those on sweated female labor in the East End. "Cheap and good," said Mr. Boldero.

"It sounds ideal," said Gumbril.

"And then," said Mr. Boldero, "there's our advertising campaign. On that I may say," he went on with a certain solemnity, "will depend the failure or success of our enterprise. I consider it of the first importance."

"Quite," said Gumbril, nodding importantly and with intelligence.

"We must set to work," said Mr. Boldero, "sci-en-tifically." Gumbril nodded again.

"We have to appeal," Mr. Boldero went on so glibly that Gumbril felt sure he must be quoting somebody else's words, "to the great instincts and feelings of humanity . . . They are the source of action. They spend the money, if I may put it like that . . ."

"That's all very well," said Gumbril. "But how do you propose to appeal to the most important of the instincts? I refer, as you may well imagine, to sex."

"I was just going to come to that," said Mr. Boldero, raising his hand as though to ask for a patient hearing. "Alas, we can't. I don't see any way of hanging our Small Clothes on the sexual peg."

"Then we are undone," said Gumbril, too, dramatically.

"No, no." Mr. Boldero was reassuring. "You make the error of the Viennese. You exaggerate the importance of sex. After all, my dear Mr. Gumbril, there is also the instinct of self-preservation; there is also," he leaned forward, wagging his finger, "the social instinct, the instinct of the herd."

"True."

"Both of them as powerful as sex. What are the Professor's famous Censors but forbidding suggestions from the herd without, made powerful and entrenched by the social instinct within?"

Gumbril had no answer; Mr. Boldero continued, smiling.

"So that we shall be all right if we stick to self-preservation and the herd. Rub in the comfort and utility, the hygienic virtues of our Small Clothes; that will catch their self-preservatory feelings. Aim at their dread of public opinion, at their ambition to be one better than their fellows and their terror of being different—at all the ludicrous weaknesses a well-developed social instinct exposes them to. We shall get them, if we set to work scientifically . . ." Mr. Bolder's birdlike eyes twinkled very brightly. "We shall get them," he repeated, and he laughed a happy little laugh, full of such a childlike diabolism, such an innocent gay malignity that it seemed as though a little leprechaun had suddenly taken the financier's place in Gumbril's best armchair.

Gumbril laughed too; for this leprechaunish mirth was infectious. "We shall get them," he echoed. "Oh, I'm sure we shall, if you set about it, Mr. Boldero."

Mr. Boldero acknowledged the compliment with a smile that expressed no false humility. It was his due and he knew it.

"I'll give you some of my ideas about the advertising campaign," he said. "Just to give you a notion. You can think them over, quietly, and make suggestions."

"Yes, yes," said Gumbril nodding.

Mr. Boldero cleared his throat. "We shall begin," he said, "by making the most simple elementary appeal to their instinct of self-preservation: we shall point out that the Patent Small Clothes are comfortable; that to wear them is to avoid pain. A few striking slogans about comfort—that's all we want. Very simple indeed. It doesn't take much to persuade a man that it's pleasanter to sit on air than on wood. But while we're on the subject of hard seats we shall have to glide off subtly at a tangent to make a flank attack on the social instincts." And joining the tip of his forefinger to the tip of his thumb, Mr. Boldero moved his hand delicately sideways, as though he were sliding it along a smooth brass rail. "We shall have to speak about the glories and the trials of sedentary labor. We must exalt its spiritual dignity and at the same time condemn its physical discomforts. 'The seat of honor,' don't you know. We could talk about that. 'The Seats of the Mighty.' 'The seat that rules the office rocks the world.' All those lines might be made something of. And then we could have little historical chats about thrones; how dignified, but how uncomfortable they've been. We must make the bank clerk and the civil servant feel proud of being what they are and at the same time feel ashamed that, being such splendid people, they should have to submit to the indignity of having blistered hindquarters. In modern advertising you must flatter your public—not in the oily, abject, tradesmanlike style of the old advertisers, crawling before clients who were their social superiors; that's all over now. It's we who are the social superiors—because we've got more money than the bank clerks and the civil servants. Our modern flattery must be manly, straightforward, sincere, the admiration of equal for equal—all the more flattering as we aren't equals." Mr. Boldero laid a finger to his nose. "They're dirt and we're capitalists . . ." He laughed.

Gumbril laughed too. It was the first time that he had ever thought of himself as a capitalist, and the thought was exhilarating.

"We flatter them," went on Mr. Boldero. "We say that honest work is glorious and ennobling—which it isn't; it's merely dull and cretinizing. And then we go on to suggest that it would be finer still, more ennobling, because less uncomfortable, if they wore Gumbril's Patent Small Clothes. You see the line?"

Gumbril saw the line.

"After that," said Mr. Boldero, "we get onto the medical side of the matter. The medical side, Mr. Gumbril—that's most important. Nobody feels really well nowadays—at any rate nobody who lives in a big town and does the kind of loathsome work that the people we're catering for do. Keeping this fact before our eyes, we have to make it clear that only those can expect to be healthy who wear pneumatic trousers."

"That will be a little difficult, won't it?" questioned Gumbril.

"Not a bit of it!" Mr. Boldero laughed with an infectious confidence. "All we have to do is to talk about the great nerve centers of the spine; the shocks they get when you sit down too hard; the wearing exhaustion to which long-protracted sitting on unpadded seats subjects them. We'll have to talk very scientifically about the great lumbar ganglia—if there are such things, which I really don't pretend to know. We'll even talk almost mystically about the ganglia. You know that sort of ganglion philosophy?" Mr. Boldero went on parenthetically. "Very interesting it is, sometimes, I think. We could put in a lot about the dark powerful sense-life, sex-life, instinct-life which is controlled by the lumbar ganglion. How important it is that that shouldn't be damaged. That already our modern conditions of civilization tend unduly to develop the intellect and the thoracic ganglia controlling the higher emotions. That we're wearing out, growing feeble, losing our balance in consequence. And that the only cure—if we are to continue our present mode of civilized life—is to be found in Gumbril's Patent Small Clothes." Mr. Boldero brought his hand with an emphatic smack onto the table as he spoke, as he fairly shouted, these last words.

"Magnificent," said Gumbril, with genuine admiration.

"This sort of medical and philosophical dope," Mr. Boldero went on, "is always very effective, if it's properly used. The public to whom we are making our appeal is, of course, almost absolutely ignorant on these, or indeed, on almost all other subjects. It is therefore very much impressed by the unfamiliar words, particularly if they have such a good juicy sound as the word 'ganglia.'"

"There was a young man of East Anglia, whose loins were a tangle of ganglia," murmured Gumbril, *improvisatore*.

"Precisely," said Mr. Boldero. "Precisely. You see how juicy it is? Well, as I say, they're impressed. And they're also grateful. They're grateful to us for having given them a piece of abstruse, unlikely information which they can pass onto their wives, or to such friends as they know don't read the paper in which our advertisement appears—can pass on airily, don't you know, with easy erudition, as though they'd known all about ganglia from their childhood. And they'll feel such a flow of superiority as they hand on the metaphysics and the pathology that they'll always think of us with affection. They'll buy our breeks and they'll get other people to buy. That's why," Mr. Boldero went off again on an instructive tangent, "that's why the day of secret patent medicines is really over.

It's no good saying you have rediscovered some secret known only, in the past, to the Egyptians. People don't know anything about Egyptology; but they have an inkling that such a science exists. And that if it does exist, it's unlikely that patent medicine makers should have found out facts unknown to the professors at the universities. And it's much the same even with secrets that don't come from Egypt. People know there's such a thing as medical science and they again feel it's improbable that manufacturers should know things ignored by the doctors. The modern democratic advertiser is entirely aboveboard. He tells you all about it. He explains that the digestive juices acting on bismuth give rise to a disinfectant acid. He points out that lactic ferment gets destroyed before it reaches the large intestine, so that Metchnikoff's cure generally won't work. And he goes on to explain that the only way of getting the ferment there is to mix it with starch and paraffin: starch to feed the ferment on, paraffin to prevent the starch being digested before it gets to the intestine. And in consequence he convinces you that a mixture of starch, paraffin and ferment is the only thing that's any good at all. Consequently you buy it; which you would never have done without the explanation. In the same way, Mr. Gumbril, we mustn't ask people to take our trousers on trust. We must explain scientifically why these trousers will be good for their health. And by means of the ganglia, as I've pointed out, we can even show that the trousers will be good for their souls and the whole human race at large. And as you probably know, Mr. Gumbril, there's nothing like a spiritual message to make things go. Combine spirituality with practicality and you've fairly got them. Got them, I may say, on toast. And that's what we can do with our trousers; we can put a message into them, a big, spiritual message. Decidedly," he concluded, "we shall have to work those ganglia all we can."

"I'll undertake to do that," said Gumbril who felt very buoyant and self-assured. Mr. Boldero's hydrogenous conversation had blown him up like a balloon.

"And I'm sure you'll do it well," said Mr. Boldero encouragingly. "There is no better training for modern commerce than a literary education. As a practical businessman, I always uphold the ancient universities, especially in their teaching of the Humanities."

Gumbril was much flattered. At the moment, it seemed supremely satisfying to be told that he was likely to make a good businessman. The businessman took on a radiance, began to glow, as it were, with a phosphorescent splendor.

"Then it's very important," continued Mr. Boldero, "to play on their snobbism; to exploit that painful sense of inferiority which the ignorant and ingenuous always feel in the presence of the knowing. We've got to make our trousers the Thing—socially right as well as merely personally comfortable. We've got to imply somehow that it's bad form not to wear them. We've got to make those who don't wear them feel rather uncomfortable. Like that film of Charlie Chaplin's, where he's the absent-minded young man about town who dresses for dinner immaculately, from the waist up—white waistcoat, tail coat, stiff shirt, top hat—and only discovers, when he gets down into the hall of the hotel, that he's forgotten to put on his trousers. We've got to make them feel like that. That's always very successful. You know those excellent American advertisements about young ladies whose engagements are broken off because they perspire too freely or have an unpleasant breath? How horribly uncomfortable those make you feel! We've got to do something of the same sort for our trousers. Or more immediately applicable would be those tailor's advertisements about correct clothes. 'Good clothes make you feel good.' You know the sort of line. And then those grave warning sentences in which you're told that a correctly cut suit may make the difference between an appointment gained and an appointment lost, an interview granted and an interview refused. But the most masterly examples I can think of," Mr. Boldero went on with growing enthusiasm, "are those American advertisements of spectacles, in which the manufacturers first assume the existence of a social law about goggles and then proceed to invoke all the sanctions which fall on the head of the committer of a solecism upon those who break it. It's masterly. For sport or relaxation, they tell you as tho' it was a social axiom you must wear spectacles of pure tortoise shell. For business, tortoise-shell rims and nickel earpieces lend incisive poise—incisive poise, we must remember that for our ads, Mr. Gumbril. 'Gumbril's Patent Small Clothes lend incisive poise to businessmen.' For semi-evening dress, shell rims with gold earpieces and gold nose bridge. And for full dress, gold-mounted rimless pince-nez are refinement itself and absolutely correct. Thus we see, a social law has been created, according to which every self-respecting myope or astigmat must have four distinct pairs of glasses. Think if he should wear the all-shell sports model with full dress! Revolting solecism! The people who read advertisements like that begin to feel uncomfortable; they have only one pair of glasses, they are afraid of being laughed at, thought low class and ignorant and suburban. And since there are few who would not rather be taken in adultery than in provincialism, they rush out to buy four new pairs of spectacles. And the manufacturer gets rich, Mr. Gumbril. Now, we must do something of the kind with our trousers. Imply somehow that they're correct, that

you're undressed without, that your fiancée would break off the engage-
ment if she saw you sitting down to dinner on anything but air." Mr.
Boldero shrugged his shoulders, vaguely waved his hand.

"It may be rather difficult," said Gumbril shaking his head.

"It may," Mr. Boldero agreed. "But difficulties are made to be overcome. We must pull the string of snobbery and shame: it's essential.
We must find out methods for bringing the weight of public opinion
to bear mockingly on those who do not wear our trousers. It is difficult
at the moment to see how it can be done. But it will have to be done;
it will have to be done." Mr. Boldero repeated emphatically. "We might
even find a way of invoking patriotism to our aid. English trousers filled
with English air, for English men. A little far-fetched, perhaps. But there
might be something in it."

Gumbril shook his head doubtfully.

"Well, it's one of the things we've got to think about in any case,"
said Mr. Boldero. "We can't afford to neglect such powerful social
emotions as these. Sex, as we've seen, is almost entirely out of the question. We must run the rest, therefore, as hard as we can. For instance,
there's the novelty business. People feel superior if they possess something new which their neighbors haven't got. The mere fact of newness
is an intoxication. We must encourage that sense of superiority, brew
up that intoxication. The most absurd and futile objects can be sold
because they're new. Not long ago I sold four million patent soap dishes
of a new and peculiar kind. The point was that you didn't screw the
fixture into the bathroom wall; you made a hole in the wall and built
the soap dish into a niche, like a holy-water stoup. My soap dishes possessed no advantages over other kinds of soap dishes, and they cost a
fantastic amount to install. But I managed to put them across, simply
because they were new. Four million of them." Mr. Boldero smiled with
satisfaction at the recollection. "We shall do the same, I hope, with our
trousers. People may be shy of being the first to appear in them; but the
shyness will be compensated for by the sense of superiority and elation
produced by the consciousness of the newness of the things."

"Quite so," said Gumbril.

"And then, of course, there's the economy slogan: One pair of Gumbril's Patent Small Clothes will outlast six pairs of ordinary trousers.
That's easy enough. So easy that it's really uninteresting." Mr. Boldero
waved it away.

"We shall have to have pictures," said Gumbril, parenthetically. He
had an idea.

"Oh, of course."

"I believe I know of the very man to do them," Gumbril went on. "His name's Lypiatt. A painter. You've probably heard of him."

"Heard of him!" exclaimed Mr. Boldero. He laughed. "But who hasn't heard of Lydgate."

"Lypiatt."

"Lypgate, I mean, of course."

"I think he'd be the very man," said Gumbril.

"I'm certain he would," said Mr. Boldero, not a whit behindhand.

Gumbril was pleased with himself. He felt he had done someone a good turn. Poor old Lypiatt; be glad of the money. Gumbril remembered also his own fiver. And remembering his own fiver, he also remembered that Mr. Boldero had as yet made no concrete suggestion about terms. He nerved himself at last to suggest to Mr. Boldero that it was time to think of this little matter. Ah, how he hated talking about money! He found it so hard to be firm in asserting his rights. He was ashamed of showing himself grasping. He always thought with consideration of the other person's point of view—poor devil, could he afford to pay? And he was always swindled and always conscious of the fact. Lord, how he hated life on these occasions! Mr. Boldero was still evasive.

"I'll write you a letter about it," he said at last.

Gumbril was delighted. "Yes, do," he said enthusiastically, "do." He knew how to cope with letters all right. He was a devil with the fountain pen. It was these personal, hand-to-hand combats that he couldn't manage. He could have been, he always felt, such a ruthless critic and satirist, such a violent, unscrupulous polemical writer. And if ever he committed his autobiography to paper, how breath-takingly intimate, how naked— naked without so much as a healthy sunburn to color the whiteness— how quiveringly sensitive a jelly it would be! All the things he had never told anyone would be in it. Confessions at long range—if anything, it would be rather agreeable.

"Yes, do write me a letter," he repeated. "Do."

Mr. Boldero's letter came at last, and the proposals it contained were derisory. A hundred pounds down and five pounds a week when the business should be started. Five pounds a week—and for that he was to act as a managing director, writer of advertisements and promoter of foreign sales. Gumbril felt thankful that Mr. Boldero had put the terms in a letter. If they had been offered point-blank across the luncheon table, he would probably have accepted them without a murmur. He wrote a few neat, sharp phrases saying that he could not consider less than five hundred pounds down and a thousand a year. Mr. Boldero's reply was amiable; would Mr. Gumbril come and see him?

See him? Well, of course, it was inevitable. He would have to see him again some time. But he would send the Complete Man to deal with the fellow. A Complete Man matched with a leprechaun—there could be no doubt as to the issue.

"DEAR MR. BOLDERO," he wrote back, "I should have come to talk over matters before this. But I have been engaged during the last days in growing a beard and until this has come to maturity, I cannot, as you will easily be able to understand, leave the house. By the day after tomorrow, however, I hope to be completely presentable and shall come to see you at your office at about three o'clock, if that is convenient to you. I hope we shall be able to arrange matters satisfactorily. Believe me, dear Mr. Boldero, yours very truly, THEODORE GUMBRIL, JR."

The day after tomorrow became in due course today; splendidly bearded and Rabelaisianly broad in his whipcord toga, Gumbril presented himself at Mr. Boldero's office in Queen Victoria Street.

"I should hardly have recognized you," exclaimed Mr. Boldero as he shook hands. "How it does alter you to be sure!"

"Does it?" The Complete Man laughed with a significant joviality.

"Won't you take off your coat?"

"No thanks," said Gumbril. "I'll keep it on."

"Well," said the leprechaun, leaning back in his chair and twinkling, birdlike, across the table.

"Well," repeated Gumbril on a different tone from behind the stooks of his cornlike beard. He smiled, feeling serenely strong and safe.

"I'm sorry we should have disagreed," said Mr. Boldero.

"So am I," the Complete Man replied. "But we shan't disagree for long," he added with significance; and as he spoke the words he brought down his fist with such a bang that the ink pots on Mr. Boldero's very solid mahogany writing table trembled and the pens danced, while Mr. Boldero himself started with a genuine alarm. He had not expected this. And now he came to look at him more closely, this young Gumbril was a great, hulking, dangerous-looking fellow. He had thought he would be easy to manage. How could he have made such a mistake?

Gumbril left the office with Mr. Boldero's check for three hundred and fifty pounds in his pocket and an annual income of eight hundred. His bruised right hand was extremely tender to the touch. He was thankful that a single blow had been enough.

Chapter XI

GUMBRIL had spent the afternoon at Bloxam Gardens. His chin was still sore from the spirit gum with which he had attached to it the symbol of the Complete Man; he was feeling also a little fatigued. Rosie had been delighted to see him; St. Jerome had gone on solemnly communicating all the time.

His father had gone out to dine, and Gumbril had eaten his rump steak and drunk his bottle of stout alone. He was sitting now in front of the open French windows which led from his father's workroom onto the balcony, with a block on his knee and a fountain pen in his hand, composing advertisements for the Patent Small Clothes. Outside in the plane trees of the square the birds had gone through their nightly performance. But Gumbril had paid no attention to them. He sat there, smoking, sometimes writing a word or two—sunk in the quagmire of his own drowsy and comfortable body. The flawless weather of the day had darkened into a blue May evening. It was agreeable merely to be alive.

He sketched out two or three advertisements in the great idealistic trans-Atlantic style. He imagined one in particular with a picture of Nelson at the head of the page and "England expects . . ." printed large beneath it. "England . . . Duty . . . these are solemn words." That was how it would begin. "These are solemn words and we use them solemnly as men who realize what Duty is and who do all that in them lies to perform it as Englishmen should. The Manufacturer's is a sacred trust. The guide and ruler of the modern world, he has, like the Monarch of other days, responsibilities toward his people; he has a Duty to fulfill. He rules, but he must also serve. We realize our responsibilities; we take them seriously. Gumbril's Patent Small Clothes have been brought into the world that they may serve. Our Duty toward you is a Duty of Service. Our proud boast is that we perform it. But besides his Duty toward Others, every man has a duty toward Himself. What is that Duty? It is to keep himself in the highest possible state of physical and spiritual fitness. Gumbril's Patent Small Clothes protect the lumbar ganglia. . . ." After that it would be plain medical and mystical sailing.

As soon as he got to the ganglia Gumbril stopped writing. He put down the block, sheathed his pen, and abandoned himself to the pleasures of pure idleness. He sat, he smoked his cigar. In the basement, two floors down, the cook and the house parlormaid were reading, one the *Daily Mirror*, the other the *Daily Sketch*. For them, Her Majesty the Queen spoke kindly words to crippled female orphans; the jockeys tumbled at the jumps; Cupid was busy in Society, and the murderers who had disemboweled their mistresses were still at large. Above him was the city of models, was a bedroom, a servant's bedroom, an attic of tanks and ancient dirt, the roof and, after that, two or three hundred light-years away, a star of the fourth magnitude. On the other side of the party wall on his right, a teeming family of Jews led their dark, compact, Jewish lives with a prodigious intensity. At this moment they were all passionately quarreling. Beyond the wall on the left lived the young journalist and his wife. Tonight it was he who had cooked the supper. The young wife lay on the sofa, feeling horribly sick; she was going to have a baby, there could be no doubt about it now. They had meant not to have one; it was horrible. And, outside, the birds were sleeping in the trees, the invading children from the slum tumbled and squealed. Ships meanwhile were walloping across the Atlantic freighted with more cigars. Rosie at this moment was probably mending Shearwater's socks. Gumbril sat and smoked, and the universe arranged itself in a pattern about him, like iron filings round a magnet.

The door opened and the house parlormaid intruded Shearwater upon his lazy felicity, abruptly in her unceremonious old way, and hurried back to the *Daily Sketch*.

"Shearwater! This is very agreeable," said Gumbril. "Come and sit down." He pointed to a chair.

Clumsily, filling the space that two ordinary men would occupy, Shearwater came zigzagging and lurching across the room, bumped against the work table and sofa as he passed, and finally sat down in the indicated chair.

It suddenly occurred to Gumbril that this was Rosie's husband; he had not thought of that before. Could it be in the marital capacity that he presented himself so unexpectedly now? After this afternoon. . . . He had come home; Rosie had confessed all. . . . Ah! but then she didn't know who he was. He smiled to himself at the thought. What a joke! Perhaps Shearwater had come to complain to him of the unknown Complete Man—to him! It was delightful. Anon—the author of all those ballads in the *Oxford Book of English* Verse: the famous Italian painter— Ignoto. Gumbril was quite disappointed when his visitor began to talk of other themes than Rosie. Sunk in the quagmire of his own comfortable guts, he felt good-humoredly obscene. The dramatic scabrousness of the situation would have charmed him in his present mood. Good old Shearwater—but what an ox of a man! If he, Gumbril, took the trouble to marry a wife, he would at least take some interest in her.

Shearwater had begun to talk in general terms about life. What could he be getting at, Gumbril wondered? What particulars were ambushed behind these generalizations? There were silences. Shearwater looked, he thought, very gloomy. Under his thick mustache the small, pouting, babyish mouth did not smile. The candid eyes had a puzzled, tired expression in them.

"People are queer," he said after one of his silences. "Very queer. One has no idea how queer they are."

Gumbril laughed. "But I have a very clear idea of their queerness," he said. "Everyone's queer, and the ordinary, respectable bourgeois people are the queerest of the lot. How do they manage to live like that? It's astonishing. When I think of all my aunts and uncles . . ." He shook his head.

"Perhaps it's because I'm rather incurious," said Shearwater. "One ought to be curious, I think. I've come to feel lately that I've not been curious enough about people." The particulars began to peep, alive and individual, out of the vagueness, like rabbits. Gumbril saw them in his fancy, at the fringe of a wood.

"Quite," he said encouragingly. "Quite."

"I think too much of my work," Shearwater went on, frowning. "Too much physiology. There's also psychology. People's minds as well as their bodies. . . . One shouldn't be limited. Not too much, at any rate. People's minds. . . ." He was silent for a moment. "I can imagine," he went on at last, as in the tone of one who puts a very hypothetical case, "I can imagine one's getting so much absorbed in somebody else's psychology that one could really think of nothing else." The rabbits seemed ready to come out into the open.

"That's a process," said Gumbril with middle-aged jocularity, speaking out of his private warm morass, "that's commonly called falling in love."

There was another silence. Shearwater broke it to begin talking about Mrs. Viveash. He had lunched with her three or four days running. He wanted Gumbril to tell him what she was really like. "She seems to me a very extraordinary woman," he said.

"Like everybody else," said Gumbril irritatingly. It amused him to see the rabbits scampering about at last.

"I've never known a woman like that before."

Gumbril laughed. "You'd say that of any woman you happened to be interested in," he said. "You've never known any women at all." He knew much more about Rosie, already, than Shearwater did, or probably ever would.

Shearwater meditated. He thought of Mrs. Viveash, her cool, pale, critical eyes; her laughter, faint and mocking; her words that pierced into the mind, goading it into thinking unprecedented thoughts.

"She interests me," he repeated. "I want you to tell me what she's really like." He emphasized the word really, as though there must, in the nature of things, be a vast difference between the apparent and the real Mrs. Viveash.

Most lovers, Gumbril reflected, picture to themselves, in their mistresses, a secret reality, beyond and different from what they see every day. They are in love with somebody else—their own invention. And sometimes there is a secret reality; and sometimes reality and appearance are the same. The discovery, in either case, is likely to cause a shock. "I don't know," he said. "How should I know? You must find out for yourself."

"But you knew her, you know her well," said Shearwater, almost with anxiety in his voice.

"Not so well as all that."

Shearwater sighed profoundly, like a whale in the night. He felt restless, incapable of concentrating. His mind was full of a horrible confusion. A violent eruptive bubbling up from below had shaken its calm clarity to pieces. All this absurd business of passion—he had always thought it nonsense, unnecessary. With a little strength of will one could shut it out. Women—only for half an hour out of the twenty-four. But she had laughed, and his quiet, his security had vanished. "I can imagine," he had said to her yesterday, "I can imagine myself giving up everything, work and all, to go running round after you." "And do you suppose I should enjoy that?" Mrs. Viveash had asked. "It would be ridiculous," he said, "it would be almost shameful." And she had thanked him for the compliment. "And at the same time," he went on, "I feel that it might be worth it. It might be the only thing." His mind was confused, full of new thoughts. "It's difficult," he said after a pause, "arranging things. Very difficult. I thought I had arranged them so well. . . ."

"I never arrange anything," said Gumbril, very much the practical philosopher. "I take things as they come." And as he spoke the words, suddenly he became rather disgusted with himself. He shook himself; he climbed up out of his own morass. "It would be better, perhaps, if I arranged things more," he added.

"'Render therefore unto Caesar the things which are Caesar's,'" said Shearwater, as though to himself; "and to God, and to sex, and to work. . . . There must be a working arrangement." He sighed again. "Everything in proportion. In proportion," he repeated, as though the word were magical and had power. "In proportion."

"Who's talking about proportion?" They turned round. In the doorway Gumbril Senior was standing, smoothing his ruffled hair and tugging at his beard. His eyes twinkled cheerfully behind his spectacles. "Preaching on my architectural ground?" he said.

"This is Shearwater," Gumbril Junior put in, and explained who he was.

The old gentleman sat down. "Proportion," he said—"I was just thinking about it, now, as I was walking back. You can't help thinking about it in these London streets, where it doesn't exist. You can't help pining for it. There are some streets . . . oh, my God!" And Gumbril Senior threw up his hands in horror. "It's like listening to a symphony of cats to walk along them. Senseless discords and a horrible disorder all the way. And the one street that was really like a symphony by Mozart—how busily and gleefully they're pulling it down now! Another year and there'll be nothing left of Regent Street. There'll only be a jumble of huge hideous buildings at three-quarters of a million apiece. A concert of Brobdingnagian cats. Order has been turned into a disgusting chaos. We need no barbarians from outside; they're on the premises, all the time."

The old man paused and pulled his beard meditatively. Gumbril Junior sat in silence, smoking; and in silence Shearwater revolved within the walls of his great round head his agonizing thoughts of Mrs. Viveash.

"It has always struck me as very curious," Gumbril Senior went on, "that people are so little affected by the vile and discordant architecture round them. Suppose, now, that all these brass bands of unemployed ex-soldiers that blow so mournfully at all the street corners were suddenly to play nothing but a series of senseless and devilish discords—why, the first policeman would move them on, and the second would put them under arrest, and the passers-by would try to lynch them on their way to the police station. There would be a real spontaneous outcry of indignation. But when at these same street corners the contractors run up enormous palaces of steel and stone that are every bit as stupid and ignoble and inharmonious as ten brass bandsmen each playing a different tune in a different key, there is no outcry. The police don't arrest the architect; the passing pedestrians don't throw stones at the workmen. They don't notice that anything's wrong. It's odd," said Gumbril Senior. "It's very odd."

"Very odd," Gumbril Junior echoed.

"The fact is, I suppose," Gumbril Senior went on, smiling with a certain air of personal triumph, "the fact is that architecture is a more difficult and intellectual art than music. Music—that's just a faculty you're born with, as you might be born with a snub nose. But the sense of plastic beauty—though that's, of course, also an inborn faculty—is something that has to be developed and intellectually ripened. It's an affair of the mind; experience and thought have to draw it out. There are infant prodigies in music; but there are no infant prodigies in architecture." Gumbril Senior chuckled with a real satisfaction. "A man can be an excellent musician and a perfect imbecile. But a good architect must also be a man of sense, a man who knows how to think and to profit by experience. Now, as almost none of the people who pass along the streets in London, or any other city of the world, do know how to think or to profit by experience, it follows that they cannot appreciate architecture. The innate faculty is strong enough in them to make them dislike discord in music; but they haven't the wits to develop that other innate faculty—the sense of plastic beauty—which would enable them to see and disapprove of the same barbarism in architecture. Come with me," Gumbril Senior added, getting up from his chair, "and I'll show you something that will illustrate what I've been saying. Something you'll enjoy, too. Nobody's seen it yet," he said mysteriously as he led the way upstairs. "It's only just finished—after months and years. It'll cause a stir when they see it—when I let them see it, if ever I do, that is. The dirty devils!" Gumbril Senior added good-humoredly.

On the landing of the next floor he paused, felt in his pocket, took out a key and unlocked the door of what should have been the second-best bedroom. Gumbril Junior wondered, without very much curiosity, what the new toy would turn out to be. Shearwater wondered only how he could possess Mrs. Viveash.

"Come on," called Gumbril Senior from inside the room. He turned on the light. They entered.

It was a big room; but almost the whole of the floor was covered by an enormous model, twenty feet long by ten or twelve wide, of a complete city traversed from end to end by a winding river and dominated at its central point by a great dome. Gumbril Junior looked at it with surprise and pleasure. Even Shearwater was roused from his bitter ruminations of desire to look at the charming city spread out at his feet.

"It's exquisite," said Gumbril Junior. "What is it? The capital of Utopia, or what?"

Delighted, Gumbril Senior laughed. "Don't you see something rather familiar in the dome?" he asked.

"Well, I had thought. . . ." Gumbril Junior hesitated, afraid that he might be going to say something stupid. He bent down to look more closely at the dome. "I had thought it looked rather like St. Paul's—and now I see that it is St. Paul's."

"Quite right," said his father. "And this is London."

"I wish it were," Gumbril Junior laughed.

"It's London as it might have been if they'd allowed Wren to carry out his plans of rebuilding after the Great Fire."

"And why didn't they allow him to?" Shearwater asked.

"Chiefly," said Gumbril Senior, "because, as I've said before, they didn't know how to think or profit by experience. Wren offered them open spaces and broad streets; he offered them sunlight and air and cleanliness; he offered them beauty, order and grandeur. He offered to build for the imagination and the ambitious spirit of man, so that even the most bestial, vaguely and remotely, as they walked those streets, might feel that they were of the same race—or very nearly—as Michelangelo; that they too might feel themselves, in spirit at least, magnificent, strong and free. He offered them all these things; he drew a plan for them, walking in peril among the still-smoldering ruins. But they preferred to re-erect the old intricate squalor; they preferred the medieval darkness and crookedness, and beastly irregular quaintness; they preferred holes and crannies and winding tunnels; they preferred foul smells, sunless, stagnant air, phthisis and rickets; they preferred ugliness and pettiness and dirt; they preferred the wretched human scale, the scale of the sickly body, not of the mind. Miserable fools! But I suppose," the old man continued, shaking his head, "we can't blame them." His hair had blown loose from its insecure anchorage; with a gesture of resignation he brushed it back into place. "We can't blame them. We would have done the same in the circumstances—undoubtedly. People offer us reason and beauty; but we will have none of them, because they don't happen to square with the notions that were grafted into our souls in youth, that have grown there and become a part of us. *Experientia docet*—nothing falser, so far as most of us are concerned, was ever said. You, no doubt, my dear Theodore, have often in the past made a fool of yourself with women. . . ."

Gumbril Junior made an embarrassed gesture that half denied, half admitted the soft impeachment. Shearwater turned away, painfully reminded of what, for a moment, he had half forgotten. Gumbril Senior swept on.

"Will that prevent you from making as great a fool of yourself again tomorrow? It will not. It will most assuredly not." Gumbril Senior shook his head. "The inconveniences and horrors of the pox are perfectly well known to everyone; but still the disease flourishes and spreads. Several million people were killed in a recent war and half the world ruined; but we all busily go on in courses that make another event of the same sort inevitable. *Experientia docet? Experientia* doesn't. And that is why we must not be too hard on these honest citizens of London who, fully appreciating the inconveniences of darkness, disorder and dirt, manfully resisted any attempt to alter conditions which they had been taught from childhood onward to consider as necessary, right and belonging inevitably to the order of things. We must not be too hard. We are doing something even worse ourselves. Knowing by a century of experience how beautiful, how graceful, how soothing to the mind is an ordered piece of town planning, we pull down almost the only specimen of it we possess and put up in its place a chaos of Portland stone that is an offense against civilization. But let us forget about these old citizens and the labyrinth of ugliness and inconveniences which we have inherited from them, and which is called London. Let us forget the contemporaries who are making it still worse than it was. Come for a walk with me through this ideal city. Look."

And Gumbril Senior began expounding it to them.

In the middle, there, of that great elliptical Piazza at the eastern end of the new City, stands, four-square, the Royal Exchange. Pierced only with small dark windows and built of rough ashlars of the silvery Portland stone, the ground floor serves as a massy foundation for the huge pilasters that slide up, between base and capital, past three tiers of pedimented windows. Upon them rest the cornice, the attic and the balustrade, and on every pier of the balustrade a statue holds up its symbol against the sky. Four great portals, rich with allegory, admit to the courtyard with its double tier of coupled columns, its cloister and its gallery. The statue of Charles the Martyr rides triumphantly in the midst, and within the windows one guesses the great rooms, rich with heavy garlands of plaster, paneled with carved wood.

Ten streets give onto the Piazza, and at either end of its ellipse the water of sumptuous fountains ceaselessly blows aloft and falls. Commerce, in that to the north of the Exchange, holds up her cornucopia, and from the midst of its grapes and apples the master jet leaps up; from the teats of all the ten Useful Arts, grouped with their symbols about the central figure, there spouts a score of fine subsidiary streams. The dolphins, the sea horses and the Tritons sport in the basin below. To the south, the ten principal cities of the Kingdom stand in a family round the Mother London, who pours from her urn an inexhaustible Thames.

Ranged round the Piazza are the Goldsmiths' Hall, the Office of Excise, the Mint, the Post Office. Their flanks are curved to the curve of the ellipse. Between pilasters their windows look out onto the Exchange and the sister statues on the balustrades beckon to one another across the intervening space.

Two master roads of ninety feet from wall to wall run westward from the Exchange. New Gate ends the more northern vista with an Arch of Triumph, whose three openings are deep, shadowy and solemn as the entries of caverns. The Guildhall and the halls of the twelve City Companies in their livery of rose-red brick, with their lacings of white stone at the coigns and round the windows, lend to the street an air of domestic and comfortable splendor. And every two or three hundred paces the line of the houses is broken and in the indentation of a square recess there rises, conspicuous and insular, the fantastic tower of a parish church. Spire out of dome; octagon on octagon diminishing upward; cylinder on cylinder; round lanterns, lanterns of many sides; towers with airy pinnacles; clusters of pillars linked by incurving cornices, and above them four more clusters and above once more; square towers pierced with pointed windows; spires uplifted on flying buttresses; spires bulbous at the base—the multitude of them beckons, familiar and friendly, on the sky. From the other shore, or sliding along the quiet river, you see them all; you tell over their names; and the great dome swells up in the midst overtopping them all.

The dome of St. Paul's.

The other master street that goes westward from the Piazza of the Exchange slants down toward it. The houses are of brick, plain-faced and square, arcaded at the base, so that the shops stand back from the street and the pedestrian walks dry shod under the harmonious succession of the vaultings. And there at the end of the street, at the base of a triangular space formed by the coming together of this with another master street that runs eastward to Tower Hill, there stands the Cathedral. To the north of it is the Deanery and under the arcades are the booksellers' shops.

From St. Paul's the main road slopes down under the swaggering Italianate arches of Ludgate, past the wide lime-planted boulevards that run north and south within and without the city wall, to the edge of the Fleet Ditch—widened now into a noble canal, on whose paved banks the barges unload their freights of country stuff—leaps it on a single flying arch to climb again to a round circus, a little to the east of Temple Bar, from which in a pair of diagonally superimposed crosses eight roads radiate; three northward toward Holborn, three from the opposite arc toward the river, one eastward to the City, and one past Lincoln's Inn Fields to the West. The Piazza is all of brick and the houses that compose it are continuous above the ground-floor level; for the roads lead out under archways. To one who stands in the center at the foot of the obelisk that commemorates the victory over the Dutch, it seems a smooth well of brickwork pierced by eight arched conduits at the base and diversified above by the three tiers of plain, unornamented windows.

Who shall describe all the fountains in the open places, all the statues and monuments? In the circus north of London Bridge where the four roads come together, stands a pyramid of nymphs and Tritons—river goddesses of Polyolbion, sea gods of the island beaches—bathing in a ceaseless tumble of white water. And here the city griffon spouts from its beak, the royal lion from between its jaws. St. George at the foot of the Cathedral rides down a dragon whose nostrils spout, not fire, but the clear water of the New River. In front of the India House four elephants of black marble, indorsed with towers of white, blow through their upturned trunks the copious symbol of Eastern wealth. In the gardens of the Tower sits Charles the Second, enthroned among a troop of Muses, Cardinal Virtues, Graces and Hours. The tower of the Customs-House is a pharos. A great water gate, the symbol of naval triumph, spans the Fleet at its junction with the Thames. The river is embanked from Blackfriars to the Tower and at every twenty paces a gravestone angel looks out from the piers of the balustrade across the water. . . .

Gumbril Senior expounded his city with passion. He pointed to the model on the ground, he lifted his arms and turned up his eyes to suggest the size and splendor of his edifices. His hair blew wispily loose and fell into his eyes, and had to be brushed impatiently back again. He pulled at his beard; his spectacles flashed, as though they were living eyes. Looking at him, Gumbril Junior could imagine that he saw before him the passionate and gesticulating silhouette of one of those old shepherds who stand at the base of Piranesi's ruins demonstrating obscurely the prodigious grandeur and the abjection of the human race.

Chapter XII

"You? Is it you?" She seemed doubtful.

Gumbril nodded. "It's me," he reassured her. "I've shaved; that's all." He had left his beard in the top right-hand drawer of the chest of drawers, among the ties and the collars.

Emily looked at him judicially. "I like you better without it," she decided at last. "You look nicer. Oh, no, I don't mean to say you weren't nice before," she hastened to add. "But—you know—gentler—" She hesitated. "It's a silly word," she said, "but there it is: sweeter."

That was the unkindest cut of all. "Milder and more melancholy?" he suggested.

"Well, if you like to put it like that," Emily agreed.

He took her hand and raised it to his lips. "I forgive you," he said.

He could forgive her anything for the sake of those candid eyes, anything for the grave, serious mouth, anything for the short brown hair that curled—oh, but never seriously, never gravely—with such a hilarious extravagance round her head. He had met her, or rather the Complete Man, flushed with his commercial triumphs as he returned from his victory over Mr. Boldero, had met her, at the National Gallery. "Old Masters, young mistresses," Coleman had recommended the National Gallery. He was walking up the Venetian Room, feeling as full of swaggering vitality as the largest composition of Veronese, when he heard, gigglingly whispered just behind him his Open Sesame to new adventure, "Beaver." He spun round on his tracks and found himself face to face with two rather startled young women. He frowned ferociously, he demanded satisfaction for the impertinence. They were both, he noticed, of gratifyingly pleasing appearance and both extremely young. One of them, the elder, it seemed and the more charming, as he had decided from the first, of the two, was dreadfully taken aback; blushed to the eyes, stammered apologetically. But the other, who had obviously pronounced the word, only laughed. It was she who made easy the forming of an acquaintance which ripened, half an hour later, over the teacups and to the strains of the most classy music on the fifth floor of Lyons' Strand Corner House.

Their names were Emily and Molly. Emily, it seemed, was married. It was Molly who let that out, and the other had been angry with her for what was evidently an indiscretion. The bald fact that Emily was married had at once been veiled with mysteries, surrounded and protected by silences; whenever the Complete Man asked a question about it, Emily did not answer and Molly only giggled. But if Emily was married and the elder of the two, Molly was decidedly the more knowledgeable about life; Mr. Mercaptan would certainly have set her down as the more civilized. Emily didn't live in London; she didn't seem to live anywhere in particular. At the moment she was staying with Molly's family at Kew.

He had seen them the next day, and the day after, and the day after that; once at lunch, to desert them precipitately for his afternoon with Rosie; once at tea in Kew Gardens, once at dinner, with a theater to follow and an extravagant taxi back to Kew at midnight. The tame decoy allays the fears of the shy wild birds; Molly who was tame, who was frankly a flirting little wanton, had served the Complete Man as a decoy for the ensnaring of Emily. When Molly went away to stay with friends in the country, Emily was already inured and accustomed to the hunter's presence; she accepted the playful attitude of gallantry, which the Complete Man, at the invitation of Molly's rolling eyes and provocative giggle, had adopted from the first, as natural and belonging to the established order of things. With giggling Molly to give her a lead, she had gone in three days much further along the path of intimacy than, by herself, she would have advanced in ten times the number of meetings.

"It seems funny," she had said the first time they met after Molly's departure, "it seems funny to be seeing you, without Molly."

"It seemed funnier with Molly;" said the Complete Man. "It wasn't Molly I wanted to see."

"Molly's a very nice dear girl," she declared loyally. "Besides, she's amusing and can talk. And I can't; I'm not a bit amusing."

It wasn't difficult to retort to that sort of thing; but Emily didn't believe in compliments; oh, quite genuinely not.

He set out to make the exploration of her; and now that she was inured to him, no longer too frightened to let him approach, now, moreover that he had abandoned the jocular insolences of the Complete Man in favor of a more native mildness, which he felt instinctively was more suitable in this particular case, she laid no difficulties in his way. She was lonely and he seemed to understand everything so well; in the unknown country of her spirit and her history she was soon going eagerly before him as his guide.

She was an orphan. Her mother she hardly remembered. Her father had died of influenza when she was fifteen. One of his business friends used to come and see her at school, take her out for treats and give her chocolates. She used to call him Uncle Stanley. He was a leather merchant, fat and jolly with a rather red face, very white teeth and a bald head that was beautifully shiny. When she was seventeen and a half he asked her to marry him and she had said yes.

"But why?" Gumbril asked. "Why on earth?" he repeated.

"He said he'd take me round the world; it was just when the war had come to an end. Around the world you know; and I didn't like school. I didn't know anything about it and he was very nice to me; he was very pressing. I didn't know what marriage meant."

"Didn't know?"

She shook her head; it was quite true. "But not in the least."

And she had been born within the twentieth century. It seemed a case for the textbooks of sexual psychology. "Mrs. Emily X, born in 1901, was found to be in a state of perfect innocence and ignorance at the time of the Armistice, November 11th, 1918, etc."

"And so you married him?"

She had nodded.

"And then?"

She had covered her face with her hands, she had shuddered. The amateur uncle, now professionally a husband, had come to claim his rights, drunk. She had fought him, she had eluded him, had run away and locked herself into another room. On the second night of her honeymoon he gave her a bruise on the forehead and a bite on the left breast which had gone on septically festering for weeks. On the fourth, more determined than ever, he seized her so violently by the throat that a blood vessel broke and she began coughing bright blood over the bedclothes. The amateur uncle had been reduced to send for a doctor and Emily had spent the next few weeks in a nursing home. That was four years ago; her husband had tried to induce her to come back, but Emily had refused. She had a little money of her own; she was able to refuse. The amateur uncle had consoled himself with other and more docile nieces.

"And has nobody tried to make love to you since then?" he asked.

"Oh, lots of them have tried."

"And not succeeded?"

She shook her head. "I don't like men," she said. "They're hateful, most of them. They're brutes."

"Anch' io?"

"What?" she asked, puzzled.

"Am I a brute too?" And behind his beard, suddenly, he felt rather a brute.

"No," said Emily, after a little hesitation, "you're different. At least I think you are; though sometimes," she added, candidly, "sometimes you do and say things which make me wonder if you really are different."

The Complete Man laughed.

"Don't laugh like that," she said. "It's rather stupid."

"You're perfectly right," said Gumbril. "It is."

And how did she spend her time? He continued the exploration.

Well, she read a lot of books; but most of the novels she got from Boots' seemed to her rather silly.

"Too much about the same thing. Always love."

The Complete Man gave a shrug. "Such is life."

"Well, it oughtn't to be," said Emily.

And then, when she was in the country—and she was often in the country, taking lodgings here and there in little villages, weeks and months at a time—she went for long walks. Molly couldn't understand why she liked the country; but she did. She was very fond of flowers. She liked them more than people, she thought.

"I wish I could paint," she said. "If I could, I'd be happy forever, just painting flowers. But I can't paint." She shook her head. "I've tried so often. Such dirty ugly smudges come out on the paper; and it's all so lovely in my head, so lovely out in the fields."

Gumbril began talking with erudition about the flora of West Surrey: where you could find butterfly orchis and green man and the bee; the wood where there was actually wild columbine growing; the best localities for butcher's broom; the outcrops of clay where you get wild daffodils. All this odd knowledge came spouting up into his mind from some underground source of memory. Flowers—he never thought about flowers nowadays from one year's end to the other. But his mother had liked flowers. Every spring and summer they used to go down to stay at their cottage in the country. All their walks, all their drives in the governess cart had been hunts after flowers. And naturally the child had hunted with all his mother's ardor. He had kept books of pressed flowers, he had mummified them in hot sand, he had drawn maps of the country and colored them elaborately with different colored inks to show where the different flowers grew. How long ago all that was! Horribly long ago! Many seeds had fallen in the stony places of his spirit, to spring luxuriantly up into stalky plants and wither again because they had no deepness of earth; many had been sown there and had died since his mother scattered the seeds of the wild flowers.

"And if you want sundew," he wound up, "you'll find it in the Punch Bowl, under Hindhead. Or round about Frensham. The little Pond, you know, not the Big."

"But you know all about them," Emily exclaimed in delight. "I'm ashamed of my poor little knowledge. And you must really love them as much as I do."

Gumbril did not deny it; they were linked henceforth by a chain of flowers.

But what else did she do?

Oh, of course she played the piano a great deal. Very badly; but at any rate it gave her pleasure. Beethoven, she liked Beethoven best. More or less, she knew all the sonatas, though she could never keep up anything like the right speed in the difficult parts.

Gumbril had again shown himself wonderfully at home. "Aha!" he said. "I bet you can't shake that low B in the last variation but one of Op. 106 so that it doesn't sound ridiculous."

And of course she couldn't, and of course she was glad that he knew all about it and how impossible it was.

In the càb, as they drove back to Kew that evening, the Complete Man had decided it was time to do something decisive. The parting kiss —more of a playful sonorous buss than a serious embracement—that was already in the protocol, as signed and sealed before her departure by giggling Molly. It was time, the Complete Man considered, that this salute should take on a character less formal and less playful. One, two, three and, decisively, as they passed through Hammersmith Broadway, he risked the gesture; Emily burst into tears. He was not prepared for that, though perhaps he should have been. It was only by imploring, only by almost weeping himself that Gumbril persuaded her to revoke her decision never, never to see him again.

"I had thought you were different," she sobbed. "And now, now——"

"Please, please," he entreated. He was on the point of tearing off his beard and confessing everything there and then. But that, on second thought, would probably only make things worse.

"Please, I promise."

In the end, she had consented to see him once again, provisionally, in Kew Gardens, on the following day. They were to meet at the little temple that stands on the hillock above the valley of the heathers.

And now, duly, they had met. The Complete Man had been left at home in the top right-hand drawer, along with the ties and collars. She would prefer, he guessed, the Mild and Melancholy One; he was quite right. She had thought him "sweeter" at a first glimpse.

"I forgive you," he said, and kissed her hand. "I forgive you."

Hand in hand they walked down toward the valley of the heather.

"I don't know why you should be forgiving me," she said, laughing. "It seems to me that I ought to be doing the forgiving. After yesterday." She shook her head at him. "You made me so wretched."

"Ah, but you've already done your forgiving."

"You seem to take it very much for granted," said Emily. "Don't be too sure."

"But I am sure," said Gumbril. "I can see——"

Emily laughed again. "I feel happy," she declared.

"So do I."

"How green the grass is!"

Green, green after these long damp months it glowed in the sunlight, as though it were lighted from inside.

"And the trees!"

The pale, high, clot-polled trees of the English spring; the dark, symmetrical pine trees, islanded here and there on the lawns, each with its own separate profile against the sky and its own shadow, impenetrably dark or freckled with moving lights, on the grass at its feet.

They walked on in silence. Gumbril took off his hat, breathed the soft air that smelled of the greenness of the garden.

"There are quiet places also in the mind," he said, meditatively. "But we build bandstands and factories on them. Deliberately—to put a stop to the quietness. We don't like the quietness. All the thoughts, all the preoccupations in my head—round and round, continually." He made a circular motion with his hand. "And the jazz bands, the music-hall songs, the boys shouting the news. What's it for, what's it all for? To put an end to the quiet, to break it up and disperse it, to pretend at any cost it isn't there. Ah, but it is, it is there, in spite of everything, at the back of everything. Lying awake at night, sometimes—not restlessly, but serenely, waiting for sleep—the quiet re-establishes itself, piece by piece; all the broken bits, all the fragments of it we've been so busily dispersing all day long. It re-establishes itself, an inward quiet, like this outward quiet of grass and trees. It fills one; it grows—a crystal quiet, a growing expanding crystal. It grows, it becomes more perfect; it is beautiful and terrifying, yes, terrifying, as well as beautiful. For one's alone in the crystal and there's no support from outside, there's nothing external and important, nothing external and trivial to pull oneself up by or to stand on, superiorly, contemptuously, so that one can look down. There's nothing to laugh at or feel enthusiastic about. But the quiet grows and grows. Beautifully and unbearably. And at last you are conscious of something approaching: it is almost a faint sound of footsteps. Something inexpressibly lovely and wonderful advances through the crystal, nearer, nearer. And, oh, inexpressibly terrifying. For if it were to touch you, if it were to seize and engulf you, you'd die; all the regular, habitual, daily part of you would die. There would be an end of bandstands and whizzing factories, and one would have to begin living arduously in the quiet, arduously in some strange unheard-of manner. Nearer, nearer come the steps; but one can't face the advancing thing. One daren't. It's too terrifying, it's too painful to die. Quickly, before it is too late, start the factory wheels, bang the drum, blow the saxophone. Think of the women you'd like to sleep with, the schemes for making money, the gossip about your friends, the last outrage of the politicians. Anything for a diversion.

Break the silence, smash the crystal to pieces. There, it lies in bits; it is easily broken, hard to build up and easy to break. And the steps? Ah, those have taken themselves off, double quick. Double quick, they were gone at the first flawing of the crystal. And by this time the lovely and terrifying thing is three infinities away, at least. And you lie tranquilly on your bed, thinking of what you'd do if you had ten thousand pounds and of all the fornications you'll never commit." He thought of Rosie's pink underclothes.

"You make things very complicated," she said, after a silence.

Gumbril spread out his greatcoat on a green bank and they sat down. Leaning back, his hands under his head, he watched her sitting there beside him. She had taken off her hat; there was a stir of wind in those childish curls and at the nape, at the temples, where the hair had sleaved out thin and fine, the sunlight made little misty haloes of gold. Her hands clasped round her knees, she sat quite still, looking out across the green expanses, at the trees, at the white clouds on the horizon. There was quiet in her mind, he thought. She was native to that crystal world; for her, the steps came comfortingly through the silence, and the lovely thing brought with it no terrors. It was all so easy for her and simple.

Ah, so simple, so simple; like the Hire Purchase System on which Rosie had bought her pink bed. And how simple it was, too, to puddle clear waters and unpetal every flower—every flower, by God! one ever passed in a governess cart at the heels of a barrel-bellied pony. How simple to spit on the floors of churches. *Si prega di non sputare.* Simple to kick one's legs and enjoy oneself—dutifully—in pink underclothing. Perfectly simple.

"It's like the Arietta, don't you think?" said Emily suddenly, "the Arietta of Op. 111." And she hummed the first bars of the air. "Don't you feel it's like that?"

"What's like that?"

"Everything," said Emily. "Today, I mean. You and me. These gardens——" And she went on humming.

Gumbril shook his head. "Too simple for me," he said.

Emily laughed. "Ah, but then think how impossible it gets a little further on." She agitated her fingers wildly, as though she were trying to play the impossible passages. "It begins easily for the sake of poor imbeciles like me; but it goes on, it goes on, more and more fully and subtly and abstrusely and embracingly. But it's still the same movement."

The shadows stretched further and further across the lawns and as the sun declined, the level light picked out among the grasses innumerable stipplings of shadow; and in the paths, that had seemed under the more perpendicular rays as level as a table, a thousand little shadowy depressions and sun-touched mountains were now apparent. Gumbril looked at his watch.

"Good Lord," he said, "we must fly." He jumped up. "Quick, quick."

"But why?"

"We shall be late." He wouldn't tell her for what. "Wait and see," was all that Emily could get out of him by her questioning. They hurried out of the gardens and in spite of her protests, he insisted on taking a taxi into town. "I have such a lot of unearned increment to get rid of," he explained. The Patent Small Clothes seemed at the moment remoter than the farthest stars.

Chapter XIII

IN SPITE of the taxi, in spite of the gobbled dinner, they were late. The concert had begun.

"Never mind," said Gumbril. "We shall get in in time for the minuetto. It's then that the fun really begins."

"Sour grapes," said Emily, putting her ear to the door. "It sounds to me simply too lovely."

They stood outside, like beggars waiting abjectly at the doors of a banquetting hall, stood and listened to the snatches of music that came out tantalizingly from within. A rattle of clapping announced at last that the first movement was over; the doors were thrown open. Hungrily they rushed in. The Sclopis Quartet and a subsidiary viola were bowing from the platform. There was a chirrup of tuning, then preliminary silence. Scolpis nodded and moved his bow. The minuetto of Mozart's G minor Quintet broke out, phrase after phrase, short and decisive, with every now and then a violent sforzando chord, startling in its harsh and sudden emphasis.

Minuetto—all civilization, Mr. Mercaptan would have said, was implied in the delicious word, the delicate pretty thing. Ladies and precious gentlemen, fresh from the wit and gallantry of Crébillon-haunted sofas, stepping gracefully to a pattern of airy notes. To this passion of one who cries out, to this obscure and angry argument with fate how would they, Gumbril wondered, how would they have tripped it?

How pure the passion, how unaffected, clear and without clot or pretension the unhappiness of that slow movement which followed! Blessed are the pure in heart, for they shall see God. Pure and unsullied;

pure and unmixed, unadulterated. "Not passionate, thank God; only
sensual and sentimental." In the name of earwig. Amen. Pure, pure. Wor-
shipers have tried to rape the statues of the gods; the statuaries who made
the images were generally to blame. And how deliciously, too, an artist
can suffer! and, in the face of the whole Albert Hall, with what an
effective gesture and grimace! But blessed are the pure in heart, for they
shall see God. The instruments come together and part again. Long
silver threads hang aerially over a murmur of waters; in the midst of
muffled sobbing, a cry. The fountains blow their architecture of slender
pillars and from basin to basin the waters fall; from basin to basin, and
every fall makes somehow possible a higher leaping of the jet, and at the
last fall the mounting column springs up into the sunlight and from
water the music has modulated up into a rainbow. Blessed are the pure
in heart, for they shall see God; they shall make God visible, too, to
other eyes.

Blood beats in the ears. Beat, beat, beat. A slow drum in the darkness,
beating in the ears of one who lies wakeful with fever, with the sickness
of too much misery. It beats unceasingly, in the ears, in the mind itself.
Body and mind are indivisible and in the spirit blood painfully throbs.
Sad thoughts droop through the mind. A small pure light comes swaying
down through the darkness, comes to rest, resigning itself to the obscurity
of its misfortune. There is resignation, but blood still beats in the ears.
Blood still painfully beats, though the mind has acquiesced. And then,
suddenly, the mind exerts itself, throws off the fever of too much suffering and, laughing, commands the body to dance. The introduction to the
last movement comes to its suspended, throbbing close. There is an
instant of expectation and then, with a series of mounting trochees and
a downward hurrying, step after tiny step, in triple time, the dance begins. Irrelevant, irreverent, out of key with all that has gone before. But
man's greatest strength lies in his capacity for irrelevance. In the midst
of pestilences, wars and famines, he builds cathedrals; and a slave, he
can think the irrelevant and unsuitable thoughts of a free man. The
spirit is slave to fever and beating blood, at the mercy of an obscure and
tyrannous misfortune. But irrelevantly, it elects to dance in triple measure
—a mounting skip, a patter of descending feet.

The G minor Quintet is at an end; the applause rattles out loudly.
Enthusiasts stand up and cry bravo. And the five men on the platform rise
and bow their acknowledgements. Great Sclopis himself receives his share
of the plaudits with a weary condescension; weary are his poached eyes,
weary his disillusioned smile. It is only his due, he knows; but he has
had so much clapping, so many lovely women. He has a Roman nose, a

colossal brow and though the tawny musical mane does much to conceal the fact, no back to his head. Garofalo, the second fiddle, is black, beady eyed and potbellied. The convex reflections of the electroliers slide back and forth over his polished bald head, as he bends, again, again, in little military salutes. Peperkoek, two meters high, bows with a sinuous politeness. His face, his hair are all of the same grayish buff color; he does not smile, his appearance is monolithic and grim. Not so exuberant Knoedler, who sweats and smiles and embraces his 'cello and lays his hand to his heart and bows almost to the ground as though all this hullaballoo were directed only at him. As for poor little Mr. Jenkins, the subsidiary viola, he has slid away, into the background and, feeling that this is really the Sclopis's show and that he, a mere intruder, has no right to any of these demonstrations, he hardly bows at all, but only smiles, vaguely and nervously, and from time to time makes a little spasmodic twitch to show that he isn't really ungrateful or haughty, as you might think, but that he feels in the circumstances—the position is a little embarrassing—it is hard to explain. . . .

"Strange," said Gumbril, "to think that those ridiculous creatures could have produced what we've just been hearing."

The poached eye of Sclopis lighted on Emily, flushed and ardently applauding. He gave her, all to herself, a weary smile. He would have a letter, he guessed, tomorrow morning signed "Your little Admirer in the Third Row." She looked a choice little piece. He smiled again to encourage her. Emily, alas, had not even noticed. She was applauding the music.

"Did you enjoy it?" he asked, as they stepped out into a deserted Bond Street.

"Did I? . . ." Emily laughed expressively. "No, I didn't enjoy," she said. "Enjoy isn't the word. You enjoy eating ices. It made me happy. It's unhappy music, but it made me happy."

Gumbril hailed a cab and gave the address of his rooms in Great Russell Street. "Happy," he repeated, as they sat there side by side in the darkness. He, too, was happy.

"Where are we going?" she asked.

"To my rooms," said Gumbril, "we shall be quiet there." He was afraid she might object to going there—after yesterday. But she made no comment.

"Some people think that it's only possible to be happy if one makes a noise," she said, after a pause. "I find it's too delicate and melancholy for noise. Being happy is rather melancholy—like the most beautiful

landscape, like those trees and the grass and the clouds and the sunshine today."

"From the outside," said Gumbril, "it even looks rather dull." They
stumbled up the dark staircase to his rooms. Gumbril lit a pair of candles
and put the kettle on the gas ring. They sat together on the divan sipping tea. In the rich, soft light of the candles she looked different, more
beautiful. The silk of her dress seemed wonderfully rich and glossy,
like the petals of a tulip, and on her face, on her bare arms and neck
the light seemed to spread an impalpable bright bloom. On the wall
behind them, their shadows ran up toward the ceiling, enormous and
profoundly black.

"How unreal it is," Gumbril whispered. "Not true. This remote secret
room. These lights and shadows out of another time. And you out of
nowhere and I, out of a past utterly remote from yours, sitting together
here, together—and being happy. That's the strangest thing of all.
Being quite senselessly happy. It's unreal, unreal."

"But why," said Emily, "why? It's here and happening now. It *is* real."

"It all might vanish, at any moment," he said.

Emily smiled rather sadly. "It'll vanish in due time," she said. "Quite
naturally, not by magic; it'll vanish the way everything else vanishes and
changes. But it's here now."

They gave themselves up to the enchantment. The candles burned,
two shining eyes of flame, without a wink, minute after minute. But for
them were no longer any minutes. Emily leaned against him, her body
held in the crook of his arm, her head resting on his shoulder. He
caressed his cheek against her hair; sometimes, very gently, he kissed her
forehead or her closed eyes.

"If I had known you years ago . . ." she sighed. "But I was a silly little
idiot then. I shouldn't have noticed any difference between you and
anybody else."

"I shall be very jealous." Emily spoke again after another timeless
silence. "There must never be anybody else, never the shadow of anybody else."

"There never will be anybody else," said Gumbril.

Emily smiled and, opening her eyes, looked up at him. "Ah, not
here," she said, "not in this real unreal room. Not during this eternity.
But there will be other rooms just as real as this."

"Not so real, not so real." He bent his face toward hers. She closed
her eyes again and the lids fluttered with a sudden tremulous movement
at the touch of his light kiss.

For them there were no more minutes. But time passed, time passed flowing in a dark stream, stanchlessly, as though from some profound mysterious wound in the world's side, bleeding, bleeding forever. One of the candles had burned down to the socket and the long smoky flame wavered unsteadily. The flickering light troubled their eyes; the shadows twitched and stirred uneasily. Emily looked up at him.

"What's the time?" she said.

Gumbril looked at his watch. It was nearly one o'clock. "Too late for you to get back," he said.

"Too late?" Emily sat up. Ah, the enchantment was breaking, was giving way, like a film of ice beneath a weight, like a web before a thrust of the wind. They looked at one another. "What shall I do?" she asked.

"You could sleep here," Gumbril answered in a voice that came from a long way away.

She sat for a long time in silence, looking through half-closed eyes at the expiring candle flame. Gumbril watched her in an agony of suspense. Was the ice to be broken, the web-work finally and forever torn? The enchantment could still be prolonged, the eternity renewed. He felt his heart beating in his breast; he held his breath. It would be terrible if she were to go now, it would be a kind of death. The flame of the candle flickered more violently, leaping up in a thin, long smoky flare, sinking again almost to darkness. Emily got up and blew out the candle. The other still burned calmly and steadily.

"May I stay?" she asked. "Will you allow me?"

He understood the meaning of her question and nodded. "Of course," he said.

"Of course? Is it as much of course as all that?"

"When I say so." He smiled at her. The eternity had been renewed, the enchantment prolonged. There was no need to think of anything now but the moment. The past was forgotten, the future abolished. There was only this secret room and the candlelight and the unreal, impossible happiness of being two. Now that this peril of a disenchantment had been averted, it would last forever. He got up from the couch, crossed the room, he took her hands and kissed them.

"Shall we sleep now?" she asked.

Gumbril nodded.

"Do you mind if I blow out the light?" And without waiting for his answer, Emily turned, gave a puff and the room was in darkness. He heard the rustling of her undressing. Hastily he stripped off his own clothing, pulled back the coverlet from the divan. The bed was made and ready; he opened it and slipped between the sheets. A dim greenish light from the gas lamp in the street below came up between the parted curtains, illuminating faintly the further end of the room. Against this tempered darkness he could see her, silhouetted, standing quite still, as if hesitating on some invisible brink.

"Emily," he whispered.

"I'm coming," Emily answered. She stood there, unmoving, a few seconds longer, then overstepped the brink. She came silently across the room, and sat down on the edge of the low couch. Gumbril lay perfectly still, without speaking, waiting in the enchanted timeless darkness. Emily lifted her knees, slid her feet in under the sheet, then stretched herself out beside him, her body, in the narrow bed, touching his. Gumbril felt that she was trembling; trembling, a sharp involuntary start, a little shudder, another start.

"You're cold," he said and slipping one arm beneath her shoulders he drew her, limp and unresisting, toward him. She lay there, pressed against him. Gradually the trembling ceased. Quite still, quite still in the calm of the enchantment. The past is forgotten, the future abolished; there is only this dark and everlasting moment. A drugged and intoxicated stupor of happiness possessed his spirit; a numbness, warm and delicious, lay upon him. And yet through the stupor he knew with a dreadful anxious certainty that the end would soon be there. Like a man on the night before his execution he looked forward through the endless present; he foresaw the end of his eternity. And after? Everything was uncertain and unsafe.

Very gently, he began caressing her shoulder, her long slender arm, drawing his finger tips lightly and slowly over her smooth skin; slowly from her neck, over her shoulder, lingeringly round the elbow to her hand. Again, again: he was learning her arm. The form of it was part of the knowledge, now, of his finger tips; his fingers knew it as they knew a piece of music, as they knew Mozart's Twelfth Sonata, for example. And the themes that crowd so quickly one after another at the beginning of the first movement played themselves aerially, glitteringly in his mind; they became a part of the enchantment.

Through the silk of her shift he learned her curving side, her smooth straight back and the ridge of her spine. He stretched down, touched her feet, her knees. Under the smock he learned her warm body, lightly, slowly caressing. He knew her; his fingers, he felt, could build her up, a warm and curving statue in the darkness. He did not desire her; to desire would have been to break the enchantment. He let himself sink deeper and deeper into his dark stupor of happiness. She was asleep in his arms; and soon he too was asleep.

Chapter XIV

MRS. VIVEASH descended the steps into King Street and standing there on the pavement looked dubiously first to the right and then to the left. Little and loud, the taxis rolled by on their white wheels; the long-snouted limousines passed with a sigh. The air smelled of watered dust, tempered in Mrs. Viveash's immediate neighborhood by those memories of Italian jasmines which were her perfume. On the opposite pavement, in the shade, two young men, looking very conscious of their gray top hats, marched gravely along.

Life, Mrs. Viveash thought, looked a little dim this morning, in spite of the fine weather. She glanced at her watch; it was one o'clock. Soon one would have to eat some lunch. But where, and with whom? Mrs. Viveash had no engagements. All the world was before her, she was absolutely free, all day long. Yesterday, when she declined all those pressing invitations, the prospect had seemed delightful. Liberty, no complications, no contacts; a pre-Adamite empty world to do what she liked in.

But today, when it came to the point, she hated her liberty. To come out like this at one o'clock into a vacuum—it was absurd; it was appalling. The prospect of immeasurable boredom opened before her. Steppes after steppes of ennui, horizon beyond horizon, forever the same. She looked again to the right and again to the left. Finally she decided to go to the left. Slowly, walking along her private knife-edge between her personal abysses, she walked toward the left. She remembered suddenly one shining day like this in the summer of 1917, when she had walked along this same street, slowly, like this, on the sunny side, with Tony Lamb. All that day, that night, it had been one long good-by. He was going back the next morning. Less than a week later, he was dead. Never again, never again: there had been a time when she could make herself cry, simply by saying those two words once or twice, under her breath. Never again, never again. She repeated them softly now. But she felt no tears behind her eyes. Grief doesn't kill, love doesn't kill; but time kills everything, kills desire, kills sorrow, kills in the end the mind that feels them; wrinkles and softens the body while it still lives, rots it like a medlar, kills it, too, at last. Never again, never again. Instead of crying, she laughed, laughed aloud. The pigeon-breasted old gentleman who had just passed her, twirling between his finger and thumb the ends of a white military mustache, turned round startled. Could she be laughing at him?

"Never again," murmured Mrs. Viveash.

"I beg your pardon?" queried the martial gentleman, in a rich port-winey, cigary voice.

Mrs. Viveash looked at him with such wide-eyed astonishment that the old gentleman was quite taken aback. "A thousand apologies, dear lady. Thought you were addressing. . . . H'm, ah'm." He replaced his hat, squared his shoulders and went off smartly, left, right, bearing preciously before him his pigeon breast. Poor thing, he thought, poor young thing. Talking to herself. Must be cracked, must be off her head. Or perhaps she took drugs. That was more likely: that was much more likely. Most of them did nowadays. Vicious young women. Lesbians, drug fiends, nymphomaniacs, dipsos—thoroughly vicious, nowadays, thoroughly vicious. He arrived at his club in an excellent temper.

Never again, never, never again. Mrs. Viveash would have liked to be able to cry.

St. James's Square opened before her. Romantically under its trees the statue pranced. The trees gave her an idea: she might go down into the country for the afternoon, take a cab and drive out, out, goodness only knew where! To the top of a hill somewhere. Box Hill, Leith Hill, Holmbury Hill, Ivinghoe Beacon—any hill where one could sit and look out over plains. One might do worse than that with one's liberty.

But not much worse, she reflected.

Mrs. Viveash had turned up toward the northern side of the square and was almost at its northwestern corner when with a thrill of genuine delight, with a sense of the most profound relief she saw a familiar figure, running down the steps of the London Library.

"Theodore!" she hallooed faintly, but penetratingly, from her inward deathbed. "Gumbril!" She waved her parasol.

Gumbril halted, looked round, came smiling to meet her. "How delightful," he said. "But how unfortunate."

"Why unfortunate?" asked Mrs. Viveash. "Am I of evil omen?"

"Unfortunate," Gumbril explained, "because I've got to catch a train and can't profit by this meeting."

"Ah no, Theodore," said Mrs. Viveash, "you're not going to catch a train. You're going to come and lunch with me. Providence has decreed it. You can't say no to Providence."

"I must," Gumbril shook his head. "I've said yes to somebody else."

"To whom?"

"Ah!" said Gumbril with a coy and saucy mysteriousness.

"And where are you going in your famous train?"

"Ah again," Gumbril answered.

"How intolerably tiresome and silly you are!" Mrs. Viveash declared.

"One would think you were a sixteen-year-old schoolboy going out for his first assignation with a shop girl. At your age, Gumbril!" She shook her head, smiled agonizingly and with contempt. "Who is she? What sordid pick-up?"

"Not sordid in the least," protested Gumbril.

"But decidedly a pick-up. Eh?" A banana skin was lying, like a bedraggled starfish, in the gutter, just in front of where they were standing. Mrs. Viveash stepped forward and with the point of her parasol lifted it carefully up and offered it to her companion.

"*Merci*," Gumbril bowed.

She tossed the skin back again into the gutter. "In any case," she said, "the young lady can wait while we have luncheon."

Gumbril shook his head. "I've made the arrangement," he said. Emily's letter was in his pocket. She had taken the loveliest cottage just out of Robertsbridge in Sussex. Ah, but the loveliest imaginable. For the whole summer. He could come and see her there. He had telegraphed that he would come today, this afternoon, by the two o'clock from Charing Cross.

Mrs. Viveash took him by the elbow. "Come along," she said. "There's a post office in that passage going from Jermyn Street to Piccadilly. You can wire from there your infinite regrets. These things always improve with a little keeping. There will be raptures when you *do* go tomorrow."

Gumbril allowed himself to be led along. "What an insufferable woman you are," he said, laughing.

"Instead of being grateful to me for asking you to luncheon!"

"Oh, I am grateful," said Gumbril. "And astonished."

He looked at her. Mrs. Viveash smiled and fixed him for a moment with her pale untroubled eyes. . . . She said nothing.

"Still," Gumbril went on, "I must be at Charing Cross by two, you know."

"But we're lunching at Verrey's."

Gumbril shook his head.

They were at the corner of Jermyn Street. Mrs. Viveash halted and delivered her ultimatum, the more impressive for being spoken in that expiring voice of one who says *in articulo* the final and supremely important things. "We lunch at Verrey's, Theodore, or I shall never, never speak to you again."

"But be reasonable, Myra," he implored. If only he'd told her that he had a business appointment . . . Imbecile, to have dropped those stupid hints—in that tone!

"I prefer not to be," said Mrs. Viveash.

Gumbril made a gesture of despair and was silent. He thought of Emily in her native quiet among the flowers; in a cottage altogether too cottagey, with honeysuckles and red ramblers and hollyhocks—though on second thoughts none of them would be blooming yet, would they?—happily, in white muslin, extracting from the cottage piano the easier sections of the Arietta. A little absurd, perhaps, when you consider her like that; but exquisite, but adorable, but pure of heart and flawless in her bright pellucid integrity, complete as a crystal in its faceted perfection. She would be waiting for him, expecting him; and they would walk through the twiddly lanes—or perhaps there would be a governess cart for hire, with a fat pony like a tub on legs to pull it—they would look for flowers in the woods and perhaps he would still remember what sort of noise a whitethroat makes; or even if he didn't remember, he could always magisterially say he did. "That's a whitethroat, Emily. Do you hear? The one that goes 'Tweedly, weedly, weedledy dee.' "

"I'm waiting," said Mrs. Viveash. "Patiently, however."

Gumbril looked at her and found her smiling like a tragic mask. After all, he reflected, Emily would still be there if he went down tomorrow. It would be stupid to quarrel with Myra about something that was really, when he came to think of it, not of enormous importance. It was stupid to quarrel with anyone about anything; and with Myra and about this, particularly so. In this white dress patterned with flowing arabesques of black she looked, he thought, more than ever enchanting. There had been times in the past. . . . The past leads on to the present. . . . No; but in any case she was excellent company.

"Well," he said, sighing decisively, "let's go and send my wire."

Mrs. Viveash made no comment, and traversing Jerymn Street they walked up the narrow passage under the lee of Wren's bald barn of St. James's, to the post office.

"I shall pretext a catastrophe," said Gumbril, as they entered; and going to the telegraph desk he wrote: "Slight accident on way to station not serious at all but a little indisposed come same train tomorrow." He addressed the form and handed it in.

"A little what?" asked the young lady behind the bars, as she read it through, prodding each successive word with the tip of her blunt pencil.

"A little indisposed," said Gumbril, and he felt suddenly very much ashamed of himself. "A little indisposed"—no, really, that was too much. He'd withdraw the telegram, he'd go after all.

"Ready?" asked Mrs. Viveash, coming up from the other end of the counter where she had been buying stamps.

Gumbril pushed a florin under the bars.

"A little indisposed," he said, hooting with laughter, and he walked toward the door, leaning heavily on his stick and limping. "Slight accident," he explained.

"What is the meaning of this clownery?" Mrs. Viveash inquired.

"What indeed?" Gumbril had limped up to the door and stood there, holding it open for her. He was taking no responsibility for himself. It was the clown's doing and the clown, poor creature, was *non compos*, but entirely there, and couldn't be called to account for his actions. He limped after her toward Piccadilly.

"*Giudicato guárabile in cinque giorni,*" Mrs. Viveash laughed. "How charming that always is in the Italian papers. The fickle lady, the jealous lover, the stab, the *colpo di rivoltella*, the mere Anglo-Saxon black eye —all judged by the house surgeon at the Misericordia curable in five days. And you, my poor Gumbril, are you curable in five days?"

"That depends," said Gumbril. "There may be complications."

Mrs. Viveash waved her parasol; a taxi came swerving to the pavement's edge in front of them. "Meanwhile," she said, "you can't be expected to walk."

At Verrey's they lunched off lobsters and white wine. "Fish suppers," Gumbril quoted jovially from the Restoration, "fish suppers will make a man hop like a flea." Through the whole meal he clowned away in the most inimitable style. The ghost of a governess cart rolled along the twiddly lanes of Robertsbridge. But one can refuse to accept responsibility; a clown cannot be held accountable. And besides, when the future and the past are abolished, when it is only the present instant, whether enchanted or unenchanted, that counts, when there are no causes or motives, no future consequences to be considered, how can there be responsibility, even for those who are not clowns? He drank a great deal of hock and when the clock struck two and the train had begun to snort out of Charing Cross, he could not refrain from proposing the health of Viscount Lascelles. After that he began telling Mrs. Viveash about his adventure as a Complete Man.

"You should have seen me," he said, describing his beard.

"I should have bowled over."

"You shall see me, then," said Gumbril. "Ah, what a Don Giovanni. *La ci darem la mano, La mi dirai di si, Vieni, non e lontano, Partiam, ben mio, da qui.* And they came, they came. Without hesitation. No '*vorrei e non vorrei,*' no '*mi trema un poco il cor.*' Straightaway."

"*Felice, io so, sarei,*" Mrs. Viveash sang very faintly under her breath, from a remote bed of agony.

"Ah, happiness, happiness; a little dull, someone had wisely said, when you looked at it from outside. An affair of duets at the cottage piano, of collecting specimens, hand in hand, for the *hortus siccus*. A matter of integrity and quietness.

"Ah, but the history of the young woman who was married four years ago," exclaimed Gumbril with clownish rapture, "and remains to this day a virgin—what an episode in my memoirs!" In the enchanted darkness he had learned her young body. He looked at his fingers; her beauty was a part of their knowledge. On the tablecloth he drummed out the first bars of the Twelfth Sonata of Mozart. "And even after singing her duet with the Don," he continued, "she is still virgin. There are chaste pleasures, sublimated sensualities. More thrillingly voluptuous," with the gesture of a restaurant keeper who praises the specialty of the house, he blew a treacly kiss, "than any of the grosser deliriums."

"What is all this about?" asked Mrs. Viveash.

Gumbril finished off his glass. "I am talking esoterically," he said, "for my own pleasure, not yours."

"But tell me more about the beard," Mrs. Viveash insisted. "I liked the beard so much."

"All right," said Gumbril, "let us try to be unworthy with coherence."

They sat for a long time over their cigarettes; it was half-past three before Mrs. Viveash suggested they should go.

"Almost time," she said, looking at her watch, "to have tea. One damned meal after another. And never anything new to eat. And every year one gets bored with another of the old things. Lobster, for instance, how I used to adore lobster once! But today—well, really, it was only your conversation, Theodore, that made it tolerable."

Gumbril put his hand to his heart and bowed. He felt suddenly extremely depressed.

"And wine: I used to think Orvieto so heavenly. But this spring, when I went to Italy, it was just a bad muddy sort of Vouvray. And those soft caramels they call Fiats; I used to eat those till I was sick. I was at the sick stage before I'd finished one of them, this time in Rome." Mrs. Viveash shook her head. "Disillusion after disillusion."

They walked down the dark passage into the street.

"We'll go home," said Mrs. Viveash. "I really haven't the spirit to do anything else this afternoon." To the commissionaire who opened the door of the cab she gave the address of her house in St. James's.

"Will one ever recapture the old thrills?" she asked rather fatiguedly as they drove slowly through the traffic of Regent Street.

"Not by chasing after them," said Gumbril, in whom the clown had quite evaporated. "If one sat still enough they might perhaps com back of their own accord." There would be the faint sound as it were of feet approaching through the quiet.

"It isn't only food," said Mrs. Viveash, who had closed her eyes and was leaning back in her corner.

"So I can well believe."

"It's everything. Nothing's the same now. I feel it never will be."

"Never more," croaked Gumbril.

"Never again," Mrs. Viveash echoed. "Never again." There were still no tears behind her eyes. "Did you ever know Tony Lamb?" she asked.

"No," Gumbril answered from his corner. "What about him?"

Mrs. Viveash did not answer. What, indeed, about him? She thought of his very clear blue eyes and the fair bright hair that had been lighter than his brown face. Brown face and neck, red-brown hands; and all the rest of his skin was as white as milk. "I was very fond of him," she said at last. "That's all. He was killed in 1917, just about this time of the year. It seems a very long time ago, don't you think?"

"Does it?" Gumbril shrugged his shoulders. "I don't know. The past is abolished. *Vivamus, mea Lesbia.* If I weren't so horribly depressed, I'd embrace you. That would be some slight compensation for my"—he tapped his foot with the end of his walking stick—"my accident."

"You're depressed too?"

"One should never drink at luncheon," said Gumbril. "It wrecks the afternoon. One should also never think of the past and never for one moment consider the future. These are treasures of ancient wisdom. But perhaps after a little tea"—he leaned forward to look at the figures on the taximeter, for the cab had come to a standstill—"after a nip of the tannin stimulant"—he threw open the door—"we may feel rather better."

Mrs. Viveash smiled excruciatingly. "For me," she said, as she stepped out on to the pavement, "even tannin has lost its virtues now."

Mrs. Viveash's drawing room was tastefully in the movement. The furniture was upholstered in fabrics designed by Dufy—race horses and roses, little tennis players clustering in the midst of enormous flowers, printed in gray and ochre on a white ground. There were a couple of lampshades by Balla. On the pale rose-stippled walls hung three portraits of herself by three different and entirely incongruous painters, a selection of the usual oranges and lemons and a rather forbidding contemporary nude painted in two tones of green.

"And how bored I am with this room and all these beastly pictures," exclaimed Mrs. Viveash as she entered. She took off her hat and, standing in front of the mirror above the mantelpiece, smoothed her coppery hair.

"You should take a cottage in the country," said Gumbril, "buy a pony and a governess cart and drive along the twiddly lanes looking for flowers. After tea you open the cottage piano," and suiting his action to the words, Gumbril sat down at the long-tailed Blüthner, "and you play, you play." Very slowly and with parodied expressiveness he played the opening theme of the Arietta. "You wouldn't be bored then," he said, turning round to her, when he had finished.

"Ah, wouldn't I!" said Mrs. Viveash. "And with whom do you propose that I should share my cottage?"

"Anyone you like," said Gumbril. His fingers hung, as though meditating over the keys.

"But I don't like anyone," cried Mrs. Viveash with a terrible vehemence from her deathbed. Ah, now it had been said, the truth. It sounded like a joke. Tony had been dead five years now. Those bright blue eyes—ah, never again. All rotted away to nothing.

"Then you should try," said Gumbril, whose hands had begun to creep softly forward into the Twelfth Sonata. "You should try."

"But I do try," said Mrs. Viveash. Her elbows propped on the mantelpiece, her chin resting on her clasped hands, she was looking fixedly at her own image in the glass. Pale eyes looked unwaveringly into pale eyes. The red mouth and its reflection exchanged their smiles of pain. She had tried; it revolted her now to think how often she had tried; she had tried to like someone, anyone, as much as Tony. She had tried to recapture, to re-evoke, to revivify. And there had never been anything, really, but a disgust. "I haven't succeeded," she added, after a pause.

The music had shifted from F major to D minor; it mounted in leaping anapaests to a suspended chord, ran down again, mounted once more, modulating to C minor, then, through a passage of trembling notes to A flat major, to the dominant of D flat, to the dominant of C, to C minor, and at last, to a new clear theme in the major.

"Then I'm sorry for you," said Gumbril, allowing his fingers to play on by themselves. He felt sorry, too, for the subjects of Mrs. Viveash's desperate experiments. She mightn't have succeeded in liking them— for their part, poor devils, they in general only too agonizingly liked her. Only too . . . He remembered the cold damp spots on his pillow, in the darkness. Those hopeless, angry tears. "You nearly killed me once," he said.

"Only time kills," said Mrs. Viveash, still looking into her own pale eyes. "I have never made anyone happy," she added, after a pause. "Never anyone," she thought, except Tony, and Tony they had killed, shot him through the head. Even the bright eyes had rotted, like any other carrion. She too had been happy then. Never again.

A maid came in with the tea things.

"Ah, the tannin," exclaimed Gumbril with enthusiasm, and broke off his playing. "The one hope of salvation." He poured out two cups and picking up one of them he came over to the fireplace and stood behind her, sipping slowly at the pale brewage and looking over her shoulder at their two reflections in the mirror.

"La ci darem," he hummed. "If only I had my beard!" He stroked his chin and with the tip of his forefinger brushed up the drooping ends of his mustache. "You'd come trembling like Zerlina, in under its golden shadow."

Mrs. Viveash smiled. "I don't ask for anything better," she said. "What more delightful part! Felice, io so, sarei: Batti, batti, o bel Mazetto. Enviable Zerlina!"

The servant made another silent entry.

"A gentleman," she said, "called Mr. Shearwater would like . . ."

"Tell him I'm not at home," said Mrs. Viveash, without looking round.

There was a silence. With raised eyebrows Gumbril looked over Mrs. Viveash's shoulder at her reflection. Her eyes were calm and without expression, she did not smile or frown. Gumbril still questioningly looked. In the end he began to laugh.

Chapter XV

THEY are playing that latest novelty from across the water, "What's He to Hecuba?" Sweet, sweet and piercing, the saxophone pierced into the very bowels of compassion and tenderness, pierced like a revelation from heaven, pierced like the angel's treacly dart into the holy Teresa's quivering and ecstasiated flank. More ripely and roundly, with a kindly and less agonizing voluptuousness, the 'cello meditated those Mohammedan ecstasies that last, under the green palms of Paradise, six hundred inerrable years apiece. Into this charged atmosphere the violin admitted refreshing drafts of fresh air, cool and thin like the breath from a still-damp squirt. And the piano hammered and rattled away unmindful of the sensibilities of other instruments, banged away all the time reminding everyone concerned, in a thoroughly businesslike way, that this was a cabaret where people came to dance the foxtrot; not a baroque

church for female saints to go into ecstasies in, not a mild, happy valley
of tumbling houris.

At each recurrence of the refrain the four Negroes of the orchestra,
or at least the three of them who played with their hands alone—
for the saxophonist always blew at this point with a redoubled sweetness,
enriching the passage with a warbling contrapuntal soliloquy that fairly
wrung the entrails and transported the pierced heart—broke into melancholy and drawling song:

> What's he to Hecuba?
> Nothing at all.
> That's why there'll be no wedding on Wednesday
>   week,
> Way down in old Bengal.

"What unspeakable sadness," said Gumbril, as he stepped, stepped
through the intricacies of the trot. "Eternal passion, eternal pain. *Les
chants désespérés sont les chants les plus beaux, Et j'en sais d'immortels
qui sont de purs sanglots.* Rum tiddle-um-tum, pom pom. Amen. What's
he to Hecuba? Nothing, at all. Nothing, mark you. Nothing, nothing."

"Nothing," repeated Mrs. Viveash. "I know all about that." She
sighed.

"I am nothing to you," said Gumbril gliding with skill between the
wall and the Charybdis of a couple dangerously experimenting with a
new step. "You are nothing to me. Thank God. And yet here we are two
bodies with but a single thought, a beast with two backs, a perfectly
united centaur trotting, trotting." They trotted.

"What's he to Hecuba?" The grinning blackamoors repeated the question, reiterated the answer on a tone of frightful unhappiness. The
saxophone warbled on the verge of anguish. The couples revolved, marked
time, stepped and stepped with a habitual precision, as though performing some ancient and profoundly significant rite. Some were in fancy
dress, for this was a gala night at the cabaret. Young women disguised
as callipygous. Florentine pages, blue-breeched Gondoliers, black-breeched
Toreadors circulated, moonlike, round the hall, clasped sometimes in the
arms of Arabs, or white clowns, or more often of untravestied partners.
The faces reflected in the mirrors were the sort of faces one feels one
ought to know by sight; the cabaret was "Artistic."

"What's he to Hecuba?"

Mrs. Viveash murmured the response, almost piously, as though she
were worshiping almighty and omnipresent Nil. "I adore this tune," she
said, "this divine tune." It filled up a space, it moved, it jigged, it set

things twitching in you, it occupied time, it gave you a sense of being alive. "Divine tune, divine tune," she repeated with emphasis, and she shut her eyes, trying to abandon herself, trying to float, trying to give Nil the slip.

"Ravishing little Toreador, that," said Gumbril, who had been following the black-breeched travesty with affectionate interest.

Mrs. Viveash opened her eyes. Nil was unescapable. "With Piers Cotton, you mean? Your tastes are a little common, my dear Theodore."

"Green-eyed monster!"

Mrs. Viveash laughed. "When I was being 'finished' in Paris," said she, "Mademoiselle always used to urge me to take fencing lessons. *C'est un exercice très gracieux. Et puis,*" Mrs. Viveash mimicked a passionate earnestness, "*et puis, ça dévelope le bassin.* Your Toreador, Gumbril, looks as though she must be a champion with the foils. *Quel bassin!*"

"Hush," said Gumbril. They were abreast of the Toreador and her partner. Piers Cotton turned his long greyhound's nose in their direction.

"How are you?" he asked across the music.

They nodded. "And you?"

"Ah, writing such a book," cried Piers Cotton, "such a brilliant, brilliant, flashing book." The dance was carrying them apart. "Like a smile of false teeth," he shouted across the widening gulf, and disappeared in the crowd.

"What's he to Hecuba?" Lachrymosely, the hilarious blackamoors chanted their question, mournfully pregnant with its foreknown reply.

Nil, omnipresent Nil, world soul, spiritual informer of all matter. Nil in the shape of a black-breeched moon-basined Toreador. Nil, the man with the greyhound's nose. Nil, as four blackamoors. Nil in the form of a divine tune. Nil, the faces, the faces one ought to know by sight, reflected in the mirrors of the hall. Nil this Gumbril whose arm is round one's waist, whose feet step in and out among one's own. Nothing at all.

That's why there'll be no wedding. No wedding at St. George's, Hanover Square—oh, desperate experiment!—with Nil Viveash, that charming boy, that charming nothing at all, engaged at the moment in hunting elephants, hunting fever and carnivors among the Tikki-tikki pygmies. That's why there'll be no wedding on Wednesday week. For Lycidas is dead, dead ere his prime. For the light strawy hair (not a lock left), the brown face, the red-brown hands and the smooth boy's body, milk-white, milk-warm, are nothing at all, nothing, now, at all—nil these five years and the shining blue eyes as much nil as the rest.

"Always the same people," complained Mrs. Viveash, looking round the room. "The old familiar faces. Never anyone new. Where's the younger generation, Gumbril? We're old, Theodore. There are millions younger than we are. Where are they?"

"I'm not responsible for them," said Gumbril. "I'm not even responsible for myself." He imagined a cottagey room, under the roof, with a window near the floor and a sloping ceiling where you were always bumping your head; and in the candlelight Emily's candid eyes, her grave and happy mouth; in the darkness, the curve, under his fingers, of her firm body.

"Why don't they come and sing for their supper?" Mrs. Viveash went on petulantly. "It's their business to amuse us."

"They're probably thinking of amusing themselves," Gumbril suggested.

"Well, then, they should do it where we can see them."

"What's he to Hecuba?"

"Nothing at all," Gumbril clownishly sang. The room in the cottage had nothing to do with him. He breathed Mrs. Viveash's memories of Italian jasmines, laid his cheek for a moment against her smooth hair. "Nothing at all." Happy clown!

Way down in old Bengal, under the green Paradisiac palms, among the ecstatic mystagogues and the saints who scream beneath the divine caresses, the music came to an end. The four Negroes wiped their glistening faces. The couples fell apart. Gumbril and Mrs. Viveash sat down and smoked a cigarette.

Chapter XVI

THE blackamoors had left the platform at the end of the hall. The curtains looped up at either side had slid down, cutting it off from the rest of the room—"making two worlds." Gumbril elegantly and allusively put it, "where only one grew before—and one of them a better world," he added too philosophically, "because unreal." There was the theatrical silence, the suspense. The curtains parted again.

On a narrow bed—on a bier perhaps—the corpse of a woman. The husband kneels beside it. At the foot stands the doctor, putting away his instruments. In a beribboned pink cradle reposes a monstrous baby.

The Husband: Margaret! Margaret!

The Doctor: She is dead.

The Husband: Margaret!

The Doctor: Of septicemia, I tell you.

The Husband: I wish that I too were dead!

The Doctor: But you won't tomorrow.

The Husband: Tomorrow! But I don't want to live to see tomorrow.

The Doctor: You will tomorrow.

The Husband: Margaret! Margaret! Wait for me there; I shall not fail to meet you in that hollow vale.

The Doctor: You will not be slow to survive her.

The Husband: Christ have mercy upon us!

The Doctor: You would do better to think of the child.

The Husband (rising and standing menacingly over the cradle): Is that the monster?

The Doctor: No worse than others.

The Husband: Begotten in a night of immaculate pleasure, monster, may you live loveless, in dirt and impurity!

The Doctor: Conceived in lust and darkness, may your own impurity always seem heavenly, monster, in your own eyes!

The Husband: Murderer, slowly die all your life long!

The Doctor: The child must be fed.

The Husband: Fed? With what?

The Doctor: With milk.

The Husband: Her milk is cold in her breasts.

The Doctor: There are still cows.

The Husband: Tubercular Shorthorns. (*Calling*) Let Short-i'-the-horn be brought!

Voices (off): Short-i'-the-horn! Short-i'-the-horn! (*Fadingly*) Short-i'-the . . .

The Doctor: In nineteen hundred and twenty-one, twenty-seven thousand, nine hundred and thirteen women died in childbirth.

The Husband: But none of them belonged to my harem.

The Doctor: Each one of them was somebody's wife.

The Husband: Doubtless. But the people we don't know are only characters in the human comedy. We are the tragedians.

The Doctor: Not in the spectator's eyes.

The Husband: Do I think of the spectators? Ah, Margaret! Margaret! . . .

The Doctor: The twenty-seven thousand, nine hundred and fourteenth.

The Husband: The only one!

The Doctor: But here comes the cow.

(*Short-i'-the-horn is led in by a Yokel.*)

The Husband: Ah, good Short-i'-the-horn! *(He pats the animal.)* She was tested last week, was she not?

The Yokel: Ay, sir.

The Husband: And found tubercular. No?

The Yokel: Even in the udders, may it please you.

The Husband: Excellent! Milk me the cow, sir, into this dirty wash pot.

The Yokel: I will, sir. *(He milks the cow.)*

The Husband: Her milk—her milk is cold already. All the woman in her chilled and curdled within her breasts. Ah, Jesus! what miraculous galactagogue will make it flow again?

The Yokel: The wash pot is full, sir.

The Husband: Then take the cow away.

The Yokel: Come, Short-i'-the-horn; come up, good Short-i'-the-horn. *(He goes out with the cow.)*

The Husband (pouring the milk into a long-tubed feeding bottle): Here's for you, monster, to drink your own health in. *(He gives the bottle to the child. Curtain.)*

"A little ponderous, perhaps," said Gumbril as the curtain came down.

"But I like the cow." Mrs. Viveash opened her cigarette case and found it empty. Gumbril offered her one of his. She shook her head. "I don't want it in the least," she said.

"Yes, the cow was in the best pantomime tradition," Gumbril agreed. Ah! but it was a long time since he had been to a Christmas pantomime. Not since Dan Leno's days. All the little cousins, the uncles and aunts on both sides of the family, dozens and dozens of them—every year they filled the best part of a row in the dress circle at Drury Lane. And buns were stickily passed from hand to hand, chocolates circulated; the grown-ups drank tea. And the pantomime went on and on, glory after glory, under the shining arch of the stage. Hours and hours; and the grownups always wanted to go away before the harlequinade. And the children felt sick from eating too much chocolate, or wanted with such extreme urgency to go to the W.C. that they had to be led out, trampling and stumbling over everybody else's feet—and every stumble making the need more agonizingly great—in the middle of the transformation scene. And there was Dan Leno, inimitable Dan Leno, dead now as poor Yorick, no more than a mere skull like anybody else's skull. And his mother, he remembered, used to laugh at him sometimes till the tears ran down her cheeks. She used to enjoy things thoroughly, with a whole heart.

"I wish they'd hurry up with the second scene," said Mrs. Viveash. "If there's anything that bores me, it's *entr'actes.*"

"Most of one's life is an *entr'acte*," said Gumbril, whose present mood of hilarious depression seemed favorable to the enunciation of apophthegms.

"None of your cracker mottoes, please," protested Mrs. Viveash. All the same, she reflected, what was she doing now but waiting for the curtain to go up again, waiting with what unspeakable weariness of spirit, for the curtain that had rung down, ten centuries ago, on those blue eyes, that bright strawy hair and the weathered face?

"Thank God," she said with an expiring earnestness, "here's the second scene!"

The curtain went up. In a bald room stood the Monster, grown now from an infant into a frail and bent young man with bandy legs. At the back of the stage a large window giving on to a street along which people pass.

The Monster (Solus): The young girls of Sparta, they say, used to wrestle naked with naked Spartan boys. The sun caressed their skins till they were brown and transparent like amber or a flask of olive oil. Their breasts were hard, their bellies flat. They were pure with the chastity of beautiful animals. Their thoughts were clear, their minds cool and untroubled. I spit blood into my handkerchief and sometimes I feel in my mouth something slimy, soft and disgusting, like a slug—and I have coughed up a shred of my lung. The rickets from which I suffered in childhood have bent my bones and made them old and brittle. All my life I have lived in this huge town, whose domes and spires are wrapped in a cloud of stink that hides the sun. The slug-dank tatters of lung that I spit out are black with the soot I have been breathing all these years. I am now come of age. Long-expected one-and-twenty has made me a fully privileged citizen of this great realm of which the owners of the *Daily Mirror*, the *News of the World* and the *Daily Express* are noble peers. Somewhere, I must logically infer, there must be other cities, built by men for men to live in. Somewhere, in the past, in the future, a very long way off . . . But perhaps the only street-improvement schemes that ever really improve the streets are schemes in the minds of those who live in them: schemes of love mostly. Ah! here she comes.

(*The Young Lady enters. She stands outside the window, in the street, paying no attention to the Monster; she seems to be waiting for somebody.*)

She is like a pear tree in flower. When she smiles, it is as though there were stars. Her hair is like the harvest in an eclogue; her cheeks are all the fruits of summer. Her arms and thighs are as beautiful as the soul of

St. Catherine of Siena. And her eyes, her eyes are plumbless with thought and limpidly pure like the water of the mountains.

The Young Lady: If I wait till the summer sale, the crepe de Chine will be reduced by at least two shillings a yard, and on six camisoles that will mean a lot of money. But the question is: can I go from May till the end of July with the underclothing I have now?

The Monster: If I knew her, I should know the universe!

The Young Lady: My present ones are so dreadfully middle class. And if Roger should . . . by any chance . . .

The Monster: Or, rather, I should be able to ignore it, having a private universe of my own.

The Young Lady: If—if he did—well, it might be rather humiliating with these I have . . . like a servant's almost . . .

The Monster: Love makes you accept the world; it puts an end to criticism.

The Young Lady: His hand already . . .

The Monster: Dare I, dare I tell her how beautiful she is?

The Young Lady: On the whole, I think I'd better get it now, though it will cost more.

The Monster (desperately advancing to the window as though to assault a battery): Beautiful! beautiful!

The Young Lady (looking at him): Ha, ha, ha!

The Monster: But I love you, flowering pear tree; I love you, golden harvest; I love you, fruitage of summer; I love you, body and limbs, with the shape of a saint's thought.

The Young Lady (redoubling her laughter): Ha, ha, ha!

The Monster (taking her hand): You cannot be cruel! *(He is seized with a violent paroxysm of coughing which doubles him up, which shakes and torments him. The handkerchief he holds to his mouth is spotted with blood.)*

The Young Lady: You disgust me! *(She draws away her skirts so that they shall not come in contact with him.)*

The Monster: But I swear to you, I love—I— *(He is once more interrupted by his cough.)*

The Young Lady: Please go away. *(In a different voice)* Ah, Roger! *(She advances to meet a snub-nosed lubber with curly hair and a face like a groom's, who passes along the street at this moment.)*

Roger: I've got the motor bike waiting at the corner.

The Young Lady: Let's go then.

Roger (pointing to the Monster): What's that?

The Young Lady: Oh, it's nothing in particular.

(Both roar with laughter. Roger escorts her out, patting her familiarly on the back as they walk along.)

The Monster *(looking after her):* There is a wound under my left pap. She has deflowered all women. I cannot . . .

"Lord!" whispered Mrs. Viveash, "how this young man bores me!"

"I confess," replied Gumbril, "I have rather a taste for moralities. There is a pleasant uplifting vagueness about these symbolical, generalized figures which pleases me."

"You were always charmingly simple-minded," said Mrs. Viveash. "But who's this? As long as the young man isn't left alone on the stage, I don't mind."

Another female figure has appeared in the street beyond the window. It is the Prostitute. Her face, painted in two tones of red, white, green, blue and black, is the most tasteful of *natures mortes.*

The Prostitute: Hullo, duckie!

The Monster: Hullo!

The Prostitute: Are you lonely?

The Monster: Yes.

The Prostitute: Would you like me to come in to see you?

The Monster: Very well.

The Prostitute: Shall we say thirty bob?

The Monster: As you like.

The Prostitute: Come along then.

(She climbs through the window and they go off together through the door on the left of the stage. The curtains descend for a moment, then rise again. The Monster and the Prostitute are seen issuing from the door at which they went out.)

The Monster *(taking out a checkbook and a fountain pen):* Thirty shillings . . .

The Prostitute: Thank you. Not a check. I don't want any checks. How do I know it isn't a dud one that they'll refuse payment for at the bank? Ready money for me, thanks.

The Monster: But I haven't got any cash on me at the moment.

The Prostitute: Well, I won't take a check. Once bitten, twice shy, I can tell you.

The Monster: But I tell you I haven't got any cash.

The Prostitute: Well, all I can say is, here I stay till I get it. And, what's more, if I don't get it quick, I'll make a row.

The Monster: But this is absurd. I offer you a perfectly good check . . .

The Prostitute: And I won't take it. So there!

The Monster: Well then, take my watch. It's worth more than thirty bob. (*He pulls out his gold half hunter.*)

The Prostitute: Thank you, and get myself arrested as soon as I take it to the popshop! No, I want cash, I tell you.

The Monster: But where in the devil do you expect me to get it at this time of night?

The Prostitute: I don't know. But you've got to get it pretty quick.

The Monster: You're unreasonable.

The Prostitute: Aren't there any servants in this house?

The Monster: Yes.

The Prostitute: Well, go and borrow it from one of them.

The Monster: But really, that would be too low, too humiliating.

The Prostitute: All right, I'll begin kicking up a noise. I'll go to the window and yell till all the neighbors are woken up and the police come to see what's up. You can borrow it from the copper then.

The Monster: You really won't take my check? I swear to you it's perfectly all right. There's plenty of money to meet it.

The Prostitute: Oh, shut up! No more dilly-dallying. Get me my money at once, or I'll start the row. One, two, three. . . . (*She opens her mouth wide as if to yell.*)

The Monster: All right. (*He goes out.*)

The Prostitute: Nice state of things we're coming to, when young rips try and swindle us poor girls out of our money! Mean, stinking skunks! I'd like to slit the throats of some of them.

The Monster (coming back again): Here you are. (*He hands her money.*)

The Prostitute (examining it): Thank you, dearie. Any other time you're lonely . . .

The Monster: No, no!

The Prostitute: Where did you get it finally?

The Monster: I woke the cook.

The Prostitute (goes off into a peal of laughter): Well, so long, duckie. (*She goes out.*)

The Monster (Solus): Somewhere there must be love like music. Love harmonious and ordered: two spirits, two bodies moving contrapuntally together. Somewhere, the stupid brutish act must be made to make sense, must be enriched, must be made significant. Lust, like Diabelli's waltz, a stupid air, turned by a genius into three-and-thirty fabulous variations. Somewhere . . .

"Oh dear!" sighed Mrs. Viveash.

"Charming!" Gumbril protested.

. . . love like sheets of silky flame; like landscapes brilliant in the sunlight against a background of purple thunder; like the solution of a cosmic problem; like faith . . .

"Crikey!" said Mrs. Viveash.

. . . Somewhere, somewhere. But in my veins creep the maggots of the pox . . .

"Really, really!" Mrs. Viveash shook her head. "Too medical!"

. . . crawling toward the brain, crawling into the mouth, burrowing into the bones. Insatiably."
The Monster threw himself to the ground and the curtain came down.

"And about time too!" declared Mrs. Viveash.
"Charming!" Gumbril stuck to his guns. "Charming! charming!"
There was a disturbance near the door. Mrs. Viveash looked round to see what was happening. "And now on top of it all," she said, "here comes Coleman, raving, with an unknown drunk."
"Have we missed it?" Coleman was shouting. "Have we missed all the lovely bloody farce?"
"Lovely bloody!" his companion repeated with drunken raptures, and he went into fits of uncontrollable laughter. He was a very young boy with straight dark hair and a face of Hellenic beauty, now distorted with tipsiness.
Coleman greeted his acquaintances in the hall, shouting a jovial obscenity to each. "And Bumbril-Gumbril," he exclaimed, catching sight of him at last in the front row. "And Hetaira-Myra!" He pushed his way through the crowd, followed unsteadily by his young disciple. "So you're here," he said, standing over them and looking down with an enigmatic malice in his bright blue eyes. "Where's the physiologue?"
"Am I the physiologue's keeper?" asked Gumbril. "He's with his glands and his hormones, I suppose. Not to mention his wife." He smiled to himself.
"Where the hormones, there moan I," said Coleman, skidding off sideways along the slippery word. "I hear, by the way, that there's a lovely prostitute in this play."
"You've missed her," said Mrs. Viveash.
"What a misfortune," said Coleman. "We've missed the delicious trull," he said, turning to the young man.

The young man only laughed.

"Let me introduce, by the way," said Coleman. "This is Dante," he pointed to the dark-haired boy. "And I am Virgil. We're making a round tour—or, rather, a descending spiral tour of hell. But we're only at the first circle so far. These, Alighieri, are two damned souls, though not as you might suppose, Paolo and Francesca."

The boy continued to laugh, happily and uncomprehendingly.

"Another of these interminable *entr'actes*," complained Mrs. Viveash. "I was just saying to Theodore here that if there's one thing I dislike more than another, it's a long *entr'acte*." Would hers ever come to an end?

"And if there's one thing *I* dislike more than another," said the boy, breaking silence for the first time, with an air of the greatest earnestness, "it's . . . it's one thing more than another."

"And you're perfectly right in doing so," said Coleman. "Perfectly right."

"I know," the boy replied modestly.

When the curtain rose again it was on an aged Monster, with a black patch over the left side of his nose, no hair, no teeth, and sitting harmlessly behind the bars of an asylum.

The Monster: Asses, apes and dogs! Milton called them that; he should have known. Somewhere there must be men, however. The variations on Diabelli prove it. Brunelleschi's dome is more than the magnification of Cléo de Mérode's breast. Somewhere there are men with power, living reasonably. Like our mythical Greeks and Romans. Living cleanly. The images of the gods are their portraits. They walk under their own protection. *(The Monster climbs onto a chair and stands in the posture of a statue.)* Jupiter, father of gods, a man, I bless myself, I throw bolts at my own disobedience, I answer my own prayers, I pronounce oracles to satisfy the questions I myself propound. I abolish all tetters, poxes, blood spitting, rotting of bones. With love I re-create the world from within. Europa puts an end to squalor, Leda does away with tyranny, Danae tempers stupidity. After establishing these reforms in the social sewer, I climb, I climb, up through the manhole, out of the manhole, beyond humanity. For the manhole, even the manhole, is dark; though not so dingy as the doghole it was before I altered it. Up through the manhole, toward the air. Up, up! *(And the Monster, suiting the action of his words, climbs up the runged back of his chair and stands, by a miraculous feat of acrobacy, on the topmost bar.)* I begin to see the stars through other eyes than my own. More than dog already, I become more than man. I begin to have inklings of the shape and sense of things. Upward, upward I strain, I peer, I reach aloft. (*The balanced Monster reaches, strains and peers.*) And I seize, I seize! (*As he shouts these words, the Monster falls heavily, head foremost, to the floor. He lies there quite still. After a little time the door opens and the Doctor of the first scene enters with a Warder.*)

The Warder: I heard a crash.

The Doctor (*Who has by this time become immensely old and has a beard like Father Thames*): It looks as though you were right. (*He examines the Monster.*)

The Warder: He was forever climbing onto his chair.

The Doctor: Well, he won't any more. His neck's broken.

The Warder: You don't say so?

The Doctor: I do.

The Warder: Well, I never!

The Doctor: Have it carried down to the dissecting room.

The Warder: I'll send for the porters at once.

(*Exeunt severally and Curtain*)

"Well," said Mrs. Viveash, "I'm glad that's over."

The music struck up again, saxophones and 'cello, with the thin draft of the violin to cool their ecstasies and the thumping piano to remind them of business. Gumbril and Mrs. Viveash slid out into the dancing crowd, revolving as though by force of habit.

"These substitutes for the genuine copulative article," said Coleman to his disciple, "are beneath the dignity of hellhounds like you and me."

Charmed, the young man laughed; he was attentive as though at the feet of Socrates. Coleman had found him in a night club, where he had gone in search of Zoe, found him very drunk in the company of two formidable women fifteen or twenty years his senior, who were looking after him, half maternally out of pure kindness of heart, half professionally; for he seemed to be carrying a good deal of money. He was incapable of looking after himself. Coleman had pounced on him at once, claimed an old friendship which the youth was too tipsy to be able to deny, and carried him off. There was something, he always thought, peculiarly interesting about the spectacle of children tobogganing down into the cesspools.

"I like this place," said the young man.

"Tastes differ!" Coleman shrugged his shoulders. "The German professors had catalogued thousands of people whose whole pleasure consists in eating dung."

The young man smiled and nodded, rather vaguely. "Is there anything to drink here?" he asked.

"Too respectable," Coleman answered, shaking his head.

"I think this is a bloody place," said the young man.

"Ah! but some people like blood. And some like boots. And some like long gloves and corsets. And some like birch rods. And some like sliding down slopes and can't look at Michelangelo's 'Night on the Medici Tombs' without dying the little death, because the statue seems to be sliding. And some. . . ."

"But I want something to drink," insisted the young man.

Coleman stamped his feet, waved his arms. "À boire! à boire!" he shouted like the newborn Gargantua. Nobody paid any attention.

The music came to an end. Gumbril and Mrs. Viveash reappeared.

"Dante," said Coleman, "calls for drink. We must leave the building."

"Yes. Anything to get out of this," said Mrs. Viveash. "What's the time?"

Gumbril looked at his watch. "Half-past one."

Mrs. Viveash sighed. "Can't possibly go to bed," she said, "for another hour at least."

They walked out into the street. The stars were large and brilliant overhead. There was a little wind that almost seemed to come from the country. Gumbril thought so, at any rate; he thought of the country.

"The question is, where?" said Coleman. "You can come to my bordello, if you like; but it's a long way off and Zoe hates us all so much, she'll probably set on us with the meat chopper. If she's back again, that is. Though she may be out all night. Zoe mou, sas agapo. Shall we risk it?"

"To me it's quite indifferent," said Mrs. Viveash faintly, as though wholly preoccupied with expiring.

"Or there's my place," Gumbril said abruptly, as though shaking himself awake out of some dream.

"But you live still farther, don't you?" said Coleman. "With venerable parents, and so forth. One foot in the grave and all that. Shall we mingle hornpipes with funerals?" He began to hum Chopin's "Funeral March" at three times its proper speed, and seizing the young stranger in his arms, two-stepped two or three turns on the pavement, then released his hold and let him go reeling against the area railings.

"No, I don't mean the family mansion," said Gumbril. "I mean my own rooms. They're quite near. In Great Russell Street."

"I never knew you had any rooms, Theodore," said Mrs. Viveash.

"Nobody did." Why should they know now? Because the wind seemed almost a country wind? "There's drink there," he said.

"Splendid!" cried the young man. They were all splendid people.

"There's some gin," said Gumbril.

"Capital aphrodisiac!" Coleman commented.

"Some light white wine."

"Diuretic."

"And some whisky."

"The great emetic," said Coleman. "Come on." And he struck up the March of the Fascisti. "*Giovinezza, giovinezza, primavera di bellezza . . .*" The noise went fading down the dark, empty streets.

The gin, the white wine, and even, for the sake of the young stranger, who wanted to sample everything, the emetic whisky, were produced.

"I like your rooms," said Mrs. Viveash, looking round her. "And I resent your secrecy about them, Theodore."

"Drink, puppy!" Coleman refilled the boy's glass.

"Here's to secrecy," Gumbril proposed. "Shut it tightly, keep it dark, cover it up. Be silent, prevaricate, lie outright." He laughed and drank. "Do you remember," he went on, "those instructive advertisements of Eno's Fruit Salt they used to have when we were young? There was one little anecdote about a doctor who advised the hypochondriacal patient who had come to consult him to go and see Grimaldi, the clown; and the patient answered, 'I am Grimaldi.' Do you remember?"

"No," said Mrs. Viveash. "And why do you?"

"Oh, I don't know. Or rather, I do know," Gumbril corrected himself, and laughed again.

The young man suddenly began to boast. "I lost two hundred pounds yesterday playing *chemin de fer*," he said, and looked round for applause.

Coleman patted his curly head. "Delicious child!" he said. "You're positively Hogarthian."

Angrily, the boy pushed him away. "What are you doing?" he shouted; then turned and addressed himself once more to the others. "I couldn't afford it, you know—not a bloody penny of it. Not my money, either." He seemed to find it exquisitely humorous. "And that two hundred wasn't all," he added, almost expiring with mirth.

"Tell Coleman how you borrowed his beard, Theodore."

Gumbril was looking intently into his glass, as though he hoped to see in its pale mixture of gin and Sauterne visions, as in a crystal, of the future. Mrs. Viveash touched him on the arm and repeated her injunction.

"Oh, that!" said Gumbril rather irritably. "No. It isn't an interesting story."

"Oh yes, it is! I insist," said Mrs. Viveash, commanding peremptorily from her deathbed.

Gumbril drank his gin and Sauterne. "Very well then," he said, reluctantly, and began.

"I don't know what my governor will say," the young man put in once or twice. But nobody paid any attention to him. He relapsed into a sulky and, it seemed to him, very dignified silence. Under the warm jolly tipsiness he felt a chill of foreboding. He poured out some more whisky.

Gumbril warmed to his anecdote. Expiringly Mrs. Viveash laughed from time to time, or smiled her agonizing smile. Coleman whooped like a redskin.

"And after the concert to these rooms," said Gumbril.

Well, let everything go. Into the mud. Leave it there and let the dogs lift their hind legs over it as they pass.

"Ah! the genuine platonic fumblers," commented Coleman.

"I am Grimaldi," Gumbril laughed. Further than this it was difficult to see where the joke could go. There, on the couch, where Mrs. Viveash and Coleman were now sitting, she had lain sleeping in his arms.

"Towsing, in Elizabethan," said Coleman.

Unreal, eternal in the secret darkness. A night that was an eternal parenthesis among the other nights and days.

"I feel I'm going to be sick," said the young man suddenly. He had wanted to go on silently and haughtily sulking; but his stomach declined to take part in the dignified game.

"Good Lord!" said Gumbril, and jumped up. But before he could do anything effective, the young man had fulfilled his own prophecy.

"The real charm about debauchery," said Coleman philosophically, "is its total pointlessness, futility, and above all its incredible tediousness. If it really were all roses and exhilaration, as these poor children seem to imagine, it would be no better than going to church or studying the higher mathematics. I should never touch a drop of wine or another harlot again. It would be against my principles. I told you it was emetic," he called to the young man.

"And what are your principles?" asked Mrs. Viveash.

"Oh, strictly ethical," said Coleman.

"You're responsible for this creature," said Gumbril, pointing to the young man, who was sitting on the floor near the fireplace, cooling his forehead against the marble of the mantel piece. "You must take him away. Really, what a bore!" His nose and mouth were all wrinkled up with disgust.

"I'm sorry," the young man whispered. He kept his eyes shut and his face was exceedingly pale.

"But with pleasure," said Coleman. "What's your name?" he asked the young man, "and where do you live?"

"My name is Porteous," murmured the young man.

"Good Lord!" cried Gumbril, letting himself fall onto the couch beside Mrs. Viveash. "That's the last straw!"

Chapter XVII

THE two o'clock snorted out of Charing Cross, but no healths were drunk, this time, to Viscount Lascelles. A desiccating sobriety made arid the corner of the third-class carriage in which Gumbril was sitting. His thoughts were an interminable desert of sand, with not a palm in sight, not so much as a comforting mirage. Once again he fumbled in his breast pocket, brought out and unfolded the flimsy paper. Once more he read. How many times had he read before?

Your telegram made me very unhappy. Not merely because of the accident—though it made me shudder to think that something terrible might have happened, poor darling—but also, selfishly, my own disappointment. I had looked forward so much. I had made a picture of it all so clearly. I should have met you at the station with the horse and trap from the Chequers and we'd have driven back to the cottage—and you'd have loved the cottage. We'd have had tea and I'd have made you eat an egg with it after your journey. Then we'd have gone for a walk; through the most heavenly wood I found yesterday to a place where there's a wonderful view—miles and miles of it. And we'd have wandered on and on, and sat down under the trees, and the sun would have set and the twilight would slowly have come to an end, and we'd have gone home again and found the lamps lighted and supper ready—not very grand, I'm afraid; for Mrs. Vole isn't the best of cooks. And then the piano; for there is a piano and I had the tuner come specially from Hastings yesterday, so that it isn't so bad now. And you'd have played; and perhaps I would have made my noises on it. And at last it would have been time for candles and bed. When I heard you were coming, Theodore, I told Mrs. Vole a lie about you. I said you were my husband, because she's fearfully respectable, of course; and it would dreadfully disturb her if you weren't. But I told myself that, too. I meant that you should be. You see, I tell you everything. I'm not ashamed. I wanted to give you everything I could and then we should always be together, loving one another. And I should have been your slave, I should have been your property and lived inside your life. But you would always have had to love me.

And then, just as I was getting ready to go and call at the Chequers for the horse and trap, your telegram came. I saw the word "accident" and I imagined you all bleeding and smashed—oh, dreadful, dreadful. But then, when you seemed to make rather a joke of it—why did you say "a little indisposed"? that seemed, somehow, so stupid, I thought—and said you were coming tomorrow, it wasn't that which upset me; it was the dreadful, dreadful disappointment. It was like a stab, that disappointment; it hurt so terribly, so unreasonably much. It made me cry and cry, so that I thought I should never be able to stop. And then, gradually, I began to see that the pain of the disappointment wasn't unreasonably great. It wasn't merely a question of your coming being put off for a day; it was a question of its being put off forever, of my never seeing you again. I saw that that accident had been something really arranged by Providence. It was meant to warn me and show me what I ought to do. I saw how hopelessly impracticable the happiness I had been imagining really was. I saw that you didn't, you couldn't love me in anything like the same way as I loved you. I was only a curious adventure, a new experience, a means to some other end. Mind, I'm not blaming you in the least. I'm only telling you what is true, what I gradually came to realize as true. If you'd come—what then? I'd have given you everything, my body, my mind, my soul, my whole life. I'd have twisted myself into the threads of your life. And then, when in due course you wanted to make an end to this curious little adventure, you would have had to cut the tangle and it would have killed me, it would also have hurt you. At least I think it would. In the end, I thanked God for the accident which had prevented you coming. In this way, Providence lets us off very lightly—you with a bruise or two (for I do hope it really is nothing, my precious darling), and me with a bruise inside, round the heart. But both will get well quite soon. And all our lives, we shall have an afternoon under the trees, an evening of music and in the darkness, a night, an eternity of happiness, to look back on. I shall go away from Robertsbridge at once. Good-by, Theodore. What a long letter! The last you'll ever get from me. The last—what a dreadful hurting word that is. I shall take it to post at once, for fear, if I leave it, I may be weak enough to change my mind and let you come tomorrow. I shall take it at once, then I shall come home again and pack up and tell some new fibs to Mrs. Vole. And after that, perhaps I shall allow myself to cry again. Good-by.

Aridly, the desert of sand stretched out with not a tree and not even a mirage, except perhaps the vague and desperate hope that he might get there before she started, that she might, conceivably, have changed her mind. Ah, if only he'd read the letter a little earlier! But he hadn't woken up before eleven, he hadn't been down before half past. Sitting at the breakfast table, he had read the letter through.

The eggs and bacon had grown still colder, if that was possible, than they were. He had read it through, he had rushed to the A. B. C. There was no practicable train before the two o'clock.

If he had taken the seven-twenty-seven he would certainly have got there before she started. Oh, if only he had woken up a little earlier! But then he would have had to go to bed a little earlier. And in order to go to bed earlier, he would have had to abandon Mrs. Viveash before she had bored herself to that ultimate point of fatigue at which she did at last feel ready for repose. And to abandon Mrs. Viveash—ah, that was really impossible; she wouldn't allow herself to be left alone. If only he hadn't gone to the London Library yesterday! A wanton, unnecessary visit it had been. For after all, the journey was short; he didn't need a book for the train. And the *Life of Beckford*, for which he had asked, proved, of course, to be out—and he had been utterly incapable of thinking of any other book, among the two or three hundred thousand on the shelves, that he wanted to read. And in any case, what the devil did he want with a *Life of Beckford?* Hadn't he his own life, the life of Gumbril, to attend to? Wasn't one life enough, without making superfluous visits to the London Library in search of other lives? And then what a stroke of bad luck to have run into Mrs. Viveash at that very moment! What an abject weakness to have let himself be bullied into sending that telegram. "A little indisposed . . ." Oh, my God! Gumbril shut his eyes and ground his teeth together; he felt himself blushing with a retrospective shame.

And of course it was quite useless taking the train, like this, to Robertsbridge. She'd be gone, of course. Still, there was always the desperate hope. There was the mirage across the desiccated plains, the mirage one knew to be deceptive and which, on a second glance, proved not even to be a mirage, but merely a few livery spots behind the eyes. Still, it was amply worth doing—as a penance, and to satisfy the conscience and to deceive oneself with an illusion of action. And then the fact that

he was to have spent the afternoon with Rosie and had put her off—
that too was highly satisfying. And not merely put her off, but—ultimate
clownery in the worst of deliriously bad taste—played a joke on her. "Impossible come to you, meet me 213 Sloane Street, second floor, a little
indisposed." He wondered how she'd get on with Mr. Mercaptan; for
it was to his rococo boudoir and Crébillon-souled sofa that he had on
the spur of the clownish moment, as he dashed into the post office
on the way to the station, sent her.

Aridly, the desiccated waste extended. Had she been right in her letter?
Would it really have lasted no more than a little while, and ended as she
prophesied, with an agonizing cutting of the tangle? Or could it be that
she had held out the one hope of happiness? Wasn't she perhaps the one,
unique being with whom he might have learned to await in quietness
the final coming of that lovely terrible thing, from before the sound of
whose secret footsteps more than once and oh! ignobly he had fled? He
could not decide; it was impossible to decide until he had seen her
again, till he had possessed her, mingled his life with hers. And now
she had eluded him; for he knew very well that he would not find her.
He sighed and looked out of the window.

The train pulled up at a small suburban station. Suburban, for though
London was already some way behind, the little sham half-timbered
houses near the station, the newer tile and rough-cast dwellings further
out on the slope of the hill proclaimed with emphasis the presence of
the businessman, the holder of the season ticket. Gumbril looked at them
with a pensive disgust which must have expressed itself on his features;
for the gentleman, sitting in the corner of the carriage facing his, suddenly leaned forward, tapped him on the knee and said, "I see you
agree with me, sir, that there are too many people in the world."

Gumbril, who up till now had merely been aware that somebody was
sitting opposite him, now looked with more attention at the stranger.
He was a large square old gentleman of robust and flourishing appearance,
with a face of wrinkled brown parchment and a white mustache that
merged, in a handsome curve, with a pair of side whiskers, in a manner
which reminded one of the photographs of the Emperor Francis Joseph.

"I perfectly agree with you, sir," Gumbril answered. If he had been
wearing his beard, he would have gone on to suggest that loquacious
old gentlemen in trains are among the supernumeraries of the planet.
As it was, however, he spoke with courtesy and smiled in his most
engaging fashion.

"When I look at all these revolting houses," the old gentleman continued, shaking his fist at the snuggeries of the season ticket holders,

"I am filled with indignation. I feel my spleen ready to burst, sir, ready to burst."

"I can sympathize with you," said Gumbril. "The architecture is certainly not very soothing."

"It's not the architecture I mind so much," retorted the old gentleman, "that's merely a question of art and all nonsense so far as I'm concerned. What disgusts me is the people inside the architecture. The number of them, sir. And the way they breed. Like maggots, sir, like maggots. Millions of them, creeping about the face of the country, spreading blight and dirt wherever they go; ruining everything. It's the people I object to."

"Ah well," said Gumbril, "if you will have sanitary conditions that don't allow plagues to flourish properly. If you will tell mothers how to bring up their children, instead of allowing nature to kill them off in her natural way. If you will import unlimited supplies of corn and meat. What can you expect? Of course the numbers go up."

The old gentleman waved all this away. "I don't care what the causes are," he said. "That's all one to me. What I do object to, sir, is the effects. Why, sir, I am old enough to remember walking through the delicious meadows beyond Swiss cottage, I remember seeing the cows milked in West Hampstead, sir. And now, what do I see now when I go there? Hideous red cities pullulating with Jews, sir. Pullulating with prosperous Jews. Am I right in being indignant, sir? Do I do well, like the prophet, Jonah, to be angry?"

"You do, sir," said Gumbril with growing enthusiasm, "and the more so since this frightful increase in population is the world's most formidable danger at the present time. With populations that in Europe alone expand by millions every year, no political foresight is possible. A few years of this mere bestial propagation will suffice to make nonsense of the wisest schemes of today—or would suffice," he hastened to correct himself, "if any wise schemes were being matured at the present."

"Very possibly, sir," said the old gentleman, "but what I object to is seeing good cornland being turned into streets, and meadows where cows used to graze, covered with houses full of useless and disgusting human beings. I resent seeing the country parceled out into back gardens."

"And is there any prospect," Gumbril earnestly asked, "of our ever being able in the future to support the whole of our population? Will unemployment ever decrease?"

"I don't know, sir," the old gentleman replied. "But the families of the unemployed will certainly increase."

"You are right, sir," said Gumbril, "they will. And the families of the employed and the prosperous will as steadily grow smaller. It is regrettable that birth control should have begun at the wrong end of the scale. There seems to be a level of poverty below which it doesn't seem worth while practicing birth control and a level of education below which birth control is regarded as morally wrong. Strange, how long it has taken for the ideas of love and procreation to dissociate themselves in the human mind. In the majority of minds they are still, even in this so-called twentieth century, indivisibly wedded. Still," he continued hopefully, "progress is being made, progress is certainly, though slowly, being made. It is gratifying to find, for example, in the latest statistics, that the clergy, as a class, are now remarkable for the smallness of their families. The old jest is out of date. Is it too much to hope that these gentlemen may bring themselves in time to preach what they already practice?"

"It is too much to hope, sir," the old gentleman answered with decision.

"You are probably right," said Gumbril.

"If we were all to preach all the things we all practice," continued the old gentleman, "the world would soon be a pretty sort of bear garden, I can tell you. Yes, and a monkey house. And a wart-hoggery. As it is, sir, it is merely a place where there are too many human beings. Vice must pay its tribute to virtue, or else we are all undone."

"I admire your wisdom, sir," said Gumbril.

The old gentleman was delighted. "And I have been much impressed by your philosophical reflections," he said. "Tell me, are you at all interested in old brandy?"

"Well, not philosophically," said Gumbril. "As a mere empiric only."

"As a mere empiric!" The old gentleman laughed. "Then let me beg you to accept a case. I have a cellar which I shall never drink dry, alas, before I die. My only wish is that what remains of it shall be distributed among those who can really appreciate it. In you, sir, I see a fitting recipient of a case of brandy."

"You overwhelm me," said Gumbril. "You are too kind, and, I may add, too flattering." The train, which was a mortally slow one, came grinding for what seemed the hundredth time to a halt.

"Not at all," said the old gentleman. "If you have a card, sir."

Gumbril searched his pockets. "I have come without one."

"Never mind," said the old gentleman. "I think I have a pencil. If you will give me your name and address, I will have the case sent to you at once."

Leisurely, he hunted for the pencil; he took out a notebook. The train gave a jerk forward.

"Now sir," he said.

Gumbril began dictating. "Theodore," he said slowly.

"The-o-dore," the old gentleman repeated, syllable by syllable.

The train crept on, with slowly gathering momentum, through the station. Happening to look out of the window at this moment, Gumbril saw the name of the place painted across a lamp. It was Robertsbridge. He made a loud inarticulate noise, flung open the door of the compartment, stepped out on the footboard and jumped. He landed safely on the platform, staggered forward a few paces with his acquired momentum and came at last to a halt. A hand reached out and closed the swinging door of his compartment and an instant afterward, through the window, a face that, at a distance, looked more than ever like the face of the Emperor Francis Joseph, looked back toward the receding platform. The mouth opened and shut; no words were audible. Standing on the platform, Gumbril made a complicated pantomime, signifying his regret by shrugging his shoulders and placing his hand on his heart; urging in excuse for his abrupt departure the necessity under which he labored of alighting at this particular station—which he did by pointing at the name on the boards and lamps, then at himself, then at the village across the fields. The old gentleman waved his hand, which still held, Gumbril noticed, the notebook in which he had been writing. Then the train carried him out of sight. There went the only case of old brandy he was ever likely to possess, thought Gumbril sadly, as he turned away. Suddenly, he remembered Emily again; for a long time he had quite forgotten her.

The cottage, when at last he found it, proved to be fully as picturesque as he had imagined. And Emily, of course, had gone, leaving as might have been expected no address. He took the evening train back to London. The aridity was now complete and even the hope of a mirage had vanished. There was no old gentleman to make a diversion. The size of clergymen's families, even the fate of Europe, seemed unimportant now, were indeed perfectly indifferent to him.

Chapter XVIII

Two hundred and thirteen Sloane Street. The address, Rosie reflected, as she vaporized synthetic lilies of the valley over all her sinuous person, was decidedly a good one. It argued a reasonable prosperity, attested a certain distinction. The knowledge of his address confirmed her already high opinion of the bearded stranger who had so surprisingly entered her

life, as though on fulfillment of all the fortunetellers' phophecies that ever
were made; had entered, yes, and intimately made himself at home. She
had been delighted, when the telegram came that morning, to think that
at last she was going to find out something more about this man of
mystery. For dark and mysterious he had remained, remote even in the
midst of the most intimate contacts. Why, she didn't even know his
name. "Call me Toto," he had suggested, when she asked him what it
was. And Toto she had had to call him, for lack of anything more definite
or committal. But today he was letting her further into his secret. Rosie
was delighted. Her pink underclothing, she decided, as she looked in the
long glass, was really ravishing. She examined herself, turning first one
way, then the other, looking over her shoulder to see the effect from
behind. She pointed a toe, bent and straightened a knee, applauding the
length of her legs ("Most women," Toto had said, "are like dachshunds"),
their slenderness and plump suavity of form. In their white stockings of
Milanese silk they looked delicious; and how marvelously, by the way,
those Selfridge people had mended those stockings by their new patent
process! Absolutely like new, and only charged four shillings. Well, it was
time to dress. Good-by, then, to the pink underclothing and the long
white legs. She opened the wardrobe door. The moving glass reflected, as
it swung through its half circle, pink bed, rose-wreathed walls, little friends
of her own age, and the dying saint at his last communion. Rosie selected
the frock she had bought the other day at one of those little shops in
Soho, where they sell such smart things so cheaply to a clientage of minor
actresses and cocottes. Toto hadn't seen it yet. She looked extremely
distinguished in it. The little hat, with its inch of veil hanging like a mask,
unconcealing and inviting, from the brim, suited her to perfection. One
last dab of powder, one last squirt of synthetic lilies of the valley, and
she was ready. She closed the door behind her. St. Jerome was left to
communicate in the untenanted pinkness.

Mr. Mercaptan sat at his writing table—an exquisitely amusing affair in
papier-mâché, inlaid with floral decorations in mother-of-pearl and painted
with views of Windsor Castle and Tintern in the romantic manner of
Prince Albert's later days—polishing to its final and gemlike perfection one
of his middle articles. It was on a splendid subject—the "Jus Primæ
Noctis, or Droit du Seigneur"—"that delicious *droit*," wrote Mr. Mercaptan, "on which, one likes to think, the Sovereigns of England insist
so firmly in their motto. *Dieu et mon Droit—de Seigneur.*" That was
charming, Mr. Mercaptan thought as he read it through. And he liked
that bit which began elegiacally: "But, alas, the Right of the First Night
belongs to a Middle Age as mythical, albeit happily different, as those

dismal epochs invented by Morris or by Chesterton. The Lord's right, as we prettily imagine it, is a figment of the baroque imagination of the seventeenth century. It never existed. Or at least it did exist, but as something deplorably different from what we love to picture it." And he went on, eruditely, to refer to that Council of Carthage which, in 398, demanded of the faithful that they should be continent on their wedding night. It was the Lord's right—the *droit* of a heavenly Seigneur. On this text of fact Mr. Mercaptan went on to preach a brilliant sermon on that melancholy sexual perversion known as continence. How much happier we all should be if the real historical *droit du Seigneur* had in fact been the mythical right of our "pretty prurient imaginations!" He looked forward to a golden age when all should be seigneurs possessing rights that should have broadened down into universal liberty. And so on. Mr. Mercaptan read through his creation with a smile of satisfaction on his face. Every here and there he made a careful correction in red ink. Over "pretty prurient imaginations" his pen hung for a full minute in conscientious hesitation. Wasn't it perhaps a little too strongly alliterative, a shade, perhaps, cheap? Perhaps "pretty lascivious" or "delicate prurient" would be better. He repeated the alternatives several times, rolling the sound of them round his tongue, judicially, like a teataster. In the end, he decided that "pretty prurient" was right. "Pretty prurient"—they were the *mots justes*, decidedly, without a question.

Mr. Mercaptan had just come to this decision and his poised pen was moving further down the page, when he was disturbed by the sound of arguing voices in the corridor, outside his room.

"What is it, Mrs. Goldie?" he called irritably, for it was not difficult to distinguish his housekeeper's loud and querulous tones. He had given orders that he was not to be disturbed. In these critical moments of correction one needed such absolute tranquillity.

But Mr. Mercaptan was to have no tranquillity this afternoon. The door of his sacred boudoir was thrown rudely open and there strode in, like a Goth into the elegant marble vomitorium of Petronius Arbiter, a haggard and disheveled person whom Mr. Mercaptan recognized, with a certain sense of discomfort, as Casimir Lypiatt.

"To what do I owe the *pleasure* of this unexpected . . . ?" Mr. Mercaptan began with an essay in offensive courtesy.

But Lypiatt, who had no feeling for the finer shades, coarsely interrupted him. "Look here, Mercaptan," he said. "I want to have a talk with you."

"Delighted, I'm sure," Mr. Mercaptan replied. "And *what*, may I ask, about?" He knew, of course, perfectly well; and the prospect of the talk disturbed him.

"About this," said Lypiatt; and he held out what looked like a roll of paper.

Mr. Mercaptan took the roll and opened it out. It was a copy of the *Weekly World.* "Ah!" said Mr. Mercaptan in a tone of delighted sur-prise, "*The World.* You have read my little article?"

"That was what I wanted to talk to you about," said Lypiatt.

Mr. Mercaptan modestly laughed. "It hardly deserves it," he said.

Preserving a calm of expression which was quite unnatural to him, and speaking in a studiedly quiet voice, Lypiatt pronounced with careful deliberation: "It is a disgusting, malicious, ignoble attack on me," he said.

"Come, come!" protested Mr. Mercaptan. "A critic must be allowed to criticize."

"But there are limits," said Lypiatt.

"Oh, I quite agree," Mr. Mercaptan eagerly conceded. "But, after all, Lypiatt you can't pretend that I have come anywhere near those limits. If I had called you a murderer, or even an adulterer—then, I admit, you would have some cause to complain. But I haven't. There's nothing like a personality in the whole thing."

Lypiatt laughed derisively and his face went all to pieces, like a pool of water into which a stone is suddenly dropped.

"You've merely said I was insincere, an actor, a mountebank, a quack, raving fustian, spouting mock heroics. That's all."

Mr. Mercaptan put on the expression of one who feels himself injured and misunderstood. He shut his eyes; he flapped deprecatingly with his hand. "I merely suggested," he said, "that you protest too much. You defeat your own ends; you lose emphasis by trying to be overemphatic. All this *folie de grandeur,* all this hankering after *terribiltà*——" sagely Mr. Mercaptan shook his head, "it's led so many people astray. And in any case, you can't really expect me to find it very sympathetic." Mr. Mercaptan uttered a little laugh and looked affectionately round his boudoir, his retired and perfumed poutery within whose walls so much civilization had finely flowered. He looked at his magnificent sofa, gilded and carved, upholstered in white satin and so deep—for it was a great square piece of furniture, almost as broad as it was long—that when you sat right back, you had of necessity to lift your feet from the floor and recline at length. It was under the white satin that Crébillon's spirit found, in these late dangerous days, a sympathetic home. He looked at his exquisite Condor fans over the mantelpiece; his lovely Marie Laurencin of two young girls, pale-skinned and berry-eyed, walking embraced in a shallow myopic landscape amid a troop of bounding heraldic dogs. He looked at his cabinet of *bibelots* in the corner where the nigger mask and the superb Chinese phallus in sculptured rock crystal contrasted so amusingly with the Chelsea china, the little ivory Madonna, which might be a fake but in any case was quite as good as any medieval French original, and the Italian medals. He looked at his comical writing desk in shining black papier-mâché and mother-of-pearl; he looked at his article on the "Jus Primæ Noctis," black and neat on the page, with the red corrections attesting his tireless search for, and his, he flattered himself, almost invariable discovery of, the inevitable word. No, really, one couldn't expect *him* to find Lypiatt's notions very sympathetic.

"But I don't expect you to," said Lypiatt, "and, good God! I don't want you to. But you call me insincere. That's what I can't and won't stand. How dare you do that?" His voice was growing louder.

Once more Mr. Mercaptan deprecatingly flapped. "At the most," he corrected, "I said that there was a certain look of insincerity about some of the pictures. Hardly avoidable, indeed, in work of this kind."

Quite suddenly, Lypiatt lost his self-control. All the accumulated anger and bitterness of the last days burst out. His show had been a hopeless failure. Not a picture sold, a press that was mostly bad, or, when good, that had praised for the wrong, the insulting reasons. "Bright and effective work." "Mr. Lypiatt would make an excellent stage designer." Damn them! damn them! And then, when the dailies had all had their yelp, here was Mercaptan in the *Weekly World* taking him as a text for what was practically an essay on insincerity in art. "How dare you?" he furiously shouted. "You—how dare you talk about sincerity? What can you know about sincerity, you disgusting little bug!" And avenging himself on the person of Mr. Mercaptan against the world that had neglected him, against the fate that had denied him his rightful share of talent, Lypiatt sprang up and, seizing the author of the "Jus Primæ Noctis" by the shoulders, he shook him, he bumped him up and down in his chair, he cuffed him over the head. "How can you have the impudence," he asked, letting go of his victim but still standing menacingly over him, "to touch anything that even attempts to be decent and big?" All these years, these wretched years of poverty and struggle and courageous hope and failure and repeated disappointment; and now this last failure, more complete than all. He was trembling with anger; at least one forgot un-happiness while one was angry.

Mr. Mercaptan had recovered from his first terrified surprise. "Really, *really*," he repeated, "*too* barbarous. Scuffling like hobbledehoys."

"If you knew," Lypiatt began; but he checked himself. If you knew, he was going to say, what those things had cost me, what they meant, what thought, what passion—— But how could Mercaptan understand? And it would sound as though he were appealing to this creature's sympathy. "Bug!" he shouted instead, "bug!" And he struck out again with the flat of his hand. Mr. Mercaptan put up his hands and ducked away from the slaps, blinking.

"Really," he protested, "*really*. . . ."

Insincere? Perhaps it was half true. Lypiatt seized his man more furiously than before and shook him, shook him. "And then that vile insult about the vermouth advertisement," he cried out. That had rankled. Those flaring vulgar posters! "You thought you could mock me and spit at me with impunity, did you? I've stood it so long, you thought I'd always stand it? Was that it? But you're mistaken." He lifted his fist. Mr. Mercaptan cowered away, raising his arm to protect his head. "Vile bug of a coward," said Lypiatt, "why don't you defend yourself like a man? You can only be dangerous with words. Very witty and spiteful and cutting about those vermouth posters, wasn't it? But you wouldn't dare to fight me if I challenged you."

"Well, as a matter of *fact*," said Mr. Mercaptan, peering up from under his defenses, "I didn't invent *that* particular piece of criticism. I borrowed the *apéritif*." He laughed feebly, more canary than bull.

"You borrowed it, did you?" Lypiatt contemptuously repeated. "And who from, may I ask?" Not that it interested him in the least to know.

"Well, if you really *want* to know," said Mr. Mercaptan, "it was from our friend Myra Viveash."

Lypiatt stood for a moment without speaking, then putting his menacing hand in his pocket, he turned away. "Oh!" he said noncommittally, and was silent again.

Relieved, Mr. Mercaptan sat up in his chair; with the palm of his right hand he smoothed his disheveled head.

Airily, outside in the sunshine, Rosie walked down Sloane Street, looking at the numbers on the doors of the houses. A hundred and ninety-nine, two hundred, two hundred and one—she was getting near now. Perhaps all the people who passed, strolling so easily and elegantly and disengagedly along, perhaps they all of them carried behind their eyes a secret, as delightful and amusing as hers. Rosie liked to think so; it made life more exciting. How nonchalantly distinguished, Rosie reflected, she herself must look. Would anyone who saw her now, sauntering along like this, would anyone guess that, ten houses further down the street, a young poet, or at least very nearly a young poet, was waiting, on the second floor, eagerly for her arrival? Of course they wouldn't and couldn't guess!

That was the fun and the enormous excitement of the whole thing. Formidable in her lighthearted detachment, formidable in the passion which at will she could give rein to and check again, the great lady swam beautifully along through the sunlight to satisfy her caprice. Like Diana, she stooped over the shepherd boy. Eagerly the striving young poet waited, waited in his garret. Two hundred and twelve, two hundred and thirteen. Rosie looked at the entrance and was reminded that the garret couldn't after all be very sordid, nor the young poet absolutely starving. She stepped in and, standing in the hall, looked at the board with the names. Ground floor: Mrs. Budge. First floor: F. de Rowbotham. Second Floor: P. Mercaptan.

P. Mercaptan . . . But it was a charming name, a romantic name, a real young poet's name! Mercaptan—she felt more than ever pleased with her selection. The fastidious lady could not have had a happier caprice. Mercaptan . . . Mercaptan . . . She wondered what the P. stood for. Peter, Philip, Patrick, Pendennis even? She could hardly have guessed that Mr. Mercaptan's father, the eminent bacteriologist, had insisted, thirty-four years ago, on calling his first born "Pasteur."

A little tremulous, under her outward elegant calm, Rosie mounted the stairs. Twenty-five steps to the first floor—one flight of thirteen, which was rather disagreeably ominous, and one of twelve. Then two flights of eleven and she was on the second landing, facing a front door, a bell push like a round eye, a brass name plate. For a great lady thoroughly accustomed to this sort of thing, she felt her heart beating rather unpleasantly fast. It was those stairs, no doubt. She halted a moment, took two deep breaths, then pushed the bell.

The door was opened by an aged servant of the most forbiddingly respectable appearance.

"Mr. Mercaptan at home?"

The person at the door burst at once into a long, rambling angry complaint, but precisely about what Rosie could not for certain make out. Mr. Mercaptan had left orders, she gathered, that he wasn't to be disturbed. But someone had come and disturbed him, "fairly shoved his way in, so rude and inconsiderate," all the same. And now he'd been once disturbed, she didn't see why he shouldn't be disturbed again. But she didn't know what things were coming to, if people fairly shoved their way in like that. Bolshevism, she called it.

Rosie murmured her sympathies and was admitted into a dark hall. Still querulously denouncing the Bolsheviks who came shoving in, the person led the way down a corridor and, throwing open a door, announced, on a tone of grievance, "A lady to see you, Master Paster"— for Mrs.

Goldie was an old family retainer and one of the few who knew the secret of Mr. Mercaptan's Christian name, one of the fewer still who were privileged to employ it. Then, as soon as Rosie had stepped across the threshold, she cut off her retreat with a bang and went off, muttering all the time, toward her kitchen.

It certainly wasn't a garret. Half a glance, the first whiff of potpourri, the feel of the carpet beneath her feet, had been enough to prove that. But it was not the room which occupied Rosie's attention; it was its occupants. One of them, thin, sharp featured and, in Rosie's very young eyes, quite old, was standing with an elbow on the mantelpiece. The other, sleeker and more genial in appearance, was sitting in front of a writing desk near the window. And neither of them—Rosie glanced desperately from one to the other, hoping vainly that she might have overlooked a blond beard—neither of them was Toto.

The sleek man at the writing desk got up, advanced to meet her.

"An unexpected pleasure," he said in a voice that alternately boomed and fluted. "*Too* delightful! But to what do I owe——? *Who*, may I ask——?"

He had held out his hand; automatically Rosie proffered hers. The sleek man shook it with cordiality, almost with tenderness.

"I . . . I think I must have made a mistake," she said. "Mr. Mercaptan . . . ?"

The sleek man smiled. "I am Mr. Mercaptan."

"You live on the second floor?"

"I never laid claims to being a mathematician," said the sleek man, smiling as though to applaud himself, "but I have always calculated that . . ." he hesitated . . . "*enfin, que ma demeure se trouve, en effet,* on the second floor. Lypiatt will bear me out, I'm sure." He turned to the thin man, who had not moved from the fireplace but had stood all the time motionlessly, his elbow on the mantelpiece, looking gloomily at the ground.

Lypiatt looked up. "I must be going," he said abruptly. And he walked toward the door. Like vermouth posters, like vermouth posters!—so that was Myra's piece of mockery! All his anger had sunk like a quenched flame. He was altogether quenched, put out with unhappiness.

Politely Mr. Mercaptan hurried across the room and opened the door for him. "*Good*-by, then," he said airily.

Lypiatt did not speak but walked out into the hall. The front door banged behind him.

"Well, *well*," said Mr. Mercaptan, coming back across the room to where Rosie was still irresolutely standing. "Talk about the *furor poeticus!*

But *do* sit down, I beg you. On Crébillon." He indicated the vast white satin sofa. "I call it Crébillon," he explained, "because the soul of that great writer undoubtedly tenants it, *undoubtedly*. You know his book, of course? You know *Le Sopha?*"

Sinking into Crébillon's soft lap, Rosie had to admit that she didn't know *Le Sopha*. She had begun to recover her self-possession. If this wasn't *the* young poet, it was certainly a young poet. And a very peculiar one, too. As a great lady she laughingly accepted the odd situation.

"Not know *Le Sopha?*" exclaimed Mr. Mercaptan. "Oh! but, my dear and mysterious young lady, let me lend you a copy of it at once. No education can be called *complete* without a knowledge of that divine book." He darted to the bookshelf and came back with a small volume bound in white vellum. "The hero's soul," he explained, handing her the volume, "passes, by the laws of metempsychosis, into a sofa. He is doomed to remain a sofa until such time as two persons consummate upon his bosom their reciprocal and equal loves. The book is the record of the poor sofa's hopes and disappointments."

"Dear me!" said Rosie, looking at the title page.

"But now," said Mr. Mercaptan, sitting down beside her on the edge of Crébillon, "won't you please explain? To what happy *quid pro quo* do I owe this sudden and altogether delightful invasion of my privacy?"

"Well," said Rosie and hesitated. It was really rather difficult to explain. "I was to meet a friend of mine."

"Quite so," said Mr. Mercaptan encouragingly.

"Who sent me a telegram," Rosie went on.

"He sent you a telegram!" Mr. Mercaptan echoed.

"Changing the—the place we had fixed and telling me to meet him at this address."

"Here?"

Rosie nodded. "On the s-second floor," she made it more precise.

"But *I* live on the second floor," said Mr. Mercaptan. "You don't mean to say your friend is also called Mercaptan and lives here too?"

Rosie smiled. "I don't know what he's called," she said with a cool ironical carelessness that was genuinely *grande dame*.

"You don't know his name?" Mr. Mercaptan gave a roar and a squeal of delighted laughter. "But that's *too* good," he said.

"S-second floor, he wrote in the telegram." Rosie was now perfectly at her ease. "When I saw your name, I thought it was his name. I must say," she added, looking sideways at Mr. Mercaptan and at once dropping the magnolia petals of her eyelids, "it seemed to me a very charming name."

"You overwhelm me," said Mr. Mercaptan, smiling all over his cheerful snouty face. "As for your name—I am too discreet a *galantuomo* to ask. And, in any case, what *does* it matter? A rose by any other name . . ."

"But, as a matter of fact," she said, raising and lowering once again her smooth white lids, "my name does happen to be Rose; or, at any rate, Rosie."

"So you are sweet by right," exclaimed Mr. Mercaptan, with a pretty gallantry which he was the first to appreciate. "Let's order tea on the strength of it." He jumped up and rang the bell. "How I congratulate myself on this astonishing piece of good fortune!"

Rosie said nothing. This Mr. Mercaptan, she thought, seemed to be even more a man of the great artistic world than Toto.

"What puzzles me," he went on, "is why your anonymous friend should have chosen my address out of all the millions of others. He must know me, or, at any rate, know about me."

"I should imagine," said Rosie, "that you have a lot of friends."

Mr. Mercaptan laughed—the whole orchestra, from bassoon to piccolo. "*Des amis, des amies*—with and without the mute 'e,' " he declared.

The aged and forbidding servant appeared at the door.

"Tea for two, Mrs. Goldie."

Mrs. Goldie looked round the room suspiciously. "The other gentleman's gone, has he?" she asked. And having assured herself of his absence, she renewed her complaint. "Shoving in like that," she said. "Bolshevism, that's what I . . ."

"All right, all right, Mrs. Goldie. Let's have our tea as quickly as possible." Mr. Mercaptan held up his hand, authoritatively, with the gesture of a policeman controlling the traffic.

"Very well, Master Paster." Mrs. Goldie spoke with resignation and departed.

"But tell me," Mr. Mercaptan went on, "if it *isn't* indiscreet—what does your friend look like?"

"W—well," Rosie answered, "he's fair and though he's quite young, he wears a beard." With her two hands she indicated on her own unemphatic bosom the contours of Toto's broad blond fan.

"A beard! But, good heavens," Mr. Mercaptan slapped his thigh, "It's Coleman, it's obviously and undoubtedly Coleman!"

"Well, whoever it was," said Rosie severely, "he played a very stupid sort of joke."

"For which I thank him. *De tout mon coeur.*"

Rosie smiled and looked sideways. "All the same," she said, "I shall give him a piece of my mind."

Poor Aunt Aggie! Oh, poor Aunt Aggie, indeed! In the light of Mr. Mercaptan's boudoir her hammered copper and her leadless glaze certainly did look a bit comical.

After tea Mr. Mercaptan played cicerone in a tour of inspection round the room. They visited the papier-mâché writing desk, the Condor fans, the Marie Laurencin, the 1914 edition of "Du Côté de chez Swann," the Madonna that probably was a fake, the nigger mask, the Chelsea figures, the Chinese object of art in sculptured crystal, the scale model of Queen Victoria in wax under a glass bell. Toto, it became clear, had been no more than a forerunner; the definitive revelation was Mr. Mercaptan's. Yes, poor Aunt Aggie! And indeed, when Mr. Mercaptan began to read her his little middle on the *Droit du Seigneur*, it was poor everybody. Poor mother, with her absurd, old-fashioned, prudish views; poor earnest father, with his Unitarianism, his *Hibbert Journal*, his letters to the papers about the necessity for a spiritual regeneration.

"Bravo!" she cried from the depths of Crébillon. She was leaning back in one corner, languid, serpentine, and at ease, her feet in their mottled snake's leather tucked up under her. "Bravo!" she cried as Mr. Mercaptan finished his reading and looked up for his applause.

Mr. Mercaptan bowed.

"You express so exquisitely what we—" and waving her hand in a comprehensive gesture, she pictured to herself all the other fastidious ladies, all the marchionesses of fable, reclining, as she herself at this moment reclined, on upholstery of white satin, "what we all only feel and aren't clever enough to say."

Mr. Mercaptan was charmed. He got up from before his writing desk, crossed the room and sat down beside her on Crébillon. "Feeling," he said, "is the important thing."

Rosie remembered that her father had once remarked, in blank verse: "The things that matter happen in the heart."

"I quite agree," she said.

Like movable raisins in the suet of his snouty face, Mr. Mercaptan's brown little eyes rolled amorous avowals. He took Rosie's hand and kissed it. Crébillon creaked discreetly as he moved a little nearer.

It was on the evening of the same day. Rosie lay on her sofa—a poor, hire-purchase thing indeed, compared with Mr. Mercaptan's grand affair in white satin and carved and gilded wood, but still a sofa—lay with her feet on the arm of it and her long suave legs exposed, by the slipping of the kimono, to the top of her wretched stockings. She was reading the little vellum-jacketed volume of Crébillon, which Mr. Mercaptan had given her when he said "good-by" (or rather, "À *bientôt, mon amie*");

given, not lent, as he had less generously offered at the beginning of their afternoon; given with the most graceful of allusive dedications inscribed on the flyleaf:

To
By-no-other-name-as-sweet,
with gratitude,
from
Crébillon Delivered.

À *bientôt*—she had promised to come again very soon. She thought of the essay on the "Jus Primæ Noctis"—ah! what we've all been feeling and none of us clever enough to say. We on the sofas, ruthless, lovely and fastidious. . . .

"I am proud to constitute myself"—Mr. Mercaptan had said of it— "*l'esprit d'escalier des dames galantes.*"

Rosie was not quite sure what he meant; but it certainly sounded very witty indeed.

She read the book slowly. Her French, indeed, wasn't good enough to permit her to read it anyhow else. She wished it were better. Perhaps if it were better she wouldn't be yawning like this. It was disgraceful: she pulled herself together. Mr. Mercaptan had said that it was a masterpiece.

In his study Shearwater was trying to write his paper on the regulative functions of the kidneys. He was not succeeding.

Why wouldn't she see me yesterday? he kept wondering. With anguish he suspected other lovers; desired her, in consequence, the more. Gumbril had said something, he remembered, that night they had met her by the coffee stall. What was it? He wished now that he had listened more attentively.

She's bored with me. Already. It was obvious.

Perhaps he was too rustic for her. Shearwater looked at his hands. Yes, the nails were dirty. He took an orange stick out of his waistcoat pocket and began to clean them. He had bought a whole packet of orange sticks that morning.

Determinedly he took up his pen. "The hydrogen ion concentration in the blood . . ." he began a new paragraph. But he got no further than the first seven words.

If, he began thinking with a frightful confusion, if—if—if— Past conditionals, hopelessly past. He might have been brought up more elegantly; his father, for example, might have been a barrister instead of a barrister's clerk. He mightn't have had to work so hard when he was young; might have been about more, danced more, seen more young women. If he had met her years ago—during the war, should one say, dressed in the uniform of a lieutenant in the Guards. . . .

He had pretended that he wasn't interested in women; that they had no effect on him; that, in fact, he was above that sort of thing. Imbecile! He might as well have said that he was above having a pair of kidneys. He had only consented to admit, graciously, that they were a physiological necessity.

O God, what a fool he had been!

And then, what about Rosie? What sort of a life had she been having while he was being above that sort of thing? Now he came to think of it, he really knew nothing about her, except that she had been quite incapable of learning correctly, even by heart, the simplest facts about the physiology of frogs. Having found that out, he had really given up exploring further. How could he have been so stupid?

Rosie had been in love with him, he supposed. Had he been in love with her? No. He had taken care not to be. On principle. He had married her as a measure of intimate hygiene; out of protective affection, too, certainly out of affection; and a little for amusement, as one might buy a puppy.

Mrs. Viveash had opened his eyes; seeing her, he had also begun to notice Rosie. It seemed to him that he had been a loutish cad as well as an imbecile.

What should he do about it? He sat for a long time wondering.

In the end he decided that the best thing would be to go and tell Rosie all about it, all about everything.

About Mrs. Viveash too? Yes, about Mrs. Viveash too. He would get over Mrs. Viveash more easily and more rapidly if he did. And he would begin to try and find out about Rosie. He would explore her. He would discover all the other things besides an incapacity to learn physiology that were in her. He would discover her, he would quicken his affection for her into something livelier and more urgent. And they would begin again; more satisfactorily this time; with knowledge and understanding; wise from their experience.

Shearwater got up from his chair before the writing table, lurched pensively toward the door, bumping into the revolving bookcase and the armchair as he went, and walked down the passage to the drawing room. Rosie did not turn her head as he came in, but went on reading without changing her position, her slippered feet still higher than her head, her legs still charmingly avowing themselves.

Shearwater came to a halt in front of the empty fireplace. He stood there with his back to it, as though warming himself before an imaginary flame. It was, he felt, the safest, the most strategic point from which to talk.

"What are you reading?" he asked.

"*Le Sopha,*" said Rosie.

"What's that?"

"What's that?" Rosie scornfully echoed. "Why, it's one of the great French classics."

"Who by?"

"Crébillon the younger."

"Never heard of him," said Shearwater. There was a silence. Rosie went on reading.

"It just occurred to me," Shearwater began again in his rather ponderous, infelicitous way, "that you mightn't be very happy, Rosie."

Rosie looked up at him and laughed. "What put that into your head?" she asked. "*I'm* perfectly happy."

Shearwater was left a little at a loss. "Well, I'm very glad to hear it," he said. "I only thought . . . that perhaps you might think . . . that I rather neglected you."

Rosie laughed again. "What is all this about?" she said.

"I have it rather on my conscience," said Shearwater. "I begin to see . . . something has made me see . . . that I've not . . . I don't treat you very well. . . ."

"But I don't n—notice it, I assure you," put in Rosie, still smiling.

"I leave you out too much," Shearwater went on with a kind of desperation, running his fingers through his thick brown hair. "We don't share enough together. You're too much outside my life."

"But after all," said Rosie, "we are a civ-vilized couple. We don't want to live in one another's pockets, do we?"

"No, but we're really no more than strangers," said Shearwater. "That isn't right. And it's my fault. I've never tried to get into touch with your life. But you did your best to understand mine . . . at the beginning of our marriage."

"Oh, *then-n!*" said Rosie, laughing. "You found out what a little idiot I was."

"Don't make a joke of it," said Shearwater. "It isn't a joke. It's very serious. I tell you, I've come to see how stupid and inconsiderate and un-understanding I've been with you. I've come to see quite suddenly. The fact is," he went on with a rush, like an uncorked fountain. "I've been seeing a woman recently whom I like very much and who doesn't like me." Speaking of Mrs. Viveash, unconsciously he spoke her language. For Mrs. Viveash people always euphemistically "liked" one another rather a lot, even when it was a case of the most frightful and excruciating passion, the most complete abandonments. "And somehow that's made me see a lot of things which I'd been blind to before—blind deliberately, I suppose. It's made me see, among other things, that I've really been to blame toward you, Rosie."

Rosie listened with an astonishment which she perfectly disguised. So James was embarking on *his* little affairs, was he? It seemed incredible, and also, as she looked at her husband's face—the face behind its bristling manly mask of a harassed baby—also rather pathetically absurd. She wondered who it could be. But she displayed no curiosity. She would find out soon enough.

"I'm sorry you should have been unhappy about it," she said.

"It's finished now." Shearwater made a decided little gesture.

"Ah, no!" said Rosie. "You should persevere." She looked at him, smiling.

Shearwater was taken aback by this display of easy detachment. He had imagined the conversation so very differently, as something so serious, so painful and at the same time so healing and soothing, that he did not know how to go on. "But I thought," he said hesitatingly, "that you . . . that we . . . after this experience . . . I would try to get closer to you . . ." (Oh, it sounded ridiculous!) ". . . we might start again, from a different place, so to speak."

"But, *cher ami*," protested Rosie, with the inflection and in the preferred tongue of Mr. Mercaptan, "you can't seriously expect us to do the Darby and Joan business, can you? You're distressing yourself quite unnecessarily on my account. I don't find you neglect me or anything like it. You have your life—naturally. And I have mine. We don't get in one another's way."

"But do you think that's the ideal sort of married life?" asked Shearwater.

"It's obviously the most civ-vilized," Rosie answered, laughing.

Confronted by Rosie's civilization, Shearwater felt helpless.

"Well, if you don't want," he said. "I'd hoped . . . I'd thought . . ."

He went back to his study to think things over. The more he thought them over, the more he blamed himself. And incessantly the memory of Mrs. Viveash tormented him.

Chapter XIX

AFTER leaving Mr. Mercaptan, Lypiatt had gone straight home. The bright day seemed to deride him. With its shining red omnibuses, its parasols, its muslin girls, its young-leaved trees, its bands at the street corners, it was too much of a garden party to be tolerable. He wanted to be alone. He took a cab back to the studio. He couldn't afford it, of course; but what did that matter, what did that matter now?

The cab drove slowly and as though with reluctance down the dirty mews. He paid it off, opened his little door between the wide stable doors, climbed the steep ladder of his stairs and was at home. He sat down and tried to think.

"Death, death, death, death," he kept repeating to himself, moving his lips as though he were praying. If he said the word often enough, if he accustomed himself completely to the idea, death would come almost by itself; he would know it already, while he was still alive, he would pass almost without noticing out of life into death. Into death, he thought, into death. Death like a well. The stone falls, falls, second after second; and at last there is a sound, a far-off horrible sound of death and then nothing more. The well at Carisbrooke, with a donkey to wind the wheel that pulls up the bucket of water, of icy water. . . . He thought for a long time of the well of death.

Outside in the mews a barrel organ struck up the tune of "Where do flies go in the wintertime?" Lypiatt lifted his head to listen. He smiled to himself. "Where *do* flies go?" The question asked itself with a dramatic, a tragical appositeness. At the end of everything—the last ludicrous touch. He saw it all from outside. He pictured himself sitting there alone, broken. He looked at his hand lying limp on the table in front of him. It needed only the stigma of the nail to make it the hand of a dead Christ.

There, he was making literature of it again. Even now. He buried his face in his hands. His mind was full of twisted darkness, of an unspeakable, painful confusion. It was too difficult, too difficult.

The inkpot, he found when he wanted to begin writing, contained nothing but a parched black sediment. He had been meaning for days past to get some more ink; and he had always forgotten. He would have to write in pencil.

"Do you remember," he wrote, "do you remember, Myra, that time we went down into the country—you remember—under the Hog's Back at that little inn they were trying to make pretentious. 'Hotel Bull'—do you remember? How we laughed over the Hotel Bull! And how we liked the country outside its doors! All the world in a few square miles. Chalk pits and blue butterflies on the Hog's Back. And at the foot of the hill, suddenly, the sand; the hard yellow sand with those queer caves, dug when and by what remote villains at the edge of the Pilgrims' Way? the fine gray sand on which the heather of Puttenham Common grows. And the flagstaff and the inscription marking the place where Queen Victoria stood to look at the view. And the enormous sloping meadows round Compton and the thick dark woods. And the lakes, the heaths, the Scotch firs at Cutt Mill. The forests of Shackleford. There was everything. Do you remember how we enjoyed it all? I did, in any case. I was happy during those three days. And I loved you, Myra. And I thought you might, you might perhaps, some day, love me. You didn't. And my love has only brought me unhappiness. Perhaps it has been my fault. Perhaps I ought to have known how to make you give me happiness. You remember that wonderful sonnet of Michelangelo's, where he says that the loved woman is like a block of marble from which the artist knows how to cut the perfect statue of his dreams. If the statue turns out a bad one, if it's death instead of love that the lover gets—why, the fault lies in the artist and in the lover, not in the marble, not in the beloved.

> Amor dunque non ha, ne tua beltate,
> O fortuna, o durezza, o gran disdegno,
> Del mio mal colpa, o mio destino, o sorte.
>
> Se dentro del tuo cor morte e pietate
> Porti in un tempo, e ch'l mio basso ingegno
> Non sappia ardendo trarne altro che morte.

Yes, it was my *basso ingegno*: my low genius which did not know how to draw love from you, nor beauty from the materials of which art is made. Ah, now you'll smile to yourself and say: Poor Casimir, he has come to admit that at last? Yes, yes, I have come to admit everything. That I couldn't paint, I couldn't write, I couldn't make music. That I was a charlatan and a quack. That I was a ridiculous actor of heroic parts who deserved to be laughed at—and *was* laughed at. But then every man is ludicrous if you look at him from outside, without taking into account what's going on in his heart and mind. You could turn Hamlet into an epigrammatic farce with an inimitable scene when he takes his adored mother in adultery. You could make the wittiest Guy de Maupassant

short story out of the life of Christ, by contrasting the mad rabbi's
pretensions with his abject fate. It's a question of the point of view.
Everyone's a walking farce and a walking tragedy at the same time. The
man who slips on a banana skin and fractures his skull describes against
the sky, as he falls, the most richly comical arabesque. And you, Myra
—what do you suppose the unsympathetic gossips say of you? What sort
of a farce of the Boulevards is your life in their eyes? For me, Myra,
you seem to move all the time through some nameless and incomprehensible tragedy. For them you are what? Merely any sort of a wanton,
with amusing adventures. And what am I? A charlatan, a quack, a
pretentious, boasting, rhodomontading imbecile, incapable of painting
anything but vermouth posters. (Why did that hurt so terribly? I don't
know. There was no reason why you shouldn't think so if you wanted
to.) I was all that—and grotesquely laughable. And very likely your
laughter was justified, your judgment was true. I don't know. I can't
tell. Perhaps I am a charlatan. Perhaps I'm insincere; boasting to others,
deceiving myself. I don't know, I tell you. Everything is confusion in
my mind now. The whole fabric seems to have tumbled to pieces; it
lies in a horrible chaos. I can make no order within myself. Have I lied
to myself? have I acted and postured the Great Man to persuade myself
that I am one? have I something in me, or nothing? have I ever achieved
anything of worth, anything that rhymed with my conceptions, my
dreams? (for those were fine; of that, I am certain). I look into the
chaos that is my soul and, I tell you, I don't know, I don't know. But
what I do know is that I've spent nearly twenty years now playing the
charlatan at whom you all laugh. That I've suffered, in mind and in
body too—almost from hunger, sometimes—in order to play it. That
I've struggled, that I've exultantly climbed to the attack, that I've been
thrown down—ah, many times!—that I've picked myself up and started
again. Well, I suppose all that's ludicrous, if you like to think of it that
way. It is ludicrous that a man should put himself to prolonged inconvenience for the sake of something which doesn't really exist at all. It's
exquisitely comic, I can see. I can see it in the abstract, so to speak. But
in this particular case, you must remember I'm not a dispassionate
observer. And if I am overcome now, it is not with laughter. It is with
an indescribable unhappiness, with the bitterness of death itself. Death,
death, death. I repeat the word to myself, again and again. I think of
death. I try to imagine it, I hang over it, looking down where the stones
fall and fall and there is one horrible noise and then silence again; looking
down into the well of death. It is so deep that there is no glittering eye
of water to be seen at the bottom. I have no candle to send down. It

is horrible, but I do not want to go on living. Living would be worse than . . ."

Lypiatt was reaching out for another sheet of paper when he was startled to hear the sound of feet on the stairs. He turned toward the door. His heart beat with violence. He was filled with a strange sense of apprehension. In terror he awaited the approach of some unknown and terrible being. The feet of the angel of death were on the stairs. Up, up, up. Lypiatt felt himself trembling as the sound came nearer. He knew for certain that in a few seconds he was going to die. The hangmen had already pinioned him; the soldiers of the firing squad had already raised their rifles. One, two, . . . he thought of Mrs. Viveash standing, bare headed, the wind blowing in her hair, at the foot of the flagstaff from the site of which Queen Victoria had admired the distant view of Selborne; he thought of her dolorously smiling; he remembered that once she had taken his head between her two hands and kissed him: "Because you're such a golden ass," she had said laughing. Three . . . There was a little tap at the door. Lypiatt pressed his hand over his heart. The door opened.

A small, birdlike man with a long sharp nose and eyes as round and black and shining as buttons stepped into the room.

"Mr. Lydgate, I presume?" he began. Then looked at a card on which a name and address were evidently written. "Lypiatt, I mean. A thousand pardons. Mr. Lypiatt, I presume?"

Lypiatt leaned back in his chair and shut his eyes. His face was as white as paper. He breathed hard and his temples were wet with sweat, as though he had been running.

"I found the door down below open; so I came straight up. I hope you'll excuse . . ." The stranger smiled apologetically.

"Who are you?" Lypiatt asked, reopening his eyes. His heart was still beating hard; after the storm it calmed itself slowly. He drew back from the brink of the fearful well; the time had not yet come to plunge.

"My name," said the stranger, "is Boldero, Herbert Boldero. Our mutual friend Mr. Gumbril, Mr. Theodore Gumbril, Junior," he made it more precise, "suggested that I might come and see you about a little matter in which he and I are interested and in which perhaps you too might be interested."

Lypiatt nodded, without saying anything.

Mr. Boldero, meanwhile, was turning his bright birdlike eyes about the studio. Mrs. Viveash's portrait, all but finished now, was clamped to the easel. He approached it, a connoisseur.

"It reminds me very much," he said, "of Bacosso. Very much indeed,

if I may say so. Also a little of . . ." he hesitated, trying to think of the
name of that other fellow Gumbril had talked about. But being unable
to remember the unimpressive syllables of Derain he played for safety
and said—"of Orpen." Mr. Boldero looked inquiringly at Lypiatt to see
if that was right.

Lypiatt still spoke no word and seemed, indeed, not to have heard
what had been said.

Mr. Boldero saw that it wasn't much good talking about modern art.
This chap, he thought, looked as though something were wrong with him.
He hoped he hadn't got influenza. There was a lot of disease about.
"This little affair I was speaking of," he pursued, in another tone, "is a
little business proposition that Mr. Gumbril and I have gone into
together. A matter of pneumatic trousers," he waved his hand airily.

Lypiatt suddenly burst out laughing, an embittered Titan. "Where
do flies go? Where do souls go? The barrel organ, and now pneumatic
trousers!" Then, as suddenly, he was silent again. More literature?
Another piece of acting? "Go on," he said, "I'm sorry."

"Not at all, not at all," said Mr. Boldero indulgently. "I know the
idea seems a little humorous, if I may say so, at first. But I assure you,
there's money in it, Mr. Lydgate—Mr. Lypiatt. Money!" Mr. Boldero
paused a moment dramatically. "Well," he went on, "our idea was to
launch the new product with a good swinging publicity campaign. Spend
a few thousands in the papers and then get it good and strong into the
Underground and on the hoardings, along with Owbridge's and John
Bull and the Golden Ballot. Now, for that, Mr. Lypiatt, we shall need,
as you can well imagine, a few good striking pictures. Mr. Gumbril
mentioned your name and suggested I should come and see you to find
out if you would perhaps be agreeable to lending us your talent for this
work. And I may add, Mr. Lypiatt," he spoke with real warmth, "that
having seen this example of your work—" he pointed to the portrait of
Mrs. Viveash, "—I feel that you would be eminently capable of . . ."

He did not finish the sentence; for at this moment Lypiatt leaped up
from his chair, and making a shrill inarticulate animal noise, rushed on
the financier, seized him with both hands by the throat, shook him,
threw him to the floor, then picked him up again by the coat collar and
pushed him toward the door, kicking him as he went. A final kick sent
Mr. Boldero tobogganing down the steep stairs. Lypiatt ran down after
him; but Mr. Boldero had picked himself up, had opened the front door,
slipped out, slammed it behind him and was running up the mews before
Lypiatt could get to the bottom of the stairs.

Lypiatt opened the door and looked out. Mr. Boldero was already far away, almost at the Piranesian arch. He watched him till he was out of sight, then went upstairs again and threw himself face downward on his bed.

Chapter XX

Zoe ended the discussion by driving half an inch of penknife into Coleman's left arm and running out of the flat, slamming the door behind her. Coleman was used to this sort of thing; this sort of thing, indeed, was what he was there for. Carefully he pulled out the penknife which had remained sticking in his arm. He looked at the blade and was relieved to see that it wasn't so dirty as might have been expected. He found some cotton wool, mopped up the blood as it oozed out and dabbed the wound with iodine. Then he set himself to bandage it up. But to tie a bandage round one's own left arm is not easy. Coleman found it impossible to keep the lint in place, impossible to get the bandage tight enough. At the end of a quarter of an hour he had only succeeded in smearing himself very copiously with blood, and the wound was still unbound. He gave up the attempt and contented himself with swabbing up the blood as it came out.

"And forthwith came there out blood and water," he said aloud and looked at the red stain on the cotton wool. He repeated the words again and again and at the fiftieth repetition burst out laughing.

The bell in the kitchen suddenly buzzed. Who could it be? He went to the front door and opened it. On the landing outside stood a tall slender young woman with slanting Chinese eyes and a wide mouth, elegantly dressed in a black frock piped with white. Keeping the cotton wool still pressed to his bleeding arm, Coleman bowed as gracefully as he could.

"Do come in," he said. "You are just in the nick of time. I am on the point of bleeding to death. And forthwith came there out blood and water. Enter, enter," he added, seeing the young woman still standing irresolutely on the threshold.

"But I wanted to see Mr. Coleman," she said, stammering a little and showing her embarrassment by blushing.

"I am Coleman." He took the cotton wool for a moment from his arm and looked with the air of a connoisseur at the blood on it. "But I shall very soon cease to be that individual unless you come and tie up my wounds."

"But you're not the Mr. Coleman I thought you were," said the young lady, still more embarrassed. "You have a beard, it is true, but . . ."

"Then I must resign myself to quit this life, must I?" He made a gesture of despair, throwing out both hands. "Out, out, brief Coleman. Out, damned spot," and he made as though to close the door.

The young lady checked him. "If you really need tying up," she said, "I'll do it of course. I passed my First Aid exam in the war."

Coleman reopened the door. "Saved," he said. "Come in."

It had been Rosie's original intention yesterday to go straight on from Mr. Mercaptan's to Toto's. She would see him at once, she would ask him what he meant by playing that stupid trick on her. She would give him a good talking to. She would even tell him that she would never see him again. But, of course, if he showed himself sufficiently contrite and reasonably explanatory, she would consent—oh, very reluctantly—to take him back into favor. In the free, unprejudiced circles in which she now moved, this sort of joke, she imagined, was a mere trifle. It would be absurd to quarrel seriously about it. But still, she was determined to give Toto a lesson.

When, however, she did finally leave Mr. Mercaptan's delicious boudoir, it was too late to think of going all the way to Pimlico, to the address which Mr. Mercaptan had given her. She decided to put it off till the next day.

And so the next day, duly, she had set out for Pimlico—to Pimlico, and to see a man called Coleman! It seemed rather dull and second-rate after Sloane Street and Mr. Mercaptan. Poor Toto!—the sparkle of Mr. Mercaptan had made him look rather tarnished. That essay on the "Jus Primæ Noctis"—ah! Walking through the unsavory mazes of Pimlico, she thought of it, and, thinking of it, smiled. Poor Toto! And also, she mustn't forget, stupid, malicious, idiotic Toto! She had made up her mind exactly what she should say to him; she had even made up her mind what Toto would say to her. And when the scene was over they would go and dine at the Café Royal—upstairs, where she had never been. And she would make him rather jealous by telling him how much she had liked Mr. Mercaptan; but not too jealous. Silence is golden, as her father used to say when she used to fly into tempers and wanted to say nasty things to everybody within range. Silence, about some things, is certainly golden.

In the rather gloomy little turning off Lupus Street to which she had been directed, Rosie found the number, found, in the row of bells and cards, the name. Quickly and decidedly she mounted the stairs.

"Well," she was going to say as soon as she saw him, "I thought you were a civilized being." Mr. Mercaptan had dropped a hint that Coleman wasn't really civilized; a hint was enough for Rosie. "But I see," she would go on, "that I was mistaken. I don't like to associate with boors." The fastidious lady had selected him as a young poet, not as a plow boy.

Well rehearsed, Rosie rang the bell. And then the door had opened on this huge bearded Cossack of a man, who smiled, who looked at her with bright, dangerous eyes, who quoted the Bible and who was bleeding like a pig. There was blood on his shirt, blood on his trousers, blood on his hands, bloody fingermarks on his face; even the blond fringe of his beard, she noticed, was dabbled here and there with blood. It was too much, at first, even for her aristocratic equanimity.

In the end, however, she followed him across a little vestibule into a bright, whitewashed room empty of all furniture but a table, a few chairs and a large box spring and mattress, which stood like an island in the middle of the floor and served as bed or sofa as occasion required. Over the mantelpiece was pinned a large photographic reproduction of Leonardo's study of the anatomy of love. There were no other pictures on the walls.

"All the apparatus is here," said Coleman, and he pointed to the table. "Lint, bandages, cotton wool, iodine, gauze, oiled silk. I have them all ready in preparation for these little accidents."

"But do you often manage to cut yourself in the arm?" asked Rosie. She took off her gloves and began to undo a fresh packet of lint.

"One gets cut," Coleman explained. "Little differences of opinion, you know. If your eye offend you, pluck it out; love your neighbor as yourself. Argal: if his eye offends you—you see? We live on Christian principles here."

"But who are 'we'?" asked Rosie, giving the cut a last dressing of iodine and laying a big square of lint over it.

"Merely myself and—how shall I put it?—my helpmate," Coleman answered. "Ah! you're wonderfully skillful at this business," he went on. "You're the real hospital-nurse type; all maternal instincts. When pain and anguish wring the brow, an interesting mangle thou, as we used to say in the good old days when the pun and the Spoonerismus were in fashion."

Rosie laughed. "Oh, I don't spend all my time tying up wounds," she said, and turned her eyes for an instant from the bandage. After the first surprise she was feeling her cool self again.

"Brava!" cried Coleman. "You make them too, do you? Make them first and cure them afterward in the grand old homeopathic way. Delightful! You see what Leonardo has to say about it." With his free hand he pointed to the photograph over the mantelpiece.

Rosie, who had noticed the picture when she came into the room, preferred not to look at it too closely a second time. "I think it's rather revolting," she said and was very busy with the bandage.

"Ah! but that's the point, that's the whole point," said Coleman, and his clear blue eyes were alive with dancing lights. "That's the beauty of the grand passion. It *is* revolting. You read what the Fathers of the Church have to say about love. They're the men. It was Odo of Cluny, wasn't it, who called woman a *saccus stercoris*, a bag of muck. *Si quis enim considerat quæ intra nares et quæ intra fauces et quæ intra ventrem lateant, sordes ubique reperiet*." The Latin rumbled like eloquent thunder in Coleman's mouth. "*Et si nec extremis digitis flegma vel stercus tangere patimur, quomodo ipsum stercoris saccum amplecti desideramus*." He smacked his lips. "Magnificent!" he said.

"I don't understand Latin," said Rosie, "and I'm glad of it. And your bandage is finished. Look."

"Interesting mangle!" Coleman smiled his thanks. "But Bishop Odo, I fear, wouldn't even have spared you; not even for your good works. Still less for your good looks, which would only have provoked him to dwell with the more insistency on the visceral secrets which they conceal."

"Really," Rosie protested. She would have liked to get up and go away, but the Cossack's blue eyes glittered at her with such a strange expression and he smiled so enigmatically that she found herself still sitting where she was, listening with a disgusted pleasure to his quick talk, his screams of deliberate and appalling laughter.

"Ah!" he exclaimed, throwing up his hands, "what sensualists these old fellows were! What a real voluptuous feeling they had for dirt and gloom and sordidness and boredom, and all the horrors of vice. They pretended they were trying to dissuade people from vice by enumerating its horrors. But they were really only making it more spicy by telling the truth about it. *O esca vermium, O massa pulveris!* What nauseating embracements! To conjugate the copulative verb, boringly, with a sack of tripes—what could be more exquisitely and piercingly and deliriously vile?" And he threw back his head and laughed; the blood-dabbled tips of his blond beard shook. Rosie looked at them, fascinated with disgust.

"There's blood on your beard," she felt compelled to say.

"What of it? Why shouldn't there be?" Coleman asked.

Confused, Rosie felt herself blushing. "Only because it's rather unpl-leasant. I don't know why. But it is."

"What a reason for immediately falling into my arms!" said Coleman.

"To be kissed by a beard is bad enough at any time. But by a bloody beard—imagine!"

Rosie shuddered.

"After all," he said, "what interest or amusement is there in doing the ordinary things in the obvious way? Life *au naturel*." He shook his head. "You must have garlic and saffron. Do you believe in God?"

"Not m-much," said Rosie, smiling.

"I pity you. You must find existence dreadfully dull. As soon as you do, everything becomes a thousand times life size. Phallic symbols five hundred feet high," he lifted his hand. "A row of grinning teeth you could run the hundred yards on." He grinned at her through his beard. "Wounds big enough to let a coach and six drive into their purulent recesses. Every slightest act eternally significant. It's only when you believe in God, and especially in hell, that you can really begin enjoying life. For instance, when in a few moments you surrender yourself to the importunities of my bloody beard, how prodigiously much more you'd enjoy it if you could believe you were committing the sin against the Holy Ghost—if you kept thinking calmly and dispassionately all the time the affair was going on: All this is not only a horrible sin, it is also ugly, grotesque, a mere defecation, a—"

Rosie held up her hand. "You're really horrible," she said. Coleman smiled at her. Still, she did not go.

"He who is not with me is against me," said Coleman. "If you can't make up your mind to be with, it's surely better to be positively against than merely negatively indifferent."

"Nonsense!" exclaimed Rosie feebly.

"When I call my lover a nymphomaniacal dog, she runs the penknife into my arm."

"Well, do you enjoy it?" asked Rosie.

"Piercingly," he answered. "It is at once sordid to the last and lowest degree and infinitely and eternally significant."

Coleman was silent and Rosie too said nothing. Futilely she wished it *had* been Toto instead of this horrible, dangerous Cossack. Mr. Mercaptan ought to have warned her. But then, of course, he supposed that she already knew the creature. She looked up at him and found his bright eyes fixed upon her; he was silently laughing.

"Don't you want to know who I am?" she asked. "And how I got here?"

Coleman blandly shook his head. "Not in the very least," he said.

Rosie felt more helpless, somehow, than ever. "Why not?" she asked as bravely and impertinently as she could.

Coleman answered with another question. "Why should I?"

"It would be natural curiosity."

"But I know all I want to know," he said. "You are a woman, or, at any rate, you have all the female stigmata. Not too sumptuously well developed, let me add. You have no wooden legs. You have eyelids that flutter up and down over your eyes like a moving shutter in front of a signaling lamp, spelling out in a familiar code the letters: A.M.O.R., and not, unless I am very much mistaken, those others: C.A.S.T.I.T.A.S. You have a mouth that looks as though it knew how to taste and how to bite. You . . ."

Rosie jumped up. "I'm going away," she said.

Coleman leaned back in his chair and hallooed with laughter. "Bite, bite, bite," he said. "Thirty-two times." And he opened and shut his mouth as fast as he could, so that his teeth clicked against one another with a little dry bony noise. "Every mouthful thirty-two times. That's what Mr. Gladstone said. And surely Mr. Gladstone—" he rattled his sharp white teeth again "—surely Mr. Gladstone should know."

"Good-by," said Rosie from the door.

"Good-by," Coleman called back; and immediately afterward jumped to his feet and made a dash across the room toward her.

Rosie uttered a cry, slipped through the door and slamming it behind her, ran across the vestibule and began fumbling with the latches of the outer door. It wouldn't open, it wouldn't open. She was trembling; fear made her feel sick. There was a rattling at the door behind her. There was a whoop of laughter, and then the Cossack's hands were on her arms, his face came peering over her shoulder and the blond beard dabbled with blood prickled against her neck and face.

"Oh, don't, don't, don't!" she implored, turning away her head. Then all at once she began violently crying.

"Tears!" exclaimed Coleman in rapture, "genuine tears!" He bent eagerly forward to kiss them away, to drink them as they fell. "What an intoxication," he said, looking up to the ceiling like a chicken that has taken a sip of water; he smacked his lips.

Sobbing uncontrollably, Rosie had never in all her life felt less like a great, fastidious lady.

Chapter XXI

"Well," said Gumbril, "here I am again."

"Already?" Mrs. Viveash had been reduced by the violence of her headache, to coming home after her luncheon with Piers Cotton for a rest. She had fed her hungry pain on Pyramidon and now she was lying down on the Dufy-upholstered sofa at the foot of her full-length portrait by Jacques-Emile Blanche. Her head was not much better, but she was bored. When the maid had announced Gumbril, she had given word that he was to be let in. "I'm very ill," she went on, expiringly. "Look at me," she pointed to herself, "and me again." She waved her hand toward the sizzling brilliance of the portrait. "Before and after. Like the advertisements, you know. Every picture tells a story." She laughed faintly, then made a little grimace and, sucking in the breath between her lips, she put her hand to her forehead.

"My poor Myra." Gumbril pulled up a chair to the sofa and sat there like a doctor at his patient's bedside. "But before and after what?" he asked, almost professionally.

Mrs. Viveash gave an all but imperceptible shrug. "I don't know," she said.

"Not influenza, I hope?"

"No, I don't think so."

"Not love, by any chance?"

Mrs. Viveash did not venture another laugh; she contented herself with smiling agonizingly.

"That would have been a just retribution," Gumbril went on, "after what you've done to me."

"What have I done to you?" Mrs. Viveash asked, opening wide her pale blue eyes.

"Merely wrecked my existence."

"But you're being childish, Theodore. Say what you mean without these grand, silly phrases." The dying voice spoke with impatience.

"Well, what I mean," said Gumbril, "is merely this. You prevented me from going to see the only person I ever really wanted to see in my life. And yesterday, when I tried to see her, she was gone. Vanished. And here am I left in the vacuum."

Mrs. Viveash shut her eyes. "We're all in the vacuum," she said. "You'll still have plenty of company, you know." She was silent for a moment. "Still, I'm sorry," she added. "Why didn't you tell me? And why didn't you just pay no attention to me and go all the same?"

"I didn't tell you," Gumbril answered, "because, then, I didn't know. And I didn't go because I didn't want to quarrel with you."

"Thank you," said Mrs. Viveash, and patted his hand. "But what are you going to do about it now? Not quarreling with me is only a rather negative satisfaction, I'm afraid."

"I propose to leave the country tomorrow morning," said Gumbril.

"Ah, the classical remedy . . . But not to shoot big game, I hope?" She thought of Viveash among the Tikki-tikkis and the tsetses. He was a charming creature; charming, but . . . but what?

"Good heavens!" exclaimed Gumbril. "What do you take me for? Big game!" He leaned back in his chair and began to laugh, heartily, for the first time since he had returned from Robertsbridge, yesterday evening. He had felt then as though he would never laugh again. "Do you see me in a pith helmet, with an elephant gun?"

Mrs. Viveash put her hand to her forehead. "I see you, Theodore," she said, "but I try to think you would look quite normal; because of my head."

"I go to Paris first," said Gumbril. "After that, I don't know. I shall go wherever I think people will buy pneumatic trousers. I'm traveling on business."

This time, in spite of her head, Mrs. Viveash laughed.

"I thought of giving myself a farewell banquet," Gumbril went on. "We'll go round before dinner, if you're feeling well enough, that is, and collect a few friends. Then, in profoundest gloom, we'll eat and drink. And in the morning, unshaved, exhausted and filled with disgust, I shall take the train from Victoria, feeling thankful to get out of England."

"We'll do it," said Mrs. Viveash faintly and indomitably from this sofa that was almost genuinely a deathbed. "And meanwhile, we'll have a second brew of tea and you shall talk to me."

The tannin was brought in. Gumbril settled down to talk and Mrs. Viveash to listen—to listen and from time to time to dab her brows with eau-de-Cologne, to take a sniff of hartshorn.

Gumbril talked. He talked of the marriage ceremonies of octopuses, of the rites intricately consummated in the submarine green grottoes of the Indian Ocean. Given a total of sixteen arms, how many permutations and combinations of caresses? And in the middle of each bunch of arms a mouth like the beak of a macaw.

On the backside of the moon, his friend Umbilikoff, the mystic, used to assure him, the souls of the dead in the form of little bladders—like so much swelled sago—are piled up and piled up till they squash and squeeze one another with an excruciating and ever-growing pressure. In the exoteric world this squeezing on the moon's backside is known, erroneously, as hell. And as for the constellation, Scorpio—he was the first of all constellations to have a proper sort of backbone. For by an effort of the will he ingurgitated his external armor, he compressed and rebuilt it within his body and so became the first vertebrate. This, you may well believe, was a notable day in cosmic history.

The rents in these new buildings in Regent Street and Piccadilly run to as much as three or four pounds a square foot. Meanwhile, all the beauty imagined by Nash has departed and chaos and barbarism once more reign supreme, even in Regent Street. The ghost of Gumbril Senior stalked across the room.

Who lives longer: the man who takes heroin for two years and dies, or the man who lives on roast beef, water and potatoes till ninety-five? One passes his twenty-four months in eternity. All the years of the beef eater are lived only in time. "I can tell you all about heroin," said Mrs. Viveash.

Lady Capricorn, he understood, was still keeping open bed. How Rubens would have admired those silk cushions, those gigantic cabbage roses, those round pink pearls of hers, vaster than those that Captain Nemo discovered in the immemorial oyster! And the warm dry rustle of flesh over flesh as she walks, moving one leg, then advancing the other.

Talking of octopuses, the swim bladders of deep-sea fishes are filled with almost absolutely pure oxygen. C'est la vie—Gumbril shrugged his shoulders.

In Alpine pastures the grasshoppers started their flight, whizzing like clockwork grasshoppers. And these brown invisible ones reveal themselves suddenly as they skim above the flowers—a streak of blue lightning, a trailing curve of scarlet. Then the overwing shuts down over the colored wing below and they are once more invisible fiddlers rubbing their thighs, like Lady Capricorn, at the foot of the towering flowers.

Forgers give patina to their medieval ivories by lending them to stout Jewesses to wear a few months hanging, like an amulet, between their breasts.

In Italian cemeteries the family vaults are made of glass and iron, like greenhouses.

Sir Henry Griddle has finally married the hog-faced gentlewoman.

Piero della Francesca's fresco of the Resurrection at San Sepolcro is the most beautiful picture in the world and the hotel there is far from bad. Scriabine=*le* Tschaikovsky *de nos jours*. The dullest landscape painter is Marchand. The best poet. . . .

"You bore me," said Mrs. Viveash.

"Must I talk of love, then?" asked Gumbril.

"It looks like it," Mrs. Viveash answered, and closed her eyes.

Gumbril told the anecdote about Jo Peters, Connie Asticot and Jim Baum. The anecdote of Lola Knopf and the Baroness Gnomon. Of Margherita Radicofani, himself and the Pastor Meyer. Of Lord Cavey and little Toby Nobes. When he had finished these, he saw that Mrs. Viveash had gone to sleep.

He was not flattered. But a little sleep would do her headache, he reflected, a world of good. And knowing that if he ceased to speak, she would probably be woken by the sudden blankness of the silence, he went on quietly talking to himself.

"When I'm abroad this time," he soliloquized, "I shall really begin writing my autobiography. There's nothing like a hotel bedroom to work in." He scratched his head thoughtfully and even picked his nose, which was one of his bad habits, when he was alone. "People who know me," he went on, "will think that what I write about the governess cart and my mother and the flowers and so on is written merely because I know in here," he scratched his head a little harder to show himself that he referred to his brain, "that that's the sort of thing one ought to write about. They'll think I'm a sort of dingy Romain Rolland, hopelessly trying to pretend that I feel the emotions and have the great spiritual experiences, which the really important people do feel and have. And perhaps they'll be right. Perhaps the Life of Gumbril will be as manifestly an *ersatz* as the Life of Beethoven. On the other hand they may be astonished to find that it's the genuine article. We shall see." Gumbril nodded his head slowly, while he transferred two pennies from his right-hand trouser pocket to his left-hand trouser pocket. He was somewhat distressed to find that these coppers had been trespassing among the silver. Silver was for the right hand, copper for the left. It was one of the laws, which it was extremely unlucky to infringe. "I have a premonition," he went on, "that one of these days I may become a saint. An unsuccessful flickering sort of saint, like a candle beginning to go out. As for love—m'yes, m'yes. And as for the people I have met—I shall point out that I have met most of the eminent men in Europe and that I have said of all of them what I said of my first love affair: 'Is that all?'"

"Did you really say that about your first love affair?" asked Mrs. Viveash, who had woken up again.

"Didn't you?"

"No. I said: This *is* all—everything, the universe. In love, it's either all or nothing at all." She shut her eyes and almost immediately went to sleep again.

Gumbril continued his lullaby—soliloquy.

"This charming little book . . . *The Scotsman.* This farrago of obscenity, slander and false psychology . . . *Darlington Echo.* 'Mr. Gumbril's first cousin is St. Francis Xavier, his second cousin is the Earl of Rochester, his third cousin is the Man of Feeling, his fourth cousin is David Hume . . .' *Court Journal.*" Gumbril was already tired of this joke. "When I consider how my light is spent," he went on, "when I consider! . . . Herr Jesu, as Fraulein Nimmernein used to exclaim at the critical moment. Consider, dear cow, consider. This is not the time of year for grass to grow. Consider, dear cow, consider, consider." He got up from his chair and tiptoed across the room to the writing table. An Indian dagger lay next to the blotting pad; Mrs. Viveash used it as a paper knife. Gumbril picked it up, executed several passes with it. "Thumb on the blade," he said, "and strike upward. On guard. Lunge. To the hilts it penetrates. Poniard at the tip"—he ran the blade between his fingers—"caress by the time it reaches the hilts. Z-zip." He put down the knife and stopping for a moment to make a grimace at himself in the mirror over the mantelpiece, he went back to his chair.

At seven o'clock Mrs. Viveash woke up. She shook her head to feel if the pain were still rolling about loose inside her skull.

"I really believe I'm all right," she said. She jumped up. "Come on," she cried. "I feel ready for anything."

"And I feel like so much food for worms," said Gumbril. "Still, *Versiam' a tazza piena il generoso umor.*" He hummed the Drinking Song out of *Robert the Devil* and to that ingenuously jolly melody they left the house.

Their taxi that evening cost them several pounds. They made the man drive back and forth, like a shuttle, from one end of London to the other. Every time they passed through Piccadilly Circus, Mrs. Viveash leaned out of the window to look at the sky signs dancing their unceasing St. Vitus's dance above the monument to the Earl of Shaftesbury.

"How I adore them!" she said the first time they passed them. "Those wheels that whizz round till the sparks fly out from under them: that rushing motor: and that lovely bottle of port filling the glass and then disappearing and reappearing and filling it again. Too lovely."

"Too revolting," Gumbril corrected her. "These things are the epileptic symbol of all that's most bestial and idiotic in contemporary life. Look at those beastly things and then look at that." He pointed to the

County Fire Office on the northern side of the Circus. "There stands decency, dignity, beauty, repose. And there flickers, there gibbers and twitches—what? Restlessness, distraction, refusal to think, anything for an unquiet life."

"What a delicious pedant you are!" She turned away from the window, put her hands on his shoulders and looked at him. "Too exquisitely ridiculous!" And she kissed him.

"You won't force me to change my opinion." Gumbril smiled at her. "*Eppur' si muove*—I stick to my guns like Galileo. They move and they're horrible."

"They're me," said Mrs. Viveash emphatically. "Those things are me."

They drove first to Lypiatt's mews. Under the Piranesian arch. The clotheslines looped from window to window across the street might have been those ropes which form so essential and so mysterious a part of the furniture of the Prisons. The place smelled; the children were shouting; the hyenalike laughter of the flappers reverberated between the close-set walls. All Gumbril's sense of social responsibility was aroused in a moment.

Shut up in his room all day, Lypiatt had been writing—writing his whole life, all his ideas and ideals, all for Myra. The pile of scribbled sheets grew higher and higher. Toward evening he made an end; he had written all that he wanted to write. He ate the remains of yesterday's loaf of bread and drank some water; for he realized suddenly that he had been fasting the whole day. Then he composed himself to think; he stretched himself out on the brink of the well and looked down into the eyeless darkness.

He still had his Service revolver. Taking it out of the drawer in which it was kept he loaded it; he laid it on the packing case which served him as a table at his bed's head and stretched himself out on the bed. He lay quite still, his muscles all relaxed, hardly breathing. He imagined himself dead. Derision! there was still the plunge into the well.

He picked up the pistol, looked down the barrel. Black and deep as the well. The muzzle against his forehead was a cold mouth.

There was nothing new to be thought about death. There was not even the possibility of a new thought. Only the old thoughts, the horrible old questions returned.

The cold mouth to his forehead, his finger pressing on the trigger. Already he would be falling, falling. And the annihilating crash would be the same as the far-away sound of death at the bottom of the well. And after that, in the silence? The old question was still the same.

After that, he would lie bleeding. The flies would drink his blood as though it were red honey. In the end the people would come and fetch him away and the coroner's jury would look at him in the mortuary and pronounce him temporarily insane. Then he would be buried in a black hole, would be buried and decay.

And meanwhile, would there be anything else? There was nothing new to be thought or asked. And there was still no answer.

In the room it began to grow dark; colors vanished, forms ran together. The easel and Myra's portrait were now a single black silhouette against the window. Near and far were fused, become one and continuous in the darkness, become a part of the darkness. Outside the window the pale twilight grew more somber. The children shouted shrilly, playing their games under the green gas lamps. The mirthless, ferocious laughter of young girls mocked and invited. Lypiatt stretched out his hand and fingered the pistol.

Down below, at his door, he heard a sharp knocking. He lifted his head and listened, caught the sound of two voices, a man's and a woman's. Myra's voice he recognized at once; the other, he supposed, was Gumbril's.

"Hideous to think that people actually live in places like this," Gumbril was saying. "Look at those children. It ought to be punishable by law to produce children in this street."

"They always take me for the Pied Piper," said Mrs. Viveash. Lypiatt got up and crept to the window. He could hear all they said.

"I wonder if Lypiatt's in. I don't see any sign of a light."

"But he has heavy curtains," said Mrs. Viveash, "and I know for a fact that he always composes his poetry in the dark. He may be composing poetry."

Gumbril laughed.

"Knock again," said Mrs. Viveash. "Poets are always absorbed, you know. And Casimir's always the poet."

"*Il Poeta*—capital P. Like d'Annunzio in the Italian papers," said Gumbril. "Did you know that d'Annunzio has books printed on mackintosh for his bath?" He rapped again at the door. "I saw it in the *Corriere della Sera* the other day at the club. He reads the *Little Flowers of St. Francis* by preference in his bath. And he has a fountain pen with waterproof ink in the soap dish, so that he can add a few Fioretti of his own whenever he feels like it. We might suggest that to Casimir."

Lypiatt stood with folded arms by the window, listening. How lightly they threw his life, his heart, from hand to hand, as though it were a ball and they were playing a game! He thought suddenly of all the times he had spoken lightly and maliciously of other people. His own person had always seemed, on those occasions, sacred. One knew in theory very well that others spoke of one contemptuously—as one spoke of them. In practice—it was hard to believe.

"Poor Casimir!" said Mrs. Viveash. "I'm afraid his show was a failure."

"I know it was," said Gumbril. "Complete and absolute. I told my tame capitalist that he ought to employ Lypiatt for our advertisements. He'd be excellent for those. And it would mean some genuine money in his pocket."

"But the worst of it is," said Mrs. Viveash, "that he'll only feel insulted by the suggestion." She looked up at the window.

"I don't know why," she went on, "this house looks most horribly dead. I hope nothing's happened to poor Casimir. I have a most disagreeable feeling that it may have."

"Ah, this famous feminine intuition," laughed Gumbril. He knocked again.

"I can't help feeling that he may be lying there dead, or delirious, or something."

"And I can't help feeling that he must have gone out to dinner. We shall have to give him up, I'm afraid. It's a pity. He's so good with Mercaptan. Like bear and mastiff. Or rather, like bear and poodle, bear and King Charles's spaniel—or whatever those little dogs are that you see ladies in eighteenth-century French engravings taking to bed with them. Let's go."

"Just knock once again," said Mrs. Viveash. "He might really be preoccupied, or asleep, or ill." Gumbril knocked. "Now listen. Hush."

They were silent; the children still went on hallooing in the distance. There was a great clop-clopping of horse's feet as a van was backed into a stable door near by. Lypiatt stood motionless, his arms still crossed, his chin on his breast. The seconds passed.

"Not a sound," said Gumbril. "He must have gone out."

"I suppose so," said Mrs. Viveash.

"Come on, then. We'll go and look for Mercaptan."

He heard their steps in the street below, heard the slamming of the taxi door. The engine was started up. Loud on the first gear, less loud on the second, whisperingly on the third it moved away, gathering speed. The noise of it was merged with the general noise of the town. They were gone.

Lypiatt walked slowly back to his bed. He wished suddenly that he had gone down to answer the last knock. These voices—at the well's edge he had turned to listen to them; at the well's extreme verge. He lay quite still in the darkness: and it seemed to him at last that he had floated away from the earth, that he was alone, no longer in a narrow dark room, but in an illimitable darkness outside and beyond. His mind grew calmer; he began to think of himself, of all that he had known, remotely, as though from a great way off.

"Adorable lights!" said Mrs. Viveash, as they drove once more through Piccadilly Circus.

Gumbril said nothing. He had said all that he had to say last time.

"And there's another," exclaimed Mrs. Viveash, as they passed, near Burlington House, a fountain of Sandeman's port. "If only they had an automatic jazz band attached to the same mechanism!" she said regretfully.

The green Park remained solitary and remote under the moon. "Wasted on us," said Gumbril, as they passed. "One should be happily in love to enjoy a summer night under the trees." He wondered where Emily could be now. They sat in silence; the cab drove on.

Mr. Mercaptan, it seemed, had left London. His housekeeper had a long story to tell. A regular Bolshevik had come yesterday, pushing in. And she had heard him shouting at Mr. Mercaptan in his own room. And then, luckily, a lady had come and the Bolshevik had gone away again. And this morning Mr. Mercaptan had decided, quite sudden like, to go away for two or three days. And it wouldn't surprise her at all if it had something to do with that horrible Bolshevik fellow. Though of course Master Paster hadn't said anything about it. Still, as she'd known him when he was so high and seen him grow up like, she thought she could say she knew him well enough to guess why he did things. It was only brutally that they contrived to tear themselves away.

Secure, meanwhile, behind a whole troop of butlers and footmen, Mr. Mercaptan was dining comfortably at Oxhanger with the most faithful of his friends and admirers, Mrs. Speegle. It was to Mrs. Speegle that he had dedicated his coruscating little "Loves of the Pachyderms"; for Mrs. Speegle it was who had suggested, casually one day at luncheon, that the human race ought to be classified in two main species—the Pachyderms and those whose skin, like her own, like Mr. Mercaptan's and a few others', was fine and "responsive," as Mr. Mercaptan himself put it, "to all caresses, including those of pure reason." Mr. Mercaptan had taken the casual hint and had developed it, richly. The barbarous Pachyderms he divided up into a number of subspecies: steatocephali, acephali, theolaters, industrious Judaeorhynci—busy, compact and hard as dung beetles—Peabodies, Russians and so on. It was all very witty and delicately savage. Mr. Mercaptan had a standing invitation at Oxhanger. With dangerous Pachyderms like Lypiatt ranging loose about the town, he thought it best to avail himself of it. Mrs. Speegle, he knew, would be delighted to see him. And indeed she was. He arrived just at lunchtime. Mrs. Speegle and Maisie Furlonger were already at the fish.

"Mercaptan!" Mrs. Speegle's soul seemed to be in the name. "Sit down," she went on, cooing as she talked, like a ringdove. There seemed to be singing in every word she spoke. She pointed to a chair next to hers. "N'you're n'just in time to tell us all about n'your Lesbian experiences."

And Mercaptan, giving vent to his fully orchestrated laugh—squeal and roar together—had sat down and speaking in French partly, he nodded toward the butler and the footman, "à cause des valets" and partly because the language lent itself more deliciously to this kind of confidence, he had begun there and then, interrupted and spurred on by the cooing of Mrs. Speegle and the happy shrieks of Maisie Furlonger, to recount at length and with all the wit in the world his experience among the Isles of Greece. How delicious it was, he said to himself, to be with really civilized people! In this happy house it seemed scarcely possible to believe that such a thing as a Pachyderm existed.

But Lypiatt still lay, face upward, on his bed, floating, it seemed to himself, far out into the dark emptiness between the stars. From those distant abstract spaces he seemed to be looking impersonally down upon his own body stretched out by the brink of the hideous well; to be looking back over his own history. Everything, even his own unhappiness, seemed very small and beautiful; every frightful convulsion had become no more than a ripple and only the fine musical ghost of sound came up to him from all the shouting.

"We have no luck," said Gumbril as they climbed once more into the cab.

"I'm not sure," said Mrs. Viveash, "that we haven't really had a great deal. Did you genuinely want very much to see Mercaptan?"

"Not in the least," said Gumbril. "But do you genuinely want to see me?"

Mrs. Viveash drew the corners of her mouth down into a painful smile and did not answer. "Aren't we going to pass through Piccadilly Circus again?" she asked. "I should like to see the lights again. They give one temporarily the illusion of being cheerful."

"No, no," said Gumbril, "we are going straight to Victoria."

"We couldn't tell the driver to . . . ?"

"Certainly not."

"Ah, well," said Mrs. Viveash. "Perhaps one's better without stimulants. I remember when I was very young, when I first began to go about at all, how proud I was of having discovered champagne. It seemed to me wonderful to get rather tipsy. Something to be exceedingly proud of. And at the same time, how much I really disliked wine! Loathed the taste of it. Sometimes, when Calliope and I used to dine quietly together, tête-à-tête, with no awful men about and no appearances to keep up, we used to treat ourselves to the luxury of a large lemon squash, or even raspberry syrup and soda. Ah, I wish I could recapture the deliciousness of raspberry syrup."

Coleman was at home. After a brief delay he appeared himself at the door. He was wearing pajamas and his face was covered with red-brown smears, the tips of his beard were clotted with the same dried pigment.

"What have you been doing to yourself?" asked Mrs. Viveash.

"Merely washing in the blood of the Lamb," Coleman answered, smiling, and his eyes sparkling blue fire, like an electric machine.

The door on the opposite side of the little vestibule was open. Looking over Coleman's shoulder, Gumbril could see through the opening a brightly lighted room and in the middle of it, like a large rectangular island, a wide divan. Reclining on the divan an odalisque by Ingres— but slimmer, more serpentine, more like a lithe pink length of boa— presented her back. That big brown mole on the right shoulder was surely familiar. But when, startled by the loudness of the voices behind her, the odalisque turned round—to see in a horribly embarrassing instant that the Cossack had left the door open and that people could look in, were looking in, indeed—the slanting eyes beneath their heavy white lids, the fine aquiline nose, the wide, full-lipped mouth, though they presented themselves for only the fraction of a second were still more recognizable and familiar. For only the fraction of a second did the odalisque reveal herself definitely as Rosie. Then a hand pulled feverishly at the counterpane, the section of buff-colored boa wriggled and rolled; and in a moment, where an odalisque had been, lay only a long packet under a white sheet, like a jockey with a fractured skull when they carry him from the course.

Well, really . . . Gumbril felt positively indignant; not jealous, but astonished and righteously indignant.

"Well, when you've finished bathing," said Mrs. Viveash, "I hope you'll come and have dinner with us." Coleman was standing between her and the further door; Mrs. Viveash had seen nothing in the room beyond the vestibule.

"I'm busy," said Coleman.

"So I see." Gumbril spoke as sarcastically as he could.

"Do you see?" asked Coleman and looked round. "So you do!" He stepped back and closed the door.

"It's Theodore's last dinner," pleaded Mrs. Viveash.

"Not even if it were his last supper," said Coleman, enchanted to have been given the opportunity to blaspheme a little. "Is he going to be crucified? Or what?"

"Merely going abroad," said Gumbril.

"He has a broken heart," Mrs. Viveash explained.

"Ah, the genuine platonic towsers?" Coleman uttered his artificial demon's laugh.

"That's just about it," said Gumbril, grimly.

Relieved by the shutting of the door from her immediate embarrassment, Rosie threw back a corner of the counterpane and extruded her head, one arm and the shoulder with a mole on it. She looked about her, opening her slanting eyes as wide as she could. She listened with parted lips to the voices that came, muffled now, through the door. It seemed to her as though she were waking up; as though now, for the first time, she were hearing that shattering laugh, were looking now for the first time on these blank white walls and the one lovely and horrifying picture. Where was she? What did it all mean? Rosie put her hand to her forehead, tried to think. Her thinking was always a series of pictures; one after another the pictures swam up before her eyes, melted again in an instant.

Her mother taking off her pince-nez to wipe them—and at once her eyes were tremulous and vague and helpless. "You should always let the gentleman get over the stile first," she said, and put on her glasses again. Behind the glasses her eyes immediately became clear, piercing, steady and efficient. Rather formidable eyes. They had seen Rosie getting over the stile in front of Willie Hoskyns and there was too much leg.

James reading at his desk; his heavy round head propped on his hand. She came up behind him and threw her arms round his neck. Very gently, and without turning his eyes from the page, he undid her embrace and with a little push that was no more than a hint, an implication, signified that he didn't want her. She had gone to her pink room and cried.

Another time James shook his head and smiled patiently under his mustache. "You'll never learn," he said. She had gone to her room and cried that time too.

Another time they were lying in bed together, in the pink bed; only you couldn't see it was pink because there was no light. They were lying very quietly. Warm and happy and remote she felt. Sometimes as it were the physical memory of pleasure plucked at her nerves, making her start, making her suddenly shiver. James was breathing as though he were asleep. All at once he stirred. He patted her shoulder two or three times in a kindly and businesslike way. "I know what that means," she said, "when you pat me like that." And she patted him—pat-pat-pat, very quickly. "It means you're going to bed." "How do you know?" he asked. "Do you think I don't know you after all this time? I know that pat by heart . . ." And suddenly all her warm quiet happiness evaporated; it was all gone. "I'm only a machine for going to bed with," she said. "That's all I am for you." She felt she would like to cry. But James only laughed and said, "Nonsense," and pulled his arm clumsily from underneath her. "You go to sleep," he said, and kissed her on the forehead. Then he got out of bed and she heard him bumping clumsily about in the darkness. "Damn!" he said once. Then he found the door, opened, and was gone.

She thought of those long stories she used to make up when she went shopping. The fastidious lady; the poets; all the adventures.

Toto's hands were wonderful.

She saw, she heard Mr. Mercaptan reading his essays. Poor father, reading aloud from the *Hibbert Journal!*

And now the Cossack, covered with blood. He too might read aloud from the *Hibbert Journal*—only backward, so to speak. She had a bruise on her arm. "You think there's nothing inherently wrong and disgusting in it?" he had asked. "There is, I tell you." He had laughed and kissed her and stripped off her clothes and caressed her. And she had cried, she had struggled, she had tried to turn away; and in the end she had been overcome by a pleasure more piercing and agonizing than anything she had ever felt before. And all the time Coleman had hung over her, with his blood-stained beard, smiling, smiling into her face and whispering, "Horrible, horrible, infamous and shameful." She lay in a kind of stupor. Then, suddenly there had been that ringing. The Cossack had left her. And now she was awake again, and it was horrible; it was shameful. She shuddered; she jumped out of bed and began as quickly as she could to put on her clothes.

"Really, really, won't you come?" Mrs. Viveash was insisting. She was not used to people saying no when she asked, when she insisted. She didn't like it.

"No." Coleman shook his head. "You may be having the last supper. But I have a date here with the Magdalen."

"O, a woman," said Mrs. Viveash. "But why didn't you say so before?"

"Well, as I'd left the door open," said Coleman, "I thought it was unnecessary."

"Fie," said Mrs. Viveash. "I find this very repulsive. Let's go away." She plucked Gumbril by the sleeve.

"Good-by," said Coleman politely. He shut the door after them and turned back across the little hall.

"What! Not thinking of going?" he exclaimed as he came in. Rosie was sitting on the edge of the bed pulling on her shoes.

"Go away," she said. "You disgust me."

"But that's splendid," Coleman declared. "That's all as it should be, all as I intended." He sat down beside her on the divan. "Really," he said admiringly, "what exquisite legs!"

Rosie would have given anything in the world to be back again in Bloxam Gardens. Even if James did live in his books all the time . . . Anything in the world.

"This time," said Mrs. Viveash, "we simply must go through Piccadilly Circus."

"It'll only be about two miles further."

"Well, that isn't much."

Gumbril leaned out and gave the word to the driver.

"And besides, I like driving about like this," said Mrs. Viveash. "I like driving for driving's sake. It's like the Last Ride Together. Dear Theodore!" She laid her hand on his.

"Thank you," said Gumbril and kissed it.

The little cab buzzed along down the empty Mall. They were silent. Through the thick air one could see the brightest of the stars. It was one of those evenings when men feel that truth, goodness and beauty are one. In the morning, when they commit their discovery to paper, when others read it written there, it looks wholly ridiculous. It was one of those evenings when love is once more invented for the first time. That too seems a little ridiculous, sometimes, in the morning.

"Here are the lights again," said Mrs. Viveash. "Hop, twitch, flick —yes, genuinely an illusion of jollity, Theodore. Genuinely."

Gumbril stopped the cab. "It's after half-past eight," he said. "At this rate we shall never get anything to eat. Wait a minute."

He ran into Appenrodt's and came back in a moment with a packet of smoked salmon sandwiches, a bottle of white wine and a glass.

"We have a long way to go," he explained as he got into the taxi.

They ate their sandwiches, they drank their wine. The taxi drove on and on.

"This is positively exhilarating," said Mrs. Viveash as they turned into the Edgeware Road.

Polished by the wheels and shining like an old and precious bronze, the road stretched before them, reflecting the lamps. It had the inviting air of a road which goes on forever.

"They used to have such good peep shows in this street," Gumbril tenderly remembered. "Little back shops where you paid twopence to see the genuine mermaid, which turned out to be a stuffed walrus, and the tattooed lady, and the dwarf, and the living statuary, which one always hoped, as a boy, was really going to be rather naked and thrilling, but which was always the most pathetic of unemployed barmaids, dressed in the thickest of pink Jaeger."

"Do you think there'd be any of those now?" asked Mrs. Viveash.

Gumbril shook his head. "They've moved on with the march of civilization. But where?" He spread out his hands interrogatively. "I don't know which direction civilization marches—whether north toward Kilburn and Golders Green, or over the river to the Elephant, to Clapham and Sydenham and all those other mysterious places. But in any case, high rents have marched up here; there are no more genuine mermaids in the Edgeware Road. What stories we shall be able to tell our children!"

"Do you think we shall ever have any?" Mrs. Viveash asked.

"One can never tell."

"I should have thought one could," said Mrs. Viveash. Children—that would be the most desperate experiment of all. The most desperate and perhaps the only one having any chance of being successful. History recorded cases. On the other hand, it recorded other cases that proved the opposite. She had often thought of this experiment. There were so many obvious reasons for not making it. But some day, perhaps—she always put it off, like that.

The cab had turned off the main road, into quieter and darker streets.

"Where are we now?" asked Mrs. Viveash.

"Penetrating into Maida Vale. We shall soon be there. Poor old Shearwater!" He laughed. Other people in love were always absurd.

"Shall we find him in, I wonder?" It would be fun to see Shearwater again. She liked to hear him talking, learnedly and like a child. But when the child is six feet high and three feet wide and two feet thick, when it tries to plunge head first into your life—then, really, no. . . . "But what did you want with me?" he had asked. "Just to look at you," she answered. Just to look; that was all. Music hall, not boudoir.

"Here we are are." Gumbril got out and rang the second-floor bell.

The door was opened by an impertinent-looking little maid.

"Mr. Shearwater's at the lavatory," she said in answer to Gumbril's question.

"Laboratory?" he suggested.

"At the 'ospital." That made it clear.

"And is Mrs. Shearwater at home?" he asked maliciously.

The little maid shook her head. "I expected 'er, but she didn't come back to dinner."

"Would you mind giving her a message when she does come in," said Gumbril. "Tell her that Mr. Toto was very sorry he hadn't time to speak to her when he saw her this evening in Pimlico."

"Mr. who?"

"Mr. Toto."

"Mr. Toto is sorry 'e 'adn't the time to speak to Mrs. Shearwater when 'e saw 'er in Pimlico this evening. Very well, Sir."

"You won't forget," said Gumbril.

"No, I won't forget."

He went back to the cab and explained that they had drawn blank once more.

"I'm rather glad," said Mrs. Viveash. "If we ever did find anybody, it would mean the end of this Last Ride Together feeling. And that would be sad. And it's a lovely night. And really, for the moment, I feel I can do without my lights. Suppose we just drove for a bit now."

But Gumbril would not allow that. "We haven't had enough to eat yet," he said, and he gave the cabman Gumbril Senior's address.

Gumbril Senior was sitting on his little iron balcony among the dried-out pots that had once held geraniums, smoking his pipe and looking earnestly out into the darkness in front of him. Clustered in the fourteen plane trees of the square, the starlings were already asleep. There was no sound but the rustling of the leaves. But sometimes, every hour or so, the birds would wake up. Something—perhaps it might be a stronger gust of wind, perhaps some happy dream of worms, some nightmare of cats simultaneously dreamed by all the flock together—would suddenly rouse them. And then they would all start to talk at once, at the tops of their shrill voices—for perhaps half a minute. Then in an instant they all went to sleep again and there was once more no sound but the rustling of the shaken leaves. At these moments Mr. Gumbril would lean forward, would strain his eyes and his ears in the hope of seeing, of hearing something—something significant, explanatory, satisfying. He never did, of course; but that in no way diminished his happiness.

Mr. Gumbril received them on his balcony with courtesy.

"I was just thinking of going in to work," he said. "And now you come and give me a good excuse for sitting out here a little longer. I'm delighted."

Gumbril Junior went downstairs to see what he could find in the way of food. While he was gone, his father explained to Mrs. Viveash the secrets of the birds. Enthusiastically, his light floss of gray hair floating up and falling again about his head as he pointed and gesticulated, he told her; the great flocks assembled—goodness only knew where!—they flew across the golden sky detaching here a little troop, there a whole legion, they flew until at last all had found their appointed resting places and there were no more to fly. He made this nightly flight sound epical, as though it were a migration of peoples, a passage of armies.

"And it's my firm belief," said Gumbril Senior adding notes to his epic, "that they made use of some sort of telepathy, some kind of direct mind-to-mind communication between themselves. You can't watch them without coming to that conclusion."

"A charming conclusion," said Mrs. Viveash.

"It's a faculty," Gumbril Senior went on, "we all possess, I believe. All we animals." He made a gesture which included himself, Mrs. Viveash and the invisible birds among the plane trees. "Why don't we use it more? You may well ask. For the simple reason, my dear young lady, that half our existence is spent in dealing with things that have no mind—things with which it is impossible to hold telepathic communication. Hence the development of the five senses. I have eyes that preserve me from running into the lamp-post, ears that warn me I'm in the neighborhood of Niagara. And having made these instruments very efficient, I use them even in holding converse with other beings having a mind. I let my telepathic faculty lie idle, preferring to employ an elaborate and cumbrous arrangement of symbols in order to make my thought known to you through your senses. In certain individuals, however, the faculty is naturally so well developed—like the musical, or the mathematical, or the chess-playing faculties in other people—that they cannot help entering into direct communication with other minds, whether they want to or not. If we knew a good method of educating and drawing out the latent faculty, most of us could make ourselves moderately efficient telepaths; just as most of us can make ourselves into moderate musicians, chess players and mathematicians. There would also be a few, no doubt, who could never communicate directly. Just as there are a few who cannot recognize 'Rule Britannia' or Bach's concerto in D minor for two violins, and a few who cannot comprehend the nature of an algebraical symbol. Look at the general development of the mathematical and musical faculties only within the last two hundred years. By the twenty-first century I believe we shall all be telepaths. Meanwhile, these delightful birds have forestalled us. Not having the wit to invent a language or an expressive pantomine, they contrive to communicate such simple thoughts as they have directly and instantaneously. They all go to sleep at once, wake at once, say the same thing at once; they turn all at once when they're flying; without a leader, without a word of command, they do everything together, in complete unison. Sitting here in the evenings, I sometimes fancy I can feel their thoughts striking against my own. It has happened to me once or twice: that I have known a second before it actually happened that the birds were going to wake up and begin their half minute of chatter in the dark. Wait! Hush." Gumbril Senior threw back his head, pressed his hand over his mouth, as though by commanding silence on himself he could command it on the whole world. "I believe they're going to wake now. I feel it."

He was silent. Mrs. Viveash looked toward the dark trees and listened. A full minute passed. Then the old gentleman burst out happily laughing.

"Completely wrong!" he said. "They've never been more soundly asleep." Mrs. Viveash laughed too. "Perhaps they all changed their minds, just as they were waking up," she suggested.

Gumbril Junior reappeared; glasses clinked as he walked and there was a little rattle of crockery. He was carrying a tray.

"Cold beef," he said, "and salad and a bit of a cold apple pie. It might be worse."

They drew up chairs to Gumbril Senior's work table, and there, among the letters and the unpaid bills and the sketchy elevations of archducal palaces, they ate the beef and the apple pie and drank the one and nine-penny vin ordinaire of the house. Gumbril Senior, who had already supped, looked on at them from the balcony.

"Did I tell you," said Gumbril Junior, "that we saw Mr. Porteous's son the other evening—very drunk?"

Gumbril Senior threw up his hands. "If you knew the calamities that young imbecile has been the cause of!"

"What's he done?"

"Gambled away I don't know how much borrowed money. And poor Porteous can't afford anything—even now." Mr. Gumbril shook his head and clutched and combed his beard. "It's a fearful blow, but of course Porteous is very steadfast and serene and . . . There!" Gumbril Senior interrupted himself, holding up his hand. "Listen!"

In the fourteen plane trees the starlings had suddenly woken up.

There was a wild outburst, like a stormy sitting in the Italian Parliament. Then all was still. Gumbril Senior listened, enchanted. His face, as he turned back toward the light, revealed itself all smiles. His hair seemed to have blown loose of its own accord, from within, so to speak; he pushed it into place.

"You heard them?" he asked Mrs. Viveash. "What can they have to say to one another, I wonder, at this time of night?"

"And did you feel they were going to wake up?" Mrs. Viveash inquired.

"No," said Gumbril Senior with candor.

"When we've finished," Gumbril Junior spoke with his mouth full, "you must show Myra your model of London. She'd adore it—except that it has no electric sky signs."

His father looked all of a sudden very much embarrassed. "I don't think it would interest Mrs. Viveash much," he said.

"Oh, yes it would. Really," she declared.

"Well, as a matter of fact it isn't here." Gumbril Senior pulled with fury at his beard.

"Not here? But what's happened to it?"

Gumbril Senior wouldn't explain. He just ignored his son's question and began to talk once more about the starlings. Later on, however, when Gumbril and Mrs. Viveash were preparing to go, the old man drew him apart into a corner and began to whisper the explanation.

"I didn't want to blare it about in front of strangers," he said, as though it were a question of the housemaid's illegitimate baby or a repair to the water closet. "But the fact is, I've sold it. The Victoria and Albert had wind that I was making it; they've been wanting it all the time. And I've let them have it."

"But why?" Gumbril Junior asked in a tone of astonishment. He knew with what a paternal affection—no, more than paternal—for he was sure that his father was more wholeheartedly attached to his models than his son—with what pride he regarded these children of his spirit.

Gumbril Senior sighed. "It's all that young imbecile," he said.

"What young imbecile?"

"Porteous's son, of course. You see, poor Porteous has had to sell his library, among other things. You don't know what that means to him. All these precious books. And collected at the price of such hardship. I thought I'd like to buy a few of the best ones back for him. They gave me quite a good price at the Museum." He came out of his corner and hurried across the room to help Mrs. Viveash with her cloak. "Allow me, allow me," he said.

Slowly and pensively Gumbril Junior followed him. Beyond good and evil? Below good and evil? The name of earwig . . . The tubby pony trotted. The wild columbines suspended, among the shadows of the hazel copse, hooked spurs, helmets of aerial purple. The Twelfth Sonata of Mozart was insecticide; no earwigs could crawl through that music. Emily's breasts were firm and pointed and she had slept at last without a tremor. In the starlight good, true and beautiful became one. Write the discovery in books—in books *quos*, in the morning, *legimus cacantes*. They descended the stairs. The cab was waiting outside.

"The Last Ride again," said Mrs. Viveash.

"Golgotha Hospital, Southwark," said Gumbril to the driver and followed her into the cab.

"Drive, drive, drive," repeated Mrs. Viveash. "I like your father, Theodore. One of these days he'll fly away with the birds. And how nice it is of those starlings to wake themselves up like that in the middle of the night, merely to amuse him. Considering how unpleasant it is to be woken in the night. Where are we going?"

"We're going to look at Shearwater in his laboratory."

"Is that a long way away?"

"Immensely," said Gumbril.

"Thank God for that," Mrs. Viveash piously and expiringly breathed.

Chapter XXII

SHEARWATER sat on his stationary bicycle, pedaling unceasingly like a man in a nightmare. The pedals were geared to a little wheel under the saddle and the rim of the wheel rubbed, as it revolved against a brake, carefully adjusted to make the work of the pedaler hard, but not impossibly hard. From a pipe which came up through the floor issued a little jet of water which played on the brake and kept it cool. But no jet of water played on Shearwater. It was his business to get hot. He did get hot.

From time to time his dog-faced young friend, Lancing, came and looked through the window of the experimenting chamber to see how he was getting on. Inside that little wooden house, which might have reminded Lancing, if he had had a literary turn of mind, of the Box in which Gulliver left Brobdingnag, the scenes of intimate life were the same every time he looked in. Shearwater was always at his post on the saddle of the nightmare bicycle, pedaling, pedaling. The water trickled over the brake. And Shearwater sweated. Great drops of sweat came oozing out from under his hair, ran down over his forehead, hung beaded on his eyebrows, ran into his eyes, down his nose, along his cheeks, fell like raindrops. His thick bull-neck was wet; his whole naked body, his arms and legs streamed and shone. The sweat poured off him and was caught as it rained down in a waterproof sheet, to trickle down its sloping folds into a large glass receptacle which stood under a hole in the center of the sheet at the focal point where all its slopes converged. The automatically controlled heating apparatus in the basement kept the temperature in the box high and steady. Peering through the damp-dimmed panes of the window, Lancing noticed with satisfaction that the mercury stood unchangingly at twenty-seven point five Centigrade. The ventilators at the side and top of the box were open; Shearwater had air enough. Another time, Lancing reflected, they'd make the box airtight and see the effect of a little carbon dioxide poisoning on top of excessive sweating. It might be very interesting, but today they were concerned with sweating only. After seeing that the thermometer was steady, that the ventilators were properly open, that water was still trickling over the brake, Lancing would tap at the window. And Shearwater who kept his eyes fixed straight before him, as he pedaled slowly and unremittingly along his nightmare road, would turn his head at the sound.

"All right?" Lancing's lips moved and his eyebrows went up inquiringly.

Shearwater would nod his big round head and the sweat drops suspended on his eyebrows and his mustache would fall like little liquid fruits shaken suddenly by the wind.

"Good," and Lancing would go back to his thick German book under the reading lamp at the other end of the laboratory.

Constant as the thermometer Shearwater pedaled steadily and slowly on. With a few brief halts for food and rest, he had been pedaling ever since lunchtime. At eleven he would go to bed on a shakedown in the laboratory and at nine tomorrow morning he would re-enter the box and start pedaling again. He would go on all tomorrow and the day after; and after that, as long as he could stand it. One, two, three, four. Pedal, pedal, pedal. . . . He must have traveled the equivalent of sixty or seventy miles this afternoon. He would be getting on for Swindon. He would be nearly at Portsmouth. He would be past Cambridge, past Oxford. He would be nearly at Harwich, pedaling through the green and golden valleys where Constable used to paint. He would be at Winchester by the bright stream. He would have ridden through the beech woods of Arundel out into the sea. . . .

In any case he was far away, he was escaping. And Mrs. Viveash followed, walking swayingly along on feet that seemed to tread between two abysses, at her leisure. Pedal, pedal. The hydrogen ion concentration in the blood. . . . Formidably, calmly, her eyes regarded. The lids cut off an arc of those pale circles. When she smiled, it was a crucifixion. The coils of her hair were copper serpents. Her small gestures loosened enormous fragments of the universe and at the faint dying sound of her voice they had fallen in ruins about him. His world was no longer safe, it had ceased to stand on its foundations. Mrs. Viveash walked among his ruins and did not even notice them. He must build up again. Pedal, pedal. He was not merely escaping; he was working a building machine. It must be built with proportion; with proportion, the old man had said. The old man appeared in the middle of the nightmare road in front of him, clutching his beard. Proportion, proportion. There were first a lot of dirty rocks lying about; then there was St. Paul's. These bits of his life had to be built up proportionably.

There was work. And there was talk about work and ideas. And there were men who could talk about work and ideas. But so far as he had been concerned that was about all they could do. He would have to find out what else they did; it was interesting. And he would have to find out what other men did; men who couldn't talk about work and not much about ideas. They had as good kidneys as anyone else.

And then there were women.

On the nightmare road he remained stationary. The pedals went round and round under his driving feet, the sweat ran off him. He was escaping and yet he was also drawing nearer. He would have to draw nearer. "Woman, what have I to do with you?" Not enough; too much.

Not enough—he was building her in, a great pillar next to the pillar of work.

Too much—he was escaping. If he had not caged himself here in this hotbox, he would have run out after her, to throw himself—all in fragments, all dissipated and useless—in front of her. And she wanted none of him. But perhaps it would be worse, perhaps it would be far, far worse if she did.

The old man stood in the road before him, clutching his beard, crying out, "Proportion, proportion." He trod and trod at his building machine, working up the pieces of his life, steadily, unremittingly working them into a proportionable whole, into a dome that should hang, light, spacious, and high, as though by a miracle, on the empty air. He trod and trod, escaping, mile after mile into fatigue, into wisdom. He was at Dover now, pedaling across the channel. He was crossing a dividing gulf and there would be safety on the other side; the cliffs of Dover were already behind him. He turned his head as though to look back at them; the drops of sweat were shaken from his eyebrows, from the shaggy fringes of his mustache. He turned his head from the blank wooden wall in front of him over his left shoulder. A face was looking through the observation window behind him—a woman's face.

It was the face of Mrs. Viveash.

Shearwater uttered a cry and at once turned back again. He redoubled his pedaling. One, two, three, four—furiously he rushed along the nightmare road. She was haunting him now in hallucinations. She was pursuing and she was gaining on him. Will, wisdom, resolution and understanding were of no avail, then? But there was always fatigue. The sweat poured down his face, streamed down the indented runnel of his spine, along the seam at the meeting place of his ribs. His loincloth was wringing wet. The drops pattered continuously on the waterproof sheet. His calves and the muscles of his thighs ached with pedaling. One, two, three, four— he trod round a hundred times with either foot. After that he ventured to turn his head once more. He was relieved, and at the same time he was disappointed, to see that there was now no face at the window. He had exorcised the hallucination. He settled down to a more leisurely pedaling.

In the annex of the laboratory the animals devoted to the service of physiology were awakened by the sudden opening of the door, the sudden irruption of light. The albino guinea pigs peered through the meshes of their hutch and their red eyes were like the rear lights of bicycles. The pregnant she-rabbits lolloped out and shook their ears and pointed their tremulous noses toward the door. The cock into which Shearwater had engrafted an ovary came out, not knowing whether to crow or cluck.

"When he's with hens," Lancing explained to his visitors, "he thinks he's a cock. When he's with a cock, he's convinced he's a pullet."

The rats who were being fed on milk from a London dairy came tumbling from their nest with an anxious hungry speaking. They were getting thinner and thinner every day; in a few days they would be dead. But the old rat, whose diet was Grade A milk from the country, hardly took the trouble to move. He was as fat and sleek as a brown furry fruit, ripe to bursting. No skim and chalky water, no dried dung and tubercle bacilli for him. He was in clover. Next week, however, the fates were plotting to give him diabetes artificially.

In their glass pagoda the little black axolotls crawled, the heraldry of Mexico, among a scanty herbage. The beetles, who had had their heads cut off and replaced by the heads of other beetles, darted uncertainly about, some obeying their heads, some their genital organs. A fifteen-year-old monkey, rejuvenated by the Steinach process, was discovered by the

light of Lancing's electric torch, shaking the bars that separated him
from the green-furred, bald-rumped, bearded young beauty in the next
cage. He was gnashing his teeth with thwarted passion.

Lancing expounded to the visitors all the secrets. The vast, unbeliev-
able, fantastic world opened out as he spoke. There were tropics, there
were cold seas busy with living beings, there were forests full of horrible
trees, silence and darkness. There were ferments and infinitesimal poisons
floating in the air. There were leviathans suckling their young; there were
flies and worms, there were men, living in cities, thinking, knowing good
and evil. And all were changing continuously, moment by moment,
and each remained all the time itself by virtue of some unimaginable
enchantment. They were all alive. And on the other side of the courtyard beyond the shed in which the animals slept or uneasily stirred, in
the huge hospital that went up sheer like a windowed cliff into the air,
men and women were ceasing to be themselves, or were struggling to
remain themselves. They were dying, they were struggling to live. The
other windows looked on to the river. The lights of London bridge were
on the right, of Blackfriars to the left. On the opposite shore St. Paul's
floated up as though self-supported in the moonlight. Like time the river
flowed, silent and black. Gumbril and Mrs. Viveash leaned their elbows
on the sill and looked out. Like time the river flower, stanchlessly, as
though from a wound in the world's side. For a long time they were
silent. They looked out, without speaking, across the flow of time, at
the stars, at the human symbol hanging miraculously in the moonlight.
Lancing had gone back to his German book; he had no time to waste,
looking out of windows.

"Tomorrow," said Gumbril at last, meditatively.

"Tomorrow," Mrs. Viveash interrupted him, "will be as awful as
today." She breathed it like a truth from beyond the grave prematurely
revealed, expiringly from her deathbed within.

"Come, come," protested Gumbril.

In his hotbox Shearwater sweated and pedaled. He was across the
channel now; he felt himself safe. Still he trod on; he would be at Amiens
by midnight if he went on at this rate. He was escaping, he had escaped.
He was building up his strong light dome of life. Proportion, cried the
old man, proportion! And it hung there proportioned and beautiful in
the dark confused horror of his desires, solid and strong and durable
among his broken thoughts. Time flowed darkly past.

"And now," said Mrs. Viveash, straightening herself up and giving
herself a little shake, "now we'll drive to Hampstead and have a look at
Piers Cotton."

POINT COUNTER POINT

Extracts

Oh, wearisome condition of humanity,
Born under one law, to another bound,
Vainly begot and yet forbidden vanity,
Created sick, commanded to be sound.
  What meaneth nature by these diverse laws
  Passion and reason, self-division's cause?

FULKE GREVILLE

I

"You won't be late?" There was anxiety in Marjorie Carling's voice, there was something like entreaty.

"No, I won't be late," said Walter, unhappily and guiltily certain that he would be. Her voice annoyed him. It drawled a little, it was too refined—even in misery.

"Not later than midnight." She might have reminded him of the time when he never went out in the evenings without her. She might have done so; but she wouldn't; it was against her principles; she didn't want to force his love in any way.

"Well, call it one. You know what these parties are." But as a matter of fact, she didn't know, for the good reason that, not being his wife, she wasn't invited to them. She had left her husband to live with Walter Bidlake; and Carling, who had Christian scruples, was feebly a sadist and wanted to take his revenge, refused to divorce her. It was two years now since they had begun to live together. Only two years; and now, already, he had ceased to love her; he had begun to love someone else. The sin was losing its only excuse, the social discomfort its sole palliation. And she was with child.

"Half-past twelve," she implored, though she knew that her importunity would only annoy him, only make him love her the less. But she could not prevent herself from speaking; she loved him too much, she was too agonizingly jealous. The words broke out in spite of her principles. It would have been better for her, and perhaps for Walter too, if she had had fewer principles and given her feelings the violent expression they demanded. But she had been well brought up in habits of the strictest self-control. Only the uneducated, she knew, made "scenes." An imploring "Half-past twelve, Walter," was all that managed to break through her principles. Too weak to move him, the feeble outburst would only annoy. She knew it, and yet she could not hold her tongue.

"If I can possibly manage it." (There; she had done it. There was exasperation in his tone.) "But I can't guarantee it; don't expect me too certainly." For of course, he was thinking (with Lucy Tantamount's image unexorcisably haunting him), it certainly wouldn't be half-past twelve.

In the street he hailed a taxi.

"Tantamount House, Pall Mall."

*   *   *

Three Italian ghosts unobtrusively haunt the eastern end of Pall Mall. The wealth of newly industrialized England and the enthusiasm, the architectural genius, of Charles Barry called them up out of the past and their native sunshine. Under the encrusting grime of the Reform Club the eye of faith recognizes something agreeably reminiscent of the Farnese Palace. A few yards further down the street, Sir Charles's recollection of the house that Raphael designed for the Pandolfini loom up through the filmy London air—the Travelers' Club. And between them, austerely classical, grim like a prison and black with soot, rises a smaller (but still enormous) version of the Cancelleria. It is Tantamount House.

Barry designed it in 1839. A hundred workmen labored for a year or two. And the third marquess paid the bills. They were heavy; but the suburbs of Leeds and Sheffield had begun to spread over the land which his ancestors had stolen from the monasteries three hundred years before. "The Catholic Church, instructed by the Holy Spirit, has from the sacred writings and the ancient traditions of the Fathers taught that there is a Purgatory and that the souls there detained are helped by the suffrages of the faithful, but principally by the acceptable sacrifice of the altar." Rich men with uneasy consciences had left their land to the monks that their souls might be helped through Purgatory by a perpetual performance of the acceptable sacrifice of the altar. But Henry VIII had lusted after

a young woman and desired a son; and because Pope Clement VII was in
the power of Henry's first wife's daughter's cousin, he would not grant
him a divorce. The monasteries were in consequence suppressed. An army
of beggars, of paupers, of the infirm died miserably of hunger. But the
Tantamounts acquired some scores of square miles of plowland, forest and
pasture. A few years later, under Edward VI, they stole the property of two
disestablished grammar schools; children remained uneducated that the
Tantamounts might be rich. They farmed their land scientifically with a
view to the highest profit. Their contemporaries regarded them as "men
that live as though there were no God at all, men that would have all in
their own hands, men that would leave nothing to others, men that be
never satisfied." From the pulpit of St. Paul's, Lever accused them of
having "offended God, and brought a common wealth into a common
ruin." The Tantamounts were unperturbed. The land was theirs, the
money came in regularly.

The corn was sown, grew and was harvested, again and again. The
beasts were born, fattened and went to the slaughter. The plowmen, the
shepherds, the cowherds labored from before dawn till sunset, year after
year, until they died. Their children took their places. Tantamount succeeded Tantamount. Elizabeth made them barons; they became viscounts
under Charles II, earls under William and Mary, marquesses under
George II. They married heiress after heiress—ten square miles of
Nottinghamshire, fifty thousand pounds, two streets in Bloomsbury, half
a brewery, a bank, a plantation and six hundred slaves in Jamaica. Meanwhile, obscure men were devising machines which made things more
rapidly than they could be made by hand. Villages were transformed into
towns, towns into great cities. On what had been the Tantamounts'
pasture and plowland, houses and factories were built. Under the grass of
their meadows, half-naked men hewed at the black and shining coal face.
The laden trucks were hauled by little boys and women. From Peru
the droppings of ten thousand generations of sea gulls were brought in
ships to enrich their fields. The corn grew thicker; the new mouths were
fed. And year by year the Tantamounts grew richer and richer and the
souls of the Black Prince's pious contemporaries continued, no doubt, to
writhe, unaided as they were by any acceptable sacrifice of the altar, in the
unquenchable fires of Purgatory. The money that might, if suitably
applied, have shortened their term among the flames served, among other
things, to call into existence a model of the Papal Chancellery in Pall
Mall.

The interior of Tantamount House is as nobly Roman as its façade.
Round a central quadrangle run two tiers of open arcades with an attic,

lit by small square windows, above. But instead of being left open to the sky, the quadrangle is covered by a glass roof, which converts it into an immense hall rising the whole height of the building. With its arcades and gallery it makes a very noble room—but too large, too public, too much like a swimming bath or a roller-skating rink to be much lived in. Tonight, however, it was justifying its existence. Lady Edward Tantamount was giving one of her musical parties. The floor was crowded with seated guests and in the hollow architectural space above them the music intricately pulsed—Bach's Suite in B minor, for flute and strings.

Young Tolley conducted with his usual inimitable grace, bending in swanlike undulations from the loins, and tracing luscious arabesques on the air with his waving arms, as though he were dancing to the music. A dozen anonymous fiddlers and 'cellists scraped at his bidding. And the great Pongileoni glueily kissed his flute. He blew across the mouth hole and a cylindrical air column vibrated; Bach's meditations filled the Roman quadrangle. In the opening *largo* John Sebastian had, with the help of Pongileoni's snout and the air column, made a statement: There are grand things in the world, noble things; there are men born kingly; there are real conquerors, intrinsic lords of the earth. But of an earth that is, oh! complex and multitudinous, he had gone on to reflect in the fugal allegro. You seem to have found the truth; clear, definite, unmistakable, it is announced by the violins; you have it, you triumphantly hold it. But it slips out of your grasp to present itself in a new aspect among the 'cellos and yet again in terms of Pongileoni's vibrating air column. The parts live their separate lives; they touch, their paths cross, they combine for a moment to create a seemingly final and perfected harmony, only to break apart again. Each is always alone and separate and individual. "I am I," asserts the violin; "the world revolves round me." "Round me," calls the 'cello. "Round me," the flute insists. And all are equally right and equally wrong; and none of them will listen to the others.

In the human fugue there are eighteen hundred million parts. The resultant noise means something perhaps to the statistician, nothing to the artist. It is only by considering one or two parts at a time that the artist can understand anything. Here, for example, is one particular part; and John Sebastian puts the case. The Rondeau begins, exquisitely and simply melodious, almost a folk song. It is a young girl singing to herself of love, in solitude, tenderly mournful. A young girl singing among the hills, with the clouds drifting overhead. But solitary as one of the floating clouds, a poet had been listening to her song. The thoughts that it provoked in him are the Sarabande that follows the Rondeau. His is a slow and lovely meditation on the beauty (in spite of squalor and stupidity), the profound goodness (in spite of all the evil), the oneness (in spite of such bewildering diversity) of the world. It is a beauty, a goodness, a unity that no intellectual research can discover, that analysis dispels, but of whose reality the spirit is from time to time suddenly and overwhelmingly convinced. A girl singing to herself under the clouds suffices to create the certitude. Even a fine morning is enough. Is it illusion or the revelation of profoundest truth? Who knows? Pongileoni blew, the fiddlers drew their rosined horsehair across the stretched intestines of lambs; through the long Sarabande the poet slowly meditated his lovely and consoling certitude.

*   *   *

Two flights up, between the *piano nobile* and the servants' quarters under the roof, Lord Edward Tantamount was busy in his laboratory. Lord Edward preferred to work at night. He found the daylight hours disagreeably noisy. Breakfasting at half-past one, he would walk for an hour or two in the afternoon and return to read or write till lunchtime at eight. At nine or half-past he would do some practical work with his assistant, and when that was over they would sit down to work on the great book or to discussion of its problems. At one, Lord Edward had his supper, and at about four or five he would go to bed.

Diminished and in fragments the B minor Suite came floating up from the great hall to the ears of the two men in the laboratory. They were too busy to realize that they were hearing it.

"Forceps," said Lord Edward to his assistant. He had a very deep voice, indistinct and without, so to speak, a clearly defined contour. "A furry voice," his daughter Lucy had called it, when she was a child.

Illidge handed him the fine bright instrument. Lord Edward made a deep noise that signified thanks and turned back with the forceps to the anesthetized newt that lay stretched out on the diminutive operating table. Illidge watched him critically, and approved. The Old Man was doing the job extraordinarily well. Illidge was always astonished by Lord Edward's skill. You would never have expected a huge, lumbering creature like the Old Man to be so exquisitely neat. His big hands could do the finest work; it was a pleasure to watch them.

"There!" said Lord Edward at last and straightened himself up as far as his rheumatically bent back would allow him. "I think that's all right, don't you?"

Illidge nodded. "Perfectly all right," he said in an accent that had certainly not been formed in any of the ancient and expensive seats of learning. It hinted of Lancashire origins. He was a small man, with a boyish-looking freckled face and red hair.

The newt began to wake up. Illidge put it away in a place of safety. The animal had no tail; it had lost that eight days ago, and tonight the little bud of regenerated tissue which would normally have grown into a new tail had been removed and grafted onto the stump of its amputated right foreleg. Transplanted to its new position, would the bud turn into a foreleg, or continue incongruously to grow as a tail? Their first experiment had been with a tailbud only just formed; it had duly turned into a leg. In the next, they had given the bud time to grow to a considerable size before they transplanted it; it had proved too far committed to tailhood to be able to adapt itself to the new conditions; they had manufactured a monster with a tail where an arm should have been. Tonight they were experimenting on a bud of intermediate age.

Lord Edward took a pipe out of his pocket and began to fill it, looking meditatively meanwhile at the newt. "Interesting to see what happens this time," he said in his profound indistinct voice. "I should think we must be just about on the borderline between . . ." He left the sentence unfinished: it was always difficult for him to find the words to express his meaning. "The bud will have a difficult choice."

"To be or not to be," said Illidge facetiously, and started to laugh; but seeing that Lord Edward showed no signs of having been amused, he checked himself. Almost put his foot in it again. He felt annoyed with himself and also, unreasonably, with the Old Man.

Lord Edward filled his pipe. "Tail becomes leg," he said meditatively. "What's the mechanism? Chemical peculiarities in the neighboring . . .? It can't obviously be the blood. Or do you suppose it has something to do with the electric tension? It does vary, of course, in different parts of the body. Though why we don't all just vaguely proliferate like cancers . . . Growing in a definite shape is very unlikely, when you come to think of it. Very mysterious and . . ." His voice trailed off into a deep and husky murmur.

Illidge listened disapprovingly. When the Old Man started off like this about the major and fundamental problems of biology, you never knew where he'd be getting to. Why, as likely as not he'd begin talking about God. It really made one blush. He was determined to prevent anything so discreditable happening this time. "The next step with these newts," he said in his most briskly practical tone, "is to tinker with the nervous system and see whether that has any influence on the grafts. Suppose, for example, we excised a piece of the spine . . ."

But Lord Edward was not listening to his assistant. He had taken his pipe out of his mouth, he had lifted his head and at the same time slightly cocked it on one side. He was frowning, as though making an effort to seize and remember something. He raised his hand in a gesture that commanded silence; Illidge interrupted himself in the middle of his sentence and also listened. A pattern of melody faintly traced itself upon the silence.

"Bach?" said Lord Edward in a whisper.

Pongileoni's blowing and the scraping of the anonymous fiddlers had shaken the air in the great hall, had set the glass of the windows looking onto it vibrating; and this in turn had shaken the air in Lord Edward's apartment on the further side. The shaking air rattled Lord Edward's *membrana tympani*; the interlocked *malleus, incus* and stirrup bones were set in motion so as to agitate the membrane of the oval window and raise an infinitesimal storm in the fluid of the labyrinth. The hairy endings of the auditory nerve shuddered like weeds in a rough sea; a vast number of obscure miracles were performed in the brain, and Lord Edward ecstatically whispered "Bach!" He smiled with pleasure, his eyes lit up. The young girl was singing to herself in solitude under the floating clouds. And then the cloud-solitary philosopher began poetically to meditate. "We must really go downstairs and listen," said Lord Edward. He got up. "Come," he said. "Work can wait. One doesn't hear this sort of thing every night."

"But what about clothes," said Illidge doubtfully. "I can't come down like this." He looked down at himself. It had been a cheap suit at the best of times. Age had not improved it.

"Oh, that doesn't matter." A dog with the smell of rabbits in his nostrils could hardly have shown a more indecent eagerness than Lord Edward at the sound of Pongileoni's flute. He took his assistant's arm and hurried him out of the door, and along the corridor toward the stairs. "It's just a little party," he went on. "I seem to remember my wife having said . . . Quite informal. And besides," he added, inventing new excuses to justify the violence of his musical appetite, "we can just slip in without . . . Nobody will notice."

Illidge had his doubts. "I'm afraid it's not a very small party," he began; he had seen the motors arriving.

"Never mind, never mind," interrupted Lord Edward, lusting irrepressibly for Bach.

Illidge abandoned himself. He would look like a horrible fool, he reflected, in his shiny blue-serge suit. But perhaps, on second thoughts, it was better to appear in shiny blue—straight from the laboratory, after all, and under the protection of the master of the house (himself in a tweed jacket), than in that old and, as he had perceived during previous excursions into Lady Edward's luscious world, deplorably shoddy and ill-made

evening suit of his. It was better to be totally different from the rich and
smart—a visitor from another intellectual planet—than a fourth-rate and
snobbish imitator. Dressed in blue, one might be stared at as an oddity;
in badly cut black (like a waiter) one was contemptuously ignored, one
was despised for trying without success to be what one obviously wasn't.

Illidge braced himself to play the part of the Martian visitor with
firmness, even assertively.

Their entrance was even more embarrassingly conspicuous than Illidge
had anticipated. The great staircase at Tantamount House comes down
from the first floor in two branches which join, like a pair of equal rivers,
to precipitate themselves in a single architectural cataract of Verona marble
into the hall. It debouches under the arcades, in the center of one of the
sides of the covered quadrangle, opposite the vestibule and the front
door. Coming in from the street, one looks across the hall and sees through
the central arch of the opposite arcade the wide stairs and shining balustrades climbing up to a landing on which a Venus by Canova, the pride
of the third marquess's collection, stands pedestaled in an alcove, screen-
ing with a modest but coquettish gesture of her two hands, or rather failing to screen, her marble charms. It was at the foot of this triumphal
slope of marble that Lady Edward had posted the orchestra; her guests
were seated in serried rows confronting it. When Illidge and Lord Edward
turned the corner in front of Canova's Venus, tiptoeing, as they approached
the music and the listening crowd, with steps ever more laboriously con-
spiratorial, they found themselves suddenly at the focus of a hundred pairs
of eyes. A gust of curiosity stirred the assembled guests. The apparition
from a world so different from theirs of this huge, bent old man, pipe-
smoking and tweed-jacketed, seemed strangely portentous. He had a certain air of the skeleton in the cupboard—broken loose; or of one of those
monsters which haunt the palaces of only the best and most aristocratic
families. The Beastie of Glamis, the Minotaur itself could hardly have
aroused more interest than did Lord Edward. Lorgnons were raised, there
was a general craning to left and right, as people tried to look round the
well-fed obstacles in front of them. Becoming suddenly aware of so many
inquisitive glances, Lord Edward took fright. A consciousness of social
sin possessed him; he took his pipe out of his mouth and put it away,
still smoking, into the pocket of his jacket. He halted irresolutely. Flight
or advance? He turned this way and that, pivoting his whole bent body
from the hips with a curious swinging motion, like the slow ponderous
balancing of a camel's neck. For a moment he wanted to retreat. But
love of Bach was stronger than his terrors. He was the bear whom the smell
of molasses constrains in spite of all his fears to visit the hunters' camp;
the lover who is ready to face an armed and outraged husband and the

divorce court for the sake of an hour in his mistress's arms. He went forward, tiptoeing down the stairs more conspiratorially than ever—Guy Fawkes discovered, but yet irrationally hoping that he might escape notice by acting as though the Gunpowder Plot were still unrolling itself according to plan. Illidge followed him. His face had gone very red with the embarrassment of the first moment; but in spite of this embarrassment, or rather because of it, he came downstairs after Lord Edward with a kind of swagger, one hand in his pocket, a smile on his lips. He turned his eyes coolly this way and that over the crowd. The expression on his face was one of contemptuous amusement. Too busy being the Martian to look where he was going, Illidge suddenly missed his footing on this unfamiliarly regal staircase with its inordinate treads and dwarfishly low risers. His foot slipped, he staggered wildly on the brink of a fall, waving his arms, to come to rest, however, still miraculously on his feet, some two or three steps lower down. He resumed his descent with such dignity as he could muster up. He felt exceedingly angry; he hated Lady Edward's guests one and all, without exception.

*　　*　　*

Pongileoni surpassed himself in the final Badinerie. Euclidean axioms made holiday with the formulae of elementary statics. Arithmetic held a wild saturnalian kermesse; algebra cut capers. The music came to an end in an orgy of mathematical merrymaking. There was applause. Tolley bowed, with all his usual grace; Pongileoni bowed, even the anonymous fiddlers bowed. The audience pushed back its chairs and got up. Torrents of pent-up chatter broke lose.

*　　*　　*

"Strange," said Mrs. Betterton, "strange that a great artist should be such a cynic." Burlap on cynicism was uplifting and Mrs. Betterton liked to be uplifted. Uplifting too on greatness, not to mention art. "For you must admit," she added, "John Bidlake *is* a great artist."

Burlap nodded slowly. He did not look directly at Mrs. Betterton, but kept his eyes averted and downcast as though he were addressing some little personage invisible to everyone but himself, standing to one side of her—his private demon, perhaps, an emanation from himself, a little Doppelgänger. He was a man of middle height with a stoop and a rather slouching gait. His hair was dark, thick and curly, with a natural tonsure as big as a medal showing pink on the crown of his head. His gray eyes were very deeply set, his nose and chin pronounced but well shaped, his mouth full lipped and rather wide. A mixture, according to old Bidlake, who was a caricaturist in words as well as with the pencil, of a movie villain and St. Anthony of Padua by a painter of the baroque, of a card-sharping Lothario and a rapturous devotee.

"Yes, a great artist," he agreed, "but not one of the greatest." He spoke slowly, ruminatively, as though he were talking to himself. All his conversation was a dialogue with himself or that little *Doppelgänger* which stood invisibly to one side of the people he was supposed to be talking to; Burlap was unceasingly and exclusively self-conscious. "Not one of the greatest," he repeated slowly. As it happened, he had just been writing an article about the subject matter of art for next week's number of the *Literary World*. "Precisely because of that cynicism." Should he quote himself? he wondered.

"How true that is!" Mrs. Betterton's applause exploded perhaps a little prematurely; her enthusiasm was always on the boil. She clasped her hands together. "*How true!*" She looked at Burlap's averted face and thought it so spiritual, so beautiful in its way.

"How can a cynic be a great artist?" Burlap went on, having decided that he'd spout his own article at her and take the risk of her recognizing it in print next Thursday. And even if she did recognize it, that wouldn't efface the personal impression he'd made by spouting it. "Though why you want to make an impression," a mocking devil had put in, "unless it's because she's rich and useful, goodness knows!" The devil was pitchforked back to where he came from. "One has responsibilities," an angel hastily explained. "The lamp mustn't be hidden under a bushel. One must let it shine, especially on people of good will." Mrs. Betterton was on the side of the angels; her loyalty should be confirmed. "A great artist," he went on aloud, "is a man who synthesizes all experience. The cynic sets out by denying half the facts—the fact of the soul, the fact of ideals, the fact of God. And yet we're aware of spiritual facts just as directly and indubitably as we're aware of physical facts."

"Of course, of course!" exclaimed Mrs. Betterton.

"It's absurd to deny either class of facts." "Absurd to deny me," said the demon, poking out his head into Burlap's consciousness.

"Absurd!"

"The cynic confines himself to only half the world of possible experience. Less than half. For there are more spiritual than bodily experiences."

"Infinitely more!"

"He may handle his limited subject matter very well. Bidlake, I grant you, does. Extraordinarily well. He has all the sheer ability of the most consummate artists. Or had, at any rate."

"Had," Mrs. Betterton sighed. "When I first knew him." The implication was that it was her influence that had made him paint so well.

"But he's always applied his powers to something small. What he synthesizes in his art was limited, comparatively unimportant."

"That's what I always told him," said Mrs. Betterton, reinterpreting those youthful arguments about Pre-Raphaelitism in a new and, for her own reputation, favorable light. "Consider Burne-Jones, I used to say." The memory of John Bidlake's huge and Rabelaisian laughter reverberated in her ears. "Not that Burne-Jones was a particularly good painter," she hastened to add. ("He painted," John Bidlake had said—and how shocked she had been, how deeply offended!—"as though he had never seen a pair of buttocks in the whole of his life.") "But his subjects were noble. If you had *his* dreams, I used to tell John Bidlake, if you had *his* ideals, you'd be a *really* great artist."

Burlap nodded, smiling his agreement. Yes, she's on the side of the angels, he was thinking; she needs encouraging. One has a responsibility. The demon winked. There was something in his smile, Mrs. Betterton reflected, that reminded one of a Leonardo or a Sodoma—something mysterious, subtle, inward.

"Though, mind you," he said regurgitating his article slowly, phrase by phrase, "the subject doesn't make the work of art. Whittier and Longfellow were fairly stuffed with *Great Thoughts*. But what they wrote was very small poetry."

"How true!"

"The only generalization one can risk is that the greatest works of art have had great subjects; and that works with small subjects, however accomplished, are never so good as . . ."

"There's Walter," said Mrs. Betterton, interrupting him. "Wandering like an unlaid ghost. Walter!"

At the sound of his name, Walter turned. The Betterton—good Lord! And Burlap! He assumed a smile. But Mrs. B. and his colleague on the *Literary World* were among the last people he wanted at this moment to see.

"We were just discussing greatness in art," Mrs. Betterton explained. "Mr. Burlap was saying such *profound* things."

She began to reproduce the profundities for Walter's benefit.

*   *   *

Mrs. Betterton had been shaken off. Walter was free to continue his search. And at last he found what he was looking for. Lucy Tantamount

had just emerged from the dining room and was standing under the
arcades, glancing in indecision this way and that. Against the mourning
of her dress the skin was luminously white. A bunch of gardenias was
pinned to her bodice. She raised a hand to touch her smooth black
hair, and the emerald of her ring shot a green signal to him across the
room. Critically, with a kind of cold intellectual hatred, Walter looked
at her and wondered why he loved. Why? There was no reason, no justification. All the reasons were against his loving her.

Suddenly she moved, she walked out of sight. Walter followed. Passing
the entrance to the dining room, he noticed Burlap, no longer the
anchorite, drinking champagne and being talked to by the Comtesse
d'Exergillod. Gosh! thought Walter, remembering his own experiences
with Molly d'Exergillod. "But Burlap probably adores her. He would . . .
He . . ." But there she was again, talking—damnation!—with General
Knoyle. Walter hung about at a little distance, waiting impatiently for an
opportunity to address her.

Turning her head, Lucy caught sight of him. She beckoned and called
his name. He pretended to be surprised and delightfully astonished.

"I hope you've not forgotten our appointment," he said.

"Do I ever forget? Except occasionally on purpose," she qualified with
a little laugh. She turned to the General. "Walter and I are going
to see your stepson this evening," she announced in the tone and with
the smile which one employs when one talks to people about those who
are dear to them. But between Spandrell and his stepfather the quarrel,
she knew very well, was mortal. Lucy had inherited all her mother's fondness for the deliberate social blunder and with it a touch of her father's
detached scientific curiosity. She enjoyed experimenting, not with frogs
and guinea pigs, but with human beings. You did unexpected things to
people, you put them in curious situations and waited to see what would
happen. It was the method of Darwin and Pasteur.

What happened in this case was that General Knoyle's face became
extremely red. "I haven't seen him for some time," he said stiffly.

"Good," she said to herself. "He's reacting."

"But he's such good company," she said aloud.

The General grew redder and frowned. What he hadn't done for that
boy! And how ungratefully the boy had responded, how abominably he
had behaved! Getting himself kicked out of every job the General had
wangled him into. A waster, an idler; drinking and drabbing; making his
mother miserable, sponging on her, disgracing the family name. And the
insolence of the fellow, the things he had ventured to say the last time

they had met and, as usual, had a scene together! The General was never likely to forget being called "an impotent old fumbler."

"And so intelligent," Lucy was saying. With an inward smile she remembered Spandrell's summary of his stepfather's career. "Superannuated from Harrow," it began, "passed out from Sandhurst at the bottom of the list, he had a most distinguished career in the Army, rising during the War to a high post in the Military Intelligence Department." The way he rolled out this anticipated obituary was really magnificent. He was the *Times* made audible. And then his remarks on Military Intelligence in general! "If you look up 'Intelligence' in the new volumes of the *Encyclopedia Britannica*," he had said, "you'll find it classified under the following three heads: Intelligence, Human; Intelligence, Animal; Intelligence, Military. My stepfather's a perfect specimen of Intelligence, Military."

"So intelligent," Lucy repeated.

"Some people think so, I know," said General Knoyle very stiffly. "But personally . . ." He cleared his throat with violence. That was *his* personal opinion.

*   *   *

Two footmen let Lucy and Walter out, obsequiously automatic. Closing the door, one winked to the other significantly. For an instant, the machines revealed themselves disquietingly as human beings.

Walter gave the address of Sbisa's restaurant to the taxi driver and stepped into the enclosed darkness of the cab. Lucy had already settled into her corner.

Meanwhile, in the dining room, Molly d'Exergillod was still talking. She prided herself on her conversation. Conversation was in the family. Her mother had been one of the celebrated Miss Geoghegans of Dublin. Her father was that Mr. Justice Brabant, so well known for his table talk and his witticisms from the bench. Moreover she had married into conversation. D'Exergillod had been a disciple of Robert de Montesquieu and had won the distinction of being mentioned in *Sodome et Gomorrhe* by Marcel Proust. Molly would have had to be a talker by marriage, if she had not already been one by birth. Nature and environment had conspired to make her a professional athlete of the tongue. Like all conscientious professionals, she was not content to be merely talented. She was industrious, she worked hard to develop her native powers. Malicious friends said that she could be heard practicing her paradoxes in bed, before she got up in the morning. She herself admitted that she kept diaries in which she recorded, as well as the complicated history of her own feelings and sensations, every trope and anecdote and witticism that caught her fancy. Did she refresh her memory with a glance at these chronicles each time she dressed to go out to dinner? The same friends who had heard her practicing in bed had also found her, like an examinee the night before his ordeal, laboriously mugging up Jean Cocteau's epigrams about art and Mr. Birrell's after-dinner stories and W. B. Yeats's anecdotes about George Moore and what Charlie Chaplin had said to and of her last time she was in Hollywood. Like all professional talkers Molly was very economical with her wit and wisdom. There are not enough *bons mots* in existence to provide any industrious conversationalist with a new stock for every social occasion. Though extensive, Molly's repertory was, like that of other more celebrated talkers, limited. A good housewife, she knew how to hash up the conversational remains of last night's dinner to furnish out this morning's lunch. Monday's funeral baked meats did service for Tuesday's wedding.

To Denis Burlap she was at this moment serving up the talk that had already been listened to with such appreciation by Lady Benger's lunch party, by the week-enders at Gobley, by Tommy Fitton, who was one of her young men, and Vladimir Pavloff, who was another, by the American Ambassador and Baron Benito Cohen. The talk turned on Molly's favorite topic.

"Do you know what Jean said about me?" she was saying (Jean was her husband). "Do you?" she repeated insistently, for she had a curious habit of demanding answers to merely rhetorical questions. She leaned toward Burlap, offering dark eyes, teeth, a décolleté.

Burlap duly replied that he didn't know.

"He said that I wasn't quite human. More like an elemental than a woman. A sort of fairy. Do you think it's a compliment or an insult?"

"That depends on one's tastes," said Burlap, making his face look arch and subtle as though he had said something rather daring, witty and at the same time profound.

"But I don't feel that it's even true," Molly went on. "I don't strike myself as at all elemental or fairylike. I've always considered myself a perfectly simple, straightforward child of nature. A sort of peasant, really." At this point in Molly's performance all her other auditors had burst into laughing protestation. Baron Benito Cohen had vehemently declared that she was "one of Nature'th Roman Empreththeth."

Burlap's reaction was unexpectedly different from that of the others. He wagged his head, he smiled with a faraway, whimsical sort of expression. "Yes," he said, "I think that's true. A child of nature, *malgré tout.* You wear disguises, but the simple genuine person shows through."

Molly was delighted by what she felt was the highest compliment Burlap could pay her. She had been equally delighted by the others' denials of her peasanthood. Denial had been *their* highest compliment. The flattering intention, the interest in her personality were the things that mattered. About the actual opinions of her admirers she cared little.

Burlap, meanwhile, was developing Rousseau's antithesis between the Man and the Citizen. She cut him short and brought the conversation back to the original theme.

"Human beings and fairies—I think it's a very good classification, don't you?" She leaned forward with offered face and bosom, intimately. "Don't you?" she repeated the rhetorical question.

"Perhaps." Burlap was annoyed at having been interrupted.

"The ordinary human—yes, let's admit it—all too human being on the one hand. And the elemental on the other. The one so attached and involved and sentimental—I'm terribly sentimental, I may say." ("About ath thentimental ath the Thirenth in the Odyththey," had been Baron Benito's classical comment.) "The other, the elemental, quite free and apart from things, like a cat; coming and going—and going just as lightheartedly as it came; charming, but never charmed; making other people feel, but never really feeling itself. Oh, I envy them their free airiness."

"You might as well envy a balloon," said Burlap, gravely. He was always on the side of the heart.

"But they have such fun."

"They haven't got enough feelings to have fun with. That's what I should have thought."

"Enough to have fun," she qualified; "but perhaps not enough to be happy. Certainly not enough to be unhappy. That's where they're so enviable. Particularly if they're intelligent. Take Philip Quarles, for example. There's a fairy if ever there was one." She launched into her regular description of Philip. "Zoologist of fiction," "learnedly elfish," "a scientific Puck" were a few of her phrases. But the best of them had slipped her memory. Desperately she hunted it, but it eluded her. Her Theophrastan portrait had to go out into the world, robbed this time of its most brilliantly effective passage, and a little marred as a whole by Molly's consciousness of the loss and her desperate efforts, as she poured forth, to make it good. "Whereas his wife," she concluded, rather painfully aware that Burlap had not smiled as frequently as he should have done, "is quite the opposite of a fairy. Neither elfish, nor learned, nor particularly intelligent." Molly smiled rather patronizingly. "A man like Philip must find her a little inadequate sometimes, to say the least." The smile persisted, a smile now of self-satisfaction. Philip had had a *faible* for her, still had. He wrote such amusing letters, almost as amusing as her own. (*"Quand je veux briller dans le monde,"* Molly was fond of quoting her husband's compliments, *"je cite des phrases de tes lettres."*) Poor Elinor! "A little bit of a bore sometimes," Molly went on. "But mind you, a most charming creature. I've known her since we were children together. Charming, but not exactly a Hypatia." Too much of a fool even to realize that Philip was bound to be attracted by a woman of his own mental stature, a woman he could talk to on equal terms. Too much of a fool to notice, when she had brought them together, how thrilled he had been. Too much of a fool to be jealous. Molly had felt the absence of jealousy as a bit of an insult. Not that she ever gave *real* cause for jealousy. She didn't sleep with husbands; she only talked to them. Still, they *did* do a lot of talking; there was no doubt of that. And wives *had* been jealous. Elinor's ingenuous confidingness had piqued her into being more than ordinarily gracious to Philip. But he had started to go round the world before much conversation had taken place. The talk, she anticipated, would be agreeably renewed on his return. Poor Elinor, she thought pityingly. Her feelings might have been a little less Christian, if she had realized that poor Elinor had noticed the admiring look in Philip's eye even before Molly had noticed it herself, and, noticing, had conscientiously proceeded to act the part of dragoman and go-between. Not that she had much hope or fear that Molly would achieve the transforming miracle. One does not fall very desperately in love with a loud-speaker, however pretty, however firmly plump (for Philip's tastes were rather old fashioned), however attractively callipygous. Her only hope was that the passions aroused by the plumpness and prettiness would be so very inadequately satisfied by the talking (for talk was all, according to report, that Molly ever conceded) that poor Philip would be reduced to a state of rage and misery most conducive to good writing.

"But of course," Molly went on, "intelligence ought never to marry intelligence. That's why Jean is always threatening to divorce me. He says I'm too stimulating. *"Tu ne m'ennuies pas assez,"* he says; and that what he needs is *une femme sédative.* And I believe he's really right. Philip Quarles has been wise. Imagine an intelligent fairy of a man like Philip married to an equally fairyish intelligent woman—Lucy Tantamount, for example. It would be a disaster, don't you think?"

"Lucy'd be rather a disaster for any man, wouldn't she, fairy or no fairy?"

"No, I must say, I like Lucy." Molly turned to her inner storehouse of Theophrastan phrases. "I like the way she floats through life instead of trudging. I like the way she flits from flower to flower—which is perhaps a rather too botanical and poetical description of Bentley and Jim Conklin and poor Reggie Tantamount and Maurice Spandrell and Tom Trivet and Poniatovsky and that young Frenchman who writes plays, what *is* his name? and the various others one has forgotten or never heard about." Burlap smiled; they all smiled at this passage. "Anyhow, she flits. Doing a good deal of damage to the flowers, I must admit." Burlap smiled again. "But getting nothing but fun out of it herself. I must say, I rather envy her. I wish I were a fairy and could float."

"She has much more reason to envy you," said Burlap, looking deep, subtle and Christian once more, and wagging his head.

"Envy me for being unhappy?"

"Who's unhappy?" asked Lady Edward breaking in on them at this moment. "Good evening, Mr. Burlap," she went on without waiting for an answer. Burlap told her how much he had enjoyed the music.

"We were just talking about Lucy," said Molly d'Exergillod, interrupting him. "Agreeing that she was like a fairy. So light and detached."

"Fairy!" repeated Lady Edward, emphatically rolling the "r" far back in her throat. "She's like a leprechaun. You've no idea, Mr. Burlap, how hard it is to bring up a leprechaun." Lady Edward shook her head. "She used really to frighten me sometimes."

"Did she?" said Molly. "But I should have thought you were a bit of a fairy yourself, Lady Edward."

"A bit," Lady Edward admitted. "But never to the point of being a leprechaun."

"Well?" said Lucy, as Walter sat down beside her in the cab. She seemed to be uttering a kind of challenge. "Well?"

The cab started. He lifted her hand and kissed it. It was his answer to her challenge. "I love you. That's all."

"Do you, Walter?" She turned toward him and, taking his face between her two hands, looked at him intently in the half darkness. "Do you?" she repeated; and as she spoke, she shook her head slowly and smiled. Then, leaning forward, she kissed him on the mouth. Walter put his arms round her; but she disengaged herself from the embrace. "No, no," she protested and dropped back into her corner. "No."

He obeyed her and drew away. There was a silence. Her perfume was of gardenias; sweet and tropical, the perfumed symbol of her being enveloped him. "I ought to have insisted," he was thinking. "Brutally. Kissed her again and again. Compelled her to love me. Why didn't I? Why?" He didn't know. Nor why she had kissed him, unless it was just provocatively, to make him desire her more violently, to make him more hopelessly her slave. Nor why, knowing this, he still loved her. Why, why? he kept repeating to himself. And echoing his thoughts out loud her voice suddenly spoke.

"Why do you love me?" she asked from her corner.

He opened his eyes. They were passing a street lamp. Through the window of the moving cab the light of it fell on her face. It stood out for a moment palely against the darkness, then dropped back into invisibility—a pale mask that had seen everything before and whose expression was one of amused detachment and a hard, rather weary langour. "I was just wondering," Walter answered. "And wishing I didn't."

"I might say the same, you know. You're not particularly amusing when you're like this."

How tiresome, she reflected, these men who imagined that nobody had ever been in love before! All the same, she liked him. He was attractive. No, "attractive" wasn't the word. Attractive, as a possible lover, was just what he wasn't. "Appealing" was more like it. An appealing lover? It wasn't exactly her style. But she liked him. There was something very nice about him. Besides, he was clever, he could be a pleasant companion. And tiresome as it was, his love sickness did at least make him very faithful. That, for Lucy, was important. She was afraid of loneliness and needed her cavalier servants in constant attendance. Walter attended with a doglike fidelity. But why did he look so like a whipped dog sometimes? So abject. What a fool! She felt suddenly annoyed by his abjection.

"Well, Walter," she said mockingly, laying her hand on his, "why don't you talk to me?"

He did not reply.

"Or is mum the word?" Her fingers brushed electrically along the back of his hand and closed round his wrist. "Where's your pulse?" she asked after a moment. "I can't feel it anywhere." She groped over the soft skin for the throbbing of the artery. He felt the touch of her finger tips, light and thrilling and rather cold against his wrist. "I don't believe you've got a pulse," she said. "I believe your blood stagnates." The tone of her voice was contemptuous. What a fool! she was thinking. What an abject fool! "Just stagnates," she repeated and suddenly, with sudden malice, she drove her sharp file-pointed nails into his flesh. Walter cried out in surprise and pain. "You deserved it," she said and laughed in his face.

He seized her by the shoulders and began to kiss her, savagely. Anger had quickened his desire; his kisses were a vengeance. Lucy shut her eyes and abandoned herself unresistingly, limply. Little premonitions of pleasure shot with a kind of panic flutter, like fluttering moths, through her skin. And suddenly sharp fingers seemed to pluck *pizzicato*, at the fiddle strings of her nerves; Walter could feel her whole body starting involuntarily within his arms, starting as though it had been suddenly hurt. Kissing her, he found himself wondering if she had expected him to react in this way to her provocation, if she had hoped he would. He took her slender neck in his two hands. His thumbs were on her windpipe. He pressed gently. "One day," he said between his clenched teeth. "I shall strangle you."

Lucy only laughed. He bent forward and kissed her laughing mouth. The touch of his lips against her own sent a thin, sharp sensation that was almost pain running unbearably through her. The panic moth wings fluttered over her body. She hadn't expected such fierce and savage ardors from Walter. She was agreeably surprised.

The taxi turned into Soho Square, slowed down, came to a halt. They had arrived. Walter let fall his hands and drew away from her.

She opened her eyes and looked at him. "Well?" she asked challengingly, for the second time that evening. There was a moment's silence.

"Lucy," he said, "let's go somewhere else. Not here; not this horrible place. Somewhere where we can be alone." His voice trembled, his eyes were imploring. The fierceness had gone out of his desire; it had become abject again, doglike. "Let's tell the man to drive on," he begged.

She smiled and shook her head. Why did he implore like that? Why was he so abject? The fool, the whipped dog!

"Please, *please!*" he begged. But he should have commanded. He should simply have ordered the man to drive on, and taken her in his arms again.

"Impossible," said Lucy and stepped out of the cab. If he behaved like a whipped dog, he could be treated like one.

Walter followed her, abject and miserable.

Sbisa himself received them on the threshold. He bowed, he waved his fat white hands, and his expanding smile raised a succession of waves in the flesh of his enormous cheeks. When Lucy arrived, the consumption of champagne tended to rise. She was an honored guest.

"Mr. Spandrell here?" she asked. "And Mr. and Mrs. Rampion?"

"Oo yez, oo yez," old Sbisa repeated with Neapolitan, almost oriental emphasis. The implication was that they were not only there, but that if it had been in his power, he would have provided two of each of them for her benefit. "And you? Quaite well, quaite well, I hope? Sooch lobster we have tonight, sooch lobster . . ." Still talking, he ushered them into the restaurant.

II

"What I complain of," said Mark Rampion, "is the horrible unwholesome tameness of our world."

Mary Rampion laughed wholeheartedly from the depths of her lungs. It was a laugh one could not hear without wishing to laugh oneself. "You wouldn't say that," she said, "if you'd been your wife instead of you. Tame? I could tell you something about tameness."

There was certainly nothing very tame about Mark Rampion's appearance. His profile was steep, with a hooked fierce nose like a cutting instrument and a pointed chin. The eyes were blue and piercing, and the very fine hair, a little on the reddish side of golden, fluttered up at every movement, every breath of wind, like wisps of blown flame.

"Well, you're not exactly a sheep either," said Rampion. "But two people aren't the world. I was talking about the world, not us. It's tame, I say. Like one of those horrible big gelded cats."

"Did you find the War so tame?" asked Spandrell, speaking from the half darkness outside the little world of pink-tinged lamplight in which their table stood. He sat leaning backward, his chair tilted on its hind legs against the wall.

"Even the War," said Rampion. "It was a domesticated outrage. People didn't go and fight because their blood was up. They went because they were told to; they went because they were good citizens. 'Man is a fighting animal,' as your stepfather is so fond of saying in his speeches. But what I complain of is that he's a domestic animal."

"And getting more domestic every day," said Mary Rampion, who shared her husband's opinions—or perhaps it would be truer to say, shared most of his feelings and, consciously or unconsciously, borrowed his opinions when she wanted to express them. "It's factories, it's Christianity, it's science, it's respectability, it's our education," she explained. "They weigh on the modern soul. They suck the life out of it. They . . ."

"Oh, for God's sake shut up!" said Rampion.

"But isn't that what you say?"

"What I say is what *I* say. It becomes quite different when you say it."

The expression of irritation which had appeared on Mary Rampion's face cleared away. She laughed. "Ah, well," she said good-humoredly, "ratiocination was never my strongest point. But you might be a little more polite about it in public."

"I don't suffer fools gladly."

"You'll suffer one very painfully, if you're not careful," she menaced laughingly.

"If you'd like to throw a plate at him," said Spandrell, pushing one over to her as he spoke, "don't mind me."

Mary thanked him. "It would do him good," she said. "He gets so bumptious."

"And it would do you no harm," retorted Rampion, "if I gave you a black eye in return."

"You just try. I'll take you on with one hand tied behind my back."

They all burst out laughing.

"I put my money on Mary," said Spandrell, tilting back his chair. Smiling with a pleasure which he would have found it hard to explain, he looked from one to the other—from the thin, fierce, indomitable little man to the big golden woman. Each separately was good; but together, as a couple, they were better still. Without realizing it, he had quite suddenly begun to feel happy.

"We'll have it out one of these days," said Rampion and laid his hand for a moment on hers. It was a delicate hand, sensitive and expressive. An aristocrat's hand if ever there was one, thought Spandrell. And hers, so blunt and strong and honest, was a peasant's. And yet by birth it was Rampion who was the peasant and she the aristocrat. Which only showed what nonsense the genealogists talked.

"Ten rounds," Rampion went on. "No gloves." He turned to Spandrell. "You ought to get married, you know," he said.

Spandrell's happiness suddenly collapsed. It was as though he had come with a jolt to his senses. He felt almost angry with himself. What business had *he* to go and sentimentalize over a happy couple?

"I can't box," he answered; and Rampion detected a bitterness in his jocularity, an inward hardening.

"No, seriously," he said, trying to make out the expression on the other's face. But Spandrell's head was in the shadow, and the light of the interposed lamp on the table between them dazzled him.

"Yes, seriously," echoed Mary. "You ought. You'd be a changed man."

Spandrell uttered a brief and snorting laugh and, letting his chair fall back onto its four legs, leaned forward across the table. Pushing aside his coffee cup and his half-emptied liqueur glass, he planted his elbows on the table and his chin in his hands. His face came into the light of the rosy lamp. Like a gargoyle, Mary thought, a gargoyle in a pink boudoir. There was one on Notre Dame in just that attitude, leaning forward with his demon's face between his claws. Only the gargoyle was a comic devil, so extravagantly diabolical that you couldn't take his devilishness very seriously. Spandrell was a real person, not a caricature; that was why his face was so much more sinister and tragical. It was a gaunt face. Cheekbone and jaw showed in hard outline through the tight skin. The gray eyes were deeply set. In the cadaverous mask only the mouth was fleshy—a wide mouth, with lips that stood out from the skin like two thick weals.

"When he smiles," Lucy Tantamount had once said of him, "it's like an appendicitis operation with ironical corners." The red scar was sensual, but firm at the same time and determined, as was the round chin below. There were lines round the eyes and at the corners of his lips. The thick brown hair had begun to retreat from the forehead.

"He might be fifty, to look at him," Mary Rampion was thinking. "And yet, what is his age?" She made calculations and decided that he couldn't be more than thirty-two or thirty-three. Just the right age for settling down.

"A changed man," she repeated.

"But I don't particularly want to be changed."

Mark Rampion nodded. "Yes, that's the trouble with you, Spandrell. You like stewing in your disgusting suppurating juice. You don't want to be made healthy. You enjoy your unwholesomeness. You're proud of it, even."

"Marriage would be the cure," persisted Mary, indefatigably enthusiastic in the cause of the sacrament to which she herself owed all her life and happiness.

"Unless, of course, it merely destroyed the wife," said Rampion. "He might infect her with his own gangrene."

Spandrell threw back his head and laughed profoundly, but, as was his custom, almost inaudibly, a muted explosion. "Admirable!" he said. "Admirable! The first really good argument in favor of matrimony I ever heard. Almost thou persuadest me, Rampion. I've never actually carried it as far as marriage."

"Carried what?" asked Rampion, frowning a little. He disliked the other's rather melodramatically cynical way of talking. So damned pleased with his naughtiness! Like a stupid child, really.

"The process of infection. I'd always stopped this side of the registry office. But I'll cross the threshold next time." He drank some more brandy. "I'm like Socrates," he went on. "I'm divinely appointed to corrupt the youth, the female youth more particularly. I have a mission to educate them in the way they shouldn't go." He threw back his head to emit that voiceless laugh of his. Rampion looked at him distastefully. So theatrical. It was as though the man were overacting in order to convince himself he was there at all.

"But if you only knew what marriage could mean," Mary earnestly put in. "If you only knew . . ."

"But, my dear woman, of course he knows," Rampion interrupted with impatience.

"We've been married more than fifteen years now," she went on, the missionary spirit strong within her. "And I assure you . . ."

"I wouldn't waste my breath, if I were you."

Mary glanced inquiringly at her husband. Wherever human relationships were concerned, she had an absolute trust in Rampion's judgment. Through those labyrinths he threaded his way with a sure tact which she could only envy, not imitate. "He can smell people's souls," she used to say of him. She herself had but an indifferent nose for souls. Wisely then, she allowed herself to be guided by him. She glanced at him. Rampion was staring into his coffee cup. His forehead was puckered into a frown; he had evidently spoken in earnest. "Oh, very well," she said and lit another cigarette.

Spandrell looked from one to the other almost triumphantly. "I have a regular technique with the young ones," he went on in the same too-cynical manner. Mary shut her eyes and thought of the time when she and Rampion had been young.

*   *   *

"A regular technique," Spandrell repeated. "One chooses them unhappy, or dissatisfied, or wanting to go on the stage, or trying to write for the magazines and being rejected and consequently thinking they're âmes incomprises." He was boastfully generalizing from the case of poor little Harriet Watkins. If he had just baldly recounted his affair with Harriet, it wouldn't have sounded such a very grand exploit. Harriet was such a pathetic, helpless little creature; anybody could have done her down. But generalized like this, as though her case was only one of hundreds, told in a language of the cookery book ("one chooses them un-happy"—it was one of Mrs. Beeton's recipes), the history sounded, he thought, most cynically impressive. "And one starts by being very, very kind, and so wise, and perfectly pure, an elder brother, in fact. And they think one's really wonderful, because, of course, they've never met anybody who wasn't just a city man, with city ideas and city ambitions. Simply wonderful, because one knows all about art and has met all the celebrities and doesn't think exclusively about money and in terms of the morning paper. And they're a little in awe of one too," he added remembering little Harriet's expression of scared admiration; "one's so unrespectable and yet so high class, so at ease and at home among the great works and the great men, so wicked but so extraordinarily good, so learned, so well traveled, so brilliantly cosmopolitan and West End (have you ever heard a suburban talking of the West End?), like that gentleman with the order of the Golden Fleece in the advertisements for De Reszke cigarettes. Yes, they're in awe of one; but at the same time they adore. One's so understanding, one knows so much about life in general and their souls in particular, and one isn't a bit flirtatious or saucy like ordinary men, not a bit. They feel they could trust one absolutely; and so they can, for the first weeks. One has to get them used to the trap; quite tame and trusting, trained not to shy at an occasional brotherly pat on the back or an occasional chaste uncle-ish kiss on the forehead. And meanwhile one coaxes out their little confidences, one makes them talk about love, one talks about it oneself in a man-to-man sort of way, as though they were one's own age and as sadly disillusioned and bitterly knowing as oneself—which they find terribly shocking (though of course they don't say so), but oh, so thrilling, so enormously flattering. They simply love you for that. Well then, finally, when the moment seems ripe and they're thoroughly domesticated and no more frightened, one stages the dénouement. Tea in one's rooms—one's got them thoroughly used to coming with absolute impunity to one's rooms—and they're going to go out to dinner with one, so that there's no hurry. The twilight deepens, one talks disillusionedly and yet feelingly about the amorous mysteries, one produces cocktails—very strong—and goes on talking so that they ingurgitate them absent-mindedly without reflection. And sitting on the floor at their feet, one begins very gently stroking their ankles in an entirely platonic way, still talking about amorous philosophy, as though one were quite unconscious of what one's hands were doing. If that's not resented and the cocktails have done their work, the rest shouldn't be difficult. So at least I've always found." Spandrell helped himself to more brandy and drank. "But it's then, when they've become one's mistress, that the fun really begins. It's then one deploys all one's Socratic talents. One develops their little temperaments, one domesticates them—still so wisely and sweetly and patiently—to every outrage of sensuality. It can be done, you know; the more easily, the more innocent they are. They can be brought in perfect ingenuousness to the most astonishing pitch of depravity."

"I've no doubt they can," said Mary indignantly. "But what's the point of doing it?"

"It's an amusement," said Spandrell with theatrical cynicism. "It passes the time and relieves the tedium."

"And above all," Mark Rampion went on, without looking up from his coffee cup, "above all it's a vengeance. It's a way of getting one's own back on women, it's a way of punishing them for being women and so attractive, it's a way of expressing one's hatred of them and of what they represent, it's a way of expressing one's hatred of oneself. The trouble with you, Spandrell," he went on, suddenly and accusingly raising his bright pale eyes to the other's face, "is that you really hate yourself. You hate the very source of your life, its ultimate basis—for there's no denying it, sex *is* fundamental. And you hate it, *hate* it."

"Me?" It was a novel accusation. Spandrell was accustomed to hearing himself blamed for his excessive love of women and the sensual pleasures.

"Not only you. All these people." With a jerk of his head he indicated the other diners. "And all the respectable ones too. Practically everyone. It's the disease of modern man. I call it Jesus's diseases on the analogy of Bright's disease. Or rather Jesus's and Newton's disease; for the scientists are as much responsible as the Christians. So are the big businessmen, for that matter. It's Jesus's and Newton's and Henry Ford's disease. Between them, the three have pretty well killed us. Ripped the life out of our bodies and stuffed us with hatred."

Rampion was full of his subject. He had been busy all day on a drawing that symbolically illustrated it. Jesus, in the loincloth of the execution morning, and an overalled surgeon were represented, scalpel in hand, one on either side of an operating table, on which, foreshortened, the soles of his feet presented to the spectator, lay crucified a half-dissected man. From the horrible wound in his belly escaped a coil of entrails which, falling to the earth, mingled with those of the gashed and bleeding woman lying in the foreground, to be transformed by an allegorical metamorphosis into a whole people of living snakes. In the background receded a landscape of hills, dotted with black collieries and chimneys. On one side of the picture, behind the figure of Jesus, two angels—the spiritual product of the vivisectors' mutilations—were trying to rise on their outspread wings. Vainly, for their feet were entangled in the coils of the serpents. For all their efforts, they could not leave the earth.

"Jesus and the scientists are vivisecting us," he went on, thinking of his picture. "Hacking our bodies to bits."

"But after all, why not?" objected Spandrell. "Perhaps they're meant to be vivisected. The fact of shame is significant. We feel spontaneously ashamed of the body and its activities. That's a sign of the body's absolute and natural inferiority."

"Absolute and natural rubbish!" said Rampion indignantly. "Shame isn't spontaneous, to begin with. It's artificial, it's acquired. You can make people ashamed of anything. Agonizingly ashamed of wearing brown boots with a black coat, or speaking with the wrong sort of accent, or having a drop at the end of their noses. Of absolutely anything, including the body and its functions. But that particular shame's just as artificial as any other. The Christians invented it, just as the tailors in Savile Row invented the shame of wearing brown boots with a black coat. There was precious little of it before Christian times. Look at the Greeks, the Etruscans."

The antique names transported Mary back to the moors above Stanton. He was just the same. Stronger now, that was all. How ill he had looked that day! She had felt ashamed of being healthy and rich. Had she loved him then as much as she loved him now?

Spandrell had lifted a long and bony hand. "I know, I know. Noble and nude and antique. But I believe they're entirely a modern invention, those Swedish-drill pagans of ours. We trot them out whenever we want to bait the Christians. But did they ever exist? I have my doubts."

"But look at their art," put in Mary, thinking of the paintings at Tarquinia. She had seen them a second time with Mark—really seen them on that occasion.

"Yes, and look at ours," retorted Spandrell. "When the Royal Academy sculpture room is dug up three thousand years hence, they'll say that twentieth-century Londoners wore fig leaves, suckled their babies in public and embraced one another in the parks, stark naked."

"I only wish they did," said Rampion.

"But they don't. And then—leaving this question of shame on one side for the moment—what about asceticism as the preliminary condition of the mystical experience?"

Rampion brought his hands together with a clap and, leaning back in his chair, turned up his eyes. "Oh, my sacred aunt!" he said. "So it's come to that, has it? Mystical experience and asceticism. The fornicator's hatred of life in a new form."

"But seriously . . ." the other began.

"No, seriously, have you read Anatole France's *Thaïs?*"

Spandrell shook his head.

"Read it," said Rampion. "Read it. It's elementary, of course. A boy's book. But one mustn't grow up without having read all the boy's books. Read it and then come and talk to me again about asceticism and mystical experiences."

"I'll read it," said Spandrell. "Meanwhile, all I wanted to say is that there are certain states of consciousness known to ascetics that are unknown to people who aren't ascetics."

"No doubt. And if you treat your body in the way nature meant you to, as an equal, you attain to states of consciousness unknown to the vivisecting ascetics."

"But the states of the vivisectors are better than the states of the indulgers."

"In other words, lunatics are better than sane men. Which I deny. The sane, harmonious, Greek man gets as much as he can of both sets of states. He's not such a fool as to want to kill part of himself. He strikes a balance. It isn't easy of course; it's even damnably difficult. The forces to be reconciled are intrinsically hostile. The conscious soul resents the activities of the unconscious, physical, instinctive part of the total being. The life of the one is the other's death and vice versa. But the sane man at least tries to strike a balance. The Christians, who weren't sane, told people that they'd got to throw half of themselves in the wastepaper basket. And now the scientists and businessmen come and tell us that we must throw away half of what the Christians left us. But I don't want to be three-quarters dead. I prefer to be alive, entirely alive. It's time there was a revolt in favor of life and wholeness."

"But from your point of view," said Spandrell, "I should have thought this epoch needed no reforming. It's the golden age of guzzling, sport and promiscuous lovemaking."

"But if you knew what a puritan Mark really was!" Mary Rampion laughed. "What a regular old puritan!"

"Not a puritan," said her husband. "Merely sane. You're like everyone else," he went on, addressing himself to Spandrell. "You seem to imagine that the cold, modern, civilized lasciviousness is the same as the healthy —what shall I call it?—phallism (that gives the religious quality of the old way of life; you've read the *Acharnians?*)—phallism, then, of the ancients."

Spandrell groaned and shook his head. "Spare us the Swedish exercises."

"But it *isn't* the same," the other went on. "It's just Christianity turned inside out. The ascetic contempt for the body expressed in a different way. Contempt and hatred. That was what I was saying just now. You hate yourselves; you hate life. Your only alternatives are promiscuity or asceticism. Two forms of death. Why, the Christians themselves understood phallism a great deal better than this godless generation. What's that phrase in the marriage service? 'With my body I thee worship.' Worshiping with the body—that's the genuine phallism. And if you imagine it has anything to do with the unimpassioned civilized promiscuity of our advanced young people, you're very much mistaken indeed."

"Oh, I'm quite ready to admit the deathliness of our civilized entertainments," Spandrell answered. "There's a certain smell," he went on, speaking in snatches between sucks at the half-smoked cigar he was trying to relight, "of cheap scent . . . and stale unwashedness . . . I often think . . . the atmosphere of hell . . . must be composed of it." He threw the match away. "But the other alternative—there's surely no death about that. No death in Jesus or St. Francis, for example."

"In spots," said Rampion. "They were dead in spots. Very much alive in others, I quite agree. But they simply left half of existence out of account. No, no, they won't do. It's time people stopped talking about them. I'm tired of Jesus and Francis, terribly tired of them."

"Well then, the poets," said Spandrell. "You can't say that Shelley's a corpse."

"Shelley?" exclaimed Rampion. "Don't talk to me of Shelley." He shook his head emphatically. "No, no. There's something very dreadful about Shelley. Not human, not a man. A mixture between a fairy and a white slug."

"Come, come," Spandrell protested.

"Oh, exquisite and all that. But what a bloodless kind of slime inside! No blood, no real bones and bowels. Only pulp and a white juice. And oh, that dreadful lie in the soul! The way he was always pretending for the benefit of himself and everybody else that the world wasn't really the world, but either heaven or hell. And that going to bed with women wasn't really going to bed with them, but just two angels holding hands. Ugh! Think of his treatment of women—shocking, really shocking. The women loved it of course—for a little. It made them feel so spiritual—that is, until it made them feel like committing suicide. So spiritual. And all the time he was just a young schoolboy with a sensual itch like anybody else's, but persuading himself and other people that he was Dante and Beatrice rolled into one, only much more so. Dreadful, dreadful! The only excuse is that, I suppose, he couldn't help it. He wasn't born a man; he was only a kind of fairy slug with the sexual appetites of a schoolboy. And then, think of that awful incapacity to call a spade a spade. He always had to pretend it was an angel's harp or a platonic imagination. Do you remember the Ode to the Skylark? 'Hail to thee, blithe spirit! Bird thou never wert!' " Rampion recited with a ludicrous parody of an elocutionist's "expression." "Just pretending, just lying to himself, as usual. The lark couldn't be allowed to be a mere bird, with blood and feathers and a nest and an appetite for caterpillars. Oh no! That wasn't nearly poetical enough, that was much too coarse. It had to be a disembodied spirit. Bloodless, boneless. A kind of ethereal flying slug. It was only to be expected. Shelley was a kind of flying slug himself; and, after all, nobody can really write about anything except himself. If you're a slug, you must write about slugs, even though your subject is supposed to be a skylark. But I wish to God," Rampion added, with a sudden burst of comically extravagant fury, "I wish to God the bird had had as much sense as those sparrows in the book of Tobit and dropped a good large mess in his eye. It would have served him damned well right for saying it wasn't a bird. Blithe spirit, indeed! Blithe spirit!"

III

In LUCY's neighborhood life always tended to become exceedingly public. The more the merrier was her principle; or if "merrier" were too strong a word, at least the noisier, the more tumultuously distracting. Within five minutes of her arrival, the corner in which Spandrell and the Rampions had been sitting all evening in the privacy of quiet conversation was invaded and in a twinkling overrun by a loud and alcoholic party from the inner room. Cuthbert Arkwright was the noisiest and the most drunken—on principle and for the love of art as well as for that of alcohol. He had an idea that by bawling and behaving offensively, he was defending art against the Philistines. Tipsy, he felt himself arrayed on the side of the angels, of Baudelaire, of Edgar Allan Poe, of De Quincey, against the dull unspiritual mob. And if he boasted of his fornications, it was because respectable people had thought Blake a madman, because Bowdler had edited Shakespeare, and the author of Madame Bovary had been prosecuted, because when one asked for the Earl of Rochester's Sodom at the Bodleian, the librarians wouldn't give it unless one had a certificate that one was engaged on bona-fide literary research. He made his living, and in the process convinced himself that he was serving the arts, by printing limited and expensive editions of the more scabrous specimens of the native and foreign literatures. Blond, beef-red, with green and bulging eyes, his large face shining, he approached vociferating greetings. Willie Weaver jauntily followed, a little man perpetually smiling, spectacles astride his long nose, bubbling with good humor and an inexhaustible verbiage. Behind him, his twin in height and also spectacled, but gray, dim, shrunken and silent, came Peter Slipe.

"They look like the advertisement of a patent medicine," said Spandrell as they approached. "Slipe's the patient before, Weaver's the same after one bottle, and Cuthbert Arkwright illustrates the appalling results of taking the complete cure."

Lucy was still laughing at the joke when Cuthbert took her hand. "Lucy!" he shouted. "My angel! But why in heaven's name do you always write in pencil? I simply cannot read what you write. It's a mere chance that I'm here tonight."

So she'd written to tell him to meet her here, thought Walter. That vulgar, stupid lout.

Willie Weaver was shaking hands with Mary Rampion and Mark. "I had no idea I was to meet the great," he said. "Not to mention the fair." He bowed toward Mary, who broke into loud and masculine laughter. Willie Weaver was rather pleased than offended. "Positively the Mermaid Tavern!" he went on.

"Still busy with the bric-a-brac?" asked Spandrell, leaning across the table to address Peter Slipe, who had taken the seat next to Walter's. Peter was an Assyriologist employed at the British Museum.

"But why in pencil, why in pencil?" Cuthbert was roaring.

"I get my fingers so dirty when I use a pen."

"I'll kiss the ink away," protested Cuthbert, and bending over the hand he was still holding, he began to kiss the thin fingers.

Lucy laughed. "I think I'd rather buy a stylo," she said.

Walter looked on in misery. Was it possible? A gross and odious clown like that?

"Ungrateful!" said Cuthbert. "But I simply must talk to Rampion."

And turning away, he gave Rampion a clap on the shoulder and simultaneously waved his other hand at Mary.

"What an agape!" Willie Weaver simmered on, like a teakettle. The spout was now turned toward Lucy, "what a symposium! What a——" he hesitated for a moment in search of the right, the truly staggering phrase—"what Athenian enlargements! What a more than Platonic orgy!"

"What *is* an Athenian enlargement?" asked Lucy.

Willie sat down and began to explain. "Enlargements, I mean, by contrast with our bourgeois and Pecksniffian smuggeries . . ."

"Why don't you give me something of yours to print?" Cuthbert was persuasively inquiring.

Rampion looked at him with distaste. "Do you think I'm ambitious of having my books sold in the rubber shops?"

"They'd be in good company," said Spandrell. "*The Works of Aristotle* . . ." Cuthbert roared in protest.

"Compare an eminent Victorian with an eminent Periclean," said Willie Weaver. He smiled; he was happy and eloquent.

On Peter Slipe the burgundy had acted as a depressant, not a stimulant. The wine had only enhanced his native dimness and melancholy.

"What about Beatrice?" he said to Walter, "Beatrice Gilray?" he hiccoughed and tried to pretend that he had coughed. "I suppose you see her often, now that she works on the *Literary World*."

Walter saw her three times a week and always found her well.

"Give her my love, when you see her next," said Slipe.

"The stertorous borborygms of the dyspeptic Carlyle!" declaimed Willie Weaver, and beamed through his spectacles. The *mot*, he flattered himself, could hardly have been more exquisitely *juste*. He gave the little cough which was his invariable comment on the best of his phrases. "I would laugh, I would applaud," the little cough might be interpreted, "but modesty forbids."

"Stertorous what?" asked Lucy. "Do remember that I've never been educated."

"Warbling your native woodnotes wild!" said Willie. "May I help myself to some of that noble brandy? The blushful Hippocrene."

"She treated me badly, extremely badly." Peter Slipe was plaintive. "But I don't want her to think that I bear her any grudge."

Willie Weaver smacked his lips over the brandy. "Solid joys and liquid pleasures none but Zion's children know," he misquoted and repeated his little cough of self-satisfaction.

"The trouble with Cuthbert," Spandrell was saying, "is that he's never quite learned to distinguish art from pornography."

"Of course," continued Peter Slipe, "she had a perfect right to do what she liked with her own house. But to turn me out at such short notice."

At another time Walter would have been delighted to listen to poor little Slipe's version of that curious story. But with Lucy on his other hand, he found it difficult to take much interest.

"But I sometimes wonder if the Victorians didn't have more fun than we did," she was saying. "The more prohibitions, the greater the fun.

If you want to see people drinking with real enjoyment, you must go to America. Victorian England was dry in every department. For example, there was a nineteenth amendment about love. They must have made it as enthusiastically as the Americans drink whisky. I don't know that I really believe in Athenian enlargements—that is, if we're one of them."

"You prefer Pecksniff to Alcibiades," Willie Weaver concluded.

Lucy shrugged her shoulders. "I've had no experience of Pecksniff."

"I don't know," Peter Slipe was saying, "whether you've ever been pecked by a goose."

"Been what?" asked Walter, recalling his attention.

"Been pecked by a goose."

"Never, that I can remember."

"It's a hard, dry sensation." Slipe jabbed the air with a tobacco-stained forefinger. "Beatrice is like that. She pecks; she enjoys pecking. But she can be very kind at the same time. She insists on being kind in her way, and she pecks if you don't like it. Pecking's part of the kindness; so I always found. I never objected. But why should she have turned me out of the house as though I were a criminal? And rooms are so difficult to find now. I had to stay in a boarding house for three weeks. The food . . ." He shuddered.

Walter could not help smiling.

"She must have been in a great hurry to install Burlap in your place."

"But why in such a hurry as all that?"

"When it's a case of off with the old love and on with the new . . ."

"But what has love to do with it?" asked Slipe. "In Beatrice's case."

"A great deal," Willie Weaver broke in. "Everything. These super-annuated virgins—always the most passionate."

"But she's never had a love affair in her life."

"Hence the violence," concluded Willie triumphantly. "Beatrice has a nigger sitting on the safety valve. And my wife assures me that her underclothes are positively Phrynean. That's most sinister."

"Perhaps she likes being well dressed," suggested Lucy.

Willie Weaver shook his head. The hypothesis was too simple.

"That woman's unconscious as a black hole." Willie hesitated a moment. "Full of batrachian grapplings in the dark," he concluded, and modestly coughed to commemorate his achievement.

Beatrice Gilray was mending a pink silk camisole. She was thirty-five, but seemed younger, or rather seemed ageless. Her skin was clear and fresh. From shallow and unwrinkled orbits the eyes looked out, shining. In a sharp, determined way her face was not unhandsome, but with something intrinsically rather comic about the shape and tilt of the nose, something slightly absurd about the bright beadiness of the eyes, the pouting mouth and round defiant chin. But one laughed with as well as at her; for the set of her lips was humorous and the expression of her round astonished eyes was mocking and mischievously inquisitive.

She stitched away. The clock ticked. The moving instant which, according to Sir Isaac Newton, separates the infinite past from the infinite future advanced inexorably through the dimension of time. Or, if Aristotle was right, a little more of the possible was every instant made real; the present stood still and drew into itself the future, as a man might suck forever at an unending piece of macaroni. Every now and then Beatrice actualized a potential yawn. In a basket by the fireplace a black she-cat lay on her side purring and suckling four blind and particolored kittens. The walls of the room were primrose yellow. On the top shelf of the bookcase the dust was thickening on the textbooks of Assyriology which she had bought when Peter Slipe was the tenant of her upper floor. A volume of Pascal's *Thoughts*, with pencil annotations by Burlap, lay open on the table. The clock continued to tick.

Suddenly the front door banged. Beatrice put down her pink silk camisole and sprang to her feet.

"Don't forget that you must drink your hot milk, Denis," she said, looking out into the hall. Her voice was clear, sharp and commanding.

Burlap hung up his coat and came to the door. "You oughtn't to have sat up for me," he said, with tender reproachfulness, giving her one of his grave and subtle Sodoma smiles.

"I had some work I simply had to get finished," Beatrice lied.

"Well, it was most awfully sweet of you." These pretty colloquialisms, with which Burlap liked to pepper his conversation, had for sensitive ears a most curious ring. "He talks slang," Mark Rampion once said, "as though he were a foreigner with a perfect command of English—but a foreigner's command. I don't know if you've ever heard an Indian calling anyone a 'jolly good sport.' Burlap's slang reminds me of that."

For Beatrice, however, that "awfully sweet" sounded entirely natural and un-alien. She flushed with a young-girlishly timid pleasure. But, "Come in and shut the door," she rapped out commandingly. Over that soft young timidity the outer shell was horny; there was a part of her being that pecked and was efficient. "Sit down there," she ordered; and while she was briskly busy over the milk jug, the saucepan, the gas ring, she asked him if he had enjoyed the party.

Burlap shook his head. "*Fascinatio nugacitatis*," he said. "*Fascinatio nugacitatis*." He had been ruminating the fascination of nugacity all the way from Piccadilly Circus.

Beatrice did not understand Latin; but she could see from his face that the words connoted disapproval. "Parties are rather a waste of time, aren't they?" she said.

Burlap nodded. "A waste of time," he echoed in his slow ruminant's voice, keeping his blank, preoccupied eyes fixed on the invisible demon standing a little to Beatrice's left. "One's forty, one has lived more than half one's life, the world is marvelous and mysterious. And yet one spends four hours chattering about nothing at Tantamount House. Why should triviality be so fascinating? Or is there something else besides the triviality that draws one? Is it some vague fantastic hope that one may meet the messianic person one's always been looking for, or hear the revealing word?" Burlap wagged his head as he spoke with a curious loose motion, as though the muscles of his neck were going limp. Beatrice was so familiar with the motion that she saw nothing strange in it any more. Waiting for the milk to boil, she listened admiringly, she watched him with a serious churchgoing face. A man whose excursions into the drawing rooms of the rich were episodes in a lifelong spiritual quest might justifiably be regarded as the equivalent of Sunday-morning church.

"All the same," Burlap added, glancing up at her with a sudden mischievous, guttersnipish grin, most startlingly unlike the Sodoma smile of a moment before, "the champagne and the caviar were really marvelous." It was the demon that had suddenly interrupted the angel at his philosophic ruminations. Burlap had allowed him to speak out loud. Why not? It amused him to be baffling. He looked at Beatrice.

Beatrice was duly baffled. "I'm sure they were," she said, readjusting her churchgoing face to make it harmonize with the grin. She laughed rather nervously and turned away to pour out the milk into a cup. "Here's your milk," she rapped out, taking refuge from her bafflement in officious command. "Mind you drink it while it's hot."

There was a long silence. Burlap sipped slowly at his steaming milk and, seated on a pouf in front of the empty fireplace, Beatrice waited, rather breathlessly, she hardly knew for what.

"You look like little Miss Muffet sitting on her tuffet," said Burlap at last.

Beatrice smiled. "Luckily there's no big spider."

"Thanks for the compliment, if it is one."

"Yes, it is," said Beatrice. That was the really delightful thing about Denis, she reflected: he was so trustworthy. Other men were liable to pounce on you and try to paw you about and kiss you. Dreadful that was, quite dreadful. Beatrice had never really got over the shock she received as a young girl, when her Aunt Maggie's brother-in-law, whom she had always looked up to as an uncle, had started pawing her about in a hansom. The incident so scared and disgusted her that when Tom Field, whom she really did like, asked her to marry him, she refused, just because he was a man, like that horrible Uncle Ben, and because she was so terrified of being made love to, she had such a panic fear of being touched. She was over thirty now and had never allowed anyone to touch her. The soft quivering little girl underneath the businesslike shell of her had often fallen in love. But the terror of being pawed about, of being even touched, had always been stronger than the love. At the first sign of danger, she had desperately pecked, she had hardened her shell, she had fled. Arrived in safety, the terrified little girl had drawn a long breath. Thank Heaven! But a little sigh of disappointment was always included in the big sigh of relief. She wished she hadn't been frightened; she wished that the happy relationship that had existed before the pawing could have gone on for-ever, indefinitely. Sometimes she was angry with herself; more often she thought there was something fundamentally wrong with love, something fundamentally dreadful about men. That was the wonderful thing about Denis Burlap; he was so reassuringly not a pouncer or a pawer. Beatrice could adore him without a qualm.

"Susan used to sit on poufs, like little Miss Muffett," Burlap resumed after a pause. His voice was melancholy. He had spent the last minutes in ruminating the theme of his dead wife. It was nearly two years now since Susan had been carried off in the influenza epidemic. Nearly two years; but the pain, he assured himself, had not diminished, the sense of loss had remained as overwhelming as ever. Susan, Susan, Susan—he had repeated the name to himself over and over again. He would never see her any more, even if he lived for a million years. A million years, a million years. Gulfs opened all round the words. "Or on the floor," he went on, reconstructing her image as vividly as he could. "I think she liked sitting on the floor best. Like a child." A child, a child, he repeated to himself. So young.

Beatrice sat in silence, looking into the empty grate. To have looked at Burlap, she felt, would have been indiscreet, indecent almost. Poor fellow! When she turned toward him at last, she saw that there were tears on his cheeks. The sight filled her with a sudden passion of maternal pity. "Like a child," he had said. But he was like a child himself. Like a poor unhappy child. Leaning forward she drew her fingers caressingly along the back of his limply hanging hand.

"Batrachian grapplings!" Lucy repeated and laughed. "That was a stroke of genius, Willie."

"All my strokes are strokes of genius," said Willie modestly. He acted himself; he was Willie Weaver in the celebrated role of Willie Weaver. He exploited artistically that love of eloquence, that passion for the rotund and reverberating phrase with which, more than three centuries too late, he had been born. In Shakespeare's youth he would have been a literary celebrity. Among his contemporaries, Willie's euphuisms only raised a laugh. But he enjoyed applause, even when it was derisive. Moreover, the laughter was never malicious; for Willie Weaver was so good-natured and obliging that everybody like him. It was to a hilariously approving audience that he played his part; and, feeling the approval through the hilarity, he played it for all it was worth. "All my strokes are strokes of genius." The remark was admirably in character. And perhaps true? Willie jested, but with a secret belief. "And mark my words," he added, "one of these days the batrachians will erump, they'll break out."

"But why batrachians?" asked Slipe. "Anything less like a batrachian than Beatrice . . ."

"And why should they break out?" put in Spandrell.

"Frogs don't peck." But Slipe's thin voice was drowned by Mary Rampion's.

"Because things do break out," she cried. "They do."

"Moral," Cuthbert concluded: "don't shut anything up. I never do."

"But perhaps the fun consists in breaking out," Lucy speculated.

"Perverse and paradoxical prohibitionist!"

"But obviously," Rampion was saying, "you get revolutions occurring inside as well as outside. It's poor against rich in the state. In the individual, it's the oppressed body and instincts against the intellect. The intellect's been exalted as the spiritual upper classes; the spiritual lower classes rebel."

"Hear, hear!" shouted Cuthbert, and banged the table.

Rampion frowned. He felt Cuthbert's approbation as a personal insult.

"I'm a counter-revolutionary," said Spandrell. "Put the spiritual lower classes in their place."

"Except in your own case, eh?" said Cuthbert grinning.

"Mayn't one theorize?"

"People have been forcibly putting them in their place for centuries," said Rampion; "and look at the result. You, among other things." He looked at Spandrell, who threw back his head and noiselessly laughed. "Look at the result," he repeated. "Inward personal revolution and consequent outward and social revolution."

"Come, come," said Willie Weaver. "You talk as though the thermidorian tumbrils were already rumbling. England still stands very much where it did."

"But what do you know of England and Englishmen?" Rampion retorted. "You've never been out of London or your class. Go to the North."

"God forbid!" Willie piously interjected.

"Go to the coal and iron country. Talk a little with the steel workers. It isn't revolution for a cause. It's revolution as an end in itself. Smashing for smashing's sake."

"Rather sympathetic it sounds," said Lucy.

"It's terrifying. It simply isn't human. Their humanity has all been squeezed out of them by civilized living, squeezed out by the weight of coal and iron. It won't be a rebellion of men. It'll be a revolution of elementals, monsters, prehuman monsters. And you just shut your eyes and pretend everything's too perfect."

"Think of the disproportion," Lord Edward was saying, as he smoked his pipe. "It's positively . . ." His voice failed. "Take coal, for example. Man's using a hundred and ten times as much as he used in 1800. But population's only two and a half times what it was. With other animals . . . Surely quite different. Consumption's proportionate to numbers."

Illidge objected. "But if animals can get more than they actually require to subsist, they take it, don't they? If there's been a battle or a plague, the hyenas and vultures take advantage of the abundance to overeat. Isn't it the same with us? Forests died in great quantities some millions of years ago. Man has unearthed their corpses, finds he can use them and is giving himself the luxury of a real good guzzle while the carrion lasts. When the supplies are exhausted, he'll go back to short rations, as the hyenas do in the intervals between wars and epidemics." Illidge spoke with gusto. Talking about human beings as though they were indistinguishable from maggots filled him with a peculiar satisfaction. "A coal field's discovered; oil's struck. Towns spring up, railways are built, ships come and go. To a long-lived observer on the moon, the swarming and crawling must look like the pullulation of ants and flies round a dead dog. Chilean niter, Mexican oil, Tunisian phosphates—at every discovery another scurrying of insects. One can imagine the comments of the lunar astronomers. 'These creatures have a remarkable and perhaps unique tropism toward fossilized carrion.'"

"Like ostriches," said Mary Rampion. "You live like ostriches."

"And not about revolutions only," said Spandrell, while Willie Weaver was heard to put in something about "strouthocamelian philosophies." "About all the important things that happen to be disagreeable. There was a time when people didn't go about pretending that death and sin

didn't exist. '*Au détour d'un sentier une charogne infâme,*'" he quoted.
"Baudelaire was the last poet of the Middle Ages as well as the first
modern. '*Et pourtant,*'" he went on, looking with a smile at Lucy and
raising his glass.

> Et pourtant vous serez semblable cette ordure,
> A cette horrible infection,
> Etoile de mes yeux, soleil de ma nature,
> Vous, mon ange et ma passion!

> Alors, ô ma beauté, dites à la vermine
> Qui vous mangera de baisers . . .

"My dear Spandrell!" Lucy held up her hand protestingly.

"Really too necrophilous!" said Willie Weaver.

"Always the same hatred of life," Rampion was thinking. "Different
kinds of death—the only alternatives." He looked observantly into
Spandrell's face.

"And when you come to think of it," Illidge was saying, "the time
it took to form the coal measures divided by the length of a human life
isn't so hugely different from the life of a sequoia divided by a generation
of decay bacteria."

Cuthbert looked at his watch. "But good God!" he shouted. "It's
twenty-five to one." He jumped up. "And I promised we'd put in an
appearance at Widdicombe's party. Peter, Willie! Quick march."

"But you can't go," protested Lucy. "Not so absurdly early."

"The call of duty," Willie Weaver explained. "Stern Daughter of the
Voice of God." He uttered his little cough of self-approbation.

"But it's ridiculous, it's not permissible." She looked from one to
other with a kind of angry anxiety. The dread of solitude was chronic
with her. And it was always possible, if one sat up another five minutes,
that something really amusing might happen. Besides, it was insufferable
that people should do things she didn't want them to do.

"And we too, I'm afraid," said Mary Rampion rising.

Thank heaven, thought Walter. He hoped that Spandrell would follow
the general example.

"But this is impossible!" cried Lucy. "Rampion, I simply cannot
allow it."

Mark Rampion only laughed. These professional sirens! he thought. She left him entirely cold; she repelled him. In desperation Lucy even appealed to the woman of the party.

"Mrs. Rampion, you *must* stay. Five minutes more. Only five minutes," she coaxed.

In vain. The waiter opened the side door. Furtively they slipped out into the darkness.

"Why *will* they insist on going?" asked Lucy, plaintively.

"Why will *we* insist on staying?" echoed Spandrell. Walter's heart sank; that meant the man didn't intend to go. "Surely, that's much more incomprehensible."

Utterly incomprehensible! On Walter the heat and alcohol were having their usual effects. He was feeling ill as well as miserable. What was the point of sitting on, hopelessly, in this poisonous air? Why not go home at once? Marjorie would be pleased.

"You, at least, are faithful, Walter." Lucy gave him a smile. He decided to postpone his departure. There was a silence.

*   *   *

Walter sat on the bed unlacing his shoes. He was wondering why he had not come three hours before, why he had ever gone out at all. He hated a crowd; alcohol disagreed with him and the twice-breathed air, the smell, the smoke of restaurants acted on him like a depressing poison. He had suffered to no purpose; except for those painful exasperating moments in the taxi, he had not been alone with Lucy the whole evening. The hours he had spent with her had been hours of boredom and impatience—endlessly long, minute after minute of torture. And the torture of desire and jealousy had been reinforced by the torture of self-conscious guilt. Every minute they lingered at Sbisa's, every minute among the revolutionaries, was a minute that retarded the consummation of his desire and that, increasing Marjorie's unhappiness, increased at the same time his own remorse and shame. It was after three when finally they left the club. Would she dismiss Spandrell and let him drive her home? He looked at her; his eyes were eloquent. He willed; he commanded.

"There'll be sandwiches and drinks at my house," said Lucy, when they were in the street.

"That's very welcome news," said Spandrell.

"Come along, Walter darling." She took his hand; she pressed it affectionately.

Walter shook his head. "I must go home." If misery could kill, he would have died there in the street.

"But you can't desert us now," she protested. "Now that you've got thus far, you really must see it through. Come along." She tugged at his hand.

"No, no." But what she said was true. He could hardly make Marjorie any more wretched than he had certainly done already. If she weren't there, he thought, if she were to die—a miscarriage, blood poisoning . . .

Spandrell looked at his watch. "Half-past three. The death rattle has almost started." Walter listened in horror; was the man reading his thoughts? "*Munie des conforts de notre sainte religion.* Your place is at the bedside. Walter. You can't go and leave the night to die like a dog in a ditch."

Like a dog in a ditch. The words were terrible; they condemned him. "I *must* go." He was firm, three hours too late. He walked away. In Oxford Street he found a taxi. Hoping, he knew vainly, to come home unobserved, he paid off the cab at Chalk Farm station and walked the last furlong to the door of the house in which he and Marjorie occupied the two upper floors. He had crept upstairs, he had opened the door with the precautions of a murderer. No sound from Marjorie's room. He undressed, he washed as though he were performing a dangerous operation. He turned out the light and got into bed. The darkness was utterly silent. He was safe.

"Walter!"

It was with the feelings of a condemned criminal when the warders come to wake him on the morning of his execution that he answered, putting an imitation of astonishment into his voice. "Are you awake, Marjorie?" He got up and walked, as though from the condemned cell to the scaffold, into her room.

"Do you want to make me die, Walter?"

Like a dog in a ditch, alone. He made as if to take her in his arms. Marjorie pushed him away. Her misery had momentarily turned to anger, her love to a kind of hatred and resentment. "Don't be a hypocrite on top of everything else," she said. "Why can't you tell me frankly that you hate me, that you'd like to get rid of me, that you'd be glad if I died? Why can't you be honest and tell me?"

"But why should I tell you what isn't true?" he protested.

"Are you going to tell me that you love me, then?" she asked sarcastically.

He almost believed it while he said so; and besides it was true, in a way.

"But I do, I do. This other thing's a kind of madness. I don't want to. I can't help it. If you knew how wretched I felt, what an unspeakable brute." All that he had ever suffered from thwarted desire, from remorse and shame and self-hatred, seemed to be crystallized by his words into a single agony. He suffered and he pitied his own sufferings. "If you knew, Marjorie." And suddenly something in his body seemed to break. An invisible hand took him by the throat, his eyes were blinded with tears and a power within him that was not himself shook his whole frame and wrenched from him, against his will, a muffled and hardly human cry.

At the sound of this dreadful sobbing in the darkness beside her, Marjorie's anger suddenly fell. She only knew that he was unhappy, that she loved him. She even felt remorse for her anger, for the bitter words she had spoken.

"Walter. My darling." She stretched out her hands; drew him down toward her. He lay there like a child in the consolation of her embrace.

* * *

Pink in her dressing gown like the tulips in the vases, Lucy lay propped on her elbow, reading. The couch was gray, the walls were hung with gray silk, the carpet was rose colored. In its gilded cage even the parrot was pink and gray. The door opened.

"Walter, darling! At last!" She threw down her book.

"Already. If you knew all the things I ought to be doing instead of being here." ("Do you promise?" Marjorie had asked. And he had answered, "I promise." But this last visit of explanation didn't count.)

The divan was wide. Lucy moved her feet toward the wall, making place for him to sit down. One of her red Turkish slippers fell.

"That tiresome manicure woman," she said, raising the bare foot a few inches so that it came into her line of sight. "She will put that horrible red stuff on my toe nails. They look like wounds."

Walter did not speak. His heart was violently beating. Like the warmth of a body transposed into another sensuous key, the scent of her gardenias enveloped him. There are hot perfumes and cold, stifling and fresh. Lucy's gardenias seemed to fill his throat and lungs with a tropical and sultry sweetness. On the gray silk of the couch, her foot was flowerlike and pale, like the pale fleshy buds of lotus flowers. The feet of Indian goddesses walking among their lotuses are themselves flowers. Time flowed in silence, but not to waste, as at ordinary moments. It was as though it flowed, pumped beat after beat by Walter's anxious heart, into some enclosed reservoir of experience to mount and mount behind the dam until at last, suddenly . . . Walter suddenly reached out and took her bare foot in his hand. Under the pressure of those silently accumulated seconds, the dam had broken. It was a long foot, long and narrow. His fingers closed round it. He bent down and kissed the instep.

"But, my dear Walter!" She laughed. "You're becoming quite oriental."

Walter said nothing, but kneeling on the ground beside the couch, he leaned over her. The face that bent to kiss her was set in a kind of desperate madness. The hands that touched her trembled. She shook her head; she shielded her face with her hand.

"No, no."

"But why not?"

"It wouldn't do," she said.

"Why not?"

"It would complicate things too much for you, to begin with."

"No, it wouldn't," said Walter. There were no complications. Marjorie had ceased to exist.

"Besides," Lucy went on, "you seem to forget me. I don't want to."

But his lips were soft, his hands touched lightly. The moth-winged premonitions of pleasure came flutteringly to life under his kisses and caresses. She shut her eyes. His caresses were like a drug, at once intoxicant and opiate. She had only to relax her will; the drug would possess her utterly. She would cease to be herself. She would become nothing but a skin of fluttering pleasure enclosing a void, a warm abysmal darkness.

"Lucy!" Her eyelids fluttered and shuddered under his lips. His hand was on her breast. "My sweetheart." She lay quite still, her eyes still closed.

A sudden and piercing shriek made both of them start, broad awake, out of their timelessness. It was as though a murder had been committed within a few feet of them, but on someone who found the process of being slaughtered rather a joke, as well as painful.

Lucy burst out laughing. "It's Polly."

Both turned toward the cage. His head cocked a little on one side, the bird was examining them out of one black and circular eye. And while they looked, a shutter of parchment skin passed like a temporary cataract across the bright expressionless regard and was withdrawn. The jocular martyr's dying shriek was once again repeated.

"You'll have to cover his cage with the cloth," said Lucy.

Walter turned back toward her and angrily began to kiss her. The parrot yelled again. Lucy's laughter redoubled.

"It's no good," she gasped. "He won't stop till you cover him."

The bird confirmed what she had said with another scream of mirthful agony. Feeling furious, outraged and a fool, Walter got up from his knees and crossed the room. At his approach the bird began to dance excitedly on its perch; its crest rose; the feathers of its head and neck stood apart from one another like the scales of a ripened fir cone. "Good morning," it said in a guttural ventriloquial voice, "good morning, Auntie, good morning, Auntie, good morning, Auntie. . . ." Walter unfolded the pink brocade that lay on the table near the cage and extinguished the creature. A last "Good morning, Auntie" came out from under the cloth. Then there was silence.

"He likes his little joke," said Lucy, as the parrot disappeared. She had lighted a cigarette.

Walter strode back across the room and without saying anything took the cigarette from between her fingers and threw it into the fireplace. Lucy raised her eyebrows, but he gave her no time to speak. Kneeling down again beside her, he began to kiss her, angrily.

"Walter," she protested. "No! What's come over you?" She tried to disengage herself, but he was surprisingly strong. "You're like a wild beast." His desire was dumb and savage. "Walter! I insist." Struck by an absurd idea, she suddenly laughed. "If you knew how like the movies you were! A great, huge, grinning close-up."

But ridicule was as unavailing as protest. And did she really desire it to be anything but unavailing? Why shouldn't she abandon herself? It was only rather humiliating to be carried away, to be compelled instead of to choose. Her pride, her will resisted him, resisted her own desire. But after all, why not? The drug was potent and delicious. Why not? She shut her eyes. But as she was hesitating, circumstances suddenly decided for her. There was a knock at the door. Lucy opened her eyes again. "I'm going to say come in," she whispered.

He scrambled to his feet and, as he did so, heard the knock repeated. "Come in!"

The door opened. "Mr. Illidge to see you, madam," said the maid.

Walter was standing by the window, as though profoundly interested in the delivery van drawn up in front of the opposite house.

"Show him up," said Lucy.

He turned round as the door closed behind the maid. His face was very pale, his lips were trembling.

"I quite forgot," she explained. "I asked him last night; this morning rather."

He averted his face and without saying a word crossed the room, opened the door and was gone.

"Walter!" she called after him, "Walter!" But he did not return.

On the stairs he met Illidge ascending behind the maid.

Walter responded to his greetings with a vague salute and hurried past. He could not trust himself to speak.

"Our friend Bidlake seemed to be in a great hurry," said Illidge, when the preliminary greetings were over. He felt exultantly certain that he had driven the other fellow away.

She observed the triumph on his face. Like a little ginger cock, she was thinking. "He'd forgotten something," she vaguely explained.

"Not himself, I hope," he questioned waggishly. And when she laughed, more at the fatuous masculinity of his expression than at his joke, he swelled with self-confidence and satisfaction. This social business was as easy as playing skittles. Feeling entirely at his ease, he stretched his legs, he looked round the room. Its richly sober elegance impressed him at once as the right thing. He sniffed the perfumed air appreciatively.

"What's under that mysterious red cloth there?" he asked, pointing at the mobled cage.

"That's a cockatoo," Lucy answered. "A cock-a-doodle-doo," she emended, breaking out into a sudden disquieting and inexplicable laughter.

There are confessable agonies, sufferings of which one can positively be proud. Of bereavement, of parting, of the sense of sin and the fear of death the poets have eloquently spoken. They command the world's sympathy. But there are also discreditable anguishes, no less excruciating than the others, but of which the sufferer dare not, cannot speak. The anguish of thwarted desire, for example. That was the anguish which Walter carried with him into the street. It was pain, anger, disappointment, shame, misery all in one. He felt as though his soul were dying in torture. And yet the cause was unavowable, low, even ludicrous. Suppose a friend were now to meet him and to ask why he looked so unhappy.

"I was making love to a woman when I was interrupted, first by the screaming of a cockatoo, then by the arrival of a visitor."

The comment would be enormous and derisive laughter. His confession would have been a smoking-room joke. And yet he could not be suffering more if he had lost his mother.

He wandered for an hour through the streets, in Regent's Park. The light gradually faded out of the white and misty afternoon; he became calmer. It was a lesson, he thought, a punishment; he had broken his promise. For his own good as well as for Marjorie's, never again. He looked at his watch and seeing that it was after seven turned homeward. He arrived at the house tired and determinedly repentant. Marjorie was sewing; the lamplight was bright on her thin fatigued face. She too was wearing a dressing gown. It was mauve and hideous; he had always thought her taste bad. The flat was pervaded with a smell of cooking. He hated kitchen smells, but that was yet another reason why he should be faithful. It was a question of honor and duty. It was not because he preferred gardenia to cabbage that he had a right to make Marjorie suffer.

"You're late," she said.

"There was a lot to do," Walter explained. "And I walked home." That at least was true. "How are you feeling?" He laid his hand on her shoulder and bent down. Dropping her sewing, Marjorie threw her hands round his neck. What a happiness, she was thinking, to have him again! Hers once more. What a comfort! But even as she pressed herself against him, she realized that she was once more betrayed. She broke away from him.

"Walter, how could you?"

The blood rushed to his face; but he tried to keep up the pretense. "How could I what?" he asked.

"You've been to see that woman again."

"But what are you talking about?" He knew it was useless; but he went on pretending all the same.

"It's no use lying." She got up so suddenly that her workbasket overturned and scattered its contents on the floor. Unheeding, she walked across the room. "Go away!" she cried, when he tried to follow her. Walter shrugged his shoulders and obeyed. "How could you?" she went on. "Coming home reeking of her perfume." So it was the gardenias. What a fool he was not to have foreseen. . . . "After all you said last night. How could you?"

"But if you'd let me explain," he protested in the tone of a victim— an exasperated victim.

"Explain why you lied," she said bitterly. "Explain why you broke your promise."

Her contemptuous anger evoked an answering anger in Walter. "Merely explain," he said with hard and dangerous politeness. What a bore she was with her scenes and jealousies! What an intolerable, infuriating bore!

"Merely go on lying," she mocked.

Again he shrugged his shoulders. "If you like to put it like that," he said politely.

"Just a despicable liar—that's what you are." And turning away from him, she covered her face with her hands and began to cry.

Walter was not touched. The sight of her heaving shoulders just exasperated and bored him. He looked at her with a cold and weary anger.

"Go away," she cried through her tears, "go away." She did not want him to be there, triumphing over her, while she cried. "Go away."

"Do you really want me to go?" he asked with the same cool, aggravating politeness.

"Yes, go, go."

"Very well," he said, and opening the door, he went.

At Camden Town he took a cab and was at Bruton Street just in time to find Lucy on the point of going out to dinner.

"You're coming out with me," he announced very calmly.

"Alas!"

"Yes, you are."

She looked at him curiously and he looked back at her, with steady eyes, smiling, with a queer look of amused triumph and invincible obstinate power, which she had never seen on his face before. "All right," she said at last and, ringing for the maid, "Telephone to Lady Sturlett, will you," she ordered, "and say I'm sorry, but I've got a very bad headache and can't come tonight." The maid retired. "Well, are you grateful now?"

"I'm beginning to be," he answered.

"Beginning?" She assumed indignation. "I like your damned impertinence."

"I know you do," said Walter, laughing. And she did. That night Lucy became his mistress.

IV

THERE was no breeze except the wind of the ship's own speed; and that was like a blast from the engine room. Stretched in their chairs Philip and Elinor watched the gradual diminution against the sky of a jagged island of bare red rock. From the deck above came the sound of people playing shuffleboard. Walking on principle or for an appetite, their fellow passengers passed and repassed with the predictable regularity of comets.

"The way people take exercise," said Elinor in a tone positively of resentment; it made her hot to look at them. "Even in the Red Sea."

"It explains the British Empire," he said.

There was a silence. Burned brown, burned scarlet, the young men on leave passed laughing, four to a girl. Sun-dried and curry-pickled veterans of the East strolled by with acrimonious words, about the Reforms and the cost of Indian living, upon their lips. Two female missionaries padded past in a rarely broken silence. The French globe-trotters reacted to the oppressively imperial atmosphere by talking very loud. The Indian students slapped one another on the back like stage subalterns in the days of Charley's Aunt; and the slang they talked would have seemed old fashioned in a preparatory school.

Time flowed. The island vanished; the air was if possible hotter.

"I'm worried about Walter," said Elinor, who had been ruminating the contents of that last batch of letters she had received from her brother just before leaving Bombay.

"He's a fool," Philip answered. "After committing one stupidity with that Carling female, he ought to have had the sense not to start again with Lucy."

"Of course he ought," said Elinor irritably. "But the point is that he hasn't had the sense. It's a question of thinking of a remedy."

"Well, it's no good thinking about it five thousand miles away."

"I'm afraid he may suddenly rush off and leave poor Marjorie in the lurch. With a baby on the way, too. She's a dreary woman. But he mustn't be allowed to treat her like that."

"No," Philip agreed. There was a pause. The sparse procession of exercise lovers marched past. "I've been thinking," he went on reflectively, "that it would make an excellent subject."

"What?"

"This business of Walter's."

"You don't propose to exploit poor Walter as copy?" Elinor was indignant. "No really, I won't have it. Botanizing on his grave—or at any rate his heart."

"But of course not!" Philip protested.

"*Mais je vous assure*," one of the Frenchwomen was shouting so loud that he had to abandon the attempt to continue, "*aux Galeries Lafayette les camisoles en flanelle pour enfant ne coûtent que . . .*"

"*Camisoles en flanelle*," repeated Philip. "Phew!"

"But seriously, Phil . . ."

"But, my dear, I never intended to use more than the situation. The young man who tries to make his life rhyme with his idealizing books and imagines he's having a great spiritual love, only to discover that he's got hold of a bore whom he really doesn't like at all."

"Poor Marjorie! But why can't she keep her face better powdered? And those artistic beads and earrings she always wears . . ."

"And who then goes down like a ninepin," Philip continued, "at the mere sight of a Siren. It's the situation that appealed to me. Not the individuals. After all, there are plenty of other nice young men besides Walter. And Marjorie isn't the only bore. Nor Lucy the only man-eater."

"Well, if it's only the situation," Elinor grudgingly allowed.

"And besides," he went on, "it isn't written and probably never will be. So there's nothing to get upset about, I assure you."

"All right. I won't say anything more till I see the book."

There was another pause.

". . . such a wonderful time at Gulmerg last summer," the young lady was saying to her four attentive cavaliers. "There was golf, and dancing every evening, and . . ."

"And in any case," Philip began again in a meditative tone, "the situation would only be a kind of . . ."

"*Mais je lui ai dit, les hommes sont comme ça. Une jeune fille bien élevée doit . . .*"

". . . a kind of excuse," bawled Philip. "It's like trying to talk in the parrot house at the Zoo," he added with parenthetic irritation. "A kind of excuse, as I was saying, for a new way of looking at things that I want to experiment with."

"I wish you'd begin by looking at me in a new way," said Elinor with a little laugh. "A more human way."

"But seriously, Elinor . . ."

"Seriously," she mocked. "Being human isn't serious. Only being clever."

"Oh, well," he shrugged his shoulders, "if you don't want to listen, I'll shut up."

"No, no, Phil. Please." She laid her hand on his. "Please."

"I don't want to bore you." He was huffy and dignified.

"I'm sorry, Phil. But you do look so comic when you're more in sorrow than in anger. Do you remember those camels at Bikaner—what an extraordinarily superior expression? But do go on!"

"This year," one female missionary was saying to the other, as they passed by, "the Bishop of Kuala Lumpur ordained six Chinese deacons and two Malays. And the Bishop of British North Borneo . . ." The quiet voices faded into inaudibility.

Philip forgot his dignity and burst out laughing. "Perhaps he ordained some orang-utangs."

"But do you remember the wife of the Bishop of Thursday Island?" asked Elinor. "The woman we met on that awful Australian ship with the cockroaches."

"The one who would eat pickles at breakfast."

"Pickled onions at that," she qualified with a shudder. "But what about your new way of looking at things? We seem to have wandered rather a long way from that."

"Well, as a matter of fact," said Philip, "we haven't. All these *camisoles en flanelle* and pickled onions and bishops of cannibal islands are really quite to the point. Because the essence of the new way of looking is multiplicity. Multiplicity of eyes and multiplicity of aspects seen. For instance, one person interprets events in terms of bishops; another in terms of the price of flannel camisoles; another, like that young lady from Gulmerg," he nodded after the retreating group, "thinks of it in terms of good times. And then there's the biologist, the chemist, the physicist, the historian. Each sees, professionally, a different aspect of the event, a different layer of reality. What I want to do is to look with all those eyes at once. With religious eyes, scientific eyes, economic eyes, homme moyen sensuel eyes . . ."

"Loving eyes too."

He smiled at her and stroked her hand. "The result . . ." he hesitated.

"Yes, what would the result be?" she asked.

"Queer," he answered. "A very queer picture indeed."

"Rather too queer, I should have thought."

"But it can't be too queer," said Philip. "However queer the picture is, it can never be half so odd as the original reality. We take it all for granted; but the moment you start thinking, it becomes queer. And the more you think, the queerer it grows. That's what I want to get in this book—the astonishingness of the most obvious things. Really any plot or situation would do. Because everything's implicit in anything. The whole book could be written about a walk from Piccadilly Circus to Charing Cross. Or you and I sitting here on an enormous ship in the Red Sea. Really, nothing could be queerer than that. When you reflect on the evolutionary processes, the human patience and genius, the social organization that have made it possible for us to be here, with stokers having heat apoplexy for our benefit and steam turbines doing five thousand revolutions a minute, and the sea being blue, and the rays of light not flowing round obstacles, so that there's a shadow, and the sun all the time providing us with energy to live and think—when you think of all this and a million other things, you must see that nothing could well be queerer and that no picture can be queer enough to do justice to the facts."

"All the same," said Elinor, after a long silence, "I wish one day you'd write a simple straightforward story about a young man and a young woman who fall in love and get married and have difficulties, but get over them, and finally settle down."

"Or why not a detective novel?" He laughed. But if, he reflected, he didn't write that kind of story, perhaps it was because he couldn't. In art there are simplicities more difficult than the most serried complications. He could manage the complications as well as anyone. But when it came to the simplicities, he lacked the talent—that talent which is of the heart, no less than of the head, of the feelings, the sympathies, the intuitions, no less than of the analytical understanding. The heart, the heart, he said to himself. "Perceive ye not, neither understand? have ye your heart yet hardened?" No heart, no understanding.

". . . a terrible flirt!" cried one of the four cavaliers, as the party rounded the corner into hearing.

"I am not!" the young lady indignantly retorted.

"You are!" they all shouted together. It was courtship in chorus and by teasing.

"It's a lie!" But, one could hear, the ticklish impeachment really delighted her.

Like dogs, he thought. But the heart, the heart . . . The heart was Burlap's specialty. "You'll never write a good book," he had said oracularly, "unless you write from the heart." It was true; Philip knew it. But was Burlap the man to say so, Burlap whose books were so heartfelt that they looked as though they had come from the stomach, after an emetic? If he went in for the grand simplicities, the results would be no less repulsive. Better to cultivate his own particular garden for all it was worth. Better to remain rigidly and loyally oneself. Oneself? But this question of identity was precisely one of Philip's chronic problems. It was so easy for him to be almost anybody, theoretically and with his intelligence. He had such a power of assimilation that he was often in danger of being unable to distinguish the assimilator from the assimilated, of not knowing among the multiplicity of his roles who was the actor. The amoeba, when it finds a prey, flows round it, incorporates it and oozes on. There was something amoeboid about Philip Quarles's mind. It was like a sea of spiritual protoplasm, capable of flowing in all directions, of engulfing every object in its path, of trickling into every crevice, of filling every mold and, having engulfed, having filled, of flowing on toward other obstacles, other receptacles, leaving the first empty and dry. At different times in his life and even at the same moment he had filled the most various molds. He had been a cynic and also a mystic, a humanitarian and also a contemptuous misanthrope; he had tried to live the life of detached and stoical reason and another time he had aspired to the unreasonableness of natural and uncivilized existence. The choice of molds depended at any given moment on the books he was reading, the people he was associating with. Burlap, for example, had redirected the flow of his mind into those mystical channels which it had not filled since he discovered Boehme in his undergraduate days. Then he had seen through Burlap and flowed out again, ready however at any time to let himself trickle back once more, whenever the circumstances seemed to require it. He was trickling back at this moment, the mold was heart-shaped. Where was the self to which he could be loyal?

The female missionaries passed in silence. Looking over Elinor's shoulder he saw that she was reading the *Arabian Nights* in Mardrus's translation. Burtt's *Metaphysical Foundations of Modern Science* lay on his knees; he picked it up and began looking for his place. Or wasn't there a self at all? he was wondering. No, no, that was untenable; that contradicted immediate experience. He looked over the top of his book at the enormous blue glare of the sea. The essential character of the self consisted precisely in that liquid and undeformable ubiquity; in that capacity to espouse all contours and yet remain unfixed in any form, to take, and with an equal facility efface, impressions. To such molds as his spirit might from time to time occupy, to such hard and burning obstacles as it might flow round, submerge, and, itself cold, penetrate to the fiery heart of, no permanent loyalty was owing. The molds were emptied as easily as they had been filled, the obstacles were passed by. But the essential liquidness that flowed where it would, the cool indifferent flux of intellectual curiosity—that persisted and to that his loyalty was due. If there was any single way of life he could lastingly believe in, it was that mixture of pyrrhonism and stoicism which had struck him, an inquiring schoolboy among the philosophers, as the height of human wisdom and into whose mold of sceptical indifference he had poured his unimpassioned adolescence. Against the pyrrhonian suspense of judgment and the stoical imperturbability he had often rebelled. But had the rebellion ever been really serious? Pascal had made him a Catholic—but only so long as the volume of *Pensées* was open before him. There were moments when, in the company of Carlyle or Whitman or bouncing Browning, he had believed in strenuousness for strenuousness' sake. And then there was Mark Rampion. After a few hours in Mark Rampion's company he really believed in noble savagery; he felt convinced that the proudly conscious intellect ought to humble itself a little and admit the claims of the heart, aye and the bowels, the loins, the bones and skin and muscles, to a fair share of life. The heart again! Burlap had been right, even though he was a charlatan, a sort of swindling thimblerigger of the emotions. The heart! But always, whatever he might do, he knew quite well in the secret depths of his being that he wasn't a Catholic, or a strenuous liver, or a mystic, or a noble savage. And though he sometimes nostalgically wished he were one or other of these beings, or all of them at once, he was always secretly glad to be none of them and at liberty, even though his liberty was in a strange paradoxical way a handicap and a confinement to his spirit.

"That simple story of yours," he said aloud; "it wouldn't do."

Elinor looked up from the *Arabian Nights*. "Which simple story?"

"That one you wanted me to write."

"Oh, *that*!" She laughed. "You've been brooding over it a long time."

"It wouldn't give me my opportunity," he explained. "It would have to be solid and deep. Whereas I'm wide; wide and liquid. It wouldn't be in my line."

"I could have told you that the first day I met you," said Elinor, and returned to Scheherazade.

"All the same," Philip was thinking, "Mark Rampion's right. In practice, too; which makes it so much more impressive. In his art and his living, as well as in his theories. Not like Burlap." He thought with disgust of Burlap's emetic leaders in the *World*. Like a spiritual channel crossing. And such a nasty, slimy sort of life. But Rampion was the proof of his own theories. "If I could capture something of his secret!" Philip sighed to himself. "I'll go and see him the moment I get home."

V

It had been raining for days. To Spandrell it seemed as though the fungi and the mildew were sprouting even in his soul.

"But why should two people stay together and be unhappy?" the barmaid was saying. "Why? When they can get a divorce and be happy?"

"Because marriage is a sacrament," replied the stranger.

"Sacrament yourself!" the barmaid retorted contemptuously. Catching sight of Spandrell, she nodded and smiled. He was a regular customer.

"Double brandy," he ordered, and leaning against the bar examined the stranger. He had a face like a choirboy's—but a choirboy suddenly overwhelmed by middle age; chubby, prettily doll-like, but withered. The mouth was horribly small, a little slit in a rosebud. The cherub's cheeks had begun to sag and were gray, like the chin, with a day's beard.

"Because," the stranger went on—and Spandrell noticed that he was never still, but must always be smiling, frowning, lifting eyebrows, cocking his head on one side or another, writhing his body in a perpetual ecstasy of self-consciousness, "because a man shall cleave unto his wife and they shall be one flesh. One flesh," he repeated and accompanied the words by a more than ordinary writhe of the body and a titter. He caught Spandrell's eye, blushed, and to keep himself in countenance, hastily emptied his glass.

"What do you think, Mr. Spandrell?" asked the barmaid as she turned to reach for the brandy bottle.

"Of what? Of being one flesh?" The barmaid nodded. "Hm. As a

matter of fact, I was just envying the Governor-General of South Melanesia and Lady Ethelberta Todhunter for being so unequivocally two
fleshes. If you were called the Governor-General of South Melanesia," he
went on, addressing himself to the withered choirboy, "and your wife
was Lady Ethelberta Todhunter, do you imagine you'd be one flesh?"
The stranger wriggled like a worm on a hook. "Obviously not. It would
be shocking if you were."

The stranger ordered another whisky. "But joking apart," he said, "the
sacrament of marriage . . ."

"But why should two people be unhappy?" persisted the barmaid.
"When it isn't necessary?"

"Why shouldn't they be unhappy?" Spandrell inquired. "Perhaps it's
what they're here for. How do you know that the earth isn't some other
planet's hell?"

A positivist, the barmaid laughed. "What rot!"

"But the Anglicans don't regard it as a sacrament," Spandrell continued.

The choirboy writhed indignantly. "Do you take me for an Anglican?"

The working day was over; the bar began to fill up with men in quest
of spiritual relaxation. Beer flowed, spirits were measured out in little
noggins, preciously. In stout, in bitter, in whisky they bought the equiv-
alents of foreign travel and mystical ecstasy, of poetry and a week end
with Cleopatra, of big-game hunting and music. The choirboy ordered
another drink.

"What an age we live in!" he said, shaking his head. "Barbarous. Such
abysmal ignorance of the most rudimentary religious truths."

"Not to mention hygienic truths," said Spandrell. "These damp
clothes! And not a window." He pulled out his handkerchief and held it
to his nose.

The choirboy shuddered and held up his hands. "But what a handkerchief!" he exclaimed, "what a horror!"

Spandrell held it out for inspection. "It seems to me a very nice handkerchief," he said. It was a silk bandana, red with bold patterns in black
and pink. "Extremely expensive, I may add."

"But the color, my dear sir. The color!"

"I like it."

"But not at this season of the year. Not between Easter and Whitsun.
Impossible! The liturgical color is white." He pulled out his own handkerchief. It was snowy. "And my socks." He lifted a foot.

"I wondered why you looked as though you were going to play tennis."

"White, white," said the choirboy. "It's prescribed. Between Easter and Pentecost the chasuble must be predominantly white. Not to mention the fact that today's the feast of St. Natalia the Virgin. And white's the color for all virgins who aren't also martyrs."

"I should have thought they were all martyrs," said Spandrell. "That is, if they've been virgins long enough."

The swing door opened and shut, opened and shut. Outside was loneliness and the damp twilight; within, the happiness of being many, of being close and in contact. The choirboy began to talk of little St. Hugh of Lincoln and St. Piran of Perranzabuloe, the patron saint of Cornish tin miners. He drank another whisky and confided to Spandrell that he was writing the lives of the English saints, in verse.

"Another wet Derby," prophesied a group of pessimists at the bar, and were happy because they could prophesy in company and with fine weather in their bellies and beery sunshine in their souls. The wet clothes steamed more suffocatingly than ever—a steam of felicity; the sound of talk and laughter was deafening. Into Spandrell's face the withered choirboy breathed alcohol and poetry.

> To and fro, to and fro,
> Piran of Perranzabuloe,

he intoned. Four whiskys had almost cured him of writhing and grimacing. He had lost his self-consciousness. The onlooker who was conscious of the self had gone to sleep. A few more whiskys and there would be no more self to be conscious of.

> Walked weightless,

he continued,

> Walked weightless on the heaving seas
> Among the Cassiterides.

"That was Piran's chief miracle," he explained; "walking from Land's End to the Scilly Islands."

"Pretty nearly the world's record, I should think," said Spandrell.

The other shook his head. "There was an Irish saint who walked to Wales. But I can't remember his name. Miss!" he called. "Here! Another whisky, please."

"I must say," said Spandrell, "you seem to make the best of both worlds. Six whiskys . . ."

"Only five," the choirboy protested. "This is only the fifth."

"Five whiskys, then, and the liturgical colors. Not to mention St. Piran of Perranzabuloe. Do you really believe in that walk to the Scillies?"

"Absolutely."

"And here's for young Sacramento," said the barmaid, pushing his glass across the counter.

The choirboy shook his head as he paid. "Blasphemies all round," he said. "Every word another wound in the Sacred Heart." He drank. "Another bleeding, agonizing wound."

"What fun you have with your Sacred Heart!"

"Fun?" said the choirboy indignantly.

"Staggering from the bar to the altar rails. And from the confessional to the bawdyhouse. It's the ideal life. Never a dull moment. I envy you."

"Mock on, mock on!" He spoke like a dying martyr. "And if you knew what a tragedy my life has been, you wouldn't say you envied me."

The swing door opened and shut, opened and shut. God-thirsty from the spiritual deserts of the workshop and the office, men came, as to a temple. Bottled and barreled by Clyde and Liffey, by Thames, Douro and Trent, the mysterious divinity revealed itself to them. For the Brahmins who pressed and drank the soma, its name was Indra; for the hemp-eating yogis, Siva. The gods of Mexico inhabited the peyotl. The Persian Sufis discovered Allah in the wine of Shiraz, the shamans of the Samoyedes ate toadstools and were filled with the spirit of Num.

"Another whisky, Miss," said the choirboy, and turning back to Spandrell almost wept over his misfortunes. He had loved, he had married—sacramentally; he insisted on that. He had been happy. They had both been happy.

Spandrell raised his eyebrows. "Did she like the smell of whisky?"

The other shook his head sadly. "I had my faults," he admitted. "I was weak. This accursed drink! Accursed!" And in a sudden enthusiasm for temperance he poured his whisky on the floor. "There!" he said triumphantly.

"Very noble!" said Spandrell. He beckoned to the barmaid. "Another whisky for this gentleman."

The choirboy protested, but without much warmth. He sighed. "It was always my besetting sin," he said. "But I was always sorry afterward. Genuinely repentant."

"I'm sure you were. Never a dull moment."

"If she'd stood by me, I might have cured myself."

"A pure woman's help, what?" said Spandrell.

"Exactly," the other nodded. "That's exactly it. But she left me. Ran off. Or rather, not ran. She was lured. She wouldn't have done it on her own. It was that horrible little snake in the grass. That little . . ." He ran through the sergeant-major's brief vocabulary. "I'd wring his neck if he were here," the choirboy went on. The Lord of Battles had been in his fifth whisky. "Dirty little swine!" He banged the counter. "You know the man who painted those pictures in the Tate; Bidlake? Well, it was that chap's son. Walter Bidlake."

Spandrell raised his eyebrows, but made no comment. The choirboy talked on.

At Sbisa's, Walter was dining with Lucy Tantamount.

"Why don't you come to Paris too?" Lucy was saying.

Walter shook his head. "I've got to work."

"I find it's really impossible to stay in one place more than a couple of months at a time. One gets so stale and wilted, so unutterably bored. The moment I step into the airplane at Croydon I feel as though I had been born again—like the Salvation Army."

"And how long does the new life last?"

Lucy shrugged her shoulders. "As long as the old one. But fortunately there's an almost unlimited supply of airplanes. I'm all for Progress."

The swing doors of the temple of the unknown god closed behind them. Spandrell and his companion stepped out into the cold and rainy darkness.

"Oof!" said the choirboy, shivering, and turned up the collar of his raincoat. "It's like jumping into a swimming bath."

"It's like reading Haeckel after Fénelon. You Christians live in such a jolly little public house of a universe."

They walked a few yards down the street.

"Look here," said Spandrell, "do you think you can get home on foot? Because you don't look as though you could."

Leaning against a lamppost the choirboy shook his head.

"We'll wait for a cab."

They waited. The rain fell. Spandrell looked at the other man with a cold distaste. The creature had amused him, while they had been in the pub, had served as a distraction. Now, suddenly, he was merely repulsive.

"Aren't you afraid of going to hell?" he asked. "They'll make you drink burning whisky there. A perpetual Christmas pudding in your belly. If you could see yourself! The revolting spectacle . . ."

The choirboy's sixth whisky had been full of contrition. "I know, I know," he groaned. "I'm disgusting. I'm contemptible. But if you knew how I'd struggled and striven and . . ."

"There's a cab." Spandrell gave a shout.

"How I'd prayed," the choirboy continued.

"Where do you live?"

"Forty-one Ossian Gardens. I've wrestled . . ."

The cab drew up in front of them. Spandrell opened the door.

"Get in, you sot," he said, and gave the other a push. "Forty-one Ossian Gardens," he said to the driver. The choirboy, meanwhile, had crawled into his seat. Spandrell followed. "Disgusting slug!"

"Go on, go on. I deserve it. You have every right to despise me."

"I know," said Spandrell. "But if you think I'm going to do you the pleasure of telling you so any more, you're much mistaken." He leaned back in his corner and shut his eyes. All his appalling weariness and disgust had suddenly returned. "God," he said to himself. "God, God, God." And like a grotesque derisive echo of his thoughts, the choirboy prayed aloud. "God have mercy upon me," the maudlin voice repeated. Spandrell burst out laughing.

Leaving the drunkard on his front doorstep, Spandrell went back to the cab. He remembered suddenly that he had not dined. "Sbisa's Restaurant," he told the driver. "God, God," he repeated in the darkness. But the night was a vacuum.

"There's Spandrell," cried Lucy, interrupting her companion in the middle of a sentence. She raised her arm and waved.

"Lucy!" Spandrell took her hand and kissed it. He sat down at their table. "It'll interest you to hear, Walter, that I've just been doing a good Samaritan to your victim."

"My victim?"

"Your cuckold. Carling; isn't that his name?" Walter blushed in an agony. "He wears his horns without any difference. Quite traditionally." He looked at Walter and was glad to see the signs of distress on his face. "I found him drowning his sorrows," he went on maliciously. "In whisky. The grand romantic remedy." It was a relief to be able to take some revenge for his miseries.

*   *   *

Quai Voltaire

The air was rough, I forgot the *Quiés* for my ears and was in a Hell of Noise for 2½ hours. Feeling very tired and consequently, sweet Walter, rather sentimental and *sola sola*. Why aren't you here to console me for the unbearable sadness of this lovely evening outside my window? The Louvre, the river, the green glass sky, the sunlight and those velvet shadows—they make me feel like bursting into tears. And not the scenery only. My arms in the sleeves of my dressing gown, my hand writing, even my bare toes, now that I've dropped my slippers—terrible, terrible. And as for my face in the

glass, and my shoulders, and the orange roses and the Chinese gold-
fish to match, and the Dufy curtains and all the rest—yes, *all*,
because everything's equally beautiful and extraordinary, even the
things that are dull and ugly—they're too much to be borne. Too
much. I can't stand it and what's more, I won't. Interval of 5
minutes. That's why I've telephoned to René Tallemant to come
and have a cocktail and take me out somewhere amusing, *malgré*
my headache. I simply won't let myself be bullied by the universe.
Do you know René? Rather a divine little man. But I wish it were
you, all the same. Must go and put on a few clothes. *A toi.* LUCY.

Quai Voltaire

Your letter was tiresome. Such yammering. And it isn't flattering
to be called a poison in the blood. It's the equivalent of being called
a stomach-ache. If you can't write more sensibly, don't write at all.
Quant à moi, je m'amuse. Pas follement. But sufficiently, sufficiently.
Theaters; mostly bad; but I like them; I'm still childish enough to
feel involved in the imbecile plots. And buying clothes; such ravish-
ments! I simply adored myself in Lanvin's looking glasses. Looking
at pictures, on the other hand, is an overrated sport. Not dancing,
though. There'd be some point if life were always like dancing with
a professional. But it ain't. And if it were, I dare say one would
long to walk. In the evenings a little pub-crawling in Mont Parnasse
through hordes of Americans, Poles, Esthonians, Rumanians, Finns,
Letts, Lapps, Wends, etcetera, and all of them (God help us!)
artists. Shall we found a league for the suppression of art? Paris
makes me long to. Also I wish one met a few more heterosexuals
for a change. I don't really like *ni les tapettes ni les gousses*. And
since Proust and Gide made them fashionable one sees nothing else
in this tiresome town. All my English respectability breaks out!
Yours, L.

Quai Voltaire

This time your letter was much better. (My only poem, and an
accident at that. Rather good, all the same.) If only everybody
would realize that being miserable or jolly about love is chiefly a
matter of fashion. Being poetically miserable is an old fashion, and
besides, the rhymes don't justify it in English. *Coure-dolore-amore*;
you can't escape it in Italian. Nor in German; *Herz* must feel
Schmerz and *Liebe* is inevitably full of *Triebe*. But in English, no.
There's no pain connected with English loves; only gloves and turtle-

doves. And the only things that, by the laws of poetry, can go straight to Englishmen's hearts are tarts and amorous arts. And I assure you, a man's much better occupied when he's thinking about those subjects than when he's telling himself how wretched he is, how jealous, how cruelly wronged and all the nonsensical rest of it. I wish that idiot René would understand this. But unfortunately cœur rhymes with *douleur*, and he's French. He's becoming almost as much of a bore as you were, my poor Walter. But I hope you're now a reformed character. I like you. L.

Quai Voltaire

Suffering from a cold and intense boredom, only momentarily relieved by your letter. Paris is really terribly dreary. I have a good mind to fly away somewhere else, only I don't know where. Eileen came to see me today. She wants to leave Tim, because he will insist on her lying naked in bed while he sets fire to newspapers over her and lets the hot ashes fall on her body. Poor Tim! It seems unkind to deprive him of his simple pleasures. But Eileen's so nervous of being grilled. She was furious with me for laughing and not being more sympathetic. I took it all as a joke. Which it is. A very mild one, however. For really, like the Queen, we are not amused. How I hate you for not being here to entertain me! One can forgive anything except absence. Unpardonably absent Walter, good-by. I have an *envie* for you tonight, for your hands and your mouth. And you? Do you remember? L.

Quai Voltaire

So Philip Quarles is going to settle in the country and be a mixture of Mrs. Gaskell and Knud Hamsun. Well, well. . . . But it's good that somebody should have illusions. At any rate he can't be more bored in his village than I am here. What straits one's reduced to! Last night I went with Tim and Eileen, who seems to be reconciled to the firework displays, to one of those places where you pay a hundred francs for the privilege of looking on at orgies (in masks —the one amusing feature) and if you want to, participating in them. Dim religious lights, little cubicles, divans, a great deal of what the French call *amour* promiscuously going on. Odd and grotesque, but terribly dreary and all so very *medical*. A sort of cross between very stupid clowns and an operating theater. Tim and Eileen wanted me to stay. I told them I'd rather pay a visit to the Morgue, and left them there. I hope they amused themselves. But

what a bore, what a hopeless unmitigated bore! I always thought
Heliogabalus was such a very sophisticated young person. But now
I've seen what amused him, I realize that he must have had a mind
like a baby's, really infantile. I have the misfortune to be rather
grown up about some things. I've a notion of going to Madrid next
week. It'll be terrifically hot, of course. But I love the heat. I blossom in ovens. (Rather a significant intimation of my particular
immortality, perhaps?) Why don't you come with me? Seriously,
I mean. You could surely get away. Murder Burlap and come and
be a tripper à la Maurice Barrès. *Du sang, de la volupté et de la mort.*
I feel rather bloodthirsty at the moment. Spain would suit me.
Meanwhile, I'll make inquiries about the bullfighting season. The
ring makes you sick; even my bloodthirstiness won't run to disemboweled cab-horses. But the spectators are marvelous. Twenty thousand simultaneous sadistic *frissons*. Really remarkable. You simply
must come, my sweet Walter. Say yes. I insist. Lucy.

Quai Voltaire
It was too sweet of you, Walter darling, to do the impossible to
come to Spain. I wish, for once, you hadn't taken my momentary
envie quite so seriously. Madrid's off—for the present, at any rate.
If it should come on again, I'll let you know at once. Meanwhile,
Paris. Hastily. L.

VI

FROM PHILIP QUARLES'S NOTEBOOK

Two things give me confidence in Rampion's opinions about the problems of living. The first is that he himself lives in a more satisfactory
way than anyone I know. He lives more satisfactorily, because he lives
more realistically than other people. Rampion, it seems to me, takes
into account all the facts (whereas other people hide from them, or try
to pretend that the ones they find unpleasant don't or shouldn't exist),
and then proceeds to make his way of living fit the facts, and doesn't
try to compel the facts to fit in with a preconceived idea of the right
way of living (like these imbecile Christians and intellectuals and moralists and efficient businessmen). The second thing which gives me
confidence in his judgment is that so many of his opinions agree with
mine. which, apart from all questions of vanity, is a good sign, because

we start from such distant points, from opposite poles in fact. Opinions on which two opponents agree (for that's what essentially, and to start with, we are: opponents) have a fair chance of being right. The chief difference between us, alas, is that his opinions are lived and mine, in the main, only thought. Like him, I mistrust intellectualism, but intellectually I disbelieve in the adequacy of any scientific or philosophical theory, any abstract moral principle, but on scientific, philosophical and abstract-moral grounds. The problem for me is to transform a detached intellectual scepticism into a way of harmonious all-round living.

The course of every intellectual, if he pursues his journey long and unflinchingly enough, ends in the obvious, from which the nonintellectuals have never stirred. The theme was developed by Burlap in one of those squelchy emetic articles of his. And there's a good deal of truth in it, in spite of Burlap. (Here we are, back again among the personalities. The thoroughly contemptible man may have valuable opinions, just as the in some ways admirable man can have detestable opinions. And I suppose, parenthetically, that I belong to the first class—though not so completely, I hope, as Burlap and in a different way.) Many intellectuals, of course, don't get far enough to reach the obvious again. They remain stuck in a pathetic belief in rationalism and the absolute supremacy of mental values and the entirely conscious will. You've got to go further than the nineteenth-century fellows, for example; as far at least as Protagoras and Pyrrho, before you get back to the obvious in which the nonintellectuals have always remained. And one must hasten to make it clear that these nonintellectuals aren't the modern canaille who read the picture papers and listen-in and jazz and are preoccupied with making money and having the awful modern "good time." No, no; one isn't paying a compliment to the hardheaded businessman or the low-brow. For, in spite of their stupidity and tastelessness and vulgarity and infantility (or rather because of all these defects), they aren't the nonintellectuals I'm talking about. They take the main intellectualist axiom for granted—that there's an intrinsic superiority in mental, conscious, voluntary life over physical, intuitive, instinctive, emotional life. The whole of modern civilization is based on the idea that the specialized function which gives a man his place in society is more important than the whole man, or rather *is* the whole man, all the rest being irrelevant or even (since the physical, intuitive, instinctive and emotional part of man doesn't contribute appreciably to making money or getting on in an industrialized world) positively harmful and detestable. The low-brow of our modern industrialized society has all the defects of the intellectual and none of his redeeming qualities. The nonintellectuals I'm thinking of are very different beings. One might still find a few of them in Italy (though Fascism has probably turned them all into bad imitations of Americans and Prussians by this time); a few perhaps in Spain, in Greece, in Provence. Not elsewhere in modern Europe. There were probably quite a lot of them three thousand years ago. But the combined efforts of Plato and Aristotle, Jesus, Newton and big business have turned their descendants into the modern bourgeoisie and proletariat. The obvious that the intellectual gets back to, if he goes far enough, isn't of course the same as the obvious of the nonintellectuals. For their obvious is life itself and his recovered obvious is only the idea of that life. Not many can put flesh and blood on the idea and turn it into reality. The intellectuals who, like Rampion, don't have to return to the obvious, but have always believed in it and lived it, while at the same time leading the life of the spirit, are rarer still.

Being with Rampion rather depresses me; for he makes me see what a great gulf separates the knowledge of the obvious from the actual living of it. And oh, the difficulties of crossing that gulf! I perceive now that the real charm of the intellectual life—the life devoted to erudition, to scientific research, to philosophy, to esthetics, to criticism—is its easiness. It's the substitution of simple intellectual schemata for the complexities of reality; of still and formal death for the bewildering movements of life. It's incomparably easier to know a lot, say, about the history of art and to have profound ideas about metaphysics and sociology, than to know personally and intuitively a lot about one's fellows and to have satisfactory relations with one's friends and lovers, one's wife and children. Living's much more difficult than Sanskrit or chemistry or economics. The intellectual life is child's play; which is why intellectuals tend to become children—and then imbeciles and finally, as the political and industrial history of the last few centuries clearly demonstrates, homicidal lunatics and wild beasts. The repressed functions don't die; they deteriorate, they fester, they revert to primitiveness. But meanwhile it's much easier to be an intellectual child or lunatic or beast than a harmonious adult man. That's why (among other reasons) there's such a demand for higher education. The rush to books and universities is like the rush to the public house. People want to drown their realization of the difficulties of living properly in this grotesque contemporary world, they want to forget their own deplorable inefficiency as artists in life. Some drown their sorrows in alcohol, but still more drown them in books and artistic dilettantism; some try to forget themselves in fornication, dancing, movies, listening-in, others in lectures and scientific hobbies. The books and lectures are better sorrow drowners than drink and fornication; they leave no headache, none of that despairing *post coitum triste* feeling. Till quite recently, I must confess, I took learning and philosophy and science—all the activities that are magniloquently lumped under the title of "The Search for Truth"—very seriously. I regarded the Search for Truth as the highest of human tasks and the Searchers as the noblest of men. But in the last year or so I have begun to see that this famous Search for Truth is just an amusement, a distraction like any other, a rather refined and elaborate substitute for genuine living; and that Truth Searchers become just as silly, infantile and corrupt in their way as the boozers, the pure esthetes, the businessmen, the Good-Timers in theirs. I also perceived that the pursuit of Truth is just a polite name for the intellectual's favorite pastime of substituting simple and therefore false abstractions for the living complexities of reality. But seeking Truth is much easier than learning the art of integral living (in which, of course, Truth Seeking will take its due and proportionate place along with the other amusements, like skittles and mountain climbing). Which explains, though it doesn't justify, my continued and excessive indulgence in the vices of informative reading and abstract generalization. Shall I ever have the strength of mind to break myself of these indolent habits of intellectualism and devote my energies to the more serious and difficult task of living integrally? And even if I did try to break these habits, shouldn't I find that heredity was at the bottom of them and that I was congenitally incapable of living wholly and harmoniously?

*   *   *

"Any letters?" Walter asked offhandedly of the porter as he entered the club. His tone was meant to imply that he expected nothing more interesting than a publisher's circular or a philanthropic offer to lend five thousand pounds without security. The porter handed him the familiar yellow envelope. He tore it open and unfolded three sheets of penciled scribble. "*Quai Voltaire*. Monday." He pored over the writing. It was almost as difficult to read as an ancient manuscript. "Why do you always write to me in pencil?" He remembered Cuthbert Arkwright's question and her answer. "I'll kiss the ink away," he had replied. The lout! Walter entered the dining room and ordered his lunch. Between the mouthfuls he deciphered Lucy's letter. "*Quai Voltaire*. Insufferable, your letter. Once and for all, I refuse to be cursed at or whined at; I simply won't be reproached, or condemned. I do what I like and I don't admit anybody's right to call my doings into question. Last week I thought it would be amusing to go to Madrid with you; this week I don't. If my changing my mind has put you to any inconvenience, I'm sorry. But I'm not in the least apologetic for having changed my mind, and if you think your howlings and jealousies make me feel sorry for you, you're much mistaken. They're intolerable, they're inexcusable. Do you really want to know why I'm not leaving Paris? Very well. 'I suppose you've found some man you like more than me.' Marvelous, my dear Holmes! And guess where I found him? In the street. Strolling along the Boulevard Saint-Germain, looking at the bookshops. I noticed I was being followed from window to window by a young man. I liked his looks. Very black, with an olive skin, rather Roman, no taller than I. At the fourth window he began to talk to me in extraordinary French, with accents on all the mute E's. '*Ma Lei è italiano.*' He was; huge delight. '*Parla italiano?*' And he began pouring out his admiration in the choicest Tuscan. I looked at him. After all, why not? Someone one has never seen before and knows nothing about—it's an exciting idea. Absolute strangers at one moment and as intimate at the next as two human beings can be. Besides, he was a beautiful creature. '*Vorrei e non vorrei,*' I said. But he'd never heard of Mozart—only Puccini, so I cut the cackle. 'All right.' We hailed a taxi and drove to a little hotel near the Jardin des Plantes. Rooms by the hour. A bed, a chair, a cupboard, a washstand with a tin basin and jug, a towel horse, a *bidet*. Sordid, but that was part of the fun. '*Dunque,*' I said. I hadn't let him touch me in the cab. He came at me as though he were going to kill me, with clenched teeth. I shut my eyes, like a Christian martyr in front of a lion. Martyrdom's exciting. Letting oneself be hurt, humiliated, used like a doormat—queer. I like it. Besides, the doormat uses the user. It's complicated. He'd just come back from a seaside holiday by the Mediterranean and his body was all brown and polished by the sun. Beautifully savage he looked, a Red Indian. And as savage as his looks. The marks are still there where he bit me on the neck. I shall have to wear a scarf for days. Where did I see that statue of Marsyas being skinned? His face was like that. I dug my nails into his arm so that the blood came. Afterward I asked him what he was called. His name's Francesco Allegri and he's an aeronautical engineer, and comes from Siena, where his father's a professor of medicine at the university. How curiously irrelevant that a brown savage should design aircraft engines and have a father who's a professor! I'm going to see him again tomorrow. So now you know, Walter, why I've changed my mind about going to Madrid. Don't ever send me another letter like the last. L."

*   *   *

Burlap came home to find Beatrice, as usual, waiting up for him. Sitting—for such was the engagingly childlike habit he had formed during the last few weeks—on the floor at her feet, his head, with the little pink tonsure in the middle of the dark curls, against her knee, he sipped his hot milk and talked of Rampion. An extraordinary man, a great man, even. Great? queried Beatrice, disapprovingly. She didn't like to hear greatness attributed to any living man (the dead were a different matter; they were dead), unless it was to Denis himself. Hardly *great*, she insisted jealously. Well, perhaps not quite. But very nearly. If he hadn't that strange insensitiveness to spiritual values, that prejudice, that blind spot. The attitude was comprehensible. Rampion was reacting against something which had gone too far in one direction; but in the process of reacting he had gone too far in the other. His incapacity to understand St. Francis, for example. The grotesque and really hideous things he could say about the saint. That was extraordinary and deplorable.

"What does he say?" asked Beatrice severely. Since knowing Burlap, she had taken St. Francis under her protection.

Burlap gave her an account, a little expurgated, of what Rampion had said. Beatrice was indignant. How could he say such things? How did he dare? It was an outrage. Yes, it was a defect in him, Burlap admitted, a real defect. But so few people, he added in charitable palliation, were born with a real feeling for spiritual beauty. Rampion was an extraordinary man in many ways, but it was as though he lacked that extra sense organ which enables men like St. Francis to see the beauty that is beyond earthly beauty. In a rudimentary form he himself, he thought, had the power. How rarely he met anyone who seemed to be like him! Almost everybody was in this respect a stranger. It was like seeing normally in a country where most people were color-blind. Didn't Beatrice feel that too? For of course she was one of the rare clear-seeing ones. He had felt it at once, the first time he met her. Beatrice nodded gravely. Yes, she too felt like that. Burlap smiled up at her; he knew it. She felt proud and important. Rampion's idea of love, for example; Burlap shook his head. So extraordinarily gross and animal and corporeal.

"Dreadful," said Beatrice feelingly. Denis, she was thinking, was so different. Tenderly she looked down at the head that reposed, so trustingly, against her knee. She adored the way his hair curled, and his very small, beautiful ears, and even the pink bare spot on the top of his crown. That little pink tonsure was somehow rather engagingly pathetic. There was a long silence.

Burlap at last profoundly sighed. "How tired I am!" he said.

"You ought to go to bed."

"Too tired even to move." He pressed his cheek more heavily against her knee and shut his eyes.

Beatrice raised her hand, hesitated a moment, dropped it again, then raised it once more and began to run her fingers soothingly through his dark curls. There was another long silence.

"Ah, don't stop," he said, when at last she withdrew her hand. "It's so comforting. Such a virtue seems to go out from you. You'd almost cured my headache."

"You've got a headache?" asked Beatrice, her solicitude running as usual to a kind of anger. "Then you simply must go to bed," she commanded.

"But I'm so happy here."

"No, I insist." Her protective motherliness was thoroughly aroused. It was a bullying tenderness.

"How cruel you are!" Burlap complained, rising reluctantly to his feet. Beatrice was touched with compunction. "I'll stroke your head when you're in bed," she promised. She too now regretted that soft warm silence, that speechless intimacy, which her outburst of domineering solicitude had too abruptly shattered. She justified herself by an explanation. The headache would return if he didn't go to sleep the moment it was cured. And so on.

Burlap had been in bed nearly ten minutes when she came to keep her promise. She was dressed in a green dressing gown and her yellow hair was plaited into a long thick pigtail that swung heavily as she moved, like the heavy plaited tail of a cart horse at a show.

"You look about twelve with that pigtail hanging down your back," said Burlap, enchanted.

Beatrice laughed, rather nervously, and sat down on the edge of the bed. He raised his hand and took hold of the thick plait. "Too charming," he said. "It simply invites pulling." He gave a little tug at it, playfully.

"Look out," she warned. "I'll pull back, in spite of your headache." She took hold of one of his dark curls.

"Pax, pax!" he begged, reverting to the vocabulary of the preparatory school. "I'll let go. The real reason," he added, "why little boys don't like fighting with little girls is simply that little girls are so much more ruthless and ferocious."

Beatrice laughed again. There was a silence. She felt a little breathless and fluttering, as one feels when one is anxiously expecting something to happen. "Head bad?" she asked.

"Rather bad."

She stretched out a hand and touched his forehead.

"Your hand's magical," he said. With a quick unexpected movement he wriggled round sideways under the sheets and laid his head on her lap. "There," he whispered and, with a sigh of contentment, closed his eyes.

For a moment Beatrice was taken aback, almost frightened. That dark head lying hard and heavy on her thighs—it seemed strange, terrifying. She had to suppress a little shudder before she could feel glad at the confiding childishness of his movement. She began stroking his forehead, stroking his scalp through the thick dark curls. Time passed. The soft warm silence enveloped them once more; the dumb intimacy of contact was re-established. She was no longer domineering in her protective solicitude, only tender. The armor of her hardness was as though melted away from her, melted away in this warm intimacy along with the terrors which made it necessary.

Burlap sighed again. He was in a kind of blissful doze of sensual passivity.

"Better?" she asked in a soft whisper.

"Still rather bad on the side," he whispered back. "Just over the ear." And he rolled his head over so that she could more easily reach the painful spot, rolled it over so that his face was pressed against her belly, her soft belly that stirred so livingly with her breathing, that was so warm and yielding against his face.

At the touch of his face against her body Beatrice felt a sudden renewal of those spasmodic creepings of apprehension. Her flesh was terrified by the nearness of that physical intimacy. But as Burlap did not stir, as he made no dangerous gesture, no movement toward a closer contact, the terrors died gradually down and their flutterings served only to enhance and intensify that wonderful warm emotion of tenderness which succeeded them. She ran her fingers through his hair, again and again. The warmth of his breathing was against her belly. She shivered a little; her happiness fluttered with apprehensions and anticipations. Her flesh trembled, but was somehow joyful; was afraid and yet curious; shrank, but took warmth at the contact and even, through its terrors, timidly desired.

"Better?" she whispered again.

He made a little movement with his head and pressed his face closer to her soft flesh.

"Shall I stop now?" she went on, "shall I go away?"

Burlap raised his head and looked at her. "No, no," he implored. "Don't go. Not yet. Don't break the magic. Stay here for a moment longer. Lie down here for a moment under the quilt. For a moment."

Without speaking she stretched herself out beside him and he drew the quilt over her, turned out the light.

The fingers that caressed her arm under its wide sleeve touched deli-

cately, touched spiritually and as it were disembodiedly, like the fingers
of those inflated rubber gloves that brush so thrillingly against one's face
in the darkness of séances, bringing comfort from the Great Beyond
and a message of affection from the loved ones who have passed over.
To caress and yet be a spiritualized rubber glove at a séance, to make
love but as though from the Great Beyond—that was Burlap's talent.
Softly, patiently, with an infinite disembodied gentleness he went on
caressing. Beatrice's armor was melted quite away. It was the soft young-
girlish, tremulous core of her that Burlap caressed with that delicate
touch of spirit fingers from the Great Beyond. Her armor was gone; but
she felt so wonderfully safe with Denis. She felt no fears, or at least
only such faint breathless flutterings of her still almost childish flesh as
served to quicken her happiness. She felt so wonderfully safe even when
—after what had seemed a delicious eternity of patiently repeated caresses
from wrist to shoulder and back again—the spirit hand reached out of
the Beyond and touched her breast. Delicately, almost disembodiedly,
it touched, like a skin of rubber stuffed with air; spiritually it slid over
the rounded flesh, and its angelic fingers lingered along the skin. At the
first touch the round breast shuddered; it had its private terrors within
Beatrice's general happiness and sense of security. But patiently, gently,
unalarmingly, the spirit hand repeated its caress again, again, till the
reassured and at last eager breast longed for its return and her whole body
was alive with the tingling ramifications of the breast's desires. In the
darkness the eternities prolonged themselves.

VII

SPANDRELL was very insistent that they should come without delay. The
*heilige Dankgesang eines Genesenen an die Gottheit, in der lydischen
Tonart* simply must be heard.

"You can't understand anything until you have heard it," he declared.
"It proves all kinds of things—God, the soul, goodness—unescapably.
It's the only real proof that exists; the only one, because Beethoven was
the only man who could get his knowledge over into expression. You
must come."

"Most willingly," said Rampion. "But . . ."

Spandrell interrupted him. "I heard quite by accident yesterday that
the A minor quartet had been recorded for the gramophone. I rushed
out and bought a machine and the records specially for you."

"For me? But why this generosity?"

"No generosity," Spandrell answered laughing. "Pure selfishness. I want you to hear and confirm my opinion."

"But why?"

"Because I believe in you and, if you confirm, I shall believe in myself."

"What a man!" mocked Rampion. "Ought to join the Church of Rome and have a confessor."

"But you *must* come." He spoke earnestly.

"But not now," said Mary.

"Not today," her husband echoed, wondering as he spoke why the man was so strangely insistent. What was the matter with him? The way he moved and spoke, the look in his eyes. . . . So excited. "I have innumerable things to do this afternoon."

"Then tomorrow."

As though he were drunk, Rampion was reflecting. "Why not the day after?" he said aloud. "It would be much easier for me. And the machine won't fly away in the interval."

Spandrell uttered his noiseless laugh. "No, but I may," he said. "I shall probably be gone by the day after tomorrow."

"You hadn't told us you were going away," said Mary. "Where?"

"Who knows?" Spandrell answered, laughing once more. "All I know is that I shan't be here any more."

"All right," said Rampion, who had been watching him curiously, "I'll make it tomorrow." Why is he so melodramatic? he wondered.

Spandrell walked slowly eastward from Chelsea along the river whistling to himself over and over again the opening phrases of the Lydian melody from the *heilige Dankgesang*. Over and over again. The river stretched away into the hot haze. The music was like water in a parched land. After so many years of drought, a spring, a fountain. A watering cart rumbled past trailing its artificial shower. The wetted dust was fragrant. That music was a proof, as he had said to Rampion. In the gutter a little torrent was hurrying a crumpled cigarette packet and a piece of orange peel toward the drain. He stopped whistling. The essential horror. Like carting garbage; that was what it had been.* Just nasty and unpleasant, like cleaning a latrine. Not terrible so much as stupid, indescribably stupid. The music was a proof; God existed. But only so long as the violins were playing. When the bows were lifted from the strings, what then? Garbage and stupidity, the pitiless drought.

* EDITOR'S NOTE: Spandrell (with the idea that "one way of knowing God is to deny him") has killed Everard Webley, leader of the fascist Brotherhood of British Freemen. The murder, in which Illidge feebly assisted, has completely baffled the police.

In the Vauxhall Bridge Road he bought a shilling packet of writing paper and envelopes. For the price of a cup of coffee and a bun he hired a table in a tea shop. With a stump of pencil he wrote. "To the Secretary General, Brotherhood of British Freemen. Sir, Tomorrow, Wednesday, at five p.m., the murderer of Everard Webley will be at 37 Catskill Street, S.W. 7. The flat is on the second floor. The man will probably answer the bell in person. He is armed and desperate."

He read it through and was reminded of those communications (written in red ink, to imitate blood, and under the influence of the serial stories in Chums and the B.O.P.) with which he and Pokinghorne Minor had hoped, at nine years old, to startle and terrify Miss Veal, the matron of their preparatory school. They had been discovered and reported to the head master. Old Nosey had given them three cuts apiece over the buttocks. "He is armed and desperate." That was pure Pokinghorne. But if he didn't say it, they wouldn't carry revolvers. And then, why, then it wouldn't happen. Nothing would happen. Let it go. He folded the paper and put it into the envelope. There was an essential silliness, as well as an essential nastiness and stupidity. He scribbled the address.

"Well, here we are," said Rampion, when Spandrell opened his door to them the next afternoon. "Where's Beethoven? Where's the famous proof of God's existence and the superiority of Jesus's morality?"

"In here." Spandrell led the way into his sitting room. The gramophone stood on the table. Four or five records lay scattered near it. "Here's the beginning of the slow movement," Spandrell went on, picking up one of them. "I won't bother you with the rest of the quartet. It's lovely. But the heilige Dankgesang is the crucial part." He wound up the clockwork; the disc revolved; he lowered the needle of the sound box on to its grooved surface. A single violin gave out a long note, then another a sixth above, dropped to the fifth (while the second violin began where the first had started), then leaped to the octave, and hung there suspended through two long beats. More than a hundred years before, Beethoven, stone deaf, had heard the imaginary music of stringed instruments expressing his inmost thoughts and feelings. He had made signs with ink on ruled paper. A century later, four Hungarians had reproduced from the printed reproduction of Beethoven's scribbles that music which Beethoven had never heard except in his imagination. Spiral grooves on a surface of shellac remembered their playing. The artificial memory revolved, a needle traveled in its grooves, and through a faint scratching and roaring that mimicked the noises of Beethoven's own deafness, the audible symbols of Beethoven's convictions and emotions quivered out into the air. Slowly, slowly, the melody unfolded itself. The archaic Lydian harmonies hung on the air. It was an unimpassioned music, transparent, pure and crystalline, like a tropical sea, an Alpine lake. Water on water, calm sliding over calm; the according of level horizons and waveless expanses, a counterpoint of serenities. And everything clear and bright; no mists, no vague twilights. It was the calm of still and rapturous contemplation, not of drowsiness or sleep. It was the serenity of the convalescent who wakes from fever and finds himself born again into a realm of beauty. But the fever was "the fever called living" and the rebirth was not into this world; the beauty was unearthly, the convalescent serenity was the peace of God. The interweaving of Lydian melodies was heaven.

Thirty slow bars had built up heaven, when the character of the music suddenly changed. From being remotely archaic, it became modern. The Lydian harmonies were replaced by those of the corresponding major key. The time quickened. A new melody leaped and bounded, but over earthly mountains, not among those of paradise.

"*Neue Kraft fühlend*," Spandrell quoted in a whisper from the score. "He's feeling stronger; but it's not so heavenly."

The new melody bounded on for another fifty bars and expired in scratchings. Spandrell lifted the needle and stopped the revolving of the disc.

"The Lydian part begins again on the other side," he explained, as he wound up the machine. "Then there's more of this lively stuff in A major. Then it's Lydian to the end, getting better and better all the time. Don't you think it's marvelous?" He turned to Rampion. "Isn't it a proof?"

The other nodded. "Marvelous. But the only thing it proves, so far as I can hear, is that sick men are apt to be very weak. It's the art of a man who's lost his body."

"But discovered his soul."

"Oh, I grant you," said Rampion, "sick men are very spiritual. But that's because they're not quite men. Eunuchs are very spiritual lovers for the same reason."

"But Beethoven wasn't a eunuch."

"I know. But why did he try to be one? Why did he make castration and bodilessness his ideal? What's this music? Just a hymn in praise of eunuchism. Very beautiful, I admit. But couldn't he have chosen something more human than castration to sing about?"

Spandrell sighed. "To me it's the beatific vision, it's heaven."

"Not earth. That's just what I've been complaining of."

"But mayn't a man imagine heaven if he wants to?" asked Mary.

"Certainly, so long as he doesn't pretend that his imagination is the last word in truth, beauty, wisdom, virtue and all the rest. Spandrell wants us to accept this disembodied eunuchism as the last word. I won't. I simply won't."

"Listen to the whole movement, before you judge." Spandrell reversed the disc and lowered the needle. The bright heaven of Lydian music vibrated on the air.

"Lovely, lovely," said Rampion, when the record was finished. "You're quite right. It is heaven, it is the life of the soul. It's the most perfect spiritual abstraction from reality I've ever known. But why should he have wanted to make that abstraction? Why couldn't he be content to be a man and not an abstract soul? Why, why?" He began walking up and down the room. "This damned soul," he went on, "this damned abstract soul—it's like a kind of cancer, eating up the real, human, natural reality, spreading and spreading at its expense. Why can't he be content with reality, your stupid old Beethoven? Why should he find it necessary to replace the real, warm, natural thing by this abstract cancer of a soul? The cancer may have a beautiful shape; but, damn it all, the body's more beautiful. I don't want your spiritual cancer."

"I won't argue with you," said Spandrell. He felt all at once extraordinarily tired and depressed. It had been a failure. Rampion had refused to be convinced. Was the proof, after all, no proof? Did the music refer to nothing outside itself and the idiosyncrasies of its inventor? He looked at his watch; it was almost five. "Hear the end of the movement at any rate," he said. "It's the best part." He wound up the gramophone. Even if it's meaningless, he thought, it's beautiful, so long as it lasts. And perhaps it isn't meaningless. After all, Rampion isn't infallible. "Listen."

The music began again. But something new and marvelous had happened in its Lydian heaven. The speed of the slow melody was doubled; its outlines became clearer and more definite; an inner part began to harp insistently on a throbbing phrase. It was as though heaven had suddenly and impossibly become more heavenly, had passed from achieved perfection into perfection yet more deeper and more absolute. The ineffable peace persisted; but it was no longer the peace of convalescence and passivity. It quivered, it was alive, it seemed to grow and intensify itself, it became an active calm, an almost passionate serenity. The miraculous paradox of eternal life and eternal repose was musically realized.

They listened, almost holding their breaths. Spandrell looked exultantly at his guest. His own doubts had vanished. How could one fail to believe in something which was there, which manifestly existed? Mark Rampion nodded. "Almost thou persuadest me," he whispered. "But it's too good."

"How can anything be too good?"

"Not human. If it lasted, you'd cease to be a man. You'd die."

They were silent again. The music played on, leading from heaven to heaven, from bliss to deeper bliss. Spandrell sighed and shut his eyes. His face was grave and serene, as though it had been smoothed by sleep or death. Yes, dead, thought Rampion as he looked at him. "He refuses to be a man. Not a man—either a demon or a dead angel. Now he's dead." A touch of discord in the Lydian harmonies gave an almost unbearable poignancy to the beatitude. Spandrell sighed again. There was a knocking at the door. He looked up. The lines of mockery came back into his face, the corners of the mouth became once more ironic.

"There, he's the demon again," thought Rampion. "He's come to life and he's the demon."

"There they are," Spandrell was saying, and without answering Mary's question, "Who?" he walked out of the room.

Rampion and Mary remained by the gramophone, listening to the revelation of heaven. A deafening explosion, a shout, another explosion and another, suddenly shattered the paradise of sound.

They jumped up and ran to the door. In the passage three men in the green uniform of British Freemen were looking down at Spandrell's body. They held pistols in their hands. Another revolver lay on the floor beside the dying man. There was a hole in the side of his head and a patch of blood on his shirt. His hands opened and shut, opened again and shut, scratching the boards.

"What has . . . ?" began Rampion.

"He fired first," one of the men interrupted.

There was a little silence. Through the open door came the sound of music. The passion had begun to fade from the celestial melody. Heaven, in those long-drawn notes, became once more the place of absolute rest, of still and blissful convalescence. Long notes, a chord repeated, protracted, bright and pure, hanging, floating, effortlessly soaring on and on. And then suddenly there was no more music; only the scratching of the needle on the revolving disc.

The afternoon was fine. Burlap walked home. He was feeling pleased with himself and the world at large. "I accept the Universe" was how, only an hour before, he had concluded his next week's leader. "I accept the Universe." He had every reason for accepting it. Mrs. Betterton had given him an excellent lunch and much flattery. The *Broad Christian Monthly* of Chicago had offered him three thousand dollars for the serial rights of his *St. Francis and the Modern Psyche*. He had cabled back demanding three thousand five hundred. The *Broad Christian's* answer had arrived that afternoon; his terms were accepted. Then there were the Affiliated Ethical Societies of the North of England. They had invited him to deliver four lectures each in Manchester, Bradford, Leeds and Sheffield. The fee would be fifteen guineas per lecture. Which for England wasn't at all bad. And there'd be very little work to do. It would just be a matter of rehashing a few of his leaders in the *World*. His mood as he walked whistling homeward was one of unmixed contentment. That night he and Beatrice pretended to be two little children and had their bath together. Two little children sitting at opposite ends of the big old-fashioned bath. And what a romp they had! The bathroom was drenched with their splashings. Of such is the Kingdom of Heaven.

Editor's Note to BRAVE NEW WORLD

THE first chapter of *Brave New World* describes how mass production has been applied to biology. Babies are decanted from bottles as socialized human beings, predestined to be Alpha-Plus Directors, Beta mechanics or Delta factory workers, hatched in Bokanovsky groups of identical twins. Throughout childhood and adolescence, sleep-hypnosis conditions everyone to be happy, instills into the individual the thoughts and tastes suitable to his particular caste.

I have selected three passages which together reflect Huxley's three-angled view of the Brave New World; some cutting was unfortunately necessary to compress the original chapters into the space available. In the first extract, Mustapha Mond, one of the ten World Controllers, explains to a group of students how the Brave New World came into being. The setting is the garden of the Central London Hatchery and Conditioning Center, where the students have been watching little children engaged in "erotic play." Huxley intersperses, between the Controller's remarks, fragments of the conversation going on among the upper-caste workers in the changing rooms of the Conditioning Center. The resulting counterpoint is an ironic introduction to the Brave New World as seen through the eyes of its brave new citizens.

The second extract describes an evening between what we would call lovers, one of whom is a misfit in the Brave New World. (There's an ugly rumor that someone made a mistake when he was still in the bottle —thought he was a Gamma and put alcohol into his blood-surrogate.) Bernard Marx gives us the same sort of picture of the Brave New World as the typical Huxleyan hero of the other novels gives us of our world.

Finally, I have included the meeting between the Savage and the World Controller, in which Huxley dramatizes the point of the fable— the choice between "insanity on the one hand and lunacy on the other."

BRAVE NEW WORLD

Extracts

Les utopies apparaissent comme bien plus réalisables qu'on ne le croyait autrefois. Et nous nous trouvons actuellement devant une question bien autrement angoissante: Comment éviter leur réalisation définitive? . . . Les utopies sont réalisables. La vie marche vers les utopies. Et peut-être un siècle nouveau commence-t-il, un siècle où les intellectuels et la classe cultivée rêveront aux moyens d'éviter les utopies et de retourner à une société non utopique, moins "parfaite" et plus libre.

NICOLAS BERDIAEFF

I

His fordship Mustapha Mond! The eyes of the saluting students almost popped out of their heads. Mustapha Mond! The Resident Controller for Western Europe! One of the Ten World Controllers. One of the Ten . . . and he sat down on the bench with the Director of Hatcheries and Conditioning, he was going to stay, to stay, yes, and actually talk to them . . . straight from the horse's mouth. Straight from the mouth of Ford himself.

Two shrimp-brown children emerged from a neighboring shrubbery, stared at them for a moment with large, astonished eyes, then returned to their amusements among the leaves.

"You all remember," said the Controller, in his strong deep voice, "you all remember, I suppose, that beautiful and inspired saying of Our Ford's: History is bunk. History," he repeated slowly, "is bunk."

He waved his hand; and it was as though, with an invisible feather whisk, he had brushed away a little dust, and the dust was Harappa, was Ur of the Chaldees; some spiderwebs, and they were Thebes and Babylon and Cnossos and Mycenae. Whisk, Whisk—and where was Odysseus, where was Job, where were Jupiter and Gotama and Jesus? Whisk—and those specks of antique dirt called Athens and Rome, Jerusalem and the Middle Kingdom—all were gone. Whisk—the place where Italy had been was empty. Whisk, the cathedrals; whisk, whisk, King Lear and the Thoughts of Pascal. Whisk, Passion; whisk, Requiem; whisk, Symphony; whisk . . .

"Going to the Feelies this evening, Henry?" inquired the Assistant Predestinator. "I hear the new one at the Alhambra is first rate. There's a love scene on a bearskin rug; they say it's marvelous. Every hair of the bear reproduced. The most amazing tactual effects."

Mustapha Mond leaned forward, shook a finger at them. "Just try to realize it," he said, and his voice sent a strange thrill quivering along their diaphragms. "Try to realize what it was like to have a viviparous mother."

That smutty word again. But none of them dreamed, this time, of smiling.

"Try to imagine what 'living with one's family' meant."

They tried; but obviously without the smallest success.

"And do you know what a 'home' was?"

They shook their heads.

From her dim crimson cellar Lenina Crowne shot up seventeen stories, turned to the right as she stepped out of the lift, walked down a long corridor and, opening the door marked GIRLS' DRESSING ROOM, plunged into a deafening chaos of arms and bosoms and underclothing. Torrents of hot water were splashing into or gurgling out of a hundred baths. Rumbling and hissing, eighty vibro-vacuum massage machines were simultaneously kneading and sucking the firm and sunburned flesh of eighty superb female specimens. Everyone was talking at the top of her voice. A Synthetic Music machine was warbling out a super-cornet solo.

"Hullo, Fanny," said Lenina to the young woman who had the pegs and locker next to hers.

Fanny worked in the Bottling Room, and her surname was also Crowne. But as the two thousand million inhabitants of the planet had only ten thousand names between them, the coincidence was not particularly surprising.

Lenina pulled at her zippers—downward on the jacket, downward with a double-handed gesture at the two that held trousers, downward again to loosen her undergarment. Still wearing her shoes and stockings, she walked off toward the bathrooms.

Home, home—a few small rooms, stiflingly overinhabited by a man, by a periodically teeming woman, by a rabble of boys and girls of all ages. No air, no space; an understerilized prison; darkness, disease, and smells.

(The Controller's evocation was so vivid that one of the boys, more sensitive than the rest, turned pale at the mere description and was on the point of being sick.)

Lenina got out of the bath, toweled herself dry, took hold of a long flexible tube plugged into the wall, presented the nozzle to her breast, as though she meant to commit suicide, pressed down the trigger. A blast of warmed air dusted her with the finest talcum powder. Eight different scents and eau-de-Cologne were laid on in little taps over the washbasin. She turned on the third from the left, dabbed herself with chypre and, carrying her shoes and stockings in her hand, went out to see if one of the vibro-vacuum machines were free.

"Who are you going out with tonight?" Lenina asked, returning from the vibro-vac like a pearl illuminated from within, pinkly glowing.

"Nobody."

Lenina raised her eyebrows in astonishment.

"I've been feeling rather out of sorts lately," Fanny explained. "Dr. Wells advised me to have a Pregnancy Substitute."

"But, my dear, you're only nineteen. The first Pregnancy Substitute isn't compulsory till twenty-one."

"I know, dear. But some people are better if they begin earlier. Dr. Wells told me that brunettes with wide pelvises, like me, ought to have their first Pregnancy Substitute at seventeen. So I'm really two years late, not two years early." She opened the door of her locker and pointed to the row of boxes and labeled phials on the upper shelf.

"SYRUP OF CORPUS LUTEUM," Lenina read the names aloud. "OVARIN, GUARANTEED FRESH: NOT TO BE USED AFTER AUGUST 1ST, A.F. 632. MAMMARY GLAND EXTRACT: TO BE TAKEN THREE TIMES DAILY, BEFORE

MEALS, WITH A LITTLE WATER. PLACENTIN: 5CC TO BE INJECTED INTRA-
VENALLY EVERY THIRD DAY . . . Ugh!" Lenina shuddered. "How I loathe
intravenals, don't you?"

"Yes. But when they do one good . . ." Fanny was a particularly sensible girl.

Our Ford—or Our Freud, as, for some inscrutable reason he chose to
call himself whenever he spoke of psychological matters—Our Freud
had been the first to reveal the appalling dangers of family life. The world
was full of fathers—was therefore full of misery; full of mothers—therefore of every kind of perversion from sadism to chastity; full of brothers,
sisters, uncles, aunts—full of madness and suicide.

"Dr. Wells says that a three months' Pregnancy Substitute now will
make all the difference to my health for the next three or four years."

"Well, I hope he's right," said Lenina. "But, Fanny, do you really
mean to say that for the next three months you're not supposed to . . ."

"Oh no, dear. Only for a week or two, that's all. I shall spend the
evening at the Club playing Musical Bridge. I suppose you're going out?"

Lenina nodded.

"Who with?"

"Henry Foster."

"Again?" Fanny's kind, rather moonlike face took on an incongruous
expression of pained and disapproving astonishment. "Do you mean to
tell me you're *still* going out with Henry Foster?"

Mothers and fathers, brothers and sisters. But there were also husbands,
wives, lovers. There were also monogamy and romance.

"Though you probably don't know what those are," said Mustapha
Mond.

They shook their heads.

Family, monogamy, romance. Everywhere exclusiveness, everywhere a
focusing of interest, a narrow channeling of impulse and energy.

"But everyone belongs to everyone else," he concluded, citing the
hypnopædic proverb.

The students nodded, emphatically agreeing with a statement which
upward of sixty-two thousand repetitions in the dark had made them

accept, not merely as true, but as axiomatic, self-evident, utterly indisputable.

"But after all," Lenina was protesting, "it's only about four months now since I've been having Henry."

"Only four months! I like that. And what's more," Fanny went on, pointing an accusing finger, "there's been nobody else except Henry all that time. Has there?"

Lenina blushed scarlet; but her eyes, the tone of her voice remained defiant. "No, there hasn't been anyone else," she answered almost truculently. "And I jolly well don't see why there should have been."

"Oh, she jolly well doesn't see why there should have been," Fanny repeated, as though to an invisible listener behind Lenina's left shoulder. Then, with a sudden change of tone, "But seriously," she said, "I really do think you ought to be careful. It's such horribly bad form to go on and on like this with one man. At forty, or thirty-five, it wouldn't be so bad. But at your age, Lenina! No, it really won't do. And you know how strongly the D.H.C. objects to anything intense or long drawn. Four months of Henry Foster, without having another man—why, he'd be furious if he knew."

"Of course there's no need to give him up. Have somebody else from time to time, that's all. He has other girls, doesn't he?"

Lenina admitted it.

"Of course he does. Trust Henry Foster to be the perfect gentleman —always correct. And then there's the Director to think of. You know what a stickler . . ."

Nodding, "He patted me on the behind this afternoon," said Lenina.

"There, you see!" Fanny was triumphant. "That shows what he stands for. The strictest conventionality."

"Stability," said the Controller, "stability. No civilization without social stability. No social stability without individual stability." His voice was a trumpet. Listening they felt larger, warmer.

The machine turns, turns and must keep on turning—forever. It is death if it stands still. A thousand millions scrabbled the crust of the earth. The wheels began to turn. In a hundred and fifty years there were two thousand millions. Stop all the wheels. In a hundred and fifty weeks there are once more only a thousand millions; a thousand thousand thousand men and women have starved to death.

Wheels must turn steadily, but cannot turn untended. There must be men to tend them, men as steady as the wheels upon their axles, sane men, obedient men, stable in contentment.

Crying: My baby, my mother, my only, only love; groaning: My sin, my terrible God; screaming with pain, muttering with fever, bemoaning old age and poverty—how can they tend the wheels? And if they cannot tend the wheels . . . The corpses of a thousand thousand thousand men and women would be hard to bury or burn.

"And after all," Fanny's tone was coaxing, "it's not as though there were anything painful or disagreeable about having one or two men besides Henry. And seeing that you *ought* to be a little more promiscuous . . ."

"Stability," insisted the Controller, "stability. The primal and the ultimate need. Stability. Hence all this."

With a wave of his hand he indicated the gardens, the huge building of the Conditioning Center, the naked children furtive in the undergrowth or running across the lawns.

Lenina shook her head. "Somehow," she mused, "I hadn't been feeling very keen on promiscuity lately. There are times when one doesn't. Haven't you found that too, Fanny?"

Fanny nodded her sympathy and understanding. "But one's got to make the effort," she said sententiously, "one's got to play the game. After all, everyone belongs to everyone else."

"Yes, everyone belongs to everyone else," Lenina repeated slowly and, sighing, was silent for a moment; then, taking Fanny's hand, gave it a little squeeze. "You're quite right, Fanny. As usual. I'll make the effort."

Impulse arrested spills over, and the flood is feeling, the flood is passion, the flood is even madness: it depends on the force of the current, the height and strength of the barrier. The unchecked stream flows smoothly down its appointed channels into a calm well-being. (The embryo is hungry; day in, day out, the blood-surrogate pump unceasingly turns its eight hundred revolutions a minute. The decanted infant howls; at once a nurse appears with a bottle of external secretion. Feeling lurks in that interval of time between desire and its consummation. Shorten that interval, break down all those old unnecessary barriers.)

"Fortunate boys!" said the Controller. "No pains have been spared to make your lives emotionally easy—to preserve you, so far as that is possible, from having emotions at all."

"Ford's in his flivver," murmured the D.H.C. "All's well with the world."

"Lenina Crowne?" said Henry Foster, echoing the Assistant Predestinator's question as he zipped up his trousers. "Oh, she's a splendid girl. Wonderfully pneumatic. I'm surprised you haven't had her."

"I can't think how it is I haven't," said the Assistant Predestinator. "I certainly will. At the first opportunity."

From his place on the opposite side of the changing-room aisle, Bernard Marx overheard what they were saying and turned pale.

"Consider your own lives," said Mustapha Mond. "Has any of you ever encountered an insurmountable obstacle?"

The question was answered by a negative silence.

"Has any of you been compelled to live through a long time-interval between the consciousness of a desire and its fulfillment?"

"Well," began one of the boys, and hesitated.

"Speak up," said the D.H.C. "Don't keep his fordship waiting."

"I once had to wait nearly four weeks before a girl I wanted would let me have her."

"And you felt a strong emotion in consequence?"

"Horrible!"

"Horrible; precisely," said the Controller. "Our ancestors were so stupid and shortsighted that when the first reformers came along and offered to deliver them from those horrible emotions, they wouldn't have anything to do with them.

"Take Ectogenesis. Pfitzner and Kawaguchi had got the whole technique worked out. But would the Governments look at it? No. There was something called Christianity. Women were forced to go on being viviparous.

"Sleep teaching was actually prohibited in England. There was something called liberalism. Parliament, if you know what that was, passed a law against it. The records survive. Speeches about liberty of the subject. Liberty to be inefficient and miserable. Freedom to be a round peg in a square hole."

"But, my dear chap, you're welcome, I assure you. You're welcome." Henry Foster patted the Assistant Predestinator on the shoulder. "Everyone belongs to everyone else, after all."

"The Nine Year's War, the great Economic Collapse. There was a choice between World Control and destruction. Between stability and . . ."

"Fanny Crowne's a nice girl too," said the Assistant Predestinator.

In the nurseries, the Elementary Class Consciousness lesson was over; the voices were adapting future demand to future industrial supply. "I do love flying," they whispered, "I do love flying, I do love having new clothes, I do love . . ."

"Not nearly so pneumatic as Lenina. Oh, not nearly."

"But old clothes are beastly," continued the untiring whisper. "We always throw away old clothes."

"Do I look all right?" Lenina asked. Her jacket was made of bottle-green acetate cloth with green viscose fur at the cuffs and collar.

"Ending is better than mending, ending is better than mending."

Green corduroy shorts and white viscose-woolen stockings turned down below the knee. A green-and-white jockey cap shaded Lenina's eyes; her shoes were bright green and highly polished. And round her waist she wore a silver-mounted, green, morocco-surrogate cartridge belt, bulging (for Lenina was not a freemartin) with the regulation supply of contraceptives.

"The discoveries of Pfitzner and Kawaguchi were at last made use of. An intensive propaganda against viviparous reproduction . . ."

"Perfect!" cried Fanny enthusiastically. She could never resist Lenina's charm for long. "And what a perfectly *sweet* Malthusian belt!"

"Accompanied by a campaign against the Past; by the closing of museums, the blowing up of historical monuments (luckily most of them had already been destroyed during the Nine Years' War); by the suppression of all books published before A.F. 150."

"It's an absolute disgrace—that bandolier of mine."

"The introduction of Our Ford's first T-Model . . ."

"I've had it nearly three months."

"Chosen as the opening date of the new era."

"Ending is better than mending; ending is better . . ."

"There was a thing, as I've said before, called Christianity. There was a thing called Heaven; but all the same they used to drink enormous quantities of alcohol. There was a thing called the soul and a thing called immortality. But they used to take morphia and cocaine. Two thousand pharmacologists and biochemists were subsidized in A.F. 178."

"He does look glum," said the Assistant Predestinator, pointing at Bernard Marx.

"Six years later it was being produced commercially. The perfect drug."

"Let's bait him."

"Euphoric, narcotic, pleasantly hallucinant."

"Glum, Marx, glum." The clap on the shoulder made him start, look up. It was that brute Henry Foster. "What you need is a gram of *soma*."

"All the advantages of Christianity and alcohol; none of their defects."

"Ford, I should like to kill him!" But all he did was to say, "No, thank you," and fend off the proffered tube of tablets.

"Take a holiday from reality whenever you like, and come back without so much as a headache or a mythology."

"Take it," insisted Henry Foster, "take it."

"Stability was practically assured."

"One cubic centimeter cures ten gloomy sentiments," said the Assistant Predestinator citing a piece of homely hypnopædic wisdom.

"It only remained to conquer old age."

"Damn you, damn you!" shouted Bernard Marx.

"Hoity-toity."

"Gonadal hormones, transfusion of young blood, magnesium salts . . ."

"And do remember that a gram is better than a damn." They went out, laughing.

"All the physiological stigmata of old age have been abolished. Along with them all the old man's mental peculiarities. Characters remain constant throughout a whole lifetime."

". . . two rounds of Obstacle Golf to get through before dark. I must fly."

"Work, play—at sixty our powers and tastes are what they were at seventeen. Old men in the bad old days used to renounce, retire, take to religion, spend their time reading, thinking—*thinking*!"

"Idiots, swine!" Bernard Marx was saying to himself, as he walked down the corridor to the lift.

"Now—such is progress—the old men work, the old men copulate, the old men have no time, no leisure from pleasure, not a moment to sit down and think—or if ever by some unlucky chance such a crevice of time should yawn in the solid substance of their distractions, there is always *soma*, delicious *soma*, half a gram for a half-holiday, a gram for a week end, two grams for a trip to the gorgeous East, three for a dark eternity on the moon; returning whence they find themselves on the other side of the crevice, safe on the solid ground of daily labor and distraction, scampering from feely to feely, from girl to pneumatic girl, from Electromagnetic Golf course to . . ."

"Go away, little girl," shouted the D.H.C. angrily. "Go away, little boy! Can't you see that his fordship's busy? Go and do your erotic play somewhere else."

"Suffer little children," said the Controller.

II

ODD, odd, *odd*, was Lenina's verdict on Bernard Marx. So odd, indeed, that in the course of the succeeding weeks she had wondered more than once whether she shouldn't change her mind about the New Mexico holiday, and go instead to the North Pole with Benito Hoover. The trouble was that she knew the North Pole, had been there with George Edzel only last summer, and, what was more, found it pretty grim. Nothing to do, and the hotel too hopelessly old fashioned—no television laid on in the bedrooms, no scent organ, only the most putrid synthetic music, and not more than twenty-five Escalator-Squash Courts for over two hundred guests. No, decidedly she couldn't face the North Pole again. Added to which, she had only been to America once before. And even then, how inadequately! A cheap week end in New York—had it been with Jean-Jacques Habibullah or Bokanovsky Jones? She couldn't remember. Anyhow, it was of absolutely no importance. The prospect of flying West again, and for a whole week, was very inviting. Moreover, for at least three days of that week they would be in the Savage Reservation. Not more than half a dozen people in the whole Center had ever been inside a Savage Reservation. As an Alpha-Plus psychologist, Bernard was one of the few men she knew entitled to a permit. For Lenina, the opportunity was unique. And yet, so unique also was Bernard's oddness that she had hesitated to take it, had actually thought of risking the Pole again with funny old Benito. At least Benito was normal. Whereas Bernard . . .

"Alcohol in his blood-surrogate," was Fanny's explanation of every eccentricity. But Henry, with whom, one evening when they were in bed together, Lenina had rather anxiously discussed her new lover, Henry had compared poor Bernard to a rhinoceros.

"You can't teach a rhinoceros tricks," he had explained in his brief and vigorous style. "Some men are almost rhinoceroses; they don't respond properly to conditioning. Poor Devils! Bernard's one of them. Luckily for him, he's pretty good at his job. Otherwise the Director would never have kept him. However," he added consolingly, "I think he's pretty harmless."

Pretty harmless, perhaps; but also pretty disquieting. That mania, to start with, for doing things in private. Which meant, in practice, not doing anything at all. For what was there that one *could* do in private. (Apart, of course, from going to bed: but one couldn't do that all the time.) Yes, what was there? Precious little. The first afternoon they went out together was particularly fine. Lenina had suggested a swim at Torquay Country Club followed by dinner at the Oxford Union. But Bernard thought there would be too much of a crowd. Then what about a round of Electromagnetic Golf at St. Andrew's? But again, no: Bernard considered that Electromagnetic Golf was a waste of time.

"Then what's time for?" asked Lenina in some astonishment.

Apparently, for going on walks in the Lake District; for that was what he now proposed. Land on the top of Skiddaw and walk for a couple of hours in the heather. "Alone with you, Lenina."

"But, Bernard, we shall be alone all night."

Bernard blushed and looked away. "I meant, alone for talking," he mumbled.

"Talking? But what about?" Walking and talking—that seemed a very odd way of spending an afternoon.

In the end she persuaded him, much against his will, to fly over to Amsterdam to see the Semi-Demi-Finals of the Women's Heavyweight Wrestling Championship.

"In a crowd," he grumbled. "As usual." He remained obstinately gloomy the whole afternoon; wouldn't talk to Lenina's friends (of whom they met dozens in the ice-cream soma bar between the wrestling bouts); and in spite of his misery absolutely refused to take the half gram raspberry sundae which she pressed upon him. "I'd rather be myself," he said. "Myself and nasty. Not somebody else, however jolly."

"A gram in time saves nine," said Lenina, producing a bright treasure of sleep-taught wisdom.

Bernard pushed away the proffered glass impatiently.

"Now don't lose your temper," she said. "Remember, one cubic centimeter cures ten gloomy sentiments."

"Oh, for Ford's sake, be quiet!" he shouted.

Lenina shrugged her shoulders. "A gram is always better than a damn," she concluded with dignity, and drank the sundae herself.

On their way back across the Channel, Bernard insisted on stopping his propeller and hovering on his helicopter screws within a hundred feet of the waves. The weather had taken a change for the worse; a southwesterly wind had sprung up, the sky was cloudy.

"Look," he commanded.

"But it's horrible," said Lenina, shrinking back from the window. She was appalled by the rushing emptiness of the night, by the black foam-flecked water heaving beneath them, by the pale face of the moon, so haggard and distracted among the hastening clouds. "Let's turn on the radio. Quick!" She reached for the dialing knob on the dashboard and turned it at random.

". . . skies are blue inside of you," sang sixteen tremoloing falsettos, "the weather's always . . ."

Then a hiccough and silence. Bernard had switched off the current.

"I want to look at the sea in peace," he said. "One can't even look with that beastly noise going on."

"But it's lovely. And I don't want to look."

"But I do," he insisted. "It makes me feel as though . . ." he hesitated, searching for words with which to express himself, "as though I were more me, if you see what I mean. More on my own, not so completely a part of something else. Not just a cell in the social body. Doesn't it make you feel like that, Lenina?"

But Lenina was crying. "It's horrible, it's horrible," she kept repeating. "And how can you talk like that about not wanting to be a part of the social body? After all, everyone works for everyone else. We can't do without anyone. Even Epsilons . . ."

"Yes, I know," said Bernard derisively. " 'Even Epsilons are useful'! So am I. And I damned well wish I weren't!"

Lenina was shocked by his blasphemy. "Bernard!" She protested in a voice of amazed distress. "How can you?"

In a different key, "How can I?" he repeated meditatively. "No, the real problem is: How is it that I can't, or rather—because, after all, I know quite well why I can't—what would it be like if I could, if I were free—not enslaved by my conditioning."

"But, Bernard, you're saying the most awful things."

"Don't you wish you were free, Lenina?"

"I don't know what you mean. I am free. Free to have the most wonderful time. Everybody's happy nowadays."

He laughed, "Yes, 'Everybody's happy nowadays.' We begin giving the children that at five. But wouldn't you like to be free to be happy in some other way, Lenina? In your own way, for example; not in everybody else's way."

"I don't know what you mean," she repeated. Then, turning to him, "Oh, do let's go back, Bernard," she besought; "I do so hate it here."

"Don't you like being with me?"

"But of course, Bernard. It's this horrible place."

"I thought we'd be more . . . more *together* here—with nothing but the sea and moon. More together than in that crowd, or even in my rooms. Don't you understand that?"

"I don't understand anything," she said with decision, determined to preserve her incomprehension intact. "Nothing. Least of all," she continued, in another tone, "why you don't take soma when you have these dreadful ideas of yours. You'd forget all about them. And instead of feeling miserable, you'd be jolly. So jolly," she repeated and smiled, for all the puzzled anxiety in her eyes, with what was meant to be an inviting and voluptuous cajolery.

He looked at her in silence, his face unresponsive and very grave—looked at her intently. After a few seconds Lenina's eyes flinched away; she uttered a nervous little laugh, tried to think of something to say and couldn't. The silence prolonged itself.

When Bernard spoke at last, it was in a small tired voice. "All right then," he said, "we'll go back." And stepping hard on the accelerator, he sent the machine rocketing up into the sky. At four thousand he started his propeller. They flew in silence for a minute or two. Then, suddenly, Bernard began to laugh. Rather oddly, Lenina thought; but still, it was laughter.

"Feeling better?" she ventured to ask.

For answer, he lifted one hand from the controls and, slipping his arm round her, began to fondle her breasts.

"Thank Ford," she said to herself, "he's all right again."

Half an hour later they were back in his rooms. Bernard swallowed four tablets of soma at a gulp, turned on the radio and television and began to undress.

"Well," Lenina inquired, with significant archness when they met next afternoon on the roof, "did you think it was fun yesterday?"

Bernard nodded. They climbed into the plane. A little jolt, and they were off.

"Everyone says I'm awfully pneumatic," said Lenina reflectively, patting her own legs.

"Awfully." But there was an expression of pain in Bernard's eyes. "Like meat," he was thinking.

She looked up with a certain anxiety. "But you don't think I'm too plump, do you?"

He shook his head. Like so much meat.

"You think I'm all right." Another nod. "In every way?"

"Perfect," he said aloud. And inwardly, "She thinks of herself that way. She doesn't mind being meat."

Lenina smiled triumphantly. But her satisfaction was premature.

"All the same," he went on, after a little pause, "I still rather wish it had all ended differently."

"Differently?" Were there other endings?

"I didn't want it to end with our going to bed," he specified.

Lenina was astonished.

"Not at once, not the first day."

"But then what . . . ?"

He began to talk a lot of incomprehensible and dangerous nonsense. Lenina did her best to stop the ears of her mind; but every now and then a phrase would insist on becoming audible. ". . . to try the effect of arresting my impulses," she heard him say. The words seemed to touch a spring in her mind.

"Never put off till tomorrow the fun you can have today," she said gravely.

"Two hundred repetitions, twice a week from fourteen to sixteen and a half," was all his comment. The mad bad talk rambled on. "I want to know what passion is," she heard him saying. "I want to feel something strongly."

"When the individual feels, the community reels," Lenina pronounced.

"Well, why shouldn't it reel a bit?"

"Bernard!"

But Bernard remained unabashed.

"Adults intellectually and during working hours," he went on. "Infants where feeling and desire are concerned."

"Our Ford loved infants."

Ignoring the interruption, "It suddenly struck me the other day," continued Bernard, "that it might be possible to be an adult all the time."

"I don't understand." Lenina's tone was firm.

"I know you don't. And that's why we went to bed together yesterday—like infants—instead of being adults and waiting."

"But it was fun," Lenina insisted. "Wasn't it?"

"Oh, the greatest fun," he answered, but in a voice so mournful, with an expression so profoundly miserable, that Lenina felt all her triumph suddenly evaporate. Perhaps he had found her too plump, after all.

"I told you so," was all that Fanny said, when Lenina came and made her confidences. "It's the alcohol they put in his surrogate."

"All the same," Lenina insisted. "I do like him. He has such awfully nice hands. And the way he moves his shoulders—that's very attractive." She sighed. "But I wish he weren't so odd."

III

MUSTAPHA MOND shook hands with all three of them; but it was to the Savage that he addressed himself. "So you don't much like civilization, Mr. Savage," he said.

The Savage shook his head. "Of course," he went on to admit, "there are some very nice things. All that music in the air, for instance . . ."

"Sometimes a thousand twangling instruments will hum about my ears and sometimes voices."

The Savage's face lit up with a sudden pleasure. "Have you read it too?" he asked. "I thought nobody knew about that book here, in England."

"Almost nobody. I'm one of the very few. It's prohibited, you see. But as I make the laws here, I can also break them. With impunity, Mr. Marx," he added, turning to Bernard. "Which I'm afraid you can't do."

Bernard sank into a yet more hopeless misery.

"But why is it prohibited?" asked the Savage. In the excitement of meeting a man who had read Shakespeare he had momentarily forgotten everything else.

The Controller shrugged his shoulders. "Because it's old; that's the chief reason. We haven't any use for old things here."

"Even when they're beautiful?"

"Particularly when they're beautiful. Beauty's attractive, and we don't want people to be attracted by old things. We want them to like the new ones."

"But the new ones are so stupid and horrible. Those plays, where there's nothing but helicopters flying about and you *feel* the people kissing." He made a grimace. "Goats and monkeys!" Only in Othello's words could he find an adequate vehicle for his contempt and hatred. "Why don't you let them see *Othello* instead?"

"I've told you; it's old. Besides, they couldn't understand it. Our world is not the same as Othello's world. You can't make flivvers without steel —and you can't make tragedies without social instability. The world's stable now. People are happy; they get what they want, and they never want what they can't get. They're well off; they're safe; they're never ill; they're not afraid of death; they're blissfully ignorant of passion and old age; they're plagued with no mothers or fathers; they've got no wives, or children, or lovers to feel strongly about; they're so conditioned that they practically can't help behaving as they ought to behave. And if anything should go wrong, there's *soma*. Which you go and chuck out of the window in the name of liberty, Mr. Savage. *Liberty!*" He laughed. "Expecting Deltas to know what liberty is! And now expecting them to understand *Othello!* My good boy!"

The Savage was silent for a little. "All the same," he insisted obstinately, "*Othello's* good, *Othello's* better than those feelies."

"Of course it is," the Controller agreed. "But that's the price we have to pay for stability. You've got to choose between happiness and what people used to call high art. We've sacrificed the high art. We have the feelies and the scent organ instead."

"But they don't mean anything."

"They mean themselves; they mean a lot of agreeable sensations to the audience."

"But they're . . . they're told by an idiot."

The Controller laughed. "You're not being very polite to your friend, Mr. Watson. One of our most distinguished Emotional Engineers . . ."

"But he's right," said Helmholtz gloomily. "Because it is idiotic. Writing when there's nothing to say . . ."

The Savage shook his head. "It all seems to me quite horrible."

"Of course it does. Actual happiness always looks pretty squalid in comparison with the overcompensations for misery. And, of course, stability isn't nearly so spectacular as instability. And being contented has none of the glamor of a good fight against misfortune, none of the picturesqueness of a struggle with temptation, or a fatal overthrow by passion or doubt. Happiness is never grand."

"I suppose not," said the Savage after a silence. "But need it be quite so bad as those twins?"

"But how useful! I see you don't like our Bokanovsky Groups; but, I assure you, they're the foundation on which everything else is built. They're the gyroscope that stabilizes the rocket plane of state on its unswerving course." The deep voice thrillingly vibrated; the gesticulating hand implied all space and the onrush of the irresistible machine. Mustapha Mond's oratory was almost up to synthetic standards.

"I was wondering," said the Savage, "why you had them at all— seeing that you can get whatever you want out of those bottles. Why don't you make everybody an Alpha Double Plus while you're about it?"

Mustapha Mond laughed. "Because we have no wish to have our throats cut," he answered. "We believe in happiness and stability. A society of Alphas couldn't fail to be unstable and miserable. Imagine a factory staffed by Alphas—that is to say by separate and unrelated individuals of good heredity and conditioned so as to be capable (within limits) of making a free choice and assuming responsibilities. Imagine it!" he repeated.

The Savage tried to imagine it, not very successfully.

"The optimum population," Mustapha Mond continued, "is modeled on the iceberg—eight-ninths below the water line, one-ninth above."

"And they're happy below the water line?"

"Happier than above it. Happier than your friend here, for example." He pointed.

"In spite of that awful work?"

"Awful? *They* don't find it so. On the contrary, they like it. It's light, it's childishly simple. No strain on the mind or the muscles. Seven and a half hours of mild, unexhausting labor, and then the *soma* ration and games and unrestricted copulation and the feelies. What more can they ask for? True," he added, "they might ask for shorter hours. And of course we could give them shorter hours. Technically, it would be perfectly simple to reduce all lower-caste working hours to three or four a day. But would they be any the happier for that? No, they wouldn't. The experiment was tried, more than a century and a half ago. The whole of Ireland was put onto the four-hour day. What was the result? Unrest and a large increase in the consumption of *soma*; that was all. Those three and a half hours of extra leisure were so far from being a source of happiness that people felt constrained to take a holiday from them. The Inventions Office is stuffed with plans for labor-saving processes. Thousands of them." Mustapha Mond made a lavish gesture. "And why don't we put them into execution? For the sake of the laborers; it would be sheer cruelty to afflict them with excessive leisure. It's the same with agriculture. We could synthesize every morsel of food, if we wanted to. But we don't. We prefer to keep a third of the population on the land. For their own sakes—because it takes *longer* to get food out of the land than out of a factory. Besides, we have our stability to think of. We don't want to change. Every change is a menace to stability. That's another reason why we're so chary of applying new inventions. Every discovery in pure science is potentially subversive; even science must sometimes be treated as a possible enemy. Yes, even science."

"What?" said Helmholtz, in astonishment. "But we're always saying that science is everything. It's a hypnopædic platitude."

"Three times a week between thirteen and seventeen," put in Bernard.

"And all the science propaganda we do at the College . . ."

"Yes; but what sort of science?" asked Mustapha Mond sarcastically. "You've had no scientific training, so you can't judge. I was a pretty good physicist in my time. Too good—good enough to realize that all our science is just a cookery book, with an orthodox theory of cooking that nobody's allowed to question, and a list of recipes that mustn't be added to except by special permission from the head cook. I'm the head cook now. But I was an inquisitive young scullion once. I started doing a bit of cooking on my own. Unorthodox cooking, illicit cooking. A bit of real science, in fact." He was silent.

"What happened?" asked Helmholtz Watson.

The Controller sighed. "Very nearly what's going to happen to you young men. I was on the point of being sent to an island."

The words galvanized Bernard into a violent and unseemly activity. "Send *me* to an island?" He jumped up, ran across the room, and stood gesticulating in front of the Controller. "Oh, please don't send me to Iceland. I promise I'll do what I ought to do. Give me another chance. Please give me another chance." The tears began to flow. "I tell you, it's their fault," he sobbed. "And not to Iceland. Oh please, your fordship, please . . ."

In the end the Controller had to ring for his fourth secretary. "Bring three men," he ordered, "and take Mr. Marx into a bedroom. Give him a good *soma* vaporization and then put him to bed and leave him."

The fourth secretary went out and returned with three green-uniformed twin footmen. Still shouting and sobbing, Bernard was carried out.

"One would think he was going to have his throat cut," said the Controller, as the door closed. "Whereas, if he had the smallest sense, he'd understand that his punishment is really a reward. He's being sent to an island. That's to say, he's being sent to a place where he'll meet the most interesting set of men and women to be found anywhere in the world. All the people who, for one reason or another, have got too self-consciously individual to fit into community life. All the people who aren't satisfied with orthodoxy, who've got independent ideas of their own. Everyone, in a word, who's anyone. I almost envy you, Mr. Watson."

"I'm interested in truth, I like science," the Controller continued. "But truth's a menace, science is a public danger. As dangerous as it's been beneficent. It has given us the stablest equilibrium in history. But we can't allow science to undo its own good work. That's why we so carefully limit the scope of its researches. We don't allow it to deal with any but the most immediate problems of the moment. All other inquiries are most sedulously discouraged. It's curious," he went on after a little pause, "to read what people in the time of Our Ford used to write about scientific progress. They seemed to have imagined that it could be allowed to go on indefinitely, regardless of everything else. Knowledge was the highest good, truth the supreme value; all the rest was secondary and subordinate. True, ideas were beginning to change even then. Our Ford himself did a great deal to shift the emphasis from truth and beauty to comfort and happiness. Mass production demanded the shift. Universal happiness keeps the wheels steadily turning; truth and beauty can't. One can't have something for nothing. Happiness has got to be paid for."

"Art, science—you seem to have paid a fairly high price for your happiness," said the Savage, when they were alone. "Anything else?"

"Well, religion, of course," replied the Controller. "There used to be something called God—before the Nine Years' War. But I was forgetting; you know all about God, I suppose."

"Then you think there is no God?"

"No, I think there quite probably is one."

"Then why? . . ."

"Call it the fault of civilization. God isn't compatible with machinery and scientific medicine and universal happiness. You must make your choice. Our civilization has chosen machinery and medicine and happiness. That's why I have to keep these books locked up in the safe. They're smut. People would be shocked if . . ."

The Savage interrupted him. "If you allowed yourselves to think of God, you wouldn't allow yourselves to be degraded by pleasant vices. You'd have a reason for bearing things patiently, for doing things with courage. I've seen it with the Indians."

"I'm sure you have," said Mustapha Mond. "But then we aren't Indians. There isn't any need for a civilized man to bear anything that's seriously unpleasant. And as for doing things—Ford forbid that he should get the idea into his head. It would upset the whole social order if men started doing things on their own."

"What about self-denial, then? If you had a God, you'd have a reason for self-denial."

"But industrial civilization is only possible when there's no self-denial. Self-indulgence up to the very limits imposed by hygiene and economics. Otherwise the wheels stop turning."

"You'd have a reason for chastity!" said the Savage, blushing a little as he spoke the words.

"But chastity means passion, chastity means neurasthenia. And passion and neurasthenia mean instability. And instability means the end of civilization. You can't have a lasting civilization without plenty of pleasant vices."

"But God's the reason for everything noble and fine and heroic. If you had a God . . ."

"My dear young friend," said Mustapha Mond, "civilization has absolutely no need of nobility or heroism. These things are symptoms of political inefficiency. In a properly organized society like ours, nobody has any opportunities for being noble or heroic. Conditions have got to be thoroughly unstable before the occasion can arise. Where there are wars, where there are divided allegiances, where there are temptations to be resisted, objects of love to be fought for or defended—there, obviously, nobility and heroism have some sense. But there aren't any wars nowadays. The greatest care is taken to prevent you from loving anyone too much. There's no such thing as a divided allegiance; you're so conditioned that you can't help doing what you ought to do. And what you ought to do is on the whole so pleasant, so many of the natural impulses are allowed free play, that there really aren't any temptations to resist. And if ever, by some unlucky chance, anything unpleasant should somehow happen, why, there's always soma to give you a holiday from the facts. And there's always soma to calm your anger, to reconcile you to your enemies, to make you patient and long-suffering. In the past you could only accomplish these things by making a great effort and after years of hard moral training. Now, you swallow two or three half-gram tablets, and there you are. Anybody can be virtuous now. You can carry at least half your morality about in a bottle. Christianity without tears—that's what soma is."

"But the tears are necessary. Don't you remember what Othello said? 'If after every tempest came such calms, may the winds blow till they have wakened death.' There's a story one of the old Indians used to tell us, about the Girl of Mátaski. The young men who wanted to marry her had to do a morning's hoeing in her garden. It seemed easy; but there were flies and mosquitoes, magic ones. Most of the young men simply couldn't stand the biting and stinging. But the one that could —he got the girl."

"Charming! But in civilized countries," said the Controller, "you can have girls without hoeing for them; and there aren't any flies or mosquitoes to sting you. We got rid of them all centuries ago."

"What you need," said the Savage, "is something with tears for a change. Nothing costs enough here."

("Twelve and a half million dollars," Henry Foster had protested when the Savage told him that. "Twelve and a half million—that's what the new Conditioning Center cost. Not a cent less.")

"Exposing what is mortal and unsure to all that fortune, death and danger dare, even for an eggshell. Isn't there something in that?" he asked, looking up at Mustapha Mond. "Quite apart from God—though of course God would be a reason for it. Isn't there something in living dangerously?"

"There's a great deal in it," the Controller replied. "Men and women must have their adrenals stimulated from time to time."

"What?" questioned the Savage, uncomprehending.

"It's one of the conditions of perfect health. That's why we've made the V.P.S. treatments compulsory."

"V.P.S.?"

"Violent Passion Surrogate. Regularly once a month. We flood the whole system with adrenin. It's the complete physiological equivalent of fear and rage. All the tonic effects of murdering Desdemona and being murdered by Othello, without any of the inconveniences."

"But I like the inconveniences."

"We don't," said the Controller. "We prefer to do things comfortably."

"But I don't want comfort. I want God, I want poetry, I want real danger, I want freedom, I want goodness. I want sin."

"In fact," said Mustapha Mond, "you're claiming the right to be unhappy."

"All right then," said the Savage defiantly. "I'm claiming the right to be unhappy."

"Not to mention the right to grow old and ugly and impotent; the right to have syphilis and cancer; the right to have too little to eat; the right to be lousy; the right to live in constant apprehension of what may happen tomorrow; the right to catch typhoid; the right to be tortured by unspeakable pains of every kind."

There was a long silence.

"I claim them all," said the Savage at last.

Mustapha Mond shrugged his shoulders. "You're welcome," he said.

II

STORIES

The Dwarfs

From *Crome Yellow*

. . . The infant who was destined to become the fourth baronet of the name of Lapith was born in the year 1740. He was a very small baby, weighing not more than three pounds at birth, but from the first he was sturdy and healthy. In honor of his maternal grandfather, Sir Hercules Occam of Bishop's Occam, he was christened Hercules. His mother, like many other mothers, kept a notebook, in which his progress from month to month was recorded. He walked at ten months, and before his second year was out he had learned to speak a number of words. At three years he weighed but twenty-four pounds, and at six, though he could read and write perfectly and showed a remarkable aptitude for music, he was no larger or heavier than a well-grown child of two. Meanwhile, his mother had borne two other children, a boy and a girl, one of whom died of croup during infancy, while the other was carried off by smallpox before it reached the age of five. Hercules remained the only surviving child.

On his twelfth birthday Hercules was still only three feet and two inches in height. His head, which was very handsome and nobly shaped, was too big for his body, but otherwise he was exquisitely proportioned and, for his size, of great strength and agility. His parents, in the hope of making him grow, consulted all the most eminent physicians of the time. Their various prescriptions were followed to the letter, but in vain. One ordered a very plentiful meat diet; another exercise; a third constructed a little rack, modeled on those employed by the Holy Inquisition, on which young Hercules was stretched, with excruciating torments, for half an hour every morning and evening. In the course of the next three years Hercules gained perhaps two inches. After that his growth stopped completely, and he remained for the rest of the life a pygmy of three feet and four inches. His father, who had built the most extravagant hopes upon his son, planning for him in his imagination a military career equal to that of Marlborough, found himself a disappointed man. "I have brought an abortion into the world," he would say, and he took so violent a dislike to his son that the boy dared scarcely come into his presence. His

temper, which had been serene, was turned by disappointment to morose-
ness and savagery. He avoided all company (being, as he said, ashamed to
show himself, the father of a *lusus naturae*, among normal, healthy human
beings), and took to solitary drinking, which carried him very rapidly to
his grave; for the year before Hercules came of age his father was taken
off by an apoplexy. His mother, whose love for him had increased with the
growth of his father's unkindness, did not long survive, but little more
than a year after her husband's death succumbed, after eating two dozen
of oysters, to an attack of typhoid fever.

Hercules thus found himself at the age of twenty-one alone in the world,
and master of considerable fortune, including the estate and mansion of
Crome. The beauty and intelligence of his childhood had survived into his
manly age, and, but for his dwarfish stature, he would have taken his place
among the handsomest and most accomplished young men of his time. He
was well read in the Greek and Latin authors, as well as in all the moderns
of any merit who had written in English, French, or Italian. He had
a good ear for music, and was no indifferent performer on the violin, which
he used to play like a bass viol, seated on a chair with the instrument
between his legs. To the music of the harpsichord and clavichord he was
extremely partial, but the smallness of his hands made it impossible for
him ever to perform upon these instruments. He had a small ivory flute
made for him, on which, whenever he was melancholy, he used to play a
simple country air or jig, affirming that this rustic music had more power
to clear and raise the spirits than the most artificial productions of the
masters. From an early age he practiced the composition of poetry, but,
though conscious of his great powers in this art, he would never publish
any specimen of his writing. "My stature," he would say, "is reflected in
my verses; if the public were to read them it would not be because I
am a poet, but because I am a dwarf." Several MS books of Sir Hercules's
poems survive. A single specimen will suffice to illustrate his qualities as a
poet.

In ancient days, while yet the world was young,
Ere Abram fed his flocks or Homer sung;
When blacksmith Tubal tamed creative fire,
And Jabel dwelt in tents and Jubal struck the lyre;
Flesh grown corrupt brought forth a monstrous birth
And obscene giants trod the shrinking earth,
Till God, impatient of their sinful brood,
Gave rein to wrath and drown'd them in the Flood.
Teeming again, repeopled Tellus bore
The lubber Hero and the Man of War;

Huge towers of Brawn, topp'd with an empty Skull,
Witlessly bold, heroically dull.
Long ages pass'd and Man grown more refin'd,
Slighter in muscle but of vaster Mind,
Smiled at his grandsire's broadsword, bow and bill,
And learn'd to wield the Pencil and the Quill.
The glowing canvas and the written page
Immortaliz'd his name from age to age,
His name emblazon'd on Fame's temple wall;
For Art grew great as Humankind grew small.
Thus man's long progress step by step we trace;
The Giant dies, the hero takes his place;
The Giant vile, the dull heroic Block:
At one we shudder and at one we mock.
Man last appears. In him the Soul's pure flame
Burns brightlier in a not inord'nate frame.
Of old when Heroes fought and Giants swarmed,
Men were huge mounds of matter scarce inform'd;
Wearied by leavening so vast a mass,
The spirit slept and all the mind was crass.
The smaller carcase of these later days
Is soon inform'd; the Soul unwearied plays
And like a Pharos darts abroad her mental rays.
But can we think that Providence will stay
Man's footsteps here upon the upward way?
Mankind in understanding and in grace
Advanc'd so far beyond the Giants' race?
Hence impious thought! Still led by GOD's own Hand,
Mankind proceeds towards the Promised Land.
A time will come (prophetic, I descry
Remoter dawns along the gloomy sky),
When happy mortals of a Golden Age
Will backward turn the dark historic page,
And in our vaunted race of Men behold
A form as gross, a Mind as dead and cold,
As we in Giants see, in warriors of old.
A time will come, wherein the soul shall be
From all superfluous matter wholly free;
When the light body, agile as a fawn's,
Shall sport with grace along the velvet lawns.
Nature's most delicate and final birth,
Mankind perfected shall possess the earth.

But ah, not yet! For still the Giants' race,
Huge, though diminish'd, tramps the Earth's fair face;
Gross and repulsive, yet perversely proud,
Men of their imperfections boast aloud.
Vain of their bulk, of all they still retain
Of giant ugliness absurdly vain;
At all that's small they point their stupid scorn
And, monsters, think themselves divinely born.
Sad is the Fate of those, ah, sad indeed,
The rare precursors of the nobler breed!
Who come man's golden glory to foretell,
But pointing Heav'nwards live themselves in Hell.

As soon as he came into the estate, Sir Hercules set about remodeling his household. For though by no means ashamed of his deformity—indeed, if we may judge from the poem quoted above, he regarded himself as being in many ways superior to the ordinary race of man—he found the presence of full-grown men and women embarrassing. Realizing, too, that he must abandon all ambitions in the great world, he determined to retire absolutely from it and to create, as it were, at Crome a private world of his own, in which all should be proportionable to himself. Accordingly, he discharged all the old servants of the house and replaced them gradually, as he was able to find suitable successors, by others of dwarfish stature. In the course of a few years he had assembled about himself a numerous household, no member of which was above four feet high and the smallest among them scarcely two feet and six inches. His father's dogs, such as setters, mastiffs, greyhounds, and a pack of beagles, he sold or gave away as too large and too boisterous for his house, replacing them by pugs and King Charles spaniels and whatever other breeds of dog were the smallest. His father's stable was also sold. For his own use, whether riding or driving, he had six black Shetland ponies, with four very choice piebald animals of New Forest breed.

Having thus settled his household entirely to his own satisfaction, it only remained for him to find some suitable companion with whom to share this paradise. Sir Hercules had a susceptible heart, and had more than once, between the ages of sixteen and twenty, felt what it was to love. But here his deformity had been a source of the most bitter humiliation, for, having once dared to declare himself to a young lady of his choice, he had been received with laughter. On his persisting, she had picked him up and shaken him like an importunate child, telling him to run away and plague her no more. The story soon got about—indeed, the young lady herself used to tell it as a particularly pleasant anecdote—and the taunts and mockery it occasioned were a source of the most acute distress to Hercules. From the poems written at this period we gather that he meditated taking his own life. In course of time, however, he lived down this humiliation; but never again, though he often fell in love, and that very passionately, did he dare to make any advances to those in whom he was interested. After coming to the estate and finding that he was in a position to create his own world as he desired it, he saw that, if he was to have a wife—which he very much desired, being of an affectionate and, indeed, amorous temper—he must choose her as he had chosen his servants— from among the race of dwarfs. But to find a suitable wife was, he found, a matter of some difficulty; for he would marry none who was not distinguished by beauty and gentle birth. The dwarfish daughter of Lord Bemboro he refused on the ground that besides being a pygmy she was hunchbacked; while another young lady, an orphan belonging to a very good family in Hampshire, was rejected by him because her face, like that of so many dwarfs, was wizened and repulsive. Finally, when he was almost despairing of success, he heard from a reliable source that Count Titimalo, a Venetian nobleman, possessed a daughter of exquisite beauty and great accomplishments, who was but three feet in height. Setting out at once for Venice, he went immediately on his arrival to pay his respects to the count, whom he found living with his wife and five children in a very mean apartment in one of the poorer quarters of the town. Indeed, the count was so far reduced in his circumstances that he was even then negotiating (so it was rumored) with a traveling company of clowns and acrobats, who had had the misfortune to lose their performing dwarf, for the sale of his diminutive daughter Filomena. Sir Hercules arrived in time to save her from this untoward fate, for he was so much charmed by Filomena's grace and beauty that at the end of three days' courtship he made her a formal offer of marriage, which was accepted by her no less joyfully than by her father, who perceived in an English son-in-law a rich and unfailing source of revenue. After an unostentatious marriage, at which the English ambassador acted as one of the witnesses, Sir Hercules and his bride returned by sea to England, where they settled down, as it proved, to a life of uneventful happiness.

Crome and its household of dwarfs delighted Filomena, who felt herself now for the first time to be a free woman living among her equals in a friendly world. She had many tastes in common with her husband, especially that of music. She had a beautiful voice, of a power surprising in one so small, and could touch A in alt without effort. Accompanied by her husband on his fine Cremona fiddle, which he played, as we have noted before, as one plays a bass viol, she would sing all the liveliest and tenderest airs from the operas and cantatas of her native country. Seated together at the harpsichord, they found that they could with their four hands play all the music written for two hands of ordinary size, a circumstance which gave Sir Hercules unfailing pleasure.

When they were not making music or reading together, which they often did, both in English and Italian, they spent their time in healthful outdoor exercises, sometimes rowing in a little boat on the lake, but more often riding or driving, occupations in which, because they were entirely new to her, Filomena especially delighted. When she had become a perfectly proficient rider, Filomena and her husband used often to go hunting in the park, at that time very much more extensive than it is now. They hunted not foxes nor hares, but rabbits, using a pack of about thirty black and fawn-colored pugs, a kind of dog which, when not overfed, can course a rabbit as well as any of the smaller breeds. Four dwarf grooms, dressed in scarlet liveries and mounted on white Exmoor ponies, hunted the pack, while their master and mistress, in green habits, followed either on the black Shetlands or on the piebald New Forest ponies. A picture of the whole hunt—dogs, horses, grooms, and masters—was painted by William Stubbs, whose work Sir Hercules admired so much that he invited him, though a man of ordinary stature, to come and stay at the mansion for the purpose of executing this picture. Stubbs likewise painted a portrait of Sir Hercules and his lady driving in their green-enameled calash drawn by four black Shetlands. Sir Hercules wears a plum-colored velvet coat and white breeches; Filomena is dressed in flowered muslin and a very large hat with pink feathers. The two figures in their gay carriage stand out sharply against a dark background of trees; but to the left of the picture the trees fall away and disappear, so that the four black ponies are seen against a pale and strangely lurid sky that has the golden-brown color of thunderclouds lighted up by the sun.

In this way four years passed happily by. At the end of that time Filomena found herself great with child. Sir Hercules was overjoyed. "If God is good," he wrote in his daybook, "the name of Lapith will be preserved and our rarer and more delicate race transmitted through the generations until in the fullness of time the world shall recognize the superiority of those beings whom now it uses to make mock of." On his wife's being brought to bed of a son he wrote a poem to the same effect. The child was christened Ferdinando in memory of the builder of the house.

With the passage of the months a certain sense of disquiet began to invade the minds of Sir Hercules and his lady. For the child was growing with an extraordinary rapidity. At a year he weighed as much as Hercules had weighed when he was three. "Ferdinando goes crescendo," wrote Filomena in her diary. "It seems not natural." At eighteen months the baby was almost as tall as their smallest jockey, who was a man of thirty-six. Could it be that Ferdinando was destined to become a man of the normal, gigantic dimensions? It was a thought to which neither of his parents dared yet give open utterance, but in the secrecy of their respective diaries they brooded over it in terror and dismay.

On his third birthday Ferdinando was taller than his mother and not more than a couple of inches short of his father's height. "Today for the first time," wrote Sir Hercules, "we discussed the situation. The hideous truth can be concealed no longer: Ferdinando is not one of us. On this, his third birthday, a day when we should have been rejoicing at the health, the strength, and beauty of our child, we wept together over the ruin of our happiness. God give us strength to bear this cross."

At the age of eight Ferdinando was so large and so exuberantly healthy that his parents decided, though reluctantly, to send him to school. He was packed off to Eton at the beginning of the next half. A profound peace settled upon the house. Ferdinando returned for the summer holidays larger and stronger than ever. One day he knocked down the butler and broke his arm. "He is rough, inconsiderate, unamenable to persuasion," wrote his father. "The only thing that will teach him manners is corporal chastisement." Ferdinando, who at this age was already seventeen inches taller than his father, received no corporal chastisement.

One summer holiday about three years later Ferdinando returned to Crome accompanied by a very large mastiff dog. He had bought it from an old man at Windsor who found the beast too expensive to feed. It was a savage, unreliable animal; hardly had it entered the house when it attacked one of Sir Hercules's favorite pugs, seizing the creature in its jaws and shaking it till it was nearly dead. Extremely put out by this occurrence, Sir Hercules ordered that the beast should be chained up in the stable yard. Ferdinando sullenly answered that the dog was his, and he would keep it where he pleased. His father, growing angry, bade him take the animal out of the house at once, on pain of his utmost displeasure. Ferdinando refused to move. His mother at this moment coming into the room, the dog flew at her, knocked her down, and in a twinkling had very severely mauled her arm and shoulder; in another instant it must infallibly have had her by the throat, had not Sir Hercules drawn his sword and stabbed the animal to the heart. Turning on his son, he ordered him to leave the room immediately, as being unfit to remain in the same place with the mother whom he had nearly murdered. So awe-inspiring was the spectacle of Sir Hercules standing with one foot on the carcass of the gigantic dog, his sword drawn and still bloody, so commanding were his voice, his gestures, and the expression of his face, that Ferdinando slunk out of the room in terror and behaved himself for all the rest of the vacation in an entirely exemplary fashion. His mother soon recovered from the bites of the mastiff, but the effect on her mind of this adventure was ineradicable; from that time forth she lived always among imaginary terrors.

The two years which Ferdinando spent on the Continent, making the Grand Tour, were a period of happy repose for his parents. But even now the thought of the future haunted them; nor were they able to solace themselves with all the diversions of their younger days. The Lady Filomena had lost her voice and Sir Hercules was grown too rheumatical to play the violin. He, it is true, still rode after his pugs, but his wife felt herself too old and, since the episode of the mastiff, too nervous for such sports. At most, to please her husband, she would follow the hunt at a distance in a little gig drawn by the safest and oldest of the Shetlands.

The day fixed for Ferdinando's return came round. Filomena, sick with vague dreads and presentiments, retired to her chamber and her bed. Sir Hercules received his son alone. A giant in a brown traveling suit entered the room. "Welcome home, my son," said Sir Hercules in a voice that trembled a little.

"I hope I see you well, sir." Ferdinando bent down to shake hands, then straightened himself up aga'. The top of his father's head reached to the level of his hip.

Ferdinando had not con alone. Two friends of his own age accompanied him, and each of the young men had brought a servant. Not for thirty years had Crome been desecrated by the presence of so many members of the common race of men. Sir Hercules was appalled and indignant, but the laws of hospitality had to be obeyed. He received the young gentlemen with grave politeness and sent the servants to the kitchen, with orders that they should be well cared for.

The old family dining table was dragged out into the light and dusted (Sir Hercules and his lady were accustomed to dine at a small table twenty inches high). Simon, the aged butler, who could only just look over the edge of the big table, was helped at supper by the three servants brought by Ferdinando and his guests.

Sir Hercules presided, and with his usual grace supported a conversation on the pleasures of foreign travel, the beauties of art and nature to be met with abroad, the opera at Venice, the singing of the orphans in the churches of the same city, and on other topics of a similar nature. The young men were not particularly attentive to his discourses; they were occupied in watching the efforts of the butler to change the plates and replenish the glasses. They covered their laughter by violent and repeated fits of coughing or choking. Sir Hercules affected not to notice, but changed the subject of the conversation to sport. Upon this one of the young men asked whether it was true, as he had heard, that he used to hunt the rabbit with a pack of pug dogs. Sir Hercules replied that it was, and proceeded to describe the chase in some detail. The young men roared with laughter.

When supper was over, Sir Hercules climbed down from his chair and, giving as his excuse that he must see how his lady did, bade them good night. The sound of laughter followed him up the stairs. Filomena was not asleep; she had been lying on her bed listening to the sound of enormous laughter and the tread of strangely heavy feet on the stairs and along the corridors. Sir Hercules drew a chair to her bedside and sat there for a long time in silence, holding his wife's hand and sometimes gently squeezing it. At about ten o'clock they were startled by a violent noise. There was a breaking of glass, a stamping of feet, with an outburst of shouts and laughter. The uproar continuing for several minutes, Sir Hercules rose to his feet and, in spite of his wife's entreaties, prepared to go and see what was happening. There was no light on the staircase, and Sir Hercules groped his way down cautiously, lowering himself from stair to stair and standing for a moment on each tread before adventuring on a new step. The noise was louder here; the shouting articulated itself into recognizable words and phrases. A line of light was visible under the dining-room door. Sir Hercules tiptoed across the hall toward it. Just as he approached the door there was another terrific crash of breaking glass and jangled metal. What could they be doing? Standing on tiptoe he managed to look through the keyhole. In the middle of the ravaged table old Simon, the butler, so primed with drink that he could scarcely keep his balance, was dancing a jig. His feet crunched and tinkled among the broken glass, and his shoes were wet with spilled wine. The three young men sat round, thumping the table with their hands or with the empty wine bottles, shouting and laughing encouragement. The three servants leaning against the wall laughed too. Ferdinando suddenly threw a handful of walnuts at the dancer's head, which so dazed and surprised the little man that he staggered and fell down on his back, upsetting a decanter and several glasses. They raised him up, gave him some brandy to drink, thumped him on the back. The old man smiled and hiccoughed. "Tomorrow," said Ferdinando, "we'll have a concerted ballet of the whole household." "With father Hercules wearing his club and lion skin," added one of his companions, and all three roared with laughter.

Sir Hercules would look and listen no further. He crossed the hall once more and began to climb the stairs, lifting his knees painfully high at each degree. This was the end; there was no place for him now in the world, no place for him and Ferdinando together.

His wife was still awake; to her questioning glance he answered, "They are making mock of old Simon. Tomorrow it will be our turn." They were silent for a time.

At last Filomena said, "I do not want to see tomorrow."

"It is better not," said Sir Hercules. Going into his closet he wrote in his daybook a full and particular account of all the events of the evening. While he was still engaged in this task he rang for a servant and ordered hot water and a bath to be made ready for him at eleven o'clock. When he had finished writing he went into his wife's room, and preparing a dose of opium twenty times as strong as that which she was accustomed to take when she could not sleep, he brought it to her, saying, "Here is your sleeping draught."

Filomena took the glass and lay for a little time, but did not drink immediately. The tears came into her eyes. "Do you remember the songs we used to sing, sitting out there *sulla terrazza* in summertime?" She began singing softly in her ghost of a cracked voice a few bars from Stradella's "*Amor, amor, non dormir piu.*" "And you playing on the violin. It seems such a short time ago, and yet so long, long, long. *Addio, amore. A rivederti.*" She drank off the draught and, lying back on the pillow, closed her eyes. Sir Hercules kissed her hand and tiptoed away, as though he were afraid of waking her. He returned to his closet, and having recorded his wife's last words to him, he poured into his bath the water that had been brought up in accordance with his orders. The water being too hot for him to get into the bath at once, he took down from the shelf his copy of Suetonius. He wished to read how Seneca had died. He opened the book at random. "But dwarfs," he read, "he held in abhorrence as being *lusus naturae* and of evil omen." He winced as though he had been struck. This same Augustus, he remembered, had exhibited in the amphitheater a young man called Lucius, of good family, who was not quite two feet in height and weighed seventeen pounds, but had a stentorian voice. He turned over the pages. Tiberius, Caligula, Claudius, Nero: it was a tale of growing horror. "Seneca, his preceptor, he forced to kill himself." And there was Petronius, who had called his friends about him at the last, bidding them talk to him, not of the consolations of philosophy, but of love and gallantry, while the life was ebbing away through his opened veins. Dipping his pen once more in the ink he wrote on the last page of his diary: "He died a Roman death." Then, putting the toes of one foot into the water and finding that it was not too hot, he threw off his dressing gown and, taking a razor in his hand, sat down in the bath. With one deep cut he severed the artery in his left wrist, then lay back and composed his mind to meditation. The blood oozed out, floating through the water in dissolving wreaths and spirals. In a little while the whole bath was tinged with pink. The color deepened; Sir Hercules felt himself mastered by an invincible drowsiness; he was sinking from vague dream to dream. Soon he was sound asleep. There was not much blood in his small body.

The Gioconda Smile

From *Mortal Coils*

"MISS SPENCE will be down directly, sir."

"Thank you," said Mr. Hutton, without turning round. Janet Spence's parlormaid was so ugly, ugly on purpose, it always seemed to him, malignantly, criminally ugly, that he could not bear to look at her more than was necessary. The door closed. Left to himself, Mr. Hutton got up and began to wander round the room, looking with meditative eyes at the familiar objects it contained.

Photographs of Greek statuary, photographs of the Roman Forum, colored prints of Italian masterpieces, all very safe and well known. Poor, dear Janet, what a prig—what an intellectual snob! Her real taste was illustrated in that water color by the pavement artist, the one she had paid half a crown for (and thirty-five shillings for the frame). How often he had heard her tell the story, how often expatiated on the beauties of that skillful imitation of an oleograph! "A real Artist in the streets," and you could hear the capital A in Artist as she spoke the words. She made you feel that part of his glory had entered into Janet Spence when she tendered him that half-crown for the copy of the oleograph. She was implying a compliment to her own taste and penetration. A genuine Old Master for half a crown. Poor, dear Janet!

Mr. Hutton came to a pause in front of a small oblong mirror. Stooping a little to get a full view of his face, he passed a white, well-manicured finger over his mustache. It was as curly, as freshly auburn as it had been twenty years ago. His hair still retained its color, and there was no sign of baldness yet—only a certain elevation of the brow. "Shakespearean," thought Mr. Hutton, with a smile, as he surveyed the smooth and polished expanse of his forehead.

Others abide our question, thou art free. . . . Footsteps in the sea . . . Majesty . . . Shakespeare, thou shouldst be living at this hour. No, that was Milton, wasn't it? Milton, the Lady of Christ's. There was no lady about him. He was what the women would call a manly man. That was why they liked him—for the curly auburn mustache and the discreet redolence of tobacco. Mr. Hutton smiled again; he enjoyed making fun of himself. Lady of Christ's? No, no. He was the Christ of Ladies. Very pretty, very pretty. The Christ of Ladies. Mr. Hutton wished there were somebody he could tell the joke to. Poor, dear Janet wouldn't appreciate it, alas!

He straightened himself up, parted his hair, and resumed his peregrination. Damn the Roman Forum; he hated those dreary photographs.

Suddenly he became aware that Janet Spence was in the room, standing near the door. Mr. Hutton started, as though he had been taken in some felonious act. To make these silent and spectral appearances was one of Janet Spence's peculiar talents. Perhaps she had been there all the time, and seen him looking at himself in the mirror. Impossible! But, still, it was disquieting.

"Oh, you gave me such a surprise," said Mr. Hutton, recovering his smile and advancing with outstretched hand to meet her.

Miss Spence was smiling too: her Gioconda smile, he had once called it in a moment of half-ironical flattery. Miss Spence had taken the compliment seriously, and always tried to live up to the Leonardo standard. She smiled on in silence while Mr. Hutton shook hands; that was part of the Gioconda business.

"I hope you're well," said Mr. Hutton. "You look it."

What a queer face she had! That small mouth pursed forward by the Gioconda expression into a little snout with a round hole in the middle, as though for whistling, was like a penholder seen from the front. Above the mouth a well-shaped nose, finely aquiline. Eyes large, lustrous, and dark, with the largeness, luster, and darkness that seem to invite sties and an occasional bloodshot suffusion. They were fine eyes, but unchangingly grave. The penholder might do its Gioconda trick, but the eyes never altered in their earnestness. Above them, a pair of boldly arched, heavily penciled black eyebrows lent a surprising air of power, as of a Roman matron, to the upper portion of the face. Her hair was dark and equally Roman; Agrippina from the brows upward.

"I thought I'd just look in on my way home," Mr. Hutton went on. "Ah, it's good to be back here——" he indicated with a wave of his hand the flowers in the vases, the sunshine and greenery beyond the windows—— "it's good to be back in the country after a stuffy day of business in town."

Miss Spence, who had sat down, pointed to a chair at her side.

"No, really, I can't sit down." Mr. Hutton protested. "I must get back to see how poor Emily is. She was rather seedy this morning." He sat down, nevertheless. "It's these wretched liver chills. She's always getting them. Women——" He broke off and coughed, so as to hide the fact that he had uttered. He was about to say that women with weak digestions ought not to marry; but the remark was too cruel, and he didn't really believe it. Janet Spence, moreover, was a believer in eternal flames and spiritual attachments. "She hopes to be well enough," he added, "to see you at luncheon tomorrow. Can you come? Do?" He smiled persuasively. "It's my invitation too, you know."

She dropped her eyes, and Mr. Hutton almost thought that he detected a certain reddening of the cheek. It was a tribute; he stroked his mustache.

"I should like to come if you think Emily's really well enough to have a visitor."

"Of course. You'll do her good. You'll do us both good. In married life three is often better company than two."

"Oh, you're cynical."

Mr. Hutton always had a desire to say "Bow-wow-wow" whenever that last word was spoken. It irritated him more than any other word in the language. But instead of barking he made haste to protest.

"No, no. I'm only speaking a melancholy truth. Reality doesn't always come up to the ideal, you know. But that doesn't make me believe any the less in the ideal. Indeed, I believe in it passionately: the ideal of a matrimony between two people in perfect accord. I think it's realizable. I'm sure it is."

He paused significantly and looked at her with an arch expression. A virgin of thirty-six, but still unwithered; she had her charms. And there was something really rather enigmatic about her. Miss Spence made no reply, but continued to smile. There were times when Mr. Hutton got rather bored with the Gioconda. He stood up.

"I must really be going now. Farewell, mysterious Gioconda." The smile grew intenser, focused itself, as it were, in a narrower snout. Mr. Hutton made a Cinquecento gesture, and kissed her extended hand. It was the first time he had done such a thing; the action seemed not to be resented. "I look forward to tomorrow."

"Do you?"

For answer Mr. Hutton once more kissed her hand, then turned to go. Miss Spence accompanied him to the porch.

"Where's your car?" she asked.

"I left it at the gate of the drive."

"I'll come and see you off."

"No, no." Mr. Hutton was playful, but determined. "You must do no such thing. I simply forbid you."

"But I should like to come," Miss Spence protested, throwing a rapid Gioconda at him.

Mr. Hutton held up his hand. "No," he repeated, and then, with a gesture that was almost the blowing of a kiss, he started to run down the drive, lightly, on his toes, with long, bounding strides like a boy's. He was proud of that run; it was quite marvelously youthful. Still, he was glad the drive was no longer. At the last bend, before passing out of sight of the house, he halted and turned round. Miss Spence was still standing on the steps, smiling her smile. He waved his hand, and this time quite definitely and overtly wafted a kiss in her direction. Then, breaking once more into his magnificent canter, he rounded the last dark promontory of trees. Once out of sight of the house he let his high paces decline to a trot, and finally to a walk. He took out his handkerchief and began wiping his neck inside his collar. What fools, what fools! Had there ever been such an ass as poor, dear Janet Spence? Never, unless it was himself. Decidedly he was the more malignant fool, since he, at least, was aware of his folly and still persisted in it. Why did he persist? Ah, the problem that was himself, the problem that was other people . . .

He had reached the gate. A large, prosperous-looking motor was standing at the side of the road.

"Home, M'Nab." The chauffeur touched his cap. "And stop at the crossroads on the way, as usual," Mr. Hutton added, as he opened the door of the car. "Well?" he said, speaking into the obscurity that lurked within.

"Oh, Teddy Bear, what an age you've been!" It was a fresh and childish voice that spoke the words. There was the faintest hint of Cockney impurity about the vowel sounds.

Mr. Hutton bent his large form and darted into the car with the agility of an animal regaining his burrow.

"Have I?" he said, as he shut the door. The machine began to move. "You must have missed me a lot if you found the time so long." He sat back in the low seat; a cherishing warmth enveloped him.

"Teddy Bear . . ." and with a sigh of contentment a charming little head declined onto Mr. Hutton's shoulder. Ravished, he looked down sideways at the round, babyish face.

"Do you know, Doris, you look like the pictures of Louise de Kerouaille." He passed his fingers through a mass of curly hair.

"Who's Louise de Kera-whatever-it-is?" Doris spoke from remote distances.

"She was, alas! *Fuit*. We shall all be 'was' one of these days. Meanwhile . . ."

Mr. Hutton covered the babyish face with kisses. The car rushed smoothly along. M'Nab's back through the front window was stonily impassive, the back of a statue.

"Your hands," Doris whispered. "Oh, you mustn't touch me. They give me electric shocks."

Mr. Hutton adored her for the virgin imbecility of the words. How late in one's existence one makes the discovery of one's body!

"The electricity isn't in me, it's in you." He kissed her again, whispering her name several times: Doris, Doris, Doris. The scientific appellation of the sea mouse, he was thinking as he kissed the throat she offered him, white and extended like the throat of a victim awaiting the sacrificial knife. The sea mouse was a sausage with iridescent fur: very peculiar. Or was Doris the sea cucumber, which turns itself inside out in moments of alarm? He would really have to go to Naples again, just to see the aquarium. These sea creatures were fabulous, unbelievably fantastic.

"Oh, Teddy Bear!" (More zoology; but he was only a land animal. His poor little jokes!) "Teddy Bear, I'm so happy."

"So am I," said Mr. Hutton. Was it true?

"But I wish I knew if it were right. Tell me, Teddy Bear, is it right or wrong?"

"Ah, my dear, that's just what I've been wondering for the last thirty years."

"Be serious, Teddy Bear. I want to know if this is right; if it's right that I should be here with you and that we should love one another, and that it should give me electric shocks when you touch me."

"Right? Well, it's certainly good that you should have electric shocks rather than sexual repressions. Read Freud; repressions are the devil."

"Oh, you don't help me. Why aren't you ever serious? If only you knew how miserable I âm sometimes, thinking it's not right. Perhaps, you know, there is a hell, and all that. I don't know what to do. Sometimes I think I ought to stop loving you."

"But could you?" asked Mr. Hutton, confident in the powers of his seduction and his mustache.

"No, Teddy Bear, you know I couldn't. But I could run away, I could hide from you, I could lock myself up and force myself not to come to you."

"Silly little thing!" He tightened his embrace.

"Oh, dear. I hope it isn't wrong. And there are times when I don't care if it is."

Mr. Hutton was touched. He had a certain protective affection for this little creature. He laid his cheek against her hair and so, interlaced, they sat in silence, while the car, swaying and pitching a little as it hastened along, seemed to draw in the white road and the dusty hedges toward it devouringly.

"Good-by, good-by."

The car moved on, gathered speed, vanished round a curve, and Doris was left standing by the signpost at the crossroads, still dizzy and weak with the languor born of those kisses and the electrical touch of those gentle hands. She had to take a deep breath, to draw herself up deliberately, before she was strong enough to start her homeward walk. She had half a mile in which to invent the necessary lies.

Alone, Mr. Hutton suddenly found himself the prey of an appalling boredom.

Mrs. Hutton was lying on the sofa in her boudoir, playing patience. In spite of the warmth of the July evening a wood fire was burning on the hearth. A black Pomeranian, extenuated by the heat and the fatigues of digestion, slept before the blaze.

"Phew! Isn't it rather hot in here?" Mr. Hutton asked as he entered the room.

"You know I have to keep warm, dear." The voice seemed breaking on the verge of tears. "I get so shivery."

"I hope you're better this evening."

"Not much, I'm afraid."

The conversation stagnated. Mr. Hutton stood leaning his back against the mantelpiece. He looked down at the Pomeranian lying at his feet, and with the toe of his right boot he rolled the little dog over and rubbed its white-flecked chest and belly. The creature lay in an inert ecstasy. Mrs. Hutton continued to play patience. Arrived at an *impasse*, she altered the position of one card, took back another, and went on playing. Her patiences always came out.

"Dr. Libbard thinks I ought to go to Llandrindod Wells this summer."

"Well, go, my dear, go, most certainly."

Mr. Hutton was thinking of the events of the afternoon: how they had driven, Doris and he, up to the hanging wood, had left the car to wait for them under the shade of the trees, and walked together out into the windless sunshine of the chalk down.

"I'm to drink the waters for my liver, and he thinks I ought to have massage and electric treatment, too."

Hat in hand, Doris had stalked four blue butterflies that were dancing together round a scabious flower with a motion that was like the flickering of blue fire. The blue fire burst and scattered into whirling sparks; she had given chase, laughing and shouting like a child.

"I'm sure it will do you good, my dear."

"I was wondering if you'd come with me, dear."

"But you know I'm going to Scotland at the end of the month."

Mrs. Hutton looked up at him entreatingly. "It's the journey," she said. "The thought of it is such a nightmare. I don't know if I can manage it. And you know I can't sleep in hotels. And then there's the luggage and all the worries. I can't go alone."

"But you won't be alone. You'll have your maid with you." He spoke impatiently. The sick woman was usurping the place of the healthy one. He was being dragged back from the memory of the sunlit down and the quick, laughing girl, back to this unhealthy, overheated room and its complaining occupant.

"I don't think I shall be able to go."

"But you must, my dear, if the doctor tells you to. And, besides, a change will do you good."

"I don't think so."

"But Libbard thinks so, and he knows what he's talking about."

"No, I can't face it. I'm too weak. I can't go alone." Mrs. Hutton pulled a handkerchief out of her black-silk bag and put it to her eyes.

"Nonsense, my dear, you must make the effort."

"I had rather be left in peace to die here." She was crying in earnest now.

"O Lord! Now do be reasonable. Listen now, please." Mrs. Hutton only sobbed more violently. "Oh, what is one to do?" He shrugged his shoulders and walked out of the room.

Mr. Hutton was aware that he had not behaved with proper patience; but he could not help it. Very early in his manhood he had discovered that not only did he not feel sympathy for the poor, the weak, the diseased, and deformed; he actually hated them. Once, as an undergraduate, he spent three days at a mission in the East End. He had returned, filled with a profound and ineradicable disgust. Instead of pitying, he loathed the unfortunate. It was not, he knew, a very comely emotion, and he had been ashamed of it at first. In the end he had decided that it was temperamental, inevitable, and had felt no further qualms. Emily had been healthy and beautiful when he married her. He had loved her then. But now—was it his fault that she was like this?

Mr. Hutton dined alone. Food and drink left him more benevolent than he had been before dinner. To make amends for his show of exasperation he went up to his wife's room and offered to read to her. She was touched, gratefully accepted the offer, and Mr. Hutton, who was particularly proud of his accent, suggested a little light reading in French.

"French? I am so fond of French." Mrs. Hutton spoke of the language of Racine as though it were a dish of green peas.

Mr. Hutton ran down to the library and returned with a yellow volume. He began reading. The effort of pronouncing perfectly absorbed his whole attention. But how good his accent was! The fact of its goodness seemed to improve the quality of the novel he was reading.

At the end of fifteen pages an unmistakable sound aroused him. He looked up; Mrs. Hutton had gone to sleep. He sat still for a little while, looking with a dispassionate curiosity at the sleeping face. Once it had been beautiful; once, long ago, the sight of it, the recollection of it, had moved him with an emotion profounder, perhaps, than any he had felt before or since. Now it was lined and cadaverous. The skin was stretched tightly over the cheekbones, across the bridge of the sharp, birdlike nose. The closed eyes were set in profound bone-rimmed sockets. The lamplight striking on the face from the side emphasized with light and shade its cavities and projections. It was the face of a dead Christ by Morales.

> Le squelette était invisible
> Au temps heureux de l'art païen.

He shivered a little, and tiptoed out of the room.

On the following day Mrs. Hutton came down to luncheon. She had had some unpleasant palpitations during the night, but she was feeling better now. Besides, she wanted to do honor to her guest. Miss Spence listened to her complaints about Llandrindod Wells, and was loud in sympathy, lavish with advice. Whatever she said was always said with intensity. She leaned forward, aimed, so to speak, like a gun, and fired her words. Bang! the charge in her soul was ignited, the words whizzed forth at the narrow barrel of her mouth. She was a machine gun riddling her hostess with sympathy. Mr. Hutton had undergone similar bombardments, mostly of a literary or philosophic character, bombardments of Maeterlinck, of Mrs. Besant, of Bergson, of William James. Today the missiles were medical. She talked about insomnia, she expatiated on the virtues of harmless drugs and beneficent specialists. Under the bombardment Mrs. Hutton opened out, like a flower in the sun.

Mr. Hutton looked on in silence. The spectacle of Janet Spence evoked in him an unfailing curiosity. He was not romantic enough to imagine that every face masked an interior physiognomy of beauty or strangeness, that every woman's small talk was like a vapor hanging over mysterious gulfs. His wife, for example, and Doris; they were nothing more than what they seemed to be. But with Janet Spence it was somehow different. Here one could be sure that there was some kind of a queer face behind the Gioconda smile and the Roman eyebrows. The only question was: What exactly was there? Mr. Hutton could never quite make out.

"But perhaps you won't have to go to Llandrindod after all," Miss Spence was saying. "If you get well quickly Dr. Libbard will let you off."

"I only hope so. Indeed, I do really feel rather better today."

Mr. Hutton felt ashamed. How much was it his own lack of sympathy that prevented her from feeling well every day? But he comforted himself by reflecting that it was only a case of feeling, not of being better. Sympathy does not mend a diseased liver or a weak heart.

"My dear, I wouldn't eat those red currants if I were you," he said, suddenly solicitous. "You know that Libbard has banned everything with skins and pips."

"But I am so fond of them," Mrs. Hutton protested, "and I feel so well today."

"Don't be a tyrant," said Miss Spence, looking first at him and then at his wife. "Let the poor invalid have what she fancies; it will do her good." She laid her hand on Mrs. Hutton's arm and patted it affectionately two or three times.

"Thank you, my dear." Mrs. Hutton helped herself to the stewed currants.

"Well, don't blame me if they make you ill again."

"Do I ever blame you, dear?"

"You have nothing to blame me for," Mr. Hutton answered playfully. "I am the perfect husband."

They sat in the garden after luncheon. From the island of shade under the old cypress tree they looked out across a flat expanse of lawn, in which the parterres of flowers shone with a metallic brilliance.

Mr. Hutton took a deep breath of the warm and fragrant air. "It's good to be alive," he said.

"Just to be alive," his wife echoed, stretching one pale, knot-jointed hand into the sunlight.

A maid brought the coffee; the silver pots and the little blue cups were set on a folding table near the group of chairs.

"Oh, my medicine!" exclaimed Mrs. Hutton. "Run in and fetch it, Clara, will you? The white bottle on the sideboard."

"I'll go," said Mr. Hutton. "I've got to go and fetch a cigar in any case."

He ran in toward the house. On the threshold he turned round for an instant. The maid was walking back across the lawn. His wife was sitting up in her deck chair, engaged in opening her white parasol. Miss Spence was bending over the table, pouring out the coffee. He passed into the cool obscurity of the house.

"Do you like sugar in your coffee?" Miss Spence inquired.

"Yes, please. Give me rather a lot. I'll drink it after my medicine to take the taste away."

Mrs. Hutton leaned back in her chair, lowering the sunshade over her eyes so as to shut out from her vision the burning sky.

Behind her, Miss Spence was making a delicate clinking among the coffee cups.

"I've given you three large spoonfuls. That ought to take the taste away. And here comes the medicine."

Mr. Hutton had reappeared, carrying a wineglass, half full of a pale liquid.

"It smells delicious," he said, as he handed it to his wife.

"That's only the flavoring." She drank it off at a gulp, shuddered, and made a grimace. "Ugh, it's so nasty. Give me my coffee."

Miss Spence gave her the cup; she sipped at it. "You've made it like syrup. But it's very nice, after that atrocious medicine."

At half-past three Mrs. Hutton complained that she did not feel as well as she had done, and went indoors to lie down. Her husband would have said something about the red currants, but checked himself; the triumph of an "I told you so" was too cheaply won. Instead, he was sympathetic and gave her his arm to the house.

"A rest will do you good," he said. "By the way, I shan't be back till after dinner."

"But why? Where are you going?"

"I promised to go to Johnson's this evening. We have to discuss the war memorial, you know."

"Oh, I wish you weren't going." Mrs. Hutton was almost in tears. "Can't you stay? I don't like being alone in the house."

"But, my dear, I promised, weeks ago." It was a bother having to lie like this. "And now I must get back and look after Miss Spence."

He kissed her on the forehead and went out again into the garden. Miss Spence received him aimed and intense.

"Your wife is dreadfully ill," she fired off at him.

"I thought she cheered up so much when you came."

"That was purely nervous, purely nervous. I was watching her closely. With a heart in that condition and her digestion wrecked—yes, wrecked —anything might happen."

"Libbard doesn't take so gloomy a view of poor Emily's health." Mr. Hutton held open the gate that led from the garden into the drive; Miss Spence's car was standing by the front door.

"Libbard is only a country doctor. You ought to see a specialist."

He could not refrain from laughing. "You have a macabre passion for specialists."

Miss Spence held up her hand in protest. "I am serious. I think poor Emily is in a very bad state. Anything might happen—at any moment."

He handed her into the car and shut the door. The chauffeur started the engine and climbed into his place, ready to drive off.

"Shall I tell him to start?" He had no desire to continue the conversation.

Miss Spence leaned forward and shot a Gioconda in his direction. "Remember, I expect you to come and see me again soon."

Mechanically he grinned, made a polite noise, and, as the car moved forward, waved his hand. He was happy to be alone.

A few minutes afterward Mr. Hutton himself drove away. Doris was waiting at the crossroads. They dined together twenty miles from home, at a roadside hotel. It was one of those bad, expensive meals which are only cooked in country hotels frequented by motorists. It revolted Mr. Hutton, but Doris enjoyed it. She always enjoyed things. Mr. Hutton ordered a not very good brand of champagne. He was wishing he had spent the evening in his library.

When they started homeward Doris was a little tipsy and extremely affectionate. It was very dark inside the car, but looking forward, past the motionless form of M'Nab, they could see a bright and a narrow universe of forms and colors scooped out of the night by the electric head lamps.

It was after eleven when Mr. Hutton reached home. Dr. Libbard met him in the hall. He was a small man with delicate hands and well-formed features that were almost feminine. His brown eyes were large and melancholy. He used to waste a great deal of time sitting at the bedside of his patients, looking sadness through those eyes and talking in a sad, low voice about nothing in particular. His person exhaled a pleasing odor, decidedly antiseptic but at the same time suave and discreetly delicious.

"Libbard?" said Mr. Hutton in surprise. "You here? Is my wife ill?"

"We tried to fetch you earlier," the soft, melancholy voice replied. "It was thought you were at Mr. Johnson's, but they had no news of you there."

"No, I was detained. I had a breakdown," Mr. Hutton answered irritably. It was tiresome to be caught out in a lie.

"Your wife wanted to see you urgently."

"Well, I can go now." Mr. Hutton moved toward the stairs.

Dr. Libbard laid a hand on his arm. "I am afraid it's too late."

"Too late?" He began fumbling with his watch; it wouldn't come out of his pocket.

"Mrs. Hutton passed away half an hour ago."

The voice remained even in its softness, the melancholy of the eyes did not deepen. Dr. Libbard spoke of death as he would speak of a local cricket match. All things were equally vain and equally deplorable.

Mr. Hutton found himself thinking of Janet Spence's words. At any moment, at any moment. She had been extraordinarily right.

"What happened?" he asked. "What was the cause?"

Dr. Libbard explained. It was heart failure brought on by a violent attack of nausea, caused in its turn by the eating of something of an irritant nature. Red currants? Mr. Hutton suggested. Very likely. It had been too much for the heart. There was chronic valvular disease: something had collapsed under the strain. It was all over; she could not have suffered much.

"It's a pity they should have chosen the day of the Eton and Harrow match for the funeral," old General Grego was saying as he stood up, his top hat in his hand, under the shadow of the lich gate, wiping his face with his handkerchief.

Mr. Hutton overheard the remark and with difficulty restrained a desire to inflict grievous bodily pain on the General. He would have liked to hit the old brute in the middle of his big red face. Monstrous great mulberry, spotted with meal! Was there no respect for the dead? Did nobody care? In theory he didn't much care; let the dead bury their dead. But here, at the graveside, he had found himself actually sobbing. Poor Emily, they had been pretty happy once. Now she was lying at the bottom of a seven-foot hole. And here was Grego complaining that he couldn't go to the Eton and Harrow match.

Mr. Hutton looked round at the groups of black figures that were drifting slowly out of the churchyard toward the fleet of cabs and motors assembled in the road outside. Against the brilliant background of the July grass and flowers and foliage, they had a horribly alien and unnatural appearance. It pleased him to think that all these people would soon be dead too.

That evening Mr. Hutton sat up late in his library reading the life of Milton. There was no particular reason why he should have chosen Milton; it was the book that first came to hand, that was all. It was after midnight when he had finished. He got up from his armchair, unbolted the French windows, and stepped out onto the little paved terrace. The night was quiet and clear. Mr. Hutton looked at the stars and at the holes between them, dropped his eyes to the dim lawns and hueless flowers of the garden, and let them wander over the farther landscape, black and gray under the moon.

He began to think with a kind of confused violence. There were the stars, there was Milton. A man can be somehow the peer of stars and night. Greatness, nobility. But is there seriously a difference between the noble and the ignoble? Milton, the stars, death, and himself, himself. The soul, the body; the higher and the lower nature. Perhaps there was something in it, after all. Milton had a god on his side and righteousness. What had he? Nothing, nothing whatever. There were only Doris's little breasts. What was the point of it all? Milton, the stars, death, and Emily in her grave, Doris and himself—always himself . . .

Oh, he was a futile and disgusting being. Everything convinced him of it. It was a solemn moment. He spoke aloud: "I will, I will." The sound of his own voice in the darkness was appalling; it seemed to him that he had sworn that infernal oath which binds even the gods: "I will, I will." There had been New Year's Days and solemn anniversaries in the past, when he had felt the same contritions and recorded similar resolutions. They had all thinned away, these resolutions, like smoke, into nothingness. But this was a greater moment and he had pronounced a more fearful oath. In the future it was to be different. Yes, he would live by reason, he would be industrious, he would curb his appetites, he would devote his life to some good purpose. It was resolved and it would be so.

In practice he saw himself spending his mornings in agricultural pursuits, riding round with the bailiff, seeing that his land was farmed in the best modern way, silos and artificial manures and continuous cropping, and all that. The remainder of the day should be devoted to serious study. There was that book he had been intending to write for so long: The Effect of Diseases on Civilization.

Mr. Hutton went to bed humble and contrite, but with a sense that grace had entered into him. He slept for seven and a half hours, and woke to find the sun brilliantly shining. The emotions of the evening before had been transformed by a good night's rest into his customary cheerfulness. It was not until a good many seconds after his return to conscious life that he remembered his resolution, his Stygian oath. Milton and death seemed somehow different in the sunlight. As for the stars, they were not there. But the resolutions were good; even in the daytime he could see that. He had his horse saddled after breakfast, and rode round the farm with the bailiff. After luncheon he read Thucydides on the plague at Athens. In the evening he made a few notes on malaria in Southern Italy. While he was undressing he remembered that there was a good anecdote in Skelton's jestbook about the Sweating Sickness. He would have made a note of it if only he could have found a pencil.

On the sixth morning of his new life Mr. Hutton found among his correspondence an envelope addressed in that peculiarly vulgar handwriting which he knew to be Doris's. He opened it, and began to read. She didn't know what to say, words were so inadequate. His wife dying like that, and so suddenly—it was too terrible. Mr. Hutton sighed, but his interest revived somewhat as he read on:

> Death is so frightening, I never think of it when I can help it. But when something like this happens, or when I am feeling ill or depressed, then I can't help remembering it is there so close, and I think about all the wicked things I have done and about you and me, and I wonder what will happen, and I am so frightened. I am so lonely, Teddy Bear, and so unhappy, and I don't know what to do. I can't get rid of the idea of dying, I am so wretched and helpless without you. I didn't mean to write to you; I meant to wait till you were out of mourning and could come and see me again, but I was so lonely and miserable, Teddy Bear, I had to write. I couldn't help it. Forgive me, I want you so much; I have nobody in the world but you. You are so good and gentle and understanding; there is nobody like you. I shall never forget how good and kind you have been to me, and you are so clever and know so much, I can't understand how you ever came to pay any attention to me, I am so dull and stupid, much less like me and love me, because you do love me a little, don't you, Teddy Bear?

Mr. Hutton was touched with shame and remorse. To be thanked like this, worshiped for having seduced the girl, it was too much. It had just been a piece of imbecile wantonness. Imbecile, idiotic: there was no other way to describe it. For, when all was said, he had derived very little pleasure from it. Taking all things together, he had probably been more bored than amused. Once upon a time he had believed himself to be a hedonist. But to be a hedonist implies a certain process of reasoning, a deliberate choice of known pleasures, a rejection of known pains. This had been done without reason, against it. For he knew beforehand —so well, so well—that there was no interest or pleasure to be derived from these wretched affairs. And yet each time the vague itch came upon him he succumbed, involving himself once more in the old stupidity. There had been Maggie, his wife's maid, and Edith, the girl on the farm, and Mrs. Pringle, and the waitress in London, and others—there seemed to be dozens of them. It had all been so stale and boring. He knew it would be; he always knew. And yet, and yet . . . Experience doesn't teach.

Poor little Doris! He would write to her kindly, comfortingly, but he wouldn't see her again. A servant came to tell him that his horse was saddled and waiting. He mounted and rode off. That morning the old bailiff was more irritating than usual.

Five days later Doris and Mr. Hutton were sitting together on the pier at Southend; Doris, in white muslin with pink garnishings, radiated happiness; Mr. Hutton, legs outstretched and chair tilted, had pushed the panama back from his forehead and was trying to feel like a tripper. That night, when Doris was asleep, breathing and warm by his side, he recaptured, in this moment of darkness and physical fatigue, the rather cosmic emotion which had possessed him that evening, not a fortnight ago, when he had made his great resolution. And so his solemn oath had already gone the way of so many other resolutions. Unreason had triumphed; at the first itch of desire he had given way. He was hopeless, hopeless.

For a long time he lay with closed eyes, ruminating his humiliation. The girl stirred in her sleep. Mr. Hutton turned over and looked in her direction. Enough faint light crept in between the half-drawn curtains to show her bare arm and shoulder, her neck, and the dark tangle of hair on the pillow. She was beautiful, desirable. Why did he lie there moaning over his sins? What did it matter? If he were hopeless, then so be it; he would make the best of his hopelessness. A glorious sense of irresponsibility suddenly filled him. He was free, magnificently free. In a kind of exaltation he drew the girl toward him. She woke, bewildered, almost frightened under his rough kisses.

The storm of his desire subsided into a kind of serene merriment. The whole atmosphere seemed to be quivering with enormous silent laughter.

"Could anyone love you as much as I do, Teddy Bear?" The question came faintly from distant worlds of love.

"I think I know somebody who does," Mr. Hutton replied. The submarine laughter was swelling, rising, ready to break the surface of silence and resound.

"Who? Tell me. What do you mean?" The voice had come very close; charged with suspicion, anguish, indignation, it belonged to this immediate world.

"Ah!"

"Who?"

"You'll never guess." Mr. Hutton kept up the joke until it began to grow tedious, and then pronounced the name: "Janet Spence."

Doris was incredulous. "Miss Spence of the Manor? That old woman?" It was too ridiculous. Mr. Hutton laughed too.

"But it's quite true," he said. "She adores me." Oh, the vast joke! He would go and see her as soon as he returned, see and conquer. "I believe she wants to marry me," he added.

"But you wouldn't . . . you don't intend . . ."

The air was fairly crepitating with humor. Mr. Hutton laughed aloud. "I intend to marry you," he said. It seemed to him the best joke he had ever made in his life.

When Mr. Hutton left Southend he was once more a married man. It was agreed that, for the time being, the fact should be kept secret. In the autumn they would go abroad together, and the world should be informed. Meanwhile he was to go back to his own house and Doris to hers.

The day after his return he walked over in the afternoon to see Miss Spence. She received him with the old Gioconda.

"I was expecting you to come."

"I couldn't keep away," Mr. Hutton gallantly replied.

They sat in the summerhouse. It was a pleasant place—a little old stucco temple bowered among dense bushes of evergreen. Miss Spence had left her mark on it by hanging up over the seat a blue-and-white Della Robbia plaque.

"I am thinking of going to Italy this autumn," said Mr. Hutton. He felt like a ginger-beer bottle, ready to pop with bubbling humorous excitement.

"Italy. . . ." Miss Spence closed her eyes ecstatically. "I feel drawn there too."

"Why not let yourself be drawn?"

"I don't know. One somehow hasn't the energy and initiative to set out alone."

"Alone. . . ." Ah, sound of guitars and throaty singing! "Yes, traveling alone isn't much fun."

Miss Spence lay back in her chair without speaking. Her eyes were still closed. Mr. Hutton stroked his mustache. The silence prolonged itself for what seemed a very long time.

Pressed to stay to dinner, Mr. Hutton did not refuse. The fun had hardly started. The table was laid in the loggia. Through its arches they looked out onto the sloping garden, to the valley below and the farther hills. Light ebbed away; the heat and silence were oppressive. A huge cloud was mounting up the sky, and there were distant breathings of thunder. The thunder drew nearer, a wind began to blow, and the first drops of rain fell. The table was cleared. Miss Spence and Mr. Hutton sat on in the growing darkness.

Miss Spence broke a long silence by saying meditatively: "I think everyone has a right to a certain amount of happiness, don't you?"

"Most certainly." But what was she leading up to? Nobody makes generalizations about life unless they mean to talk about themselves. Happiness: he looked back on his own life, and saw a cheerful, placid existence disturbed by no great griefs or discomforts or alarms. He had always had money and freedom; he had been able to do very much as he wanted. Yes, he supposed he had been happy, happier than most men. And now he was not merely happy; he had discovered in irresponsibility the secret of gaiety. He was about to say something about his happiness when Miss Spence went on speaking.

"People like you and me have a right to be happy some time in our lives."

"Me?" said Mr. Hutton surprised.

"Poor Henry! Fate hasn't treated either of us very well."

"Oh, well, it might have treated me worse."

"You're being cheerful. That's brave of you. But don't think I can't see behind the mask."

Miss Spence spoke louder and louder as the rain came down more and more heavily. Periodically the thunder cut across her utterances. She talked on, shouting against the noise.

"I have understood you so well and for so long."

A flash revealed her, aimed and intent, leaning toward him. Her eyes were two profound and menacing gun barrels. The darkness re-engulfed her.

"You were a lonely soul seeking a companion soul. I could sympathize with you in your solitude. Your marriage . . ."

The thunder cut short the sentence. Miss Spence's voice became audible once more with the words:

". . . could offer no companionship to a man of your stamp. You needed a soul mate."

A soul mate—he! A soul mate! It was incredibly fantastic. "Georgette Leblanc, the ex-soul mate of Maurice Maeterlinck." He had seen that in the paper a few days ago. So it was thus that Janet Spence had painted him in her imagination—as a soul-mater. And for Doris he was a picture of goodness and the cleverest man in the world. And actually, really, he was what? Who knows?

"My heart went out to you. I could understand; I was lonely, too."

Miss Spence laid her hand on his knee. "You were so patient." Another flash. She was still aimed, dangerously. "You never complained. But I could guess, I could guess."

"How wonderful of you!" So he was an *âme incomprise*. "Only a woman's intuition . . ."

The thunder crashed and rumbled, died away, and only the sound of the rain was left. The thunder was his laughter, magnified, externalized. Flash and crash, there it was again, right on top of them.

"Don't you feel that you have within you something that is akin to this storm?" He could imagine her leaning forward as she uttered the words. "Passion makes one the equal of the elements."

What was his gambit now? Why, obviously, he should have said, "Yes," and ventured on some unequivocal gesture. But Mr. Hutton suddenly took fright. The ginger beer in him had gone flat. The woman was serious —terribly serious. He was appalled.

Passion? "No," he desperately answered. "I am without passion."

But his remark was either unheard or unheeded, for Miss Spence went on with a growing exaltation, speaking so rapidly, however, and in such a burningly intimate whisper that Mr. Hutton found it very difficult to distinguish what she was saying. She was telling him, as far as he could make out, the story of her life. The lightning was less frequent now, and there were long intervals of darkness. But at each flash he saw her still aiming toward him, still yearning forward with a terrifying intensity. Darkness, the rain, and then flash! her face was there, close at hand. A pale mask, greenish white; the large eyes, the narrow barrel of the mouth, the heavy eyebrows. Agrippina, or wasn't it rather—yes, wasn't it rather George Robey?

He began devising absurd plans for escaping. He might suddenly jump up, pretending he had seen a burglar—Stop thief! stop thief!— and dash off into the night in pursuit. Or should he say that he felt faint, a heart attack, or that he had seen a ghost—Emily's ghost—in the garden? Absorbed in his childish plotting, he had ceased to pay any attention to Miss Spence's words. The spasmodic clutching of her hand recalled his thoughts.

"I honored you for that, Henry," she was saying.

Honored him for what?

"Marriage is a sacred tie, and your respect for it, even when the marriage was, as it was in your case, an unhappy one, made me respect you and admire you, and—shall I dare say the word?—"

Oh, the burglar, the ghost in the garden! But it was too late.

". . . yes, love you, Henry, all the more. But we're free now, Henry."

Free? There was a movement in the dark, and she was kneeling on the floor by his chair.

"Oh, Henry, Henry, I have been unhappy too."

Her arms embraced him, and by the shaking of her body he could feel that she was sobbing. She might have been a suppliant crying for mercy. "You mustn't, Janet," he protested. Those tears were terrible, terrible. "Not now, not now! You must be calm; you must go to bed." He patted her shoulder, then got up, disengaging himself from her embrace. He left her still crouching on the floor beside the chair on which he had been sitting.

Groping his way into the hall, and without waiting to look for his hat, he went out of the house, taking infinite pains to close the front door noiselessly behind him. The clouds had blown over, and the moon was shining from a clear sky. There were puddles all along the road, and a noise of running water rose from the gutters and ditches. Mr. Hutton splashed along, not caring if he got wet.

How heart-rendingly she had sobbed! With the emotions of pity and remorse that the recollection evoked in him there was a certain resentment: why couldn't she have played the game that he was playing, the heartless, amusing game? Yes, but he had known all the time that she wouldn't, she couldn't, play that game; he had known and persisted.

What had she said about passion and the elements? Something absurdly stale, but true, true. There she was, a cloud black-bosomed and charged with thunder, and he, like some absurd little Benjamin Franklin, had sent up a kite into the heart of the menace. Now he was complaining that his toy had drawn the lightning.

She was probably still kneeling by that chair in the loggia, crying.

But why hadn't he been able to keep up the game? Why had his irresponsibility deserted him, leaving him suddenly sober in a cold world? There were no answers to any of his questions. One idea burned steady and luminous in his mind, the idea of flight. He must get away at once.

"What are you thinking about, Teddy Bear?"

"Nothing."

There was a silence. Mr. Hutton remained motionless, his elbows on the parapet of the terrace, his chin in his hands, looking down over Florence. He had taken a villa on one of the hilltops to the south of the city. From a little raised terrace at the end of the garden one looked down a long fertile valley on to the town and beyond it to the bleak mass of Monte Morello and, eastward of it, to the peopled hill of Fiesole, dotted with white houses. Everything was clear and luminous in the September sunshine.

"Are you worried about anything?"

"No, thank you."

"Tell me, Teddy Bear."

"But, my dear, there's nothing to tell." Mr. Hutton turned round, smiled, and patted the girl's hand. "I think you'd better go in and have your siesta. It's too hot for you here."

"Very well, Teddy Bear. Are you coming too?"

"When I've finished my cigar."

"All right. But do hurry up and finish it, Teddy Bear." Slowly, reluctantly, she descended the steps of the terrace and walked toward the house.

Mr. Hutton continued his contemplation of Florence. He had need to be alone. It was good sometimes to escape from Doris and the restless solicitude of her passion. He had never known the pains of loving hopelessly, but he was experiencing now the pains of being loved. These last weeks had been a period of growing discomfort. Doris was always with him, like an obsession, like a guilty conscience. Yes, it was good to be alone.

He pulled an envelope out of his pocket and opened it, not without reluctance. He hated letters; they always contained something unpleasant, nowadays, since his second marriage. This was from his sister. He began skimming through the insulting home-truths of which it was composed. The words "indecent haste," "social suicide," "scarcely cold in her grave," "person of the lower classes," all occurred. They were inevitable now in any communication from a well-meaning and right-thinking relative. Impatient, he was about to tear the stupid letter to pieces when his eye fell on a sentence at the bottom of the third page. His heart beat with uncomfortable violence as he read it. It was too monstrous! Janet Spence was going about telling everyone that he had poisoned his wife in order to marry Doris. What damnable malice! Ordinarily a man of the suavest temper, Mr. Hutton found himself trembling with rage. He took the childish satisfaction of calling names—he cursed the woman.

Then suddenly he saw the ridiculous side of the situation. The notion that he should have murdered anyone in order to marry Doris! If they only knew how miserably bored he was. Poor, dear Janet! She had tried to be malicious; she had only succeeded in being stupid.

A sound of footsteps aroused him; he looked round. In the garden below the little terrace the servant girl of the house was picking fruit. A Neapolitan, strayed somehow as far north as Florence, she was a specimen of the classical type a little debased. Her profile might have been taken from a Sicilian coin of a bad period. Her features, carved floridly in the grand tradition, expressed an almost perfect stupidity. Her mouth was the most beautiful thing about her; the calligraphic hand of nature had richly curved it into an expression of mulish bad temper. Under her hideous black clothes, Mr. Hutton divined a powerful body, firm and massive. He had looked at her before with a vague interest and curiosity. Today the curiosity defined and focused itself into a desire. An idyll of Theocritus. Here was the woman; he, alas, was not precisely like a goatherd on the volcanic hills. He called to her.

"Armida!"

The smile with which she answered him was so provocative, attested so easy a virtue, that Mr. Hutton took fright. He was on the brink once more —on the brink. He must draw back, oh! quickly, quickly, before it was too late. The girl continued to look up at him.

"*Ha chiamato?*" she asked at last.

Stupidity or reason? Oh, there was no choice now. It was imbecility every time.

"*Scendo,*" he called back to her. Twelve steps led from the garden to the terrace. Mr. Hutton counted them. Down, down, down, down. . . . He saw a vision of himself descending from one circle of the inferno to the next, from a darkness full of wind and hail to an abyss of stinking mud.

For a good many days the Hutton case had a place on the front page of every newspaper. There had been no more popular murder trial since George Smith had temporarily eclipsed the European War by drowning in a warm bath his seventh bride. The public imagination was stirred by this tale of a murder brought to light months after the date of the crime. Here, it was felt, was one of those incidents in human life, so notable because they are so rare, which do definitely justify the ways of God to man. A wicked man had been moved by an illicit passion to kill his wife. For months he had lived in sin and fancied security, only to be dashed at last more horribly into the pit he had prepared for himself. "Murder will out," and here was a case of it. The readers of the newspapers were in a position to follow every movement of the hand of God. There had been vague, but persistent rumors in the neighborhood; the police had taken action at last. Then came the exhumation order, the post-mortem examination, the inquest, the evidence of the experts, the verdict of the coroner's jury, the trial, the condemnation. For once Providence had done its duty, obviously, grossly, didactically, as in a melodrama. The newspapers were right in making of the case the staple intellectual food of a whole season.

Mr. Hutton's first emotion when he was summoned from Italy to give evidence at the inquest was one of indignation. It was a monstrous, a scandalous thing that the police should take such idle, malicious gossip seriously. When the inquest was over he would bring an action for malicious prosecution against the Chief Constable; he would sue the Spence woman for slander.

The inquest was opened; the astonishing evidence unrolled itself. The experts had examined the body, and had found traces of arsenic; they were of opinion that the late Mrs. Hutton had died of arsenic poisoning.

Arsenic poisoning . . . Emily had died of arsenic poisoning? After that, Mr. Hutton learned with surprise that there was enough arsenicated insecticide in his greenhouses to poison an army.

It was now, quite suddenly, that he saw it: there was a case against him. Fascinated, he watched it growing, growing, like some monstrous tropical plant. It was enveloping him, surrounding him; he was lost in a tangled forest.

When was the poison administered? The experts agreed that it must have been swallowed eight or nine hours before death. About lunchtime? Yes, about lunchtime. Clara, the parlormaid, was called. Mrs. Hutton, she remembered, had asked her to go and fetch her medicine. Mr. Hutton had volunteered to go instead; he had gone alone. Miss Spence—ah, the memory of the storm, the white face, the horror of it all!—Miss Spence confirmed Clara's statement, and added that Mr. Hutton had come back with the medicine already poured out in a wineglass, not in the bottle.

Mr. Hutton's indignation evaporated. He was dismayed, frightened. It was all too fantastic to be taken seriously, and yet this nightmare was a fact, it was actually happening.

M'Nab had seen them kissing, often. He had taken them for a drive on the day of Mrs. Hutton's death. He could see them reflected in the wind screen, sometimes out of the tail of his eye.

The inquest was adjourned. That evening Doris went to bed with a headache. When he went to her room after dinner, Mr. Hutton found her crying.

"What's the matter?" He sat down on the edge of her bed and began to stroke her hair. For a long time she did not answer, and he went on stroking her hair mechanically, almost unconsciously; sometimes, even, he bent down and kissed her bare shoulder. He had his own affairs, how-ever, to think about. What had happened? How was it that the stupid gossip had actually come true? Emily had died of arsenic poisoning. It was absurd, impossible. The order of things had been broken, and he was at the mercy of an irresponsibility. What had happened, what was going to happen? He was interrupted in the midst of his thoughts.

"It's my fault, it's my fault!" Doris suddenly sobbed out. "I shouldn't have loved you; I oughtn't to have let you love me. Why was I ever born?"

Mr. Hutton didn't say anything, but looked down in silence at the abject figure of misery lying on the bed.

"If they do anything to you I shall kill myself."

She sat up, held him for a moment at arm's length, and looked at him with a kind of violence, as though she were never to see him again.

"I love you, I love you, I love you." She drew him, inert and passive, toward her, clasped him, pressed herself against him. "I didn't know you loved me as much as that, Teddy Bear. But why did you do it, why did you do it?"

Mr. Hutton undid her clasping arms and got up. His face became very red. "You seem to take it for granted that I murdered my wife," he said. "It's really too grotesque. What do you all take me for? A cinema hero?" He had begun to lose his temper. All the exasperation, all the fear and bewilderment of the day, was transformed into a violent anger against her. "It's all such damned stupidity. Haven't you any conception of a civilized man's mentality? Do I look the sort of man who'd go about slaughtering people? I suppose you imagined I was so insanely in love with you that I could commit any folly. When will you women understand that one isn't insanely in love? All one asks for is a quiet life, which you won't allow one to have. I don't know what the devil ever induced me to marry you. It was all a damned stupid, practical joke. And now you go about saying I'm a murderer. I won't stand it."

Mr. Hutton stamped toward the door. He had said horrible things, he knew, odious things that he ought speedily to unsay. But he wouldn't. He closed the door behind him.

"Teddy Bear!" He turned the handle; the latch clicked into place. "Teddy Bear!" The voice that came to him through the closed door was agonized. Should he go back? He ought to go back. He touched the handle, then withdrew his fingers and quickly walked away. When he was halfway down the stairs he halted. She might try to do something silly— throw herself out of the window or God knows what! He listened attentively; there was no sound. But he pictured her very clearly, tiptoeing across the room, lifting the sash as high as it would go, leaning out into the cold night air. It was raining a little. Under the window lay the paved terrace. How far below? Twenty-five or thirty feet? Once, when he was walking along Piccadilly, a dog had jumped out of a third-story window of the Ritz. He had seen it fall; he had heard it strike the pavement. Should he go back? He was damned if he would; he hated her.

He sat for a long time in the library. What had happened? What was happening? He turned the question over and over in his mind and could find no answer. Suppose the nightmare dreamed itself out to its horrible conclusion. Death was waiting for him. His eyes filled with tears; he wanted so passionately to live. "Just to be alive." Poor Emily had wished it too, he remembered: "Just to be alive." There were still so many places in this astonishing world unvisited, so many queer delightful people still unknown, so many lovely women never so much as seen. The huge white oxen would still be dragging their wains along the Tuscan roads, the cypresses would still go up, straight as pillars, to the blue heaven; but he would not be there to see them. And the sweet southern wines—Tears of Christ and Blood of Judas—others would drink them, not he. Others would walk down the obscure and narrow lanes between the bookshelves in the London Library, sniffing the dusty perfume of good literature, peer-ing at strange titles, discovering unknown names, exploring the fringes of vast domains of knowledge. He would be lying in a hole in the ground. And why, why? Confusedly he felt that some extraordinary kind of justice was being done. In the past he had been wanton and imbecile and irresponsible. Now Fate was playing as wantonly, as irresponsibly, with him. It was tit for tat, and God existed after all.

He felt that he would like to pray. Forty years ago he used to kneel by his bed every evening. The nightly formula of his childhood came to him almost unsought from some long-unopened chamber of the memory. "God bless Father and Mother, Tom and Cissie and the Baby, Made-moiselle and Nurse, and everyone that I love, and make me a good boy. Amen." They were all dead now, all except Cissie.

His mind seemed to soften and dissolve; a great calm descended upon his spirit. He went upstairs to ask Doris's forgiveness. He found her lying on the couch at the foot of the bed. On the floor beside her stood a blue bottle of liniment, marked NOT TO BE TAKEN; she seemed to have drunk about half of it.

"You didn't love me," was all she said when she opened her eyes to find him bending over her.

Dr. Libbard arrived in time to prevent any very serious consequences. "You mustn't do this again," he said while Mr. Hutton was out of the room.

"What's to prevent me?" she asked defiantly.

Dr. Libbard looked at her with his large, sad eyes. "There's nothing to prevent you," he said. "Only yourself and your baby. Isn't it rather bad luck on your baby, not allowing it to come into the world because you want to go out of it?"

Doris was silent for a time. "All right," she whispered, "I won't."

Mr. Hutton sat by her bedside for the rest of the night. He felt himself now to be indeed a murderer. For a time he persuaded himself that he loved this pitiable child. Dozing in his chair, he woke up, stiff and cold, to find himself drained dry, as it were, of every emotion. He had become nothing but a tired and suffering carcass. At six o'clock he undressed and went to bed for a couple of hours' sleep. In the course of the same afternoon the coroner's jury brought in a verdict of "Willful Murder," and Mr. Hutton was committed for trial.

Miss Spence was not at all well. She had found her public appearances in the witness box very trying, and when it was all over she had something that was very nearly a breakdown. She slept badly, and suffered from nervous indigestion. Dr. Libbard used to call every other day. She talked to him a great deal, mostly about the Hutton case. Her moral indignation was always on the boil. Wasn't it appalling to think that one had had a murderer in one's house? Wasn't it extraordinary that one could have been for so long mistaken about the man's character? (But she had had an inkling from the first.) And then the girl he had gone off with—so low class, so little better than a prostitute. The news that the second Mrs. Hutton was expecting a baby, the posthumous child of a condemned and executed criminal, revolted her; the thing was shocking, an obscenity. Dr. Libbard answered her gently and vaguely, and prescribed bromide.

One morning he interrupted her in the midst of her customary tirade. "By the way," he said in his soft, melancholy voice, "I suppose it was really you who poisoned Mrs. Hutton."

Miss Spence stared at him for two or three seconds with enormous eyes, and then quietly said, "Yes." After that she started to cry.

"In the coffee, I suppose."

She seemed to nod assent. Dr. Libbard took out his fountain pen, and in his neat, meticulous calligraphy wrote out a prescription for a sleeping draught.

Nuns at Luncheon

From *Mortal Coils*

"WHAT have I been doing since you saw me last?" Miss Penny repeated my question in her loud, emphatic voice. "Well, when did you see me last?"

"It must have been June," I computed.

"Was that after I'd been proposed to by the Russian General?"

"Yes; I remember hearing about the Russian General."

Miss Penny threw back her head and laughed. Her long earrings swung and rattled—corpses hanging in chains: an agreeably literary simile. And her laughter was like brass, but that had been said before.

"That was an uproarious incident. It's sad you should have heard of it. I love my Russian General story. 'Vos yeux me rendent fou.'" She laughed again.

Vos yeux—she had eyes like a hare's, flush with her head and very bright with a superficial and expressionless brightness. What a formidable woman. I felt sorry for the Russian General.

"'Sans cœur et sans entrailles,'" she went on quoting the poor devil's words. "Such a delightful motto, don't you think? Like 'Sans peur et sans reproche.' But let me think; what have I been doing since then?" Thoughtfully she bit into the crust of her bread with long, sharp, white teeth.

"Two mixed grills," I said parenthetically to the waiter.

"But of course," exclaimed Miss Penny suddenly. "I haven't seen you since my German trip. All sorts of adventures. My appendicitis; my nun."

"Your nun?"

"My marvelous nun. I must tell you all about her."

"Do." Miss Penny's anecdotes were always curious. I looked forward to an entertaining luncheon.

"You knew I'd been in Germany this autumn?"

"Well, I didn't, as a matter of fact. But still——"

"I was just wandering round." Miss Penny described a circle in the air with her gaudily jeweled hand. She always twinkled with massive and improbable jewelry. "Wandering round, living on three pounds a week, partly amusing myself, partly collecting material for a few little articles. 'What it Feels Like to be a Conquered Nation'—sob stuff for the Liberal press, you know—and 'How the Hun is Trying to Wriggle out of the Indemnity,' for the other fellows. One has to make the best of all possible worlds, don't you find? But we mustn't talk shop. Well, I was wandering round, and very pleasant I found it. Berlin, Dresden, Leipzig. Then down to Munich and all over the place. One fine day I got to Grauburg. You know Grauburg? It's one of those picture-book German towns with a castle on a hill, hanging beer gardens, a Gothic church, an old university, a river, a pretty bridge, and forests all round. Charming. But I hadn't much opportunity to appreciate the beauties of the place. The day after I arrived there—bang!—I went down with appendicitis —screaming, I may add."

"But how appalling!"

"They whisked me off to a hospital, and cut me open before you could say knife. Excellent surgeon, highly efficient Sisters of Charity to nurse me—I couldn't have been in better hands. But it was a bore being tied there by the leg for four weeks—a great bore. Still, the thing had its compensations. There was my nun, for example. Ah, here's the food, thank Heaven!"

The mixed grill proved to be excellent. Miss Penny's description of the nun came to me in scraps and snatches. A round, pink, pretty face in a winged coif; blue eyes and regular features; teeth altogether too perfect —false, in fact; but the general effect extremely pleasing. A youthful Teutonic twenty-eight.

"She wasn't my nurse," Miss Penny explained. "But I used to see her quite often when she came in to have a look at the *tolle Engländerin*. Her name was Sister Agatha. During the war, they told me, she had converted any number of wounded soldiers to the true faith—which wasn't surprising, considering how pretty she was."

"Did she try and convert you?" I asked.

"She wasn't such a fool." Miss Penny laughed, and rattled the miniature gallows of her ears.

I amused myself for a moment with the thought of Miss Penny's conversion—Miss Penny confronting a vast assembly of Fathers of the Church, rattling her earrings at their discourses on the Trinity, laughing her appalling laugh at the doctrine of the Immaculate Conception, meeting the stern look of the Grand Inquisitor with a flash of her bright, emotionless, hare's eyes. What was the secret of the woman's formidableness?

But I was missing the story. What had happened? Ah yes, the gist of it was that Sister Agatha had appeared one morning, after two or three days' absence, dressed, not as a nun, but in the overalls of a hospital charwoman, with a handkerchief instead of a winged coif on her shaven head.

"Dead," said Miss Penny; "she looked as though she were dead. A walking corpse, that's what she was. It was a shocking sight. I shouldn't have thought it possible for anyone to change so much in so short a time. She walked painfully, as though she had been ill for months, and she had great burned rings round her eyes and deep lines in her face. And the general expression of unhappiness—that was something quite appalling."

She leaned out into the gangway between the two rows of tables, and caught the passing waiter by the end of one of his coattails. The little Italian looked round with an expression of surprise that deepened into terror on his face.

"Half a pint of Guinness," ordered Miss Penny. "And, after this, bring me some jam roll."

"No jam roll today, madam."

"Damn!" said Miss Penny. "Bring me what you like, then."

She let go of the waiter's tail and resumed her narrative.

"Where was I? Yes, I remember. She came into my room, I was telling you, with a bucket of water and a brush, dressed like a charwoman. Naturally I was rather surprised. 'What on earth are you doing, Sister Agatha?' I asked. No answer. She just shook her head, and began to scrub the floor. When she'd finished, she left the room without so much as looking at me again. 'What's happened to Sister Agatha?' I asked my nurse when she next came in. 'Can't say.'—'Won't say,' I said. No answer. It took nearly a week to find out what really had happened. Nobody dared tell me; it was *strengst verboten*, as they used to say in the good old days. But I wormed it out in the long run. My nurse, the doctor, the charwomen—I got something out of all of them. I always get what I want in the end." Miss Penny laughed like a horse.

"I'm sure you do," I said politely.

"Much obliged," acknowledged Miss Penny. "But to proceed. My information came to me in fragmentary whispers. 'Sister Agatha ran away with a man.'—Dear me!—'One of the patients.'—You don't say so.—'A criminal out of the jail.'—The plot thickens.—'He ran away from her.'—It seems to grow thinner again.—'They brought her back here; she's been disgraced. There's been a funeral service for her in the chapel—coffin and all. She had to be present at it—her own funeral. She isn't a nun any more. She has to do charwoman's work now, the roughest in the hospital. She's not allowed to speak to anybody, and nobody's allowed to speak to her. She's regarded as dead.'" Miss Penny paused to signal to the harassed little Italian. "My small 'Guinness,'" she called out.

"Coming, coming," and the foreign voice cried "Guinness" down the lift, and from below another voice echoed, "Guinness."

"I filled in the details bit by bit. There was our hero, to begin with; I had to bring him into the picture, which was rather difficult, as I had never seen him. But I got a photograph of him. The police circulated one when he got away; I don't suppose they ever caught him." Miss Penny opened her bag. "Here it is," she said. "I always carry it about with me; it's become a superstition. For years, I remember, I used to carry a little bit of heather tied up with string. Beautiful, isn't it? There's a sort of Renaissance look about it, don't you think? He was half Italian, you know."

Italian. Ah, that explained it. I had been wondering how Bavaria could have produced this thin-faced creature with the big dark eyes, the finely modeled nose and chin, and the fleshy lips so royally and sensually curved.

"He's certainly very superb," I said, handing back the picture.

Miss Penny put it carefully away in her bag. "Isn't he?" she said. "Quite marvelous. But his character and his mind were even better. I see him as one of those innocent, childlike monsters of iniquity who are simply unaware of the existence of right and wrong. And he had genius —the real Italian genius for engineering, for dominating and exploiting nature. A true son of the Roman aqueduct builders he was, and a brother of the electrical engineers. Only Kuno—that was his name—didn't work in water; he worked in women. He knew how to harness the natural energy of passion; he made devotion drive his mills. The commercial exploitation of love power, that was his specialty. I sometimes wonder," Miss Penny added in a different tone, "whether I shall ever be exploited, when I get a little more middle aged and celibate, by one of these young engineers of the passions. It would be humiliating, particularly as I've done so little exploiting from my side."

She frowned and was silent for a moment. No, decidedly, Miss Penny was not beautiful; you could not even honestly say that she had charm or was attractive. That high Scotch coloring, those hare's eyes, the voice, the terrifying laugh, and the size of her, the general formidableness of the woman. No, no, no.

"You said he had been in prison," I said. The silence, with all its implications, was becoming embarrassing.

Miss Penny sighed, looked up, and nodded. "He was fool enough," she said, "to leave the straight and certain road of female exploitation for the dangerous courses of burglary. We all have our occasional accesses of folly. They gave him a heavy sentence, but he succeeded in getting pneumonia, I think it was, a week after entering jail. He was transferred to the hospital. Sister Agatha, with her known talent for saving souls, was given him as his particular attendant. But it was he, I'm afraid, who did the converting."

Miss Penny finished off the last mouthful of the ginger pudding which the waiter had brought in lieu of jam roll.

"I suppose you don't smoke cheroots," I said, as I opened my cigar case.

"Well, as a matter of fact, I do," Miss Penny replied. She looked sharply round the restaurant. "I must just see if there are any of those horrible little gossip paragraphers here today. One doesn't want to figure in the social and personal column tomorrow morning: 'A fact which is not so generally known as it ought to be is that Miss Penny, the well-known woman journalist, always ends her luncheon with a six-inch Burma cheroot. I saw her yesterday in a restaurant—not a hundred miles from Carmelite Street—smoking like a house on fire.' You know the touch. But the coast seems to be clear, thank goodness."

She took a cheroot from the case, lit it at my proffered match, and went on talking.

"Yes, it was young Kuno who did the converting. Sister Agatha was converted back into the worldly Melpomene Fugger she had been before she became the bride of holiness."

"Melpomene Fugger?"

"That was her name. I had her history from my old doctor. He had seen all Grauburg, living and dying and propagating, for generations. Melpomene Fugger—why, he had brought little Melpel into the world, little Melpchen. Her father was Professor Fugger, the great Professor Fugger, the *berümter Geolog*. Oh, yes, of course, I know the name. So well . . . He was the man who wrote the standard work on Lemuria— you know, the hypothetical continent where the lemurs come from. I showed due respect. Liberal minded he was, a disciple of Herder, a world burgher, as they beautifully call it over there. Anglophile, too, and always ate porridge for breakfast—up till August 1914. Then, on the radiant morning of the fifth, he renounced it forever, solemnly and with tears in his eyes. The national food of a people who had betrayed culture and civilization—how could he go on eating it? It would stick in his throat. In future he would have a lightly boiled egg. He sounded, I thought, altogether charming. And his daughter, Melpomene—she sounded charming, too; and such thick, yellow pigtails when she was young! Her mother was dead, and a sister of the great Professor's ruled the house with an iron rod. Aunt Bertha was her name. Well, Melpomene grew up, very plump and appetizing. When she was seventeen, something very odious and disagreeable happened to her. Even the doctor didn't know exactly what it was; but he wouldn't have been surprised if it had had something to do with the then professor of Latin, an old friend of the family's, who combined, it seems, great erudition with a horrid fondness for very young ladies."

Miss Penny knocked half an inch of cigar ash into her empty glass.

"If I wrote short stories," she went on reflectively "(but it's too much bother), I should make this anecdote into a sort of potted life history, beginning with a scene immediately after this disagreeable event in Melpomene's life. I see the scene so clearly. Poor little Melpel is leaning over the bastions of Grauburg Castle, weeping into the June night and the mulberry trees in the garden thirty feet below. She is besieged by the memory of what happened this dreadful afternoon. Professor Engelmann, her father's old friend, with the magnificent red Assyrian beard . . . Too awful—too awful! But then, as I was saying, short stories are really too much bother; or perhaps I'm too stupid to write them. I bequeath it to you. You know how to tick these things off."

"You're generous."

"Not at all," said Miss Penny. "My terms are ten per cent commission on the American sale. Incidentally there won't be an American sale. Poor Melpchen's history is not for the chaste public of Those States. But let me hear what you propose to do with Melpomene now you've got her on the castle bastions."

"That's simple," I said. "I know all about German university towns and castles on hills. I shall make her look into the June night, as you suggest; into the violet night with its points of golden flame. There will be the black silhouette of the castle, with its sharp roofs and hooded turrets, behind her. From the hanging beer gardens in the town below the voices of the students, singing in perfect four-part harmony, will float up through the dark-blue spaces. 'Röslein, Röslein, Röslein rot' and 'Das Ringlein sprang in zwei'—the heart-rendingly sweet old songs will make her cry all the more. Her tears will patter like rain among the leaves of the mulberry trees in the garden below. Does that seem to you adequate?"

"Very nice," said Miss Penny. "But how are you going to bring the sex problem and all its horrors into your landscape?"

"Well, let me think." I called to memory those distant foreign summers when I was completing my education. "I know I shall suddenly bring a swarm of moving candles and Chinese lanterns under the mulberry trees. You imagine the rich lights and shadows, the jewel-bright leafage, the faces and moving limbs of men and women, seen for an instant and gone again. They are students and girls of the town come out to dance, this windless, blue, June night, under the mulberry trees. And now they begin, thumping round and round in a ring, to the music of their own singing:

> Wir können spielen
> Vio-vio-vio-lin,
> Wir können spielen
> Vi-o-lin.

Now the rhythm changes, quickens:

> Und wir können tanzen Bumstarara,
> Bumstarara, Bumstarara,
> Und wir können tanzen Bumstarara,
> Bumstarara-rara.

The dance becomes a rush, an elephantine prancing on the dry lawn under the mulberry trees. And from the bastion Melpomene looks down and perceives, suddenly and apocalyptically, that everything in the world is sex, sex, sex. Men and women, male and female—always the same, and all, in the light of the horror of the afternoon, disgusting. That's how I should do it, Miss Penny."

"And very nice, too. But I wish you could find a place to bring in my conversation with the doctor. I shall never forget the way he cleared his throat, and coughed before embarking on the delicate subject. 'You may know, ahem, gracious Miss,' he began—'you may know that religious phenomena are often, ahem, closely connected with sexual causes.' I replied that I had heard rumors which might justify me in believing this to be true among Roman Catholics, but that in the Church of England —and I for one was a practitioner of Anglicanismus—it was very different. That might be, said the doctor; he had had no opportunity in the course of his long medical career of personally studying Anglicanismus. But he could vouch for the fact that among his patients, here in Grauburg, mysticismus was very often mixed up with the Geschlechtsleben. Melpomene was a case in point. After that hateful afternoon she had become extremely religious; the Professor of Latin had diverted her emotions out of their normal channels. She rebelled against the placid Agnosticismus of her father, and at night, in secret, when Aunt Bertha's dragon eyes were closed, she would read such forbidden books as The Life of St. Theresa, The Little Flowers of St. Francis, The Imitation of Christ, and the horribly enthralling *Book of Martyrs*. Aunt Bertha confiscated these works whenever she came upon them; she considered them more pernicious than the novels of Marcel Prévost. The character of a good potential housewife might be completely undermined by reading of this kind. It was rather a relief for Melpomene when Aunt Bertha shuffled off, in the summer of 1911, this mortal coil. She was one of those indispensables of whom one makes the discovery, when they are gone, that one can get on quite as well without them. Poor Aunt Bertha!"

"One can imagine Melpomene trying to believe she was sorry, and horribly ashamed to find that she was really, in secret, almost glad." The suggestion seemed to me ingenious, but Miss Penny accepted it as obvious.

"Precisely," she said, "and the emotion would only further confirm and give new force to the tendencies which her aunt's death left her free to indulge as much as she liked. Remorse, contrition—they would lead to the idea of doing penance. And for one who was now wallowing in the martyrology, penance was the mortification of the flesh. She used to kneel for hours, at night, in the cold; she ate too little, and when her teeth ached, which they often did—for she had a set, the doctor told me, which had given trouble from the very first—she would not go and see the dentist, but lay awake at night, savoring to the full her excruciations, and feeling triumphantly that they must, in some strange way, be pleasing to the Mysterious Powers. She went on like that for two or three years, till she was poisoned through and through. In the end she went down with gastric ulcer. It was three months before she came out of hospital, well for the first time in a long space of years, and with a brand-new set of imperishable teeth, all gold and ivory. And in mind, too, she was changed—for the better, I suppose. The nuns who nursed her had made her see that in mortifying herself she had acted supererogatively and through spiritual pride; instead of doing right, she had sinned. The only road to salvation, they told her, lay in discipline, in the orderliness of established religion, in obedience to authority. Secretly, so as not to distress her poor father, whose Agnosticismus was extremely dogmatic, for all its unobtrusiveness, Melpomene became a Roman Catholic. She was twenty-two. Only a few months later came the war and Professor Fugger's eternal renunciation of porridge. He did not long survive the making of that patriotic gesture. In the autumn of 1914 he caught a fatal influenza. Melpomene was alone in the world. In the spring of 1915 there was a new and very conscientious Sister of Charity at work among the wounded in the hospital of Grauburg. Here," explained Miss Penny, jabbing the air with her forefinger, "you put a line of asterisks or dots to signify a six years' gulf in the narrative. And you begin again right in the middle of a dialogue between Sister Agatha and the newly convalescent Kuno."

"What's their dialogue to be about?" I asked.

"Oh, that's easy enough," said Miss Penny. "Almost anything would do. What about this, for example? You explain that the fever has just abated; for the first time for days the young man is fully conscious. He feels himself to be well, reborn, as it were, in a new world—a world so bright and novel and jolly that he can't help laughing at the sight of it. He looks about him; the flies on the ceiling strike him as being extremely comic. How do they manage to walk upside down? They have suckers on their feet, says Sister Agatha, and wonders if her natural history is quite sound. Suckers on their feet—ha, ha! What an uproarious notion! Suckers on their feet—that's good, that's damned good! You can say charming, pathetic, positively tender things about the irrelevant mirth of convalescents—the more so in this particular case, where the mirth is expressed by a young man who is to be taken back to jail as soon as he can stand firmly on his legs. Ha, ha! Laugh on, unhappy boy! It is the quacking of the Fates, the Parcae, the Norns!"

Miss Penny gave an exaggerated imitation of her own brassy laughter. At the sound of it the few lunchers who still lingered at the other tables looked up, startled.

"You can write pages about Destiny and its ironic quacking. It's tremendously impressive, and there's money in every line."

"You may be sure I shall."

"Good! Then I can get on with my story. The days pass and the first hilarity of convalescence fades away. The young man remembers and grows sullen; his strength comes back to him, and with it a sense of despair. His mind broods incessantly on the hateful future. As for the consolations of religion, he won't listen to them. Sister Agatha perseveres —oh, with what anxious solicitude!—in the attempt to make him understand and believe and be comforted. It is all so tremendously important, and in this case, somehow, more important than in any other. And now you see the Geschlechtsleben working yeastily and obscurely, and once again the quacking of the Norns is audible. By the way," said Miss Penny, changing her tone and leaning confidentially across the table, "I wish you'd tell me something. Tell me, do you really—honestly, I mean—do you seriously believe in literature?"

"Believe in literature?"

"I was thinking," Miss Penny explained, "of Ironic Fate and the quacking of the Norns and all that."

" 'M yes."

"And then there's this psychology and introspection business; and construction and good narrative and word pictures and *le mot juste* and verbal magic and striking metaphors."

I remembered that I had compared Miss Penny's tinkling earrings to skeletons hanging in chains.

"And then, finally, and to begin with—Alpha and Omega—there's ourselves: two professionals gloating, with an absolute lack of sympathy, over a seduced nun, and speculating on the best method of turning her misfortunes into cash. It's all very curious, isn't it?—when one begins to think about it dispassionately."

"Very curious," I agreed. "But, then, so is everything else if you look at it like that."

"No, no," said Miss Penny. "Nothing's so curious as our business. But I shall never get to the end of my story if I get started on first principles."

Miss Penny continued her narrative. I was still thinking of literature. Do you believe in it? Seriously? Ah! Luckily the question was quite meaningless. The story came to me rather vaguely, but it seemed that the young man was getting better; in a few more days, the doctor had said, he would be well—well enough to go back to jail. No, no. The question was meaningless. I would think about it no more. I concentrated my attention again.

"Sister Agatha," I heard Miss Penny saying, "prayed, exhorted, indoctrinated. Whenever she had half a minute to spare from her other duties she would come running into the young man's room. 'I wonder if you fully realize the importance of prayer?' she would ask, and, before he had time to answer, she would give him a breathless account of the uses and virtues of regular and patient supplication. Or else, it was: 'May I tell you about St. Theresa?' or 'St. Stephen, the first martyr—you know about him, don't you?' Kuno simply wouldn't listen at first. It seemed so fantastically irrelevant, such an absurd interruption to his thoughts, his serious, despairing thoughts about the future. Prison was real, imminent, and this woman buzzed about him with her ridiculous fairy tales. Then suddenly, one day he began to listen, he showed signs of contrition and conversion. Sister Agatha announced her triumph to the other nuns, and there was rejoicing over the one lost sheep. Melpomene had never felt so happy in her life, and Kuno, looking at her radiant face, must have wondered how he could have been such a fool as not to see from the first what was now so obvious. The woman had lost her head about him. And he had only four days now—four days in which to tap the tumultuous love power, to canalize it, to set it working for his escape. Why hadn't he started a week ago? He could have made certain of it then. But now? There was no knowing. Four days was a horribly short time."

"How did he do it?" I asked, for Miss Penny had paused.

"That's for you to say," she replied, and shook her earrings at me. "I don't know. Nobody knows, I imagine, except the two parties concerned and perhaps Sister Agatha's confessor. But one can reconstruct the crime, as they say. How would you have done it? You're a man, you ought to be familiar with the processes of amorous engineering."

"You flatter me," I answered. "Do you seriously suppose——" I extended my arms. Miss Penny laughed like a horse. "No. But, seriously, it's a problem. The case is a very special one. The person, a nun; the place, a hospital; the opportunities, few. There could be no favorable circumstances—no moonlight, no distant music; and any form of direct attack would be sure to fail. That audacious confidence which is your amorist's best weapon would be useless here."

"Obviously," said Miss Penny. "But there are surely other methods. There is the approach through pity and the maternal instincts. And there's the approach through Higher Things, through the soul. Kuno must have worked on those lines, don't you think? One can imagine him letting himself be converted, praying with her, and at the same time appealing for her sympathy and even threatening—with a great air of seriousness—to kill himself rather than go back to jail. You can write that up easily and convincingly enough. But it's the sort of thing that bores me so frightfully to do. That's why I can never bring myself to write fiction. What is the point of it all? And the way you literary men think yourselves so important—particularly if you write tragedies. It's all very queer, very queer indeed."

I made no comment. Miss Penny changed her tone and went on with the narrative.

"Well," she said, "whatever the means employed, the engineering process was perfectly successful. Love was made to find out a way. On the afternoon before Kuno was to go back to prison, two Sisters of Charity walked out of the hospital gates, crossed the square in front of it, glided down the narrow streets toward the river, boarded a tram at the bridge, and did not descend till the car had reached its terminus in the farther suburbs. They began to walk briskly along the high road out into the country. 'Look!' said one of them, when they were clear of the houses, and with the gesture of a conjurer produced from nowhere a red leather purse. 'Where did it come from?' asked the other, opening her eyes. Memories of Elisha and the ravens, of the widow's cruse, of the loaves and fishes, must have floated through the radiant fog in poor Melpomene's mind. 'The old lady I was sitting next to in the tram left her bag open. Nothing could have been simpler.' 'Kuno! You don't mean to say you stole it?' Kuno swore horribly. He had opened the purse. 'Only sixty marks. Who'd have thought that an old camel, all dressed up in silk and furs, would only have sixty marks in her purse. And I must have a thousand at least to get away.' It's easy to reconstruct the rest of the conversation down to the inevitable 'For God's sake, shut up,' with which Kuno put an end to Melpomene's dismayed moralizing. They trudged on in silence. Kuno thinks desperately. Only sixty marks; he can do nothing with that. If only he had something to sell, a piece of jewelry, some gold or silver—anything, anything. He knows such a good place for selling things. Is he to be caught again for lack of a few marks? Melpomene is also thinking. Evil must often be done that good may follow. After all, had not she herself stolen Sister Mary of the Purification's clothes when she was asleep after night duty? Had not she run away from the convent, broken her vows? And yet how convinced she was that she was doing rightly! The mysterious Powers emphatically approved; she felt sure of it. And now there was the red purse. But what was a red purse in comparison with a saved soul—and, after all, what was she doing but saving Kuno's soul?" Miss Penny, who had adopted the voice and gestures of a debater asking rhetorical questions, brought her hand with a slap on to the table. "Lord, what a bore this sort of stuff is!" she exclaimed. "Let's get to the end of this dingy anecdote as quickly as possible. By this time, you must imagine, the shades of night were falling fast—the chill November twilight, and so on; but I leave the natural descriptions to you. Kuno gets into the ditch at the roadside and takes off his robes. One imagines that he would feel himself safer in trousers, more capable of acting with decision in a crisis. They tramp on for miles. Late in the evening they leave the high road and strike up through the fields toward the forest. At the fringe of the wood they find one of those wheeled huts where the shepherds sleep in the lambing season.

"The real 'Maison du Berger.' "

"Precisely," said Miss Penny, and she began to recite:

> Si ton coeur gémissant du poids de notre vie
> Se traine et se débat comme un aigle blessé. . . .

How does it go on? I used to adore it all so much when I was a girl:

> Le seuil est perfumé l'alcôve est large et sombre,
> Et là parmi les fleurs, nous trouverons dans l'ombre,
> Pour nos cheveux unis un lit silencieux.

I could go on like this indefinitely."

"Do," I said.

"No, no. No, no. I'm determined to finish this wretched story. Kuno broke the padlock of the door. They entered. What happened in that little hut?" Miss Penny leaned forward at me. Her large hare's eyes glittered; the long earrings swung and faintly tinkled. "Imagine the emotions of a virgin of thirty, and a nun at that, in the terrifying presence of desire. Imagine the easy, familiar brutalities of the young man. Oh, there's pages to be made out of this—the absolutely impenetrable darkness, the smell of straw, the voices, the strangled crying, the movements! And one likes to fancy that the emotions pulsing about in that confined space made palpable vibrations like a deep sound that shakes the air. Why, it's ready-made literature, this scene. In the morning," Miss Penny went on, after a pause, "two woodcutters on their way to work noticed that the door of the hut was ajar. They approached the hut cautiously, their axes raised and ready for a blow if there should be need of it. Peeping in, they saw a woman in a black dress lying face downward in the straw. Dead? No; she moved, she moaned. 'What's the matter?' a blubbered face, smeared with streaks of tear-clotted gray dust, it lifted toward them. 'What's the matter?'—'He's gone!' What a queer, indistinct utterance. The woodcutters regard one another. What does she say? She's a foreigner, perhaps. 'What's the matter?' they repeat once more. The woman bursts out violently crying. 'Gone, gone! He's gone,' she sobs out in her vague, inarticulate way. 'Oh, gone.' That's what she says. 'Who's gone?'—'He's left me.'—'What?'—'Left me . . .'—'What the devil . . . ? Speak a little more distinctly.'—'I can't,' she wails; 'he's taken my teeth.' —'Your what?'—'My teeth!'—and the shrill voice breaks into a scream, and she falls back sobbing into the straw. The woodcutters look significantly at one another. They nod. One of them applies a thick yellow-nailed forefinger to his forehead."

Miss Penny looked at her watch.

"Good heavens!" she said, "it's nearly half-past three. I must fly. Don't forget about the funeral service," she added, as she put on her coat. "The tapers, the black coffin in the middle of the aisle, the nuns in their white-winged coifs, the gloomy chanting, and the poor cowering creature without any teeth, her face all caved in like an old woman's, wondering whether she wasn't really and in fact dead—wondering whether she wasn't already in hell. Good-by."

Half-Holiday

From *Two or Three Graces*

I

IT WAS Saturday afternoon and fine. In the hazy spring sunlight London was beautiful, like a city of the imagination. The lights were golden, the shadows blue and violet. Incorrigibly hopeful, the sooty trees in the Park were breaking into leaf; and the new green was unbelievably fresh and light and aerial, as though the tiny leaves had been cut out of the central emerald stripe of a rainbow. The miracle, to all who walked in the Park that afternoon, was manifest. What had been dead now lived; soot was budding into rainbow green. Yes, it was manifest. And, moreover, those who perceived this thaumaturgical change from death to life were themselves changed. There was something contagious about the vernal miracle. Loving more, the loitering couples under the trees were happier—or much more acutely miserable. Stout men took off their hats and, while the sun kissed their bald heads, made good resolutions—about whisky, about the pretty typist at the office, about early rising. Accosted by spring-intoxicated boys, young girls consented, in the teeth of all their upbringing and their alarm, to go for walks. Middle-aged gentlemen, strolling homeward through the Park, suddenly felt their crusted, business-grimy hearts burgeoning, like these trees, with kindness and generosity. They thought of their wives, thought of them with a sudden gush of affection, in spite of twenty years of marriage. "Must stop on the way back," they said to themselves, "and buy the missus a little present." What should it be? A box of candied fruits? She liked candied fruits. Or a pot of azaleas? Or . . . And then they remembered that it was Saturday afternoon. The shops would all be shut. And probably, they thought, sighing, the missus's heart would also be shut; for the missus had not walked under the budding trees. Such is life, they reflected, looking sadly at the boats on the glittering Serpentine, at the playing children, at the lovers sitting, hand in hand, on the green grass. Such is life; when the heart is open, the shops are generally shut. But they resolved nevertheless to try, in future, to control their tempers.

On Peter Brett, as on everyone else who came within their range of influence, this bright spring sunlight and the new-budded trees profoundly worked. They made him feel, all at once, more lonely, more heartbroken than he had ever felt before. By contrast with the brightness round him, his soul seemed darker. The trees had broken into leaf; but he remained dead. The lovers walked in couples; he walked alone. In spite of the spring, in spite of the sunshine, in spite of the fact that today was Saturday and that tomorrow would be Sunday—or rather because of all these things which should have made him happy and which did make other people happy—he loitered through the miracle of Hyde Park feeling deeply miserable.

As usual, he turned for comfort to his imagination. For example, a lovely young creature would slip on a loose stone just in front of him and twist her ankle. Grown larger than life and handsomer, Peter would rush forward to administer first aid. He would take her in a taxi (for which he had money to pay) to her home—in Grosvenor Square. She turned out to be a peer's daughter. They loved each other. . . .

Or else he rescued a child that had fallen into the Round Pond and so earned the eternal gratitude, and more than the gratitude, of its rich young widowed mother. Yes, widowed; Peter always definitely specified her widowhood. His intentions were strictly honorable. He was still very young and had been well brought up.

Or else there was no preliminary accident. He just saw a young girl sitting on a bench by herself, looking very lonely and sad. Boldly, yet courteously, he approached, he took off his hat, he smiled. "I can see that you're lonely," he said; and he spoke elegantly and with ease, without a trace of his Lancashire accent, without so much as a hint of that dreadful stammer which, in real life, made speech such a torment to him. "I can see that you're lonely. So am I. May I sit down beside you?" She smiled, and he sat down. And then he told her that he was an orphan and that all he had was a married sister who lived in Rochdale. And she said, "I'm an orphan too." And that was a great bond between them. And they told one another how miserable they were. And she began to cry. And then he said, "Don't cry. You've got me." And at that she cheered up a little. And then they went to the pictures together. And finally, he supposed, they got married. But that part of the story was a little dim.

But of course, as a matter of fact, no accidents ever did happen and he never had the courage to tell anyone how lonely he was; and his stammer was something awful; and he was small, he wore spectacles, and nearly always had pimples on his face; and his dark-gray suit was growing very shabby and rather short in the sleeves; and his boots, though carefully blacked, looked just as cheap as they really were.

It was the boots which killed his imaginings this afternoon. Walking with downcast eyes, pensively, he was trying to decide what he should say to the peer's lovely young daughter in the taxi on the way to Grosvenor Square, when he suddenly became aware of his alternately striding boots, blackly obtruding themselves through the transparent phantoms of his inner life. How ugly they were! And how sadly unlike those elegant and sumptuously shining boots which encase the feet of the rich! They had been ugly enough when they were new; age had rendered them positively repulsive. No boot trees had corrected the effects of walking, and the uppers, just above the toecaps, were deeply and hideously wrinkled. Through the polish he could see a network of innumerable little cracks in the parched and shoddy leather. On the outer side of the left boot the toecap had come unstitched and had been coarsely sewn up again; the scar was only too visible. Worn by much lacing and unlacing, the eyeholes had lost their black enamel and revealed themselves obtrusively in their brassy nakedness.

Oh, they were horrible, his boots; they were disgusting! But they'd have to last him a long time yet. Peter began to remake the calculations he had so often and often made before. If he spent three-halfpence less every day on his lunch; if, during the fine weather, he were to walk to the office every morning instead of taking the bus . . . But however carefully and however often he made his calculations, twenty-seven and sixpence a week always remained twenty-seven and six. Boots were dear; and when he had saved up enough to buy a new pair, there was still the question of his suit. And, to make matters worse, it was spring; the leaves were coming out, the sun shone, and among the amorous couples he walked alone. Reality was too much for him today; he could not escape. The boots pursued him whenever he tried to flee, and dragged him back to the contemplation of his misery.

II

The two young women turned out of the crowded walk along the edge of the Serpentine, and struck uphill by a smaller path in the direction of Watts's statue. Peter followed them. An exquisite perfume lingered in the air behind them. He breathed it greedily and his heart began to beat with unaccustomed violence. They seemed to him marvelous and hardly human beings. They were all that was lovely and unattainable. He had met them walking down there, by the Serpentine, had been overwhelmed by that glimpse of a luxurious and arrogant beauty, had turned immediately and followed them. Why? He hardly knew himself. Merely in order that he might be near them; and perhaps with the fantastic, irrepressible hope that something might happen, some miracle, that should project him into their lives.

Greedily he sniffed their delicate perfume; with a kind of desperation, as though his life depended on it, he looked at them, he studied them. Both were tall. One of them wore a gray cloth coat, trimmed with dark-gray fur. The other's coat was all of fur; a dozen or two of ruddily golden foxes had been killed in order that she might be warm among the chilly shadows of this spring afternoon. One of them wore gray and the other buff-colored stockings. One walked on gray kid, the other on serpent's leather. Their hats were small and close-fitting. A small black French bulldog accompanied them, running now at their heels, now in front of them. The dog's collar was trimmed with brindled wolf's fur that stuck out like a ruff round its black head.

Peter walked so close behind them that, when they were out of the crowd, he could hear snatches of their talk. One had a cooing voice; the other spoke rather huskily.

"Such a divine man," the husky voice was saying, "such a really divine man!"

"So Elizabeth told me," said the cooing one.

"Such a perfect party, too," Husky went on. "He kept us laughing the whole evening. Everybody got rather buffy, too. When it was time to go, I said I'd walk and trust to luck to find a taxi on the way. Whereupon he invited me to come and look for a taxi in his heart. He said there were so many there, and all of them disengaged."

They both laughed. The chatter of a party of children who had come up from behind and were passing at this moment prevented Peter from hearing what was said next. Inwardly he cursed the children. Beastly little devils—they were making him lose his revelation. And what a revelation! Of how strange, unfamiliar and gaudy a life! Peter's dreams had always been idyllic and pastoral. Even with the peer's daughter he meant to live in the country, quietly and domestically. The world in which there are perfect parties where everybody gets rather buffy and divine men invite young goddesses to look for taxis in their hearts was utterly unknown to him. He had had a glimpse of it now; it fascinated him by its exotic and tropical strangeness. His whole ambition was now to enter this gorgeous world, to involve himself, somehow and at all costs, in the lives of these young goddesses. Suppose, now, they were both simultaneously to trip over that projecting root and twist their ankles. Suppose . . . But they both stepped over it in safety. And then, all at once, he saw a hope—in the bulldog.

The dog had left the path to sniff at the base of an elm tree growing a few yards away on the right. It had sniffed, it had growled, it had left a challenging souvenir of its visit and was now indignantly kicking up earth and twigs with its hinder paws against the tree, when a yellow Irish terrier trotted up and began in its turn to sniff, first at the tree, then at the bulldog. The bulldog stopped its scrabbling in the dirt and sniffed at the terrier. Cautiously, the two beasts walked round one another sniffing and growling as they went. Peter watched them for a moment with a vague and languid curiosity. His mind was elsewhere; he hardly saw the two dogs. Then, in an illuminating flash, it occurred to him that they might begin to fight. If they fought, he was a made man. He would rush in and separate them, heroically. He might even be bitten. But that didn't matter. Indeed, it would be all the better. A bite would be another claim on the goddesses' gratitude. Ardently, he hoped that the dogs would fight. The awful thing would be if the goddesses or the owners of the yellow terrier were to notice and interfere before the fight could begin. "Oh God," he fervently prayed, "don't let them call the dogs away from each other now. But let the dogs fight. For Jesus Christ's sake. Amen." Peter had been piously brought up.

The children had passed. The voices of the goddesses once more became audible.

". . . Such a fearful bore," the cooing one was saying. "I can never move a step without finding him there. And nothing penetrates his hide. I've told him that I hate Jews, that I think he's ugly and stupid and tactless and impertinent and boring. But it doesn't seem to make the slightest difference."

"You should make him useful, at any rate," said Husky.

"Oh, I do," affirmed Coo.

"Well, that's something."

"Something," Coo admitted. "But not much."

There was a pause. "Oh, God," prayed Peter, "don't let them see."

"If only," began Coo meditatively, "if only men would understand that . . ." A fearful noise of growling and barking violently interrupted her. The two young women turned in the direction from which the sound came.

"Pongo!" they shouted in chorus, anxiously and commandingly. And again, more urgently, "Pongo!"

But their cries were unavailing. Pongo and the yellow terrier were already fighting too furiously to pay any attention.

"Pongo! Pongo!"

And, "Benny!" the little girl and her stout nurse to whom the yellow
terrier belonged as unavailingly shouted. "Benny, come here!"

The moment had come, the passionately anticipated, the richly pregnant moment. Exultantly, Peter threw himself on the dogs. "Get away,
you brute," he shouted, kicking the Irish terrier. For the terrier was the
enemy, the French bulldog—*their* French bulldog—the friend whom he
had come, like one of the Olympian gods in the Iliad, to assist. "Get
away!" In his excitement, he forgot that he had a stammer. The letter G
was always a difficult one for him; but he managed on this occasion to
shout "Get away" without a trace of hesitation. He grabbed at the dogs
by their stumpy tails, by the scruffs of their necks, and tried to drag them
apart. From time to time he kicked the yellow terrier. But it was the
bulldog which bit him. Stupider even than Ajax, the bulldog had failed
to understand that the immortal was fighting on his side. But Peter felt
no resentment and, in the heat of the moment, hardly any pain. The
blood came oozing out of a row of jagged holes in his left hand.

"Ooh!" cried Coo, as though it were her hand that had been bitten.

"Be careful," anxiously admonished Husky. "Be careful."

The sound of their voices nerved him to further efforts. He kicked
and he tugged still harder; and at last, for a fraction of a second, he managed to part the angry beasts. For a fraction of a second neither dog had
any portion of the other's anatomy in his mouth. Peter seized the opportunity, and catching the French bulldog by the loose skin at the back
of his neck, he lifted him, still furiously snapping, growling and struggling, into the air. The yellow terrier stood in front of him, barking and
every now and then leaping up in a frantic effort to snap the dangling
black paws of his enemy. But Peter, with the gesture of Perseus raising
on high the severed head of the Gorgon, lifted the writhing Pongo out
of danger to the highest stretch of his arm. The yellow dog he kept off
with his foot; and the nurse and the little girl, who had by this time
somewhat recovered their presence of mind, approached the furious
animal from behind and succeeded at last in hooking the leash to his
collar. His four rigidly planted paws skidding over the grass, the yellow
terrier was dragged away by main force, still barking, though feebly—for
he was being half strangled by his efforts to escape. Suspended six feet
above the ground by the leathery black scruff of his neck, Pongo vainly
writhed.

Peter turned and approached the goddesses. Husky had narrow eyes
and a sad mouth; it was a thin, tragic-looking face. Coo was rounder,
pinker and whiter, bluer-eyed. Peter looked from one to the other and
could not decide which was the more beautiful.

He lowered the writhing Pongo. "Here's your dog," was what he wanted to say. But the loveliness of these radiant creatures suddenly brought back all his self-consciousness and with his self-consciousness his stammer. "Here's your . . ." he began; but could not bring out the dog. For Peter, D was always a difficult letter.

For all common words beginning with a difficult letter Peter had a number of easier synonyms in readiness. Thus, he always called cats "pussies," not out of any affectation of childishness, but because P was more pronounceable than the impossible C. Coal he had to render in the vaguer form of "fuel." Dirt, with him, was always "muck." In the discovery of synonyms he had become almost as ingenious as those Anglo-Saxon poets who, using alliteration instead of rhyme, were compelled, in their efforts to make (shall we say) the sea begin with the same letter as its waves or its billows, to call it the "whale-road" or the "bath of the swans." But Peter, who could not permit himself the full poetic license of his Saxon ancestors, was reduced sometimes to spelling the most difficult words to which there happened to be no convenient and prosaic equivalent. Thus, he was never quite sure whether he should call a cup a mug or a c-u-p. And since "ovum" seemed to be the only synonym for egg, he was always reduced to talkings of e-g-g-s.

At the present moment, it was the miserable little word "dog" that was holding him up. Peter had several synonyms for dog. P being a slightly easier letter than D, he could, when not too nervous, say "pup." Or if the P's weren't coming easily, he could call the animal, rather facetiously and mock-heroically, a "hound." But the presence of the two goddesses was so unnerving that Peter found it as hopelessly impossible to pronounce a P or an H as a D. He hesitated painfully, trying to bring out in turn, first dog, then pup, then hound. His face became very red. He was in an agony.

"Here's your whelp," he managed to say at last. The word, he was conscious, was a little too Shakespearean for ordinary conversation. But it was the only one which came.

"Thank you most awfully," said Coo.

"You were splendid, really splendid," said Husky. "But I'm afraid you're hurt."

"Oh, it's n-nothing," Peter declared. And twisting his handkerchief round the bitten hand, he thrust it into his pocket.

Coo, meanwhile, had fastened the end of her leash to Pongo's collar. "You can put him down now," she said.

Peter did as he was told. The little black dog immediately bounded forward in the direction of his reluctantly retreating enemy. He came to the end of his tether with a jerk that brought him up on to his hind legs and kept him, barking, in the position of a rampant lion on a coat of arms.

"But are you sure it's nothing?" Husky insisted. "Let me look at it."

Obediently, Peter pulled off the handkerchief and held out his hand. It seemed to him that all was happening as he had hoped. Then he noticed with horror that the nails were dirty. If only, if only he had thought of washing before he went out! What would they think of him? Blushing, he tried to withdraw his hand. But Husky held it.

"Wait," she said. And then added: "It's a nasty bite."

"Horrid," affirmed Coo, who had also bent over it. "I'm so awfully sorry that my stupid dog should have . . ."

"You ought to go straight to a chemist," said Husky, interrupting her, "and get him to disinfect it and tie it up."

She lifted her eyes from his hand and looked into his face.

"A chemist," echoed Coo, and also looked up.

Peter looked from one to the other, dazzled equally by the wide-open blue eyes and the narrowed, secret eyes of green. He smiled at them vaguely and vaguely shook his head. Unobtrusively he wrapped up his hand in his handkerchief and thrust it away, out of sight.

"It's n-nothing," he said.

"But you must," insisted Husky.

"You must," cried Coo.

"N-nothing," he repeated. He didn't want to go to a chemist. He wanted to stay with the goddesses.

Coo turned to Husky. "Qu'est-ce qu'on donne à ce petit bonhomme?" she asked, speaking very quickly and in a low voice.

Husky shrugged her shoulders and made a little grimace suggestive of uncertainty. "Il serait offensé, peut-être," she suggested.

"Tu crois?"

Husky stole a rapid glance at the subject of their discussion, taking him in critically from his cheap felt hat to his cheap boots, from his pale, spotty face to his rather dirty hands, from his steel-framed spectacles to his leather watch guard. Peter saw that she was looking at him and smiled at her with shy, vague rapture. How beautiful she was! He wondered what they had been whispering about together. Perhaps they were debating whether they should ask him to tea. And no sooner had the idea occurred to him than he was sure of it. Miraculously, things were happening just as they happened in his dreams. He wondered if he would have the face to tell them—this first time—that they could look for taxis in his heart.

Husky turned back to her companion. Once more she shrugged her shoulders. "Vraiment, je ne sais pas," she whispered.

"Si on lui donnait une livre?" suggested Coo.

Husky nodded. "*Comme tu voudras.*" And while the other turned away to fumble unobtrusively in her purse, she addressed herself to Peter.

"You were awfully brave," she said, smiling.

Peter could only shake his head, blush and lower his eyes from before that steady, self-assured, cool gaze. He longed to look at her; but when it came to the point, he simply could not keep his eyes steadily fixed on those unwavering eyes of hers.

"Perhaps you're used to dogs," she went on. "Have you got one of your own?"

"N-no," Peter managed to say.

"Ah, well, that makes it all the braver," said Husky. Then, noticing that Coo had found the money she had been looking for, she took the boy's hand and shook it, heartily. "Well, good-by," she said, smiling more exquisitely than ever. "We're so awfully grateful to you. Most awfully," she repeated. And as she did so, she wondered why she used that word "awfully" so often. Ordinarily she hardly ever used it. It had seemed suitable somehow, when she was talking with this creature. She was always very hearty and emphatic and schoolboyishly slangy when she was with the lower classes.

"G-g-g . . ." began Peter. Could they be going, he wondered in an agony, suddenly waking out of his comfortable and rosy dream. Really going, without asking him to tea or giving him their addresses? He wanted to implore them to stop a little longer, to let him see them again. But he knew that he wouldn't be able to utter the necessary words. In the face of Husky's good-by he felt like a man who sees some fearful catastrophe impending and can do nothing to arrest it. "G-g . . ." he feebly stuttered. But he found himself shaking hands with the other one before he had got to the end of that fatal good-by.

"You were really splendid," said Coo, as she shook his hand. "Really splendid. And you simply must go to a chemist and have the bite disinfected at once. Good-by, and thank you very, very much." As she spoke these last words she slipped a neatly folded one-pound note into his palm and with her two hands shut his fingers over it. "Thank you so much," she repeated.

Violently blushing, Peter shook his head. "N-n . . ." he began, and tried to make her take the note back.

But she only smiled more sweetly. "Yes, yes," she insisted. "Please." And without waiting to hear any more, she turned and ran lightly after Husky, who had walked on, up the path, leading the reluctant Pongo, who still barked and strained heraldically at his leash.

"Well, that's all right," she said, as she came up with her companion.

"He accepted it?" asked Husky.

"Yes, yes." She nodded. Then changing her tone, "Let me see," she went on, "what were we saying when this wretched dog interrupted us?"

"N-no," Peter managed to say at last. But she had already turned and was hurrying away. He took a couple of strides in pursuit; then checked himself. It was no good. It would only lead to further humiliation if he tried to explain. Why, they might even think, while he was standing there, straining to bring out his words, that he had run after them to ask for more. They might slip another pound into his hand and hurry away still faster. He watched them till they were out of sight, over the brow of the hill; then turned back toward the Serpentine.

In his imagination he re-acted the scene, not as it had really happened, but as it ought to have happened. When Coo slipped the note into his hand he smiled and courteously returned it, saying: "I'm afraid you've made a mistake. A quite justifiable mistake, I admit. For I look poor, and indeed I am poor. But I am a gentleman, you know. My father was a doctor in Rochdale. My mother was a doctor's daughter. I went to a good school till my people died. They died when I was sixteen, within a few months of one another. So I had to go to work before I'd finished my schooling. But you see that I can't take your money." And then, becoming more gallant, personal and confidential, he went on: "I separated those beastly dogs because I wanted to do something for you and your friend. Because I thought you so beautiful and wonderful. So that even if I weren't a gentleman, I wouldn't take your money." Coo was deeply touched by this little speech. She shook him by the hand and told him how sorry she was. And he put her at her ease by assuring her that her mistake had been perfectly comprehensible. And then she asked if he'd care to come along with them and take a cup of tea. And from this point onward Peter's imaginings became vaguer and rosier, till he was dreaming the old familiar dream of the peer's daughter, the grateful widow and the lonely orphan; only there happened to be two goddesses this time, and their faces, instead of being dim creations of fancy, were real and definite.

But he knew, even in the midst of his dreaming, that things hadn't happened like this. He knew that she had gone before he could say anything; and that even if he had run after them and tried to make his speech of explanation, he could never have done it. For example, he would have had to say that his father was a "medico," not a doctor (M being an easier letter than D). And when it came to telling them that his people had died, he would have had to say that they had "perished" —which would sound facetious, as though he were trying to make a joke of it. No, no, the truth must be faced. He had taken the money and they had gone away thinking that he was just some sort of a street loafer, who had risked a bite for the sake of a good tip. They hadn't even dreamed of treating him as an equal. As for asking him to tea and making him their friend . . .

But his fancy was still busy. It struck him that it had been quite unnecessary to make any explanation. He might simply have forced the note back into her hand, without saying a word. Why hadn't he done it? He had to excuse himself for his remissness. She had slipped away too quickly; that was the reason.

Or what if he had walked on ahead of them and ostentatiously given the money to the first street boy he happened to meet? A good idea, that. Unfortunately it had not occurred to him at the time.

All that afternoon Peter walked and walked, thinking of what had happened, imagining creditable and satisfying alternatives. But all the time he knew that these alternatives were only fanciful. Sometimes the recollection of his humiliation was so vivid that it made him physically wince and shudder.

The light began to fail. In the gray and violet twilight the lovers pressed closer together as they walked, more frankly clasped one another beneath the trees. Strings of yellow lamps blossomed in the increasing darkness. High up in the pale sky overhead, a quarter of the moon made itself visible. He felt unhappier and lonelier than ever.

His bitten hand was by this time extremely painful. He left the Park and walked along Oxford Street till he found a chemist. When his hand had been disinfected and bandaged he went into a tea shop and ordered a poached e-g-g, a roll, and a mug of mocha, which he had to translate for the benefit of the uncomprehending waitress as a c-u-p of c-o-f-f-e-e.

"You seem to think I'm a loafer or a tout." That's what he ought to have said to her, indignantly and proudly. "You've insulted me. If you were a man, I'd knock you down. Take your dirty money." But then, he reflected, he could hardly have expected them to become his friends, after that. On second thoughts, he decided that indignation would have been no good.

"Hurt your hand?" asked the waitress sympathetically, as she set down his egg and his mug of mocha.

Peter nodded. "B-bitten by a d-d . . . by a h-h-hound." The word burst out at last, explosively.

Remembered shame made him blush as he spoke. Yes, they had taken him for a tout; they had treated him as though he didn't really exist, as though he were just an instrument whose services you hired and to which, when the bill had been paid, you gave no further thought. The remembrance of humiliation was so vivid, the realization of it so profound and complete, that it affected not only his mind but his body too. His heart beat with unusual rapidity and violence; he felt sick. It was with the greatest difficulty that he managed to eat his egg and drink his mug of mocha.

Still remembering the painful reality, still feverishly constructing his fanciful alternatives to it, Peter left the tea shop and, though he was very tired, resumed his aimless walking. He walked along Oxford Street as far as the Circus, turned down Regent Street, halted in Piccadilly to look at the epileptically twitching sky signs, walked up Shaftesbury Avenue, and turning southward made his way through bystreets toward the Strand.

In a street near Covent Garden a woman brushed against him. "Cheer up, dearie," she said. "Don't look so glum."

Peter looked at her in astonishment. Was it possible that she should have been speaking to him? A woman—was it possible? He knew, of course, that she was what people called a bad woman. But the fact that she should have spoken to him seemed none the less extraordinary; and he did not connect it, somehow, with her "badness."

"Come along with me," she wheedled.

Peter nodded. He could not believe it was true. She took his arm.

"You got money?" she asked anxiously.

He nodded again.

"You look as though you'd been to a funeral," said the woman.

"I'm l-lonely," he explained. He felt ready to weep. He even longed to weep—to weep and to be comforted. His voice trembled as he spoke.

"Lonely? That's funny. A nice-looking boy like you's got no call to be lonely." She laughed significantly and without mirth.

Her bedroom was dimly and pinkly lighted. A smell of cheap scent and unwashed underlinen haunted the air.

"Wait a tick," she said, and disappeared through a door into an inner room.

He sat there, waiting. A minute later she returned, wearing a kimono and bedroom slippers. She sat on his knees, threw her arms round his neck and began to kiss him. "Lovey," she said in her cracked voice, "lovey." Her eyes were hard and cold. Her breath smelt of spirits. Seen at close range she was indescribably horrible.

Peter saw her, it seemed to him, for the first time—saw and completely realized her. He averted his face. Remembering the peer's daughter who had sprained her ankle, the lonely orphan, the widow whose child had tumbled into the Round Pond; remembering Coo and Husky, he untwined her arms, he pushed her away from him, he sprang to his feet.

"S-sorry," he said. "I must g-g . . . I'd forg-gotten something. I . . ." He picked up his hat and moved toward the door.

The woman ran after him and caught him by the arm. "You young devil, you," she screamed. Her abuse was horrible and filthy. "Asking a girl and then trying to sneak away without paying. Oh, no you don't, no you don't. You . . ."

And the abuse began again.

Peter dipped his hand into his pocket, and pulled out Coo's neatly folded note. "L-let me g-go," he said as he gave it her.

While she was suspiciously unfolding it, he hurried away, slamming the door behind him, and ran down the dark stairs, into the street.

After the Fireworks

From *Brief Candles*

I

"Late as usual. Late." Judd's voice was censorious. The words fell sharp, like beakblows. "As though I were a nut," Miles Fanning thought resentfully, "and he were a woodpecker. And yet he's devotion itself, he'd do anything for me. Which is why, I suppose, he feels entitled to crack my shell each time he sees me." And he came to the conclusion, as he had so often come before, that he really didn't like Colin Judd at all. "My oldest friend, whom I quite definitely don't like. Still . . ." Still, Judd was an asset, Judd was worth it.

"Here are your letters," the sharp voice continued.

Fanning groaned as he took them. "Can't one ever escape from letters? Even here, in Rome? They seem to get through everything. Like filter-passing bacteria. Those blessed days before post offices!" Sipping, he examined, over the rim of his coffee cup, the addresses on the envelopes.

"You'd be the first to complain if people didn't write," Judd rapped out. "Here's your egg. Boiled for three minutes exactly. I saw to it myself."

Taking his egg, "On the contrary," Fanning answered, "I'd be the first to rejoice. If people write, it means they exist; and all I ask for is to be able to pretend that the world doesn't exist. The wicked flee when no man pursueth. How well I understand them! But letters don't allow you to be an ostrich. The Freudians say . . ." He broke off suddenly. After all he was talking to Colin—to *Colin*. The confessional, self-accusatory manner was wholly misplaced. Pointless to give Colin the excuse to say something disagreeable. But what he had been going to say about the Freudians was amusing. "The Freudians," he began again.

But taking advantage of forty years of intimacy, Judd had already started to be disagreeable. "But you'd be miserable," he was saying, "if the post didn't bring you your regular dose of praise and admiration and sympathy and . . ."

"And humiliation," added Fanning, who had opened one of the envelopes and was looking at the letter within. "Listen to this. From my

American publishers. Sales and Publicity Department. 'My dear Mr. Fanning.' My dear, mark you. Wilbur F. Schmalz's dear. 'My dear Mr. Fanning—Won't you take us into your confidence with regard to your plans for the Summer Vacation? What aspect of the Great Outdoors are you favoring this year? Ocean or Mountain, Woodland or purling Lake? I would esteem it a great privilege if you would inform me, as I am preparing a series of notes for the Literary Editors of our leading journals, who are, as I have often found in the past, exceedingly receptive to such personal material, particularly when accompanied by well-chosen snapshots. So won't you co-operate with us in providing this service? Very cordially yours, Wilbur F. Schmalz.' Well, what do you think of that?"

"I think you'll answer him," said Judd. "Charmingly," he added, envenoming his malice. Fanning gave a laugh, whose very ease and heartiness betrayed his discomfort. "And you'll even send him a snapshot."

Contemptuously—too contemptuously (he felt it at the time)—Fanning crumpled up the letter and threw it into the fireplace. The really humiliating thing, he reflected, was that Judd was quite right: he *would* write to Mr. Schmalz about the Great Outdoors, he *would* send the first snapshot anybody took of him. There was a silence. Fanning ate two or three spoonfuls of egg. Perfectly boiled, for once. But still, what a relief that Colin was going away! After all, he reflected, there's a great deal to be said for a friend who has a house in Rome and who invites you to stay, even when he isn't there. To such a man much must be forgiven —even his infernal habit of being a woodpecker. He opened another envelope and began to read.

Possessive and preoccupied, like an anxious mother, Judd watched him. With all his talents and intelligence, Miles wasn't fit to face the world alone. Judd had told him so (peck, peck!) again and again. "You're a child!" He had said it a thousand times. "You ought to have somebody to look after you." But if anyone other than himself offered to do it, how bitterly jealous and resentful he became! And the trouble was that there were always so many applicants for the post of Fanning's bear-leader. Foolish men or, worse and more frequently, foolish women, attracted to him by his reputation and then conquered by his charm. Judd hated and professed to be loftily contemptuous of them. And the more Fanning liked his admiring bear-leaders, the loftier Judd's contempt became. For that was the bitter and unforgivable thing: Fanning manifestly preferred their bear-leading to Judd's. They flattered the bear, they caressed and even worshiped him; and the bear, of course, was charming to them, until such time as he growled, or bit, or, more often, quietly slunk away. Then they were surprised; they were pained. Because, as Judd would say with a grim satisfaction, they didn't know what Fanning was *really* like. Whereas he did know and had known since they were school-boys together, nearly forty years before. Therefore he had a right to like him—a right and, at the same time, a duty to tell him all the reasons why he ought not to like him. Fanning didn't much enjoy listening to these reasons; he preferred to go where the bear was a sacred animal. With that air, which seemed so natural on his gray sharp face, of being dispassionately impersonal, "You're afraid of healthy criticism," Judd would tell him. "You always were, even as a boy."

"He's Jehovah," Fanning would complain. "Life with Judd is one long Old Testament. Being one of the Chosen People must have been bad enough. But to be *the* Chosen Person, in the singular . . ." And he would shake his head. "Terrible!"

And yet he had never seriously quarreled with Colin Judd. Active unpleasantness was something which Fanning avoided as much as possible. He had never even made any determined attempt to fade out of Judd's existence as he had faded, at one time or another, out of the existence of so many once intimate bear-leaders. The habit of their intimacy was of too long standing and, besides, old Colin was so useful, so bottomlessly reliable. So Judd remained for him the Oldest Friend whom one definitely dislikes; while for Judd, he was the Oldest Friend whom one adores and at the same time hates for not adoring back, the Oldest Friend whom one never sees enough of, but whom, when he *is* there, one finds insufferably exasperating, the Oldest Friend whom, in spite of all one's efforts, one is always getting on the nerves of.

"If only," Judd was thinking, "he could have faith!" The Catholic Church was there to help him. (Judd himself was a convert of more than twenty years' standing.) But the trouble was that Fanning didn't want to be helped by the Church; he could only see the comic side of Judd's religion. Judd was reserving his missionary efforts till his friend should be old or ill. But if only, meanwhile, if only, by some miracle of grace . . . So thought the good Catholic; but it was the jealous friend who felt and who obscurely schemed. Converted, Miles Fanning would be separated from his other friends and brought, Judd realized, nearer to himself.

Watching him, as he read his letter, Judd noticed, all at once, that Fanning's lips were twitching involuntarily into a smile. They were full lips, well cut, sensitive and sensual; his smiles were a little crooked. A dark fury suddenly fell on Colin Judd.

"Telling me that you'd like to get no letters!" he said with an icy vehemence. "When you sit there grinning to yourself over some silly woman's flatteries."

Amazed, amused, "But what an outburst!" said Fanning, looking up from his letter.

Judd swallowed his rage; he had made a fool of himself. It was in a tone of calm dispassionate flatness that he spoke. Only his eyes remained angry. "Was I right?" he asked.

"So far as the woman was concerned," Fanning answered. "But wrong about the flattery. Women have no time nowadays to talk about anything except themselves."

"Which is only another way of flattering," said Judd obstinately. "They confide in you, because they think you'll like being treated as a person who understands."

"Which is what, after all, I am. By profession even." Fanning spoke with an exasperating mildness. "What *is* a novelist, unless he's a person who understands?" He paused; but Judd made no answer, for the only words he could have uttered would have been whirling words of rage and jealousy. He was jealous not only of the friends, the lovers, the admiring correspondents; he was jealous of a part of Fanning himself, of the artist, the public personage; for the artist, the public personage seemed so often to stand between his friend and himself. He hated, while he gloried in them.

Fanning looked at him for a moment, expectantly; but the other kept his mouth tight shut, his eyes averted. In the same exasperatingly gentle tone, "And flattery or no flattery," Fanning went on, "this is a charming letter. And the girl's adorable."

He was having his revenge. Nothing upset poor Colin Judd so much as having to listen to talk about women or love. He had a horror of anything connected with the act, the mere thought, of sex. Fanning called it his perversion. "You're one of those unspeakable chastity-perverts," he would say, when he wanted to get his own back after a bout of pecking. "If I had children, I'd never allow them to frequent your company. Too dangerous." When he spoke of the forbidden subject, Judd would either writhe, a martyr, or else unchristianly explode. On this occasion he writhed and was silent. "Adorable," Fanning repeated, provocatively. "A ravishing little creature. Though of course she may be a huge great camel. That's the danger of unknown correspondents. The best letter writers are often camels. It's a piece of natural history I've learned by the bitterest experience." Looking back at the letter, "All the same," he went on, "when a young girl writes to one that she's sure one's the only person in the world who can tell her exactly who and what (both heavily underlined) she is—well, one's rather tempted, I must confess, to try yet once more. Because even if she were a camel she'd be a very young one. Twenty-one—isn't that what she says?" He turned over a page of the letter. "Yes; twenty-one. Also she writes in orange ink. And doesn't like the Botticelli's at the Uffizi. But I hadn't told you; she's at Florence. This letter has been to London and back. We're practically neighbors. And here's something that's really rather good. Listen. 'What I like about the Italian women is that they don't seem to be rather ashamed of being women, like so many English girls are, because English girls seem to go about apologizing for their figures, as though they were punctured, the way they hold themselves—it's really rather abject. But here they're all pleased and proud and not a bit apologetic or punctured, but just the opposite, which I really like, don't you?' Yes, I do," Fanning answered, looking up from the letter. "I like it very much indeed. I've always been opposed to these modern Ars est celare arsem fashions. I like unpuncturedness and I'm charmed by the letter. Yes, charmed. Aren't you?"

In a voice that trembled with hardly restrained indignation, "No, I'm not!" Judd answered; and without looking at Fanning, he got up and walked quickly out of the room.

II

Judd had gone to stay with his old Aunt Caroline at Montreux. It was an annual affair; for Judd lived chronometrically. Most of June and the first half of July were always devoted to Aunt Caroline and devoted, invariably, at Montreux. On the fifteenth of July, Aunt Caroline was rejoined by her friend Miss Gaskin and Judd was free to proceed to England. In England he stayed till September the thirteenth, when he returned to Rome—"for the praying season," as Fanning irreverently put it. The beautiful regularity of poor Colin's existence was a source of endless amusement to his friend. Fanning never had any plans. "I just accept what turns up," he would explain. "Heads or tails—it's the only rational way of living. Chance generally knows so much better than we do. The Greeks elected most of their officials by lot—how wisely! Why shouldn't we toss up for Prime Ministers? We'd be much better governed. Or a sort of Calcutta Sweep for all the responsible posts in Church and State. The only horror would be if one were to win the sweep oneself. Imagine drawing the Permanent Under-Secretaryship for Education! Or the Archbishopric of Canterbury! Or the Vice-royalty of India! One would just have to drink weed killer. But as things are, luckily . . ."

Luckily, he was at liberty, under the present dispensation, to stroll, very slowly, in a suit of cream-colored silk, down the shady side of the Via Condotti toward the Spanish Steps. Slowly, slowly. The air was streaked with invisible bars of heat and cold. Coolness came flowing out of shadowed doorways, and at every transverse street the sun breathed fiercely. Like walking through the ghost of a zebra, he thought.

Three beautiful young women passed him talking and laughing together. Like laughing flowers, like deer, like little horses. And of course absolutely unpunctured, unapologetic. He smiled to himself, thinking of the letter and also of his own reply to it.

A pair of pink and white monsters loomed up, as though from behind the glass of an aquarium. But not speechless. For "Grossartig!" fell enthusiastically on Fanning's ear as they passed, and "Fabelhaft!" These Nordics! He shook his head. Time they were put a stop to.

In the looking glasses of a milliner's window a tall man in creamy white walked slowly to meet him, hat in hand. The face was aquiline and eager, brown with much exposure to the sun. The waved, rather wiry hair was dark almost to blackness. It grew thickly, and the height of the forehead owed nothing to the approach of baldness. But what pleased Fanning most was the slimness and straightness of the tall figure. Those sedentary men of letters, with their sagging tremulous paunches —they were enough to make one hate the very thought of literature. What had been Fanning's horror when, a year before, he had realized that his own paunch was showing the first preliminary signs of sagging! But Mr. Hornibrooke's exercises had been wonderful. "The Culture of the Abdomen." So much more important, as he had remarked in the course of the last few months at so many dinner tables, than the culture of the mind! For of course he had taken everybody into his confidence about the paunch. He took everybody into his confidence about almost everything. About his love affairs and his literary projects; about his illnesses and his philosophy; his vices and his bank balance. He lived a rich and variegated private life in public; it was one of the secrets of his charm. To the indignant protests of poor jealous Colin, who reproached him with being an exhibitionist, shameless, a self-exploiter, "You take everything so moralistically," he had answered. "You seem to imagine people do everything on purpose. But people do hardly anything on purpose. They behave as they do because they can't help it; that's what they happen to be like. 'I am that I am'; Jehovah's is the last word in realistic psychology. I am what I am—a sort of soft transparent jellyfish. While you're what you are—very tightly shut, opaque, heavily armored: in a word, a giant clam. Morality doesn't enter; it's a case for scientific classification. You should be more of a Linnaeus, Colin, and less the Samuel Smiles." Judd had been reduced to a grumbling silence. What he really resented was the fact that Fanning's confidences were given to upstart friends, to strangers even, before they were given to him. It was only to be expected. The clam's shell keeps the outside things out as effectually as it keeps the inside things in. In Judd's case, moreover, the shell served as an instrument of reproachful pinching.

From his cool street Fanning emerged into the Piazza di Spagna. The sunlight was stinging hot and dazzling. The flower venders on the steps sat in the midst of great explosions of color. He bought a gardenia from one of them and stuck it in his buttonhole. From the windows of the English bookshop *The Return of Eurydice* by Miles Fanning stared at him again and again. They were making a regular display of his latest volume in Tauchnitz. Satisfactory, no doubt; but also, of course, rather ridiculous and even humiliating, when one reflected that the book would be read by people like that estimable upper-middle-class couple there, with their noses at the next window—that Civil Servant, he guessed, with the sweet little artistic wife and the artistic little house on Campden Hill—would be read by them dutifully (for of course they worked hard to keep abreast of everything) and discussed at their charming little dinner parties and finally condemned as "extraordinarily brilliant, but..." Yes, but, but, but. For they were obviously regular subscribers to *Punch*, were vertebrae in the backbone of England, were upholders of all that was depressingly finest, all that was lifelessly and genteelly best in the English upper-class tradition. And when they recognized him (as it was obvious to Fanning, in spite of their discreet politeness, that they did) his vanity, instead of being flattered, was hurt. Being recognized by people like that—such was fame! What a humiliation, what a personal insult!

At Cook's, where he now went to draw some money on his letter of credit, Fame still pursued him, trumpeting. From behind the brass bars of his cage the cashier smiled knowingly as he counted out the bank notes. "Of course your name's very familiar to me, Mr. Fanning," he said; and his tone was at once ingratiating and self-satisfied; the compliment to Fanning was at the same time a compliment to himself. "And if I may be permitted to say so," he went on, pushing the money through the bars, as one might offer a piece of bread to an ape, "gratters on your last book. Gratters," he repeated, evidently delighted with his very public-schooly colloquialism.

"All gratitude for gratters," Fanning answered, and turned away. He was half amused, half annoyed. Amused by the absurdity of those more than Etonian congratulations, annoyed at the damned impertinence of the congratulator. So intolerably patronizing! he grumbled to himself. But most admirers were like that; they thought they were doing you an enormous favor by admiring you. And how much more they admired themselves for being capable of appreciating than they admired the object of their appreciation! And then there were the earnest ones who thanked you for giving such a perfect expression to their ideas and sentiments. They were the worst of all. For, after all, what were they thanking you for? For being *their* interpreter, *their* dragoman, for playing John the Baptist to *their* Messiah. Damn their impertinence! Yes, damn their impertinence!

"Mr. Fanning." A hand touched his elbow.

Still indignant with the thought of damned impertinences, Fanning turned round with an expression of such ferocity on his face that the young woman who had addressed him involuntarily fell back.

"Oh . . . I'm so sorry," she stammered; and her face, which had been bright, deliberately, with just such an impertinence as Fanning was damning, was discomposed into a childlike embarrassment. The blood tingled painfully in her cheeks. Oh, what a fool, she thought, what a fool she was making of herself! This idiotic blushing! But the way he had turned round on her, as if he were going to bite . . . Still, even that was no excuse for blushing and saying she was sorry, as though she were still at school and he were Miss Huss. Idiot! she inwardly shouted at herself. And making an enormous effort, she readjusted her still scarlet face, giving it as good an expression of smiling nonchalance as she could summon up. "I'm sorry," she repeated, in a voice that was meant to be light, easy, ironically polite, but which came out (oh, idiot, idiot!) nervously shaky and uneven. "I'm afraid I disturbed you. But I just wanted to introduce . . . I mean, as you were passing . . ."

"But how charming of you!" said Fanning, who had had time to realize that this latest piece of impertinence was one to be blessed, not damned. "Charming!" Yes, charming it was, that young face with the gray eyes and the little straight nose, like a cat's, and the rather short upper lip. And the heroic way she had tried, through all her blushes, to be the accomplished woman of the world—that too was charming. And touchingly charming, even, were those rather red, large-wristed English hands, which she wasn't yet old enough to have learned the importance of tending into whiteness and softness. They were still the hands of a child, a tomboy. He gave her one of those quick, those brilliantly and yet mysteriously significant smiles of his; those smiles that were still so youthfully beautiful when they came spontaneously. But they could also be put on; he knew how to exploit their fabricated charm, deliberately. To a sensitive eye, the beauty of his expression was, on these occasions, subtly repulsive.

Reassured, "I'm Pamela Tarn," said the young girl, feeling warm with gratitude for the smile. He was handsomer, she was thinking, than in his photographs. And much more fascinating. It was a face that had to be seen in movement.

"Pamela Tarn?" he repeated questioningly.

"The one who wrote you a letter." Her blush began to deepen again. "You answered so nicely. I mean, it was so kind . . . I thought . . ."

"But of course!" he cried, so loudly, that people looked round, startled. "Of course!" He took her hand and held it, shaking it from time to time, for what seemed to Pamela hours. "The most enchanting letter. Only I'm so bad at names. So you're Pamela Tarn." He looked at her appraisingly. She returned his look for a moment, then flinched away in confusion from his bright dark eyes.

"Excuse me," said a chilly voice; and a very large suit of plus fours edged past them to the door.

"I like you," Fanning concluded, ignoring the plus fours; she uttered an embarrassed little laugh. "But then, I liked you before. You don't know how pleased I was with what you said about the difference between English and Italian women." The color rose once more into Pamela's cheeks. She had only written those sentences after long hesitation, and had written them then recklessly, dashing them down with a kind of anger, just because Miss Huss would have been horrified by their unwomanliness, just because Aunt Edith would have found them so distressing, just because they had, when she spoke them aloud one day in the streets of Florence, so shocked the two schoolmistresses from Boston whom she had met at the pension and was doing the sights with. Fanning's mention of them pleased her and at the same time made her feel dreadfully guilty. She hoped he wouldn't be too specific about those differences; it seemed to her that every one was listening. "So profound," he went on in his musical ringing voice. "But out of the mouths of babes, with all due respect." He smiled again, "And 'punctured'—that was really the mot juste. I shall steal it and use it as my own."

"Permesso." This time it was a spotted muslin and brown arms and a whiff of synthetic carnations.

"I think we're rather in the way," said Pamela, who was becoming more and more uncomfortably aware of being conspicuous. And the spirit

presences of Miss Huss, of Aunt Edith, of the two American ladies at
Florence seemed to hang about her, hauntingly. "Perhaps we'd better
. . . I mean . . ." And, turning, she almost ran to the door.

"Punctured, punctured," repeated his pursuing voice behind her.
"Punctured with the shame of being warm-blooded mammals. Like those
poor lank creatures that were standing at the counter in there," he added,
coming abreast with her as they stepped over the threshold into the heat
and glare. "Did you see them? So pathetic. But, oh dear!" he shook his
head. "Oh dear, oh dear!"

She looked up at him, and Fanning saw in her face a new expression,
an expression of mischief and laughing malice and youthful impertinence.
Even her breasts, he now noticed with an amused appreciation, even her
breasts were impertinent. Small, but, beneath the pale-blue stuff of
her dress, pointed, firm, almost comically insistent. No ashamed de-
flation here.

"Pathetic," she mockingly echoed, "but, oh dear, how horrible, how
disgusting! Because they are disgusting," she added defiantly, in answer
to his look of humorous protest. Here in the sunlight and with the noise
of the town isolating her from everyone except Fanning, she had lost
her embarrassment and her sense of guilt. The spiritual presences had
evaporated. Pamela was annoyed with herself for having felt so uncomfortable among those awful old English cats at Cook's. She thought of
her mother; her mother had never been embarrassed, or at any rate she
had always managed to turn her embarrassment into something else.
Which was what Pamela was doing now. "Really disgusting," she almost
truculently insisted. She was reasserting herself, she was taking a revenge.

"You're very ruthless to the poor old things," said Fanning. "So worthy
in spite of their mangy dimness, so obviously good."

"I hate goodness," said Pamela with decision, speeding the parting
ghosts of Miss Huss and Aunt Edith and the two ladies from Boston.

Fanning laughed aloud. "Ah, if only we all had the courage to say so,
like you, my child!" And with a familiar affectionate gesture, as though
she were indeed a child and he had known her from the cradle, he
dropped a hand on her shoulder. "To say so and to act up to our beliefs.
As you do, I'm sure." And he gave the slim hard little shoulder a pat.
"A world without goodness—it'd be Paradise."

They walked some steps in silence. His hand lay heavy and strong on
her shoulder, and a strange warmth that was somehow intenser than the
warmth of mere flesh and blood seemed to radiate through her whole
body. Her heart quickened its beating; an anxiety oppressed her lungs;
her very mind was as though breathless.

"Putting his hand on my shoulder like that!" she was thinking. "It would have been cheek if someone else . . . Perhaps I ought to have been angry, perhaps . . ." No, that would have been silly. "It's silly to take things like that too seriously, as though one were Aunt Edith." But meanwhile his hand lay heavy on her shoulder, broodingly hot, its weight, its warmth insistently present in her consciousness.

She remembered characters in his books. Her namesake Pamela in *Pastures New*. Pamela the cold, but for that very reason an experimenter with passion; cold and therefore dangerous, full of power, fatal. Was she like Pamela? She had often thought so. But more recently she had often thought she was like Joan in *The Return of Eurydice*—Joan, who had emerged from the wintry dark underworld of an unawakened life with her husband (that awful, good, disinterested husband—so like Aunt Edith) into the warmth and brilliance of that transfiguring passion for Walter, for the adorable Walter whom she had always imagined must be so like Miles Fanning himself. She was sure of it now. But what of her own identity? Was she Joan, or was she Pamela? And which of the two would it be nicer to be? Warm Joan, with her happiness—but at the price of surrender? Or the cold, the unhappy, but conquering, dangerous Pamela? Or wouldn't it perhaps be best to be a little of both at once? Or first one and then the other? And in any case there was to be no goodness in the Aunt Edith style; he had been sure she wasn't good.

In her memory the voice of Aunt Edith sounded, as it had actually sounded only a few weeks before, in disapproving comment on her reference to the passionless experimental Pamela of *Pastures New*. "It's a book I don't like. A most unnecessary book." And then, laying her hand on Pamela's, "Dear child," she had added, with that earnest, that dutifully willed affectionateness, which Pamela so bitterly resented, "I'd rather you didn't read any of Miles Fanning's books."

"Mother never objected to my reading them. So I don't see . . ." The triumphant consciousness of having at this very moment the hand that had written those unnecessary books upon her shoulder was promising to enrich her share of the remembered dialogue with a lofty impertinence which the original had hardly possessed. "I don't see that you have the smallest right . . ."

Fanning's voice fell startlingly across the eloquent silence. "A penny for your thoughts, Miss Pamela," it said.

He had been for some obscure reason suddenly depressed by his own last words. "A world without goodness—it'd be paradise." But it wouldn't, no more than now. The only paradises were fools' paradises, ostriches' paradises. It was as though he had suddenly lifted his head

out of the sand and seen time bleeding away—like the stabbed bull at
the end of a bullfight, swaying on his legs and soundlessly spouting the
red blood from his nostrils—bleeding, bleeding away stanchlessly into
the darkness. And it was all, even the loveliness and the laughter and the
sunlight, finally pointless. This young girl at his side, this beautiful
pointless creature pointlessly walking down the Via del Babuino . . . The
feelings crystallized themselves, as usual, into whole phrases in his mind,
and suddenly the phrases were metrical.

> Pointless and arm in arm with pointlessness,
> I pace and pace the Street of the Baboon.

Imbecile! Annoyed with himself, he tried to shake off his mood of maudlin depression; he tried to force his spirit back into the ridiculous and
charming universe it had inhabited, on the whole so happily, all the
morning.

"A penny for your thoughts," he said, with a certain rather forced
jocularity, giving her shoulder a little clap. "Or forty centesimi, if you
prefer them." And, dropping his hand to his side, "In Germany," he
went on, "just after the War one could afford to be more munificent.
There was a time when I regularly offered a hundred and ninety million
marks for a thought—yes, and gained on the exchange. But now . . ."

"Well, if you really want to know," said Pamela, deciding to be bold,
"I was thinking how much my Aunt Edith disapproved of your books."

"Did she? I suppose it was only to be expected. Seeing that I don't
write for aunts—at any rate, not for aunts in their specifically auntly
capacity. Though, of course, when they're off duty . . ."

"Aunt Edith's never off duty."

"And I'm never on. So you see." He shrugged his shoulders. "But I'm
sure," he added, "you never paid much attention to her disapproval."

"None," she answered, playing the un-good part for all it was worth.
"I read Freud this spring," she boasted, "and Gide's autobiography, and
Krafft-Ebbing. . . ."

"Which is more than I've ever done," he laughed.

The laugh encouraged her. "Not to mention all your books, years ago.
You see," she added, suddenly fearful lest she might have said something
to offend him, "my mother never minded my reading your books. I
mean, she really encouraged me, even when I was only seventeen or
eighteen. My mother died last year," she explained. There was a silence.
"I've lived with Aunt Edith ever since," she went on. "Aunt Edith's
my father's sister. Older than he was. Father died in 1923."

"So you're all alone now?" he questioned. "Except, of course, for Aunt Edith."

"Whom I've now left." She was almost boasting again. "Because when I was twenty-one . . ."

"You stuck out your tongue at her and ran away. Poor Aunt Edith!"

"I won't have you being sorry for her," Pamela answered hotly. "She's really awful, you know. Like poor Joan's husband in *The Return of Eurydice*." How easy it was to talk to him!

"So you even know," said Fanning, laughing, "what it's like to be unhappily married. Already. Indissolubly wedded to a virtuous aunt."

"No joke, I can tell you. *I'm* the one to be sorry for. Besides, she didn't mind my going away, whatever she might say."

"She did say something, then?"

"Oh yes. She always says things. More in sorrow than in anger, you know. Like head mistresses. So gentle and good, I mean. When all the time she really thought me too awful. I used to call her Hippo, because she was such a hypocrite—and so fat. Enormous. Don't you *hate* enormous people? No, she's really delighted to get rid of me," Pamela concluded, "simply delighted." Her face was flushed and as though luminously alive; she spoke with a quick eagerness.

"What a tremendous hurry she's in," he was thinking, "to tell me all about herself. If she were older or uglier, what an intolerable egotism it would be! As intolerable as mine would be if I happened to be less intelligent. But as it is . . ." His face, as he listened to her, expressed a sympathetic attention.

"She always disliked me," Pamela had gone on. "Mother too. She couldn't abide my mother, though she was always sweetly hippo-ish with her."

"And your mother—how did she respond?"

"Well, not hippo-ishly, of course. She couldn't be that. She treated Aunt Edith—well, how *did* she treat Aunt Edith?" Pamela hesitated, frowning. "Well, I suppose you'd say she was just natural with the Hippo. I mean . . ." She bit her lip. "Well, if she ever *was* really natural. *I* don't know. Is anybody natural?" She looked up questioningly at Fanning. "Am I natural, for example?"

Smiling a little at her choice of an example, "I should think almost certainly not," Fanning answered, more or less at random.

"You're right, of course," she said despairingly, and her face was suddenly tragic, almost there were tears in her eyes. "But isn't it awful? I mean, isn't it simply hopeless?"

Pleased that his chance shot should have gone home, "At your age," he said consolingly, "you can hardly expect to be natural. Naturalness is something you learn, painfully, by trial and error. Besides," he added, "there are some people who are unnatural by nature."

"Unnatural by nature." Pamela nodded, as she repeated the words, as though she were inwardly marshaling evidence to confirm their truth. "Yes, I believe that's us," she concluded. "Mother and me. Not hippos, I mean, not *poseuses*, but just unnatural by nature. You're quite right. As usual," she added, with something that was almost resentment in her voice.

"I'm sorry," he apologized.

"How is it you manage to know so much?" Pamela asked in the same resentful tone. By what right was he so easily omniscient, when she could only grope and guess in the dark?

Taking to himself a credit that belonged, in this case, to chance, "Child's play, my dear Watson," he answered banteringly. "But I suppose you're too young to have heard of Sherlock Holmes. And anyhow," he added, with an ironical seriousness, "don't let's waste any more time talking about me."

Pamela wasted no more time. "I get so depressed with myself," she said with a sigh. "And after what you've told me I shall get still more depressed. Unnatural by nature. And by upbringing too. Because I see now that my mother was like that. I mean, she was unnatural by nature too."

"Even with you?" he asked, thinking that this was becoming interesting. She nodded without speaking. He looked at her closely. "Were you very fond of her?" was the question that now suggested itself.

After a moment of silence, "I loved my father more," she answered slowly. "He was more . . . more reliable. I mean, you never quite knew where you were with my mother. Sometimes she almost forgot about me; or else she didn't forget me enough and spoiled me. And then sometimes she used to get into the most terrible rages with me. She really frightened me then. And said such terribly hurting things. But you mustn't think I didn't love her. I did." The words seemed to release a spring; she was suddenly moved. There was a little silence. Making an effort, "But that's what she was like," she concluded at last.

"But I don't see," said Fanning gently, "that there was anything specially unnatural in spoiling you and then getting cross with you." They were crossing the Piazza del Popolo; the traffic of four thronged streets intricately merged and parted in the open space. "You must have been a charming child. And also . . . look out!" He laid a hand on her arm. An electric bus passed noiselessly, a whispering monster. "Also maddeningly exasperating. So where the unnaturalness came in . . ."

"But if you'd known her," Pamela interrupted, "you'd have seen exactly where the unnaturalness . . ."

"Forward!" he called, and, still holding her arm, he steered her on across the Piazza.

She suffered herself to be conducted blindly. "It came out in the way she spoiled me," she explained, raising her voice against the clatter of a passing lorry. "It's so difficult to explain, though; because it's something I felt. I mean, I've never really tried to put it into words till now. But it was as if . . . as if she weren't just herself spoiling me, but the picture of a young mother—do you see what I mean?—spoiling the picture of a little girl. Even as a child I kind of felt it wasn't quite as it should be. Later on I began to know it too, here." She tapped her forehead. "Particularly after father's death, when I was beginning to grow up. There were times when it was almost like listening to recitations—dreadful. One feels so blushy and prickly; you know the feeling."

He nodded. "Yes, I know. Awful!"

"Awful," she repeated. "So you can understand what a beast I felt, when it took me that way. So disloyal, I mean. So ungrateful. Because she was being so wonderfully sweet to me. You've no idea. But it was just when she was being her sweetest that I got the feeling worst. I shall never forget when she made me call her Clare—that was her Christian name. 'Because we're going to be companions,' she said, and all that sort of thing. Which was simply too sweet and too nice of her. But if you'd heard the way she said it! So dreadfully unnatural. I mean, it was almost as bad as Aunt Edith reading *Prospice*. And yet I know she meant it; I know she wanted me to be her companion. But somehow something kind of went wrong on the way between the wanting and the saying. And then the doing seemed to go just as wrong as the saying. She always wanted to do things excitingly, romantically, like in a play. But you can't make things be exciting and romantic, can you?" Fanning shook his head. "She wanted to kind of force things to be thrilling by thinking and wishing, like Christian Science. But it doesn't work. We had wonderful times together; but she always tried to make out that they were more wonderful than they really were. Which only made them less wonderful. Going to the Paris Opera on a gala night is wonderful; but it's never as wonderful as when Rastignac goes, is it?"

"I should think it wasn't!" he agreed. "What an insult to Balzac to imagine that it could be!"

"And the real thing's less wonderful," she went on, "when you're being asked all the time to see it as Balzac, and to *be* Balzac yourself. When you aren't anything of the kind. Because, after all, what am I? Just good, ordinary, middle-class English."

She pronounced the words with a kind of defiance. Fanning imagined that the defiance was for him and, laughing, prepared to pick up the ridiculous little glove. But the glove was not for him; Pamela had thrown it down to a memory, to a ghost, to one of her own sceptical and mocking selves. It had been on the last day of their last stay together in Paris—that exciting, exotic Paris of poor Clare's imagination, to which their tickets from London never seemed quite to take them. They had gone to lunch at La Pérouse. "Such a marvelous, *fantastic* restaurant! It makes you feel as though you were back in the Second Empire." (Or was it the First Empire? Pamela could not exactly remember.) The rooms were so crowded with Americans that it was with some difficulty that they secured a table. "We'll have a marvelous lunch," Clare had said, as she unfolded her napkin. "And some day, when you're in Paris with your lover, you'll come here and order just the same things as we're having today. And perhaps you'll think of me. Will you, darling?" And she had smiled at her daughter with that intense, expectant expression that was so often on her face, and the very memory of which made Pamela feel subtly uncomfortable. "How should I ever forget?" she had answered, laying her hand on her mother's and smiling. But after a second her eyes had wavered away from that fixed look, in which the intensity had remained as desperately on the stretch, the expectancy as wholly unsatisfied, as hungrily insatiable as ever. The waiter, thank goodness, had created a timely diversion; smiling at him confidentially, almost amorously, Clare had ordered like a princess in a novel of high life. The bill, when it came, was enormous. Clare had had to scratch the bottom of her purse for the last stray piece of nickel. "It looks as though we should have to carry our own bags at Calais and Dover. I didn't realize I'd run things so fine." Pamela had looked at the bill. "But, Clare," she had protested, looking up again at her mother with an expression of genuine horror, "it's wicked! Two hundred and sixty francs for a lunch! It wasn't worth it." The blood had risen darkly into Clare's face. "How can you be so disgustingly *bourgeoise*, Pamela? So crass, so crawling?" Incensed by the heaping up of this abuse, "I think it's stupid to do things one can't afford," the girl had answered; "stupid and vulgar." Trembling with rage, Clare had risen to her feet. "I'll never take you out again. Never." (How often since then Pamela had recalled that terribly prophetic word!) "You'll never understand life, you'll never be anything but a sordid little middle-class Englishwoman. Never, never." And she had swept out of the room, like an insulted queen. Overheard by Pamela, as she undignifiedly followed, "Gee!" an American voice had remarked, "it's a regular cat fight."

The sound of another, real voice overlaid the remembered Middle Western accents.

"But after all," Fanning was saying, "it's better to be a good ordinary bourgeois than a bad ordinary bohemian, or a sham aristocrat, or a second-rate intellectual. . . ."

"I'm not even third rate," said Pamela mournfully. There had been a time when, under the influence of the now abhorred Miss Huss, she had thought she would like to go up to Oxford and read Greats. But Greek grammar was so awful . . . "Not even fourth rate."

"Thank goodness," said Fanning. "Do you know what third- and fourth-rate intellectuals are? They're professors of philology and organic chemistry at the minor universities; they're founders and honorary life presidents of the Nuneaton Poetry Society and the Baron's Court Debating Society; they're the people who organize and sedulously attend all those Conferences for promoting international good will and the spread of culture that are perpetually being held at Buda-Pesth and Prague and Stockholm. Admirable and indispensable creatures, of course! But impossibly dreary; one simply cannot have any relations with them. And how virtuously they disapprove of those of us who have something better to do than disseminate culture or foster good will—those of us who are concerned, for example, with creating beauty—like me; or, like you, my child, in deliciously *being* beauty."

Pamela blushed with pleasure, and for that reason felt it necessary immediately to protest. "All the same," she said, "it's rather humiliating not to be able to do anything but be. I mean, even a cow can be."

"Damned well, too," said Fanning. "If I were as intensely as a cow *is*, I'd be uncommonly pleased with myself. But this is getting almost too metaphysical. And do you realize what the time is?" He held out his watch; it was ten past one. "And where we are? At the Tiber. We've walked miles." He waved his hand; a passing taxi swerved into the pavement beside them. "Let's go and eat some lunch. You're free?"

"Well . . ." She hesitated. It was marvelous, of course; so marvelous that she felt she ought to refuse. "If I'm not a bore. I mean, I don't want to impose . . . I mean . . ."

"You mean you'll come and have lunch. Good. Do you like marble halls and bands? Or local color?"

Pamela hesitated. She remembered her mother once saying that Valadier and the Ulpia were the only two restaurants in Rome.

"Personally," Fanning went on, "I'm slightly avaricious about marble halls. I rather resent spending four times as much for eating about two-thirds as well. But I'll overcome my avarice if you prefer them."

Pamela duly voted for local color; he gave an address to the driver and they climbed into the cab.

"It's a genuinely Roman place," Fanning explained. "I hope you'll like it."

"Oh, I'm sure I shall." All the same, she did rather wish they were going to Valadier's.

III

Fanning's old friend, Dodo del Grillo, was in Rome for that one night and had urgently summoned him to dine. His arrival was loud and exclamatory.

"Best of all possible Dodos!" he cried, as he advanced with outstretched hands across the enormous baroque saloon. "What an age! But what a pleasure!"

"At last, Miles," she said reproachfully; he was twenty minutes late.

"But I know you'll forgive me." And laying his two hands on her shoulders he bent down and kissed her. He made a habit of kissing all his women friends.

"And even if I didn't forgive, you wouldn't care two pins."

"Not one." He smiled his most charming smile. "But if it gives you the smallest pleasure, I'm ready to say I'd be inconsolable." His hands still resting on her shoulders, he looked at her searchingly, at arm's length. "Younger than ever," he concluded.

"I couldn't look as young as you do," she answered. "You know, Miles, you're positively indecent. Like Dorian Gray. What's your horrible secret?"

"Simply Mr. Hornibrooke," he explained. "The culture of the abdomen. So much more important than the culture of the mind." Dodo only faintly smiled; she had heard the joke before. Fanning was sensitive to smiles; he changed the subject. "And where's the marquis?" he asked.

The marchesa shrugged her shoulders. Her husband was one of those dear old friends whom somehow one doesn't manage to see anything of nowadays. "Filippo's in Tanganyika," she explained. "Hunting lions."

"While you hunt them at home. And with what success! You've bagged what's probably the finest specimen in Europe this evening. Congratulations!"

"Merci, cher maître!" she laughed. "Shall we go in to dinner?"

The words invited, irresistibly. "If only I had the right to answer:

Oui, chère maîtresse!" Though as a matter of fact, he reflected, he had never really found her at all interesting in that way. A woman without temperament. But very pretty once—that time (how many years ago?) when there had been that picnic on the river at Bray, and he had drunk a little too much champagne. "If only!" he repeated; and then was suddenly struck by a grotesque thought. Suppose she were to say yes, now —now! "If only I had the right!"

"But luckily," said Dodo, turning back toward him, as she passed through the monumental door into the dining room, "luckily you haven't the right. You ought to congratulate me on my immense good sense. Will you sit there?"

"Oh, I'll congratulate. I'm always ready to congratulate people who have sense." He unfolded his napkin. "And to condole." Now that he knew himself safe, he could condole as much as he liked. "What you must have suffered, my poor sensible Dodo, what you must have missed!"

"Suffered less," she answered, "and missed more unpleasantnesses than the women who didn't have the sense to say no."

"What a mouthful of negatives! But that's how sensible people always talk about love—in terms of negatives. Never of positives; they ignore those and go about sensibly avoiding the discomforts. Avoiding the pleasures and exultations too, poor sensible idiots! Avoiding all that's valuable and significant. But it's always like that. The human soul is a fried whiting. (What excellent red mullet this is, by the way! Really excellent.) Its tail is in its mouth. All progress finally leads back to the beginning again. The most sensible people—dearest Dodo, believe me—are the most foolish. The most intellectual are the stupidest. I've never met a really good metaphysician, for example, who wasn't in one way or another bottomlessly stupid. And as for the really spiritual people, look what they revert to. Not merely to silliness and stupidity, but finally to crass nonexistence. The highest spiritual state is ecstasy, which is just not being there at all. No, no; we're all fried whitings. Heads are invariably tails."

"In which case," said Dodo, "tails must also be heads. So that if you want to make intellectual or spiritual progress, you must behave like a beast—is that it?"

Fanning held up his hand. "Not at all. If you rush too violently toward the tail, you run the risk of shooting down the whiting's open mouth into its stomach, and even further. The wise man . . ."

"So the whitings are fried without being cleaned?"

"In parables," Fanning answered reprovingly, "whitings are always fried that way. The wise man, as I was saying, oscillates lightly from head to tail and back again. His whole existence—or shall we be more frank and say 'my' whole existence?—is one continual oscillation. I am never too consistently sensible, like you; or too consistently featherheaded like some of my other friends. In a word," he wagged a finger, "I oscillate."

Tired of generalizations, "And where exactly," Dodo inquired, "have you oscillated to at the moment? You've left me without your news so long. . . ."

"Well, at the moment," he reflected aloud, "I suppose you might say I was at a dead point between desire and renunciation, between sense and sensuality."

"Again?" She shook her head. "And who is she this time?"

Fanning helped himself to asparagus before replying. "Who is she?" he echoed. "Well, to begin with, she's the writer of admiring letters."

Dodo made a grimace of disgust. "What a horror!" For some reason she felt it necessary to be rather venomous about this new usurper of Fanning's heart. "Vamping by correspondence—it's really the lowest . . ."

"Oh, I agree," he said. "On principle and in theory I entirely agree."

"Then why . . ." she began, annoyed by his agreement; but he interrupted her.

"Spiritual adventuresses," he said. "That's what they generally are, the women who write you letters. Spiritual adventuresses. I've suffered a lot from them in my time."

"I'm sure you have."

"They're a curious type," he went on, ignoring her sarcasms. "Curious and rather horrible. I prefer the good old-fashioned vampire. At least one knew where one stood with her. There she was—out for money, for power, for a good time, occasionally, perhaps, for sensual satisfactions. It was all entirely aboveboard and obvious. But with the spiritual adventuress, on the contrary, everything's most horribly turbid and obscure and slimy. You see, she doesn't want money or the commonplace good time. She wants Higher Things—damn her neck! Not large pearls and a large motorcar, but a large soul—that's what she pines for: a large soul and a large intellect, and a huge philosophy, and enormous culture, and outsizes in great thoughts."

Dodo laughed. "You're fiendishly cruel, Miles."

"Cruelty can be a sacred duty," he answered. "Besides, I'm getting a little of my own back. If you knew what these spiritual vamps had done to me! I've been one of their appointed victims. Yes, appointed; for, you see, they can't have their Higher Things without attaching themselves to a Higher Person."

"And are you one of the Higher People, Miles?"

"Should I be dining here with you, my dear, if I weren't?" And without waiting for Dodo's answer, "They attach themselves like lice," he went on. "The contact with the Higher Person makes them feel high themselves; it magnifies them, it gives them significance, it satisfies their parasitic will to power. In the past they could have gone to religion —fastened themselves on the nearest priest (that's what the priest was there for), or sucked the spiritual blood of some saint. Nowadays they've got no professional victims; only a few charlatans and swamis and higher-thought mongers. Or alternatively the artists. Yes, the artists. They find our souls particularly juicy. What I've suffered! Shall I ever forget that American woman who got so excited by my book on Blake that she came specially to Tunis to see me? She had an awful way of opening her mouth very wide when she talked, like a fish. You were perpetually seeing her tongue; and, what made it worse, her tongue was generally white. Most distressing. And how the tongue wagged! In spite of its white-ness. Wagged like mad, and mostly about the Divine Mind."

"The Divine Mind?"

He nodded. "It was her specialty. In Rochester, N. Y., where she lived, she was never out of touch with it. You've no idea what a lot of Divine Mind there is floating about in Rochester, particularly in the neighbor-hood of women with busy husbands and incomes of over fifteen thousand dollars. If only she could have stuck to the Divine Mind! But the Divine Mind has one grave defect: it won't make love to you. That was why she'd come all the way to Tunis in search of a merely human speci-men."

"And what did you do about it?"

"Stood it nine days and then took the boat to Sicily. Like a thief in the night. The wicked flee, you know. God, how they can flee!"

"And she?"

"Went back to Rochester, I suppose. But I never opened any more of her letters. Just dropped them into the fire whenever I saw the writing. Ostrichism—it's the only rational philosophy of conduct. Accord-ing to the Freudians we're all unconsciously trying to get back to . . ."

"But poor woman!" Dodo burst out. "She must have suffered."

"Nothing like what I suffered. Besides, she had the Divine Mind to go back to; which was her version of the Freudians' prenatal . . ."

"But I suppose you'd encouraged her to come to Tunis?"

Reluctantly, Fanning gave up his Freudians. "She could write good letters," he admitted. "Inexplicably good, considering what she was at close range."

"But then you treated her abominably."

"But if you'd seen her, you'd realize how abominably she'd treated me."

"You?"

"Yes, abominably—by merely existing. She taught me to be very shy of letters. That was why I was so pleasantly surprised this morning when my latest correspondent suddenly materialized at Cook's. Really ravishing. One could forgive her everything for the sake of her face and that charming body. Everything, even the vamping. For a vamp I sup-pose she is, even this one. That is, if a woman can be a spiritual adven-turess when she's so young and pretty and well made. Absolutely and sub specie aeternitatis, I suppose she can. But from the very sublunary point of view of the male victim, I doubt whether, at twenty-one . . ."

"Only twenty-one?" Dodo was disapproving. "But Miles!"

Fanning ignored her interruption. "And another thing you must re-member," he went on, "is that the spiritual vamp who's come of age this year is not at all the same as the spiritual vamp who came of age fifteen, twenty, twenty-five years ago. She doesn't bother much about Mysticism, or the Lower Classes, or the Divine Mind, or any nonsense of that sort. No, she goes straight to the real point—the point which the older vamps approached in such a tiresomely circuitous fashion—she goes straight to herself. But straight!" He stabbed the air with his fruit knife. "A beeline. Oh, it has a certain charm that directness. But whether it won't be rather frightful when they're older is another question. But then almost everything is rather frightful when people are older."

"Thank you," said Dodo. "And what about you?"

"Oh, an old satyr," he answered with that quick, brilliantly mysterious smile of his. "A superannuated faun. I know it; only too well. But at the same time, most intolerably, a Higher Person. Which is what draws the spiritual vamps. Even the youngest ones. Not to talk to me about the Divine Mind, of course, or their views about Social Reform. But about themselves. Their Individualities, their Souls, their Inhibitions, their Un-consciouses, their Pasts, their Futures. For them, the Higher Things are all frankly and nakedly personal. And the function of the Higher Person is to act as a sort of psychoanalytical father confessor. He exists to tell them all about their strange and wonderful psyches. And meanwhile, of course, his friendship inflates their egotism. And if there should be any question of love, what a personal triumph!"

"Which is all very well!" objected Dodo. "But what about the old satyr? Wouldn't it also be a bit of a triumph for him? You know, Miles," she added gravely, "it would really be scandalous if you were to take advantage . . ."

"But I haven't the slightest intention of taking any advantages. If only for my own sake. Besides, the child is too ingenuously absurd. The most hair-raising theoretical knowledge of life, out of books. You should hear her prattling away about inverts and perverts and birth control— but prattling from unplumbed depths of innocence and practical ignorance. Very queer. And touching too. Much more touching than the old-fashioned innocences of the young creatures who thought babies were brought by storks. Knowing all about love and lust, but in the same way as one knows all about quadratic equations. And her knowledge of the other aspects of life is really of the same kind. What she's seen of the world she's seen in her mother's company. The worst guide imaginable, to judge from the child's account. (Dead now, incidentally.) The sort of woman who could never live on top gear so to speak—only at one or two imaginative removes from the facts. So that, in her company, what was nominally real life became actually just literature—yet more literature. Bad, inadequate Balzac in flesh and blood instead of genuine, good Balzac out of a set of nice green volumes. The child realizes it herself. Obscurely, of course; but distressfully. It's one of the reasons why she's applied to me: she hopes I can explain what's wrong. And correct it in practice. Which I won't do in any drastic manner, I promise you. Only mildly, by precept—that is, if I'm not too bored to do it at all."

"What's the child's name?" Dodo asked.

"Pamela Tarn."

"Tarn? But was her mother by any chance Clare Tarn?"

He nodded. "That was it. She even made her daughter call her by her Christian name. The companion stunt."

"But I used to know Clare Tarn quite well," said Dodo in an astonished, feeling voice. "These last years I'd hardly seen her. But when I was more in London just after the War . . ."

"But this begins to be interesting," said Fanning. "New light on my little friend. . . ."

"Whom I absolutely forbid you," said Dodo emphatically, "to . . ."

"Tamper with the honor of," he suggested. "Let's phrase it as nobly as possible."

"No, seriously, Miles. I really won't have it. Poor Clare Tarn's daughter. If I didn't have to rush off tomorrow I'd ask her to come and see me, so as to warn her."

Fanning laughed. "She wouldn't thank you. And besides, if anyone is to be warned, I'm the one who's in danger. But I shall be firm, Dodo—a rock. I won't allow her to seduce me."

"You're incorrigible, Miles. But mind, if you dare . . ."

"But I won't. Definitely." His tone was reassuring. "Meanwhile I must hear something about the mother."

The marchesa shrugged her shoulders. "A woman who couldn't live on top gear. You've really said the last word."

"But I want first words," he answered. "It's not the verdict that's interesting. It's the whole case; it's all the evidence. You're *subpoenaed*, my dear. Speak up."

"Poor Clare!"

"Oh, *nil nisi bonum*, of course, if that's what disturbs you."

"She'd have so loved it to be not *bonum*, poor dear!" said the marchesa, tempering her look of vague condolence with a little smile. "That was her great ambition—to be thought rather wicked. She'd have liked to have the reputation of a vampire. Not a spiritual one, mind you. The other sort. Lola Montes—that was her ideal."

"It's an ideal," said Fanning, "that takes some realizing, I can tell you."

Dodo nodded. "And that's what she must have found out, pretty soon. She wasn't born to be a fatal woman; she lacked the gifts. No staggering beauty, no mysterious fascination or intoxicating vitality. She was just very charming; that was all; and at the same time rather impossible and absurd. So that there weren't any aspiring victims to be fatal to. And a vampire without victims is—well, *what*?"

"Certainly not a vampire," he concluded.

"Except, of course, in her own imagination, if she chooses to think so. In her own imagination Clare certainly was a vampire."

"Reduced, in fact, to being her own favorite character in fiction."

"Precisely. You always find the phrase."

"Only too fatally!" He made a little grimace. "I often wish I didn't. The luxury of being inarticulate! To be able to wallow indefinitely long in every feeling and sensation, instead of having to clamber out at once on to a hard, dry, definite phrase. But what about your Clare?"

"Well, she started, of course, by being a riddle to me. Unanswerable, or rather answerable, answered, but so very strangely that I was still left wondering. I shall never forget the first time Filippo and I went to dine there. Poor Roger Tarn was still alive then. While the men were drinking their port, Clare and I were alone in the drawing room. There was a little chitchat, I remember, and then, with a kind of determined desperation, as though she'd that second screwed herself up to jumping off the Eiffel Tower, suddenly, out of the blue, she asked me if I'd ever had one of those *wonderful* Sicilian peasants—I can't possibly reproduce the tone, the expression—as a lover. I was a bit taken aback, I must confess. 'But we don't live in Sicily,' was the only thing I could think of answering—too idiotically! 'Our estates are all in Umbria and Tuscany.' 'But the Tuscans are superb creatures too,' she insisted. Superb, I agreed. But, as it happens, I don't have affairs with even the superbest peasants. Nor with anybody else, for that matter. Clare was dreadfully disappointed. I think she'd expected the most romantic confidences— moonlight and mandolines and *stretti, stretti, nell'estasi d'amor*. She was really very ingenuous. 'Do you mean to say you've really never . . .' she insisted. I ought to have got angry, I suppose; but it was all so ridiculous that I never thought of it. I just said 'Never,' and felt as though I were refusing her a favor. But she made up for my churlishness by being lavish to herself. But lavish! You can't imagine what a tirade she let fly at me. How *wonderful* it was to get away from self-conscious, complicated, sentimental love! How profoundly *satisfying* to feel oneself at the mercy of the dumb, dark forces of physical passion! How *intoxicating* to humiliate one's culture and one's class feeling before some *magnificent* primitive, some *earthly* beautiful satyr, some *divine* animal! And so on, *crescendo*. And it ended with her telling me the story of her *extraordinary* affair with—was it a gamekeeper? or a young farmer? I forget. But there was something about rabbit-shooting in it, I know."

"It sounds like a chapter out of George Sand."

"It was."

"Or still more, I'm afraid," he said, making a wry face, "like a most deplorable parody of my *Endymion and the Moon*."

"Which I've never read, I'm ashamed to say."

"You should, if only to understand this Clare of yours."

"I will. Perhaps I'd have solved her more quickly, if I'd read it at the time. As it was I could only be amazed—and a little horrified. That rabbit-shooter!" She shook her head. "He ought to have been so romantic. But I could only think of that awful yellow kitchen soap he'd be sure to wash himself with, or perhaps carbolic, so that he'd smell like washed dogs—dreadful! And the flannel shirts, not changed quite often enough. And the hands, so horny, with very short nails, perhaps broken. No, I simply couldn't understand her."

"Which is to your discredit, Dodo, if I may say so."

"Perhaps. But you must admit, I never pretended to be anything but what I am—a perfectly frivolous and respectable member of the upper classes. With a taste, I must confess, for the scandalous. Which was one of the reasons, I suppose, why I became so intimate with poor Clare. I was really fascinated by her confidences."

"Going on the tiles vicariously, eh?"

"Well, if you choose to put it grossly and vulgarly. . . ."

"Which I do choose," he interposed. "To be tactfully gross and appositely vulgar—that, my dear, is one of the ultimate artistic refinements. One day I shall write a monograph on the esthetics of vulgarity. But meanwhile shall we say that you were inspired by an intense scientific curiosity to . . ."

Dodo laughed. "One of the tiresome things about you, Miles, is that one can never go on being angry with you."

"Yet another subject for a monograph!" he answered, and his smile was at once confidential and ironical, affectionate and full of mockery. "But let's hear what the scientific curiosity elicited?"

"Well, to begin with, a lot of really rather embarrassingly intimate confidences and questions, which I needn't repeat."

"No, don't. I know what those feminine conversations are. I have a native modesty. . . ."

"Oh, so have I. And, strangely enough, so had Clare. But somehow she wanted to outrage herself. You felt it all the time. She always had that desperate jumping-off-the-Eiffel-Tower manner, when she began to talk like that. It was a kind of martyrdom. But enjoyable. Perversely." Dodo shook her head. "Very puzzling. I used to have to make quite an effort to change the conversation from gynecology to romance. Oh, those lovers of hers! Such stories! The most fantastic adventures in East End opium dens, in airplanes, and even, I remember (it was that very hot summer of 'twenty-two), even in a refrigerator!"

"My dear!" protested Fanning.

"Honestly! I'm only repeating what she told me."

"But do you mean to say you believed her?"

"Well, by that time, I must admit, I was beginning to be rather sceptical. You see, I could never elicit the names of these creatures. Nor any detail. It was as though they didn't exist outside the refrigerator and the airplane."

"How many of them were there?"

"Only two at that particular moment. One was a Grand Passion, and the other a Caprice. A Caprrice," she repeated, rolling the r. "It was one of poor Clare's favorite words. I used to try and pump her. But she was mum. 'I want them to be mysterious,' she told me the last time I pressed her for details, 'anonymous, without an état civil. Why should I show you their passports and identity cards?' 'Perhaps they haven't got any,' I suggested. Which was malicious. I could see she was annoyed. But a week later she showed me their photographs. There they were; the camera cannot lie; I had to be convinced. The Grand Passion, I must say, was a very striking-looking creature. Thin faced, worn, a bit Roman and sinister.

The Caprice was more ordinarily the nice young Englishman. Rather childish and simple, Clare explained; and she gave me to understand that she was initiating him. It was the other, the Grand P., who thought of such refinements as the refrigerator. Also, she now confided to me for the first time, he was mildly a sadist. Having seen his face, I could believe it. 'Am I ever likely to meet him?' I asked. She shook her head. He moved in a very different world from mine."

"A rabbit-shooter?" Fanning asked.

"No: an intellectual. That's what I gathered."

"Golly!"

"So there was not the slightest probability, as you can see, that I should ever meet him," Dodo laughed. "And yet almost the first face I saw on leaving Clare that afternoon was the Grand P.'s."

"Coming to pay his sadistic respects?"

"Alas for poor Clare, no. He was behind glass in the showcase of a photographer in the Brompton Road, not a hundred yards from the Tarns' house in Ovington Square. The identical portrait. I marched straight in. 'Can you tell me who that is?' But it appears that photography is done under the seal of confession. They wouldn't say. Could I order a copy? Well, yes, as a favor, they'd let me have one. Curiously enough, they told me, as they were taking down my name and address, another lady had come in only two or three days before and also ordered a copy. 'Not by any chance a rather tall lady with light auburn hair and a rather amusing mole on the left cheek?' That did sound rather like the lady. 'And with a very confidential manner,' I suggested, 'as though you were her oldest friends?' Exactly, exactly; they were unanimous. That clinched it. Poor Clare, I thought, as I walked on toward the Park, poor, poor Clare!"

There was a silence.

"Which only shows," said Fanning at last, "how right the Church has always been to persecute literature. The harm we imaginative writers do! Enormous! We ought all to be on the Index, every one. Consider your Clare, for example. If it hadn't been for books, she'd never have known that such things as passion and sensuality and perversity even existed. Never."

"Come, come," she protested.

But, "Never," Fanning repeated. "She was congenitally as cold as a fish; it's obvious. Never had a spontaneous, untutored desire in her life. But she'd read a lot of books. Out of which she'd fabricated a theory of passion and perversity. Which she then consciously put into practice."

"Or rather didn't put into practice. Only daydreamed that she did."

He nodded. "For the most part. But sometimes, I don't mind betting, she realized the daydreams in actual life. Desperately, as you so well described it, with her teeth clenched and her eyes shut, as though she were jumping off the Eiffel Tower. That rabbit-shooter, for instance. . . ."

"But do you think the rabbit-shooter really existed?"

"Perhaps not that particular one. But a rabbit-shooter, perhaps several rabbit-shooters—at one time or another, I'm sure, they genuinely existed. Though never *genuinely*, of course, for her. For her, it's obvious, they were just phantoms, like the other inhabitants of her dreamery. Phantoms of flesh and blood, but still phantoms. I see her as a kind of Midas, turning everything she touched into imagination. Even in the embraces of a genuine, solid rabbit-shooter, she was still only indulging in her solitary sultry dream—a dream inspired by Shakespeare, or Mrs. Barclay, or the Chevalier de Nerciat, or D'Annunzio, or whoever her favorite author may have been."

"Miles Fanning, perhaps," Dodo mockingly suggested.

"Yes, I feared as much."

"What a responsibility!"

"Which I absolutely refuse to accept. What have I ever written but solemn warnings against the vice of imagination? Sermons against mental licentiousness of every kind—intellectual licentiousness, mystical licentiousness, fantastic-amorous licentiousness. No, no. I'll accept no responsibility. Or at least no special responsibility—only the generic responsibility of being an imaginative author, the original sin of writing in such a way as to influence people. And when I say 'influence,' of course I don't really mean *influence*. Because a writer can't influence people, in the sense of making them think and feel and act as he does. He can only influence them to be more, or less, like one of their own selves. In other words, he's never understood. (Thank goodness! because it would be very humiliating to be really understood by one's readers.) What readers get out of him is never, finally, *his* ideas, but theirs. And when they try to imitate him or his creations, all that they can ever do is to act one of their own potential roles. Take this particular case. Clare read and, I take it, was impressed. She took my warnings against mental licentiousness to heart and proceeded to do—what? Not to become a creature of spontaneous, unvitiated impulses—for the good reason that that wasn't in her power—but only to imagine that she was such a creature. She imagined herself a woman like the one I put into *Endymion and the Moon* and acted accordingly—or else didn't act, only dreamed; it makes very little difference. In a word, she did exactly what all my books told her not to do. Inevitably; it was her nature. I'd influenced her, yes.

But she didn't become more like one of my heroines. She only became more intensely like herself. And then, you must remember, mine weren't the only books on her shelves. I think we can take it that she'd read *Les Liaisons Dangereuses* and Casanova and some biography, shall we say, of the Maréchal de Richelieu. So that those spontaneous, unvitiated impulses—how ludicrous they are, anyhow, when you *talk* about them! —became identified in her mind with the most elegant forms of 'caprice'—wasn't that the word? She was a child of nature—but with qualifications. The kind of child of nature that lived at Versailles or on the Grand Canal about 1760. Hence those rabbit-shooters and hence also those sadistic intellectuals, whether real or imaginary—and imaginary even when real. I may have been a favorite author. But I'm not responsible for the rabbit-shooters or the Grand P.'s. Not more responsible than anyone else. She'd heard of the existence of love before she'd read me. We're all equally to blame, from Homer downward. Plato wouldn't have any of us in his Republic. He was quite right, I believe. Quite right."

"And what about the daughter?" Dodo asked, after a silence.

He shrugged his shoulders. "In reaction against the mother, so far as I could judge. In reaction, but also influenced by her, unconsciously. And the influence is effective because, after all, she's her mother's daughter and probably resembles her mother, congenitally. But consciously, on the surface, she knows she doesn't want to live as though she were in a novel. And yet can't help it, because that's her nature, that's how she was brought up. But she's miserable, because she realizes that fiction-life *is* fiction. Miserable and very anxious to get out—out through the covers of the novel into the real world."

"And are you her idea of the real world?" Dodo inquired.

He laughed. "Yes, I'm the real world. Strange as it may seem. And also, of course, pure fiction. The Writer, the Great Man—the Official Biographer's fiction, in a word. Or, better still, the autobiographer's fiction. Chateaubriand, shall we say? And her breaking out—that's fiction too. A pure Miles Fanningism, if ever there was one. And, poor child, she knows it. Which makes her so cross with herself. Cross with me too, in a curious obscure way. But at the same time she's thrilled. What a thrilling situation! And herself walking about in the middle of it. She looks on and wonders and wonders what the next installment of the feuilleton's going to contain."

"Well, there's one thing we're quite certain it's not going to contain, aren't we? Remember your promise, Miles."

"I think of nothing else," he bantered.

"Seriously, Miles, seriously."

"I think of nothing else," he repeated in a voice that was the parody of a Shakespearean actor's.

Dodo shook her finger at him. "Mind," she said, "mind!" Then pushing back her chair, "Let's move into the drawing room," she went on. "We shall be more comfortable there."

IV

"And to think," Pamela was writing in her diary, "how nervous I'd been beforehand, and the trouble I'd taken to work out the whole of our first meeting, question and answer, like the Shorter Catechism, instead of which I was like a fish in water, really at home, for the first time in my life, I believe. No, perhaps not more at home than with Ruth and Phyllis, but then they're girls, so they hardly count. Besides, when you've once been at home in the sea, it doesn't seem much fun being at home in a little glass bowl, which is rather unfair to Ruth and Phyllis, but after all it's not their fault and they can't help being little bowls, just as M. F. can't help being a sea, and when you've swum about a bit in all that intelligence and knowledge and really *devilish* understanding, well, you find the bowls rather narrow, though of course they're sweet little bowls and I shall always be very fond of them, especially Ruth. Which makes me wonder if what he said about Clare and me—unnatural by nature—is always true, because hasn't every unnatural person got somebody she can be natural with, or even that she can't help being natural with, like oxygen and that other stuff making water? Of course it's not guaranteed that you find the other person who makes you natural, and I think perhaps Clare never did find her person, because I don't believe it was Daddy. But in my case there's Ruth and Phyllis and now today M. F.; and he really proves it, because I was natural with him more than with anyone, even though he did say I was unnatural by nature. No, I feel that if I were with him always, I should always be my *real* self, just kind of easily spouting, like those lovely fountains we went to look at this afternoon, not all tied up in knots and squirting about vaguely in every kind of direction, and muddy at that, but beautifully clear in a big gushing spout, like what Joan in *The Return of Eurydice* finally became when she'd escaped from that awful, awful man and found Walter. But does that mean I'm in love with him?"

Pamela bit the end of her pen and stared, frowning, at the page before her. Scrawled large in orange ink, the question stared back. Disquietingly and insistently stared. She remembered a phrase of her mother's. "But if you knew," Clare had cried (Pamela could see her, wearing the black afternoon dress from Patou, and there were yellow roses in the bowl on the table under the window), "if you knew what certain writers were to me! *Shrines*—there's no other word. I could worship the Tolstoy of Anna Karenina." But Harry Braddon, to whom the words were addressed, had laughed at her. And, though she hated Harry Braddon, so had Pamela, mockingly. For it was absurd; nobody was a shrine, nobody. And anyhow, what was a shrine? Nothing. Not nowadays, not when one had stopped being a child. She told herself these things with a rather unnecessary emphasis, almost truculently, in the style of the professional atheists in Hyde Park. One didn't worship—for the good reason that she herself once had worshiped. Miss Figgis, the classical mistress, had been her pash for more than a year. Which was why she had gone to Early Service so frequently in those days and been so keen to go up to Oxford and take Greats. (Besides, she had even, at that time, rather liked and admired Miss Huss. Ghastly old Hussy! It seemed incredible now.) But oh, that grammar! And Caesar was such a bore, and Livy still worse, and as for Greek . . . She had tried very hard for a time. But when Miss Figgis so obviously preferred that priggish little beast Kathleen, Pamela had just let things slide. The bad marks had come in torrents and old Hussy had begun being more sorrowful than angry, and finally more angry than sorrowful. But she hadn't cared. What made not caring easier was that she had her mother behind her. "I'm so delighted," was what Clare had said when she heard that Pamela had given up wanting to go to Oxford. "I'd have felt so terribly inferior if you'd turned out a bluestocking. Having my frivolity rebuked by my own daughter!" Clare had always boasted of her frivolity. Once, under the influence of old Hussy and for the love of Miss Figgis, an earnest disapprover, Pamela had become an apostle of her mother's gospel. "After all," she had pointed out to Miss Figgis, "Cleopatra didn't learn Greek." And though Miss Figgis was able to point out, snubbingly, that the last of the Ptolemies had probably spoken nothing but Greek, Pamela could still insist that in principle she was quite right: Cleopatra hadn't learnt Greek, or what, if you were a Greek, corresponded to Greek. So why should she? She began to parade a violent and childish cynicism, a cynicism which was still (though she had learned, since leaving school, to temper the ridiculous expression of it) her official creed. There were no shrines—though she sometimes wistfully and rather shamefacedly wished there were. One didn't, determinedly didn't worship. She herself might admire Fanning's books, *did* admire them, enormously. But as for worshiping—no, she absolutely declined. Clare had overdone it all somehow—as usual. Pamela was resolved that there should be no nonsense about her feelings.

"But does that mean I'm in love with him?" insisted the orange scrawl.

As though in search of an answer, Pamela turned back the pages of her diary (she had already covered nearly eight of them with her account of this memorable twelfth of June). "His face," she read, "is very brown, almost like an Arab's, except that he has blue eyes, as he lives mostly in the South, because he says that if you don't live in the sun, you go slightly mad, which is why people in the North, like us and the Germans and the Americans, are so tiresome, though of course you go still madder where there's too much sun, like in India, where they're even more hopeless. He's very good-looking and you don't think of him as being either old or young, but as just being there, like that; and the way he smiles is really very extraordinary, and so are his eyes, and I simply adored his white silk suit." But the question was not yet answered. His silk suit wasn't him, nor was his voice, even though he had "an awfully nice one, rather like that man who talks about books on the wireless, only nicer." She turned over a page. "But M. F. is different from most clever people," the orange scrawl proclaimed, "because he doesn't make you feel a fool even when he does laugh at you, and never, which is so ghastly with men like Professor Cobley, talks down to you in that awful patient, gentle way, which makes you feel a million times more of a worm than being snubbed or ignored, because, if you have any pride, that sort of intelligence without tears is just loathsome, as though you were being given milk pudding out of charity. No, M. F. talks to you on the level, and the extraordinary thing is that, while he's talking to you and you're talking to him, you are on a level with him, or at any rate you feel as though you were, which comes to the same thing. He's like influenza: you catch his intelligence." Pamela let the leaves of the notebook flick past, one by one, under her thumb. The final words on the half-blank page once more stared at her, questioningly. "But does that mean I'm in love with him?" Taking her pen from between her teeth, "Certainly," she wrote, "I do find him terribly attractive physically." She paused for a moment to reflect, then added, frowning as though with the effort of raising an elusive fact from the depths of memory, of solving a difficult problem in algebra: "Because really, when he put his hand on my shoulder, which would have been simply intolerable if anyone else had done it, but somehow with him I didn't mind, I felt all thrilled with an absolute frisson." She ran her pen through the last word and substituted "thrill," which she underlined to make it seem less lamely a repetition. "Frisson" had been one of Clare's favorite words; hearing it pronounced in her mother's remembered voice, Pamela had felt a sudden mistrust of it; it seemed to cast a kind of doubt on the feelings it stood for, a doubt of which she was ashamed—it seemed so disloyal and the voice had sounded so startlingly, so heart-rendingly clear and near—but which she still couldn't help experiencing. She defended herself; "frisson" had simply had to go, because the thrill was genuine, absolutely genuine, she insisted. "For a moment," she went on, writing very fast, as though she were trying to run away from the sad, disagreeable thoughts that had intruded upon her, "I thought I was going to faint when he touched me, like when one's coming to after chloroform, which I've certainly never felt like with anyone else." As a protest against the doubts inspired by that unfortunate frisson she underlined "never," heavily. Never; it was quite true. When Harry Braddon had tried to kiss her, she had been furious and disgusted—disgusting beast! Saddening and reproachful, Clare's presence hovered round her once more; Clare had liked Harry Braddon. Still, he was a beast. Pamela had never told her mother about that kiss. She shut her eyes excludingly and thought instead of Cecil Rudge, poor, timid, unhappy little Cecil, whom she liked so much, was so genuinely sorry for. But when, that afternoon at Aunt Edith's, when at last, after an hour's visibly laborious screwing to the sticking point, he had had the courage to take her hand and say "Pamela" and kiss it, she had just laughed, oh! unforgivably, but she simply couldn't help it; he was so ridiculous. Poor lamb, he had been terribly upset. "But I'm so sorry," she had gasped between the bursts of her laughter, "so dreadfully sorry. Please don't be hurt." But his face, she could see, was agonized. "Please! Oh, I feel so miserable." And she had gone off into another explosion of laughter which almost choked her. But when she could breathe again, she had run to him where he stood, averted and utterly unhappy, by the window; she had taken his hand and, when he still refused to look at her, had put her arm round his neck and kissed him. But the emotion that had filled her eyes with tears was nothing like passion. As for Hugh Davies—why, it certainly had been rather thrilling when Hugh kissed her. It had been thrilling, but certainly not to fainting point. But then had she really felt like fainting today? a small voice questioned. She drowned the small voice with the scratching of her pen. "Consult the oracles of passion," she wrote and, laying down her pen, got up and crossed the room. A copy of The Return of Eurydice was lying on the bed; she picked it up and turned over the pages. Here it was! "Consult the oracles of passion," she read aloud, and her own voice sounded, she thought, strangely oracular in the solitude. "A god speaks in them, or else a devil, one can never tell which beforehand, nor even, in most cases, afterward. And, when all is said, does it very much matter? God and devil are equally supernatural; that is the important thing; equally supernatural and therefore, in this all too flatly natural world of sense and science and society, equally desirable, equally significant." She shut the book and walked back to the table. "Which is what he said this afternoon," she went on writing, "but in that laughing way, when I said I could never see why one shouldn't do what one liked, instead of all this Hussy and Hippo rigamarole about service and duty, and he said yes, that was what Rabelais had said" (there seemed to be an awful lot of "saids" in this sentence, but it couldn't be helped; she scrawled on); "which I pretended I'd read—why can't one tell the truth? particularly as I'd just been saying at the same time that one ought to say what one thinks as well as do what one likes; but it seems to be hopeless—and he said he entirely agreed, it was perfect, so long as you had the luck to like the sort of things that kept you on the right side of the prison bars and think the sort of things that don't get you murdered when you say them. And I said I'd rather say what I thought and do what I liked and be murdered and put in jail than be a Hippo, and he said I was an idealist, which annoyed me and I said I certainly wasn't, all I was was someone who didn't want to go mad with inhibitions. And he laughed, and I wanted to quote him his own words about the oracles, but somehow it was so shy-making that I didn't. All the same, it's what I intensely feel, that one *ought* to consult the oracles of passion. And I shall consult them." She leaned back in her chair and shut her eyes. The orange question floated across the darkness: "But does that mean I'm in love with him?" The oracle seemed to be saying yes. But oracles, she resolutely refused to remember, can be rigged to suit the interests of the questioner. Didn't the admirer of *The Return of Eurydice* secretly want the oracle to say yes? Didn't she think she'd almost fainted, because she'd wished she'd almost fainted, because she'd come desiring to faint? Pamela sighed; then, with a gesture of decision, she slapped her notebook to and put away her pen. It was time to get ready for dinner; she bustled about efficiently and distractingly among her trunks. But the question returned to her as she lay soaking in the warm other-world of her bath. By the time she got out she had boiled herself to such a pitch of giddiness that she could hardly stand.

For Pamela, dinner in solitude, especially the public solitude of hotels, was a punishment. Companionlessness and compulsory silence depressed her. Besides, she never felt quite eyeproof; she could never escape from the obsession that everyone was looking at her, judging, criticizing. Under a carapace of rather impertinent uncaringness she writhed distressfully.

At Florence her loneliness had driven her to make friends with two not very young American women who were staying in her hotel. They were a bit earnest and good and dreary. But Pamela preferred even dreariness to solitude. She attached herself to them inseparably. They were touched. When she left for Rome, they promised to write to her, they made her promise to write to them. She was so young; they felt responsible; a steadying hand, the counsel of older friends. . . . Pamela had already received two steadying letters. But she hadn't answered them, never would answer them. The horrors of lonely dining cannot be alleviated by correspondence.

Walking down to her ordeal in the restaurant, she positively yearned for her dreary friends. But the hall was a desert of alien eyes and faces; and the waiter who led her through the hostile dining room had bowed, it seemed to her, with an ironical politeness, had mockingly smiled. She sat down haughtily at her table and almost wished she were under it. When the sommelier appeared with his list, she ordered half a bottle of something absurdly expensive, for fear he might think she didn't know anything about wine.

She had got as far as the fruit, when a presence loomed over her; she looked up. "You?" Her delight was an illumination; the young man was dazzled. "What marvelous luck!" Yet it was only Guy Browne, Guy whom she had met a few times at dances and found quite pleasant— that was all. "Think of your being in Rome!" She made him sit down at her table. When she had finished her coffee, Guy suggested that they should go out and dance somewhere. They went. It was nearly three when Pamela got to bed. She had had a most enjoyable evening.

V

But how ungratefully she treated poor Guy when, next day at lunch, Fanning asked her how she had spent the evening! True, there were extenuating circumstances, chief among which was the fact that Fanning had kissed her when they met. By force of habit he himself would have explained, if anyone had asked him why, because he kissed every presentable face. Kissing was in the great English tradition. "It's the only way I can be like Chaucer," he liked to affirm. "Just as knowing a little Latin and less Greek is my only claim to resembling Shakespeare and as lying in bed till ten's the nearest I get to Descartes." In this particular case, as perhaps in every other particular case, the force of habit had been seconded by a deliberate intention; he was accustomed to women being rather in love with him; he liked the amorous atmosphere and could use the simplest as well as the most complicated methods to create it. Moreover he was an experimentalist: he genuinely wanted to see what would happen. What happened was that Pamela was astonished, embarrassed, thrilled, delighted, bewildered. And what with her confused excitement and the enormous effort she had made to take it all as naturally and easily as he had done, she was betrayed into what, in other circumstances, would have been a scandalous ingratitude. But when one has just been kissed, for the first time and at one's second meeting with him, kissed offhandedly and yet (she felt it) significantly, by Miles Fanning— actually Miles Fanning!—little men like Guy Browne do seem rather negligible, even though one did have a very good time with them the evening before.

"I'm afraid you must have been rather lonely last night," said Fanning, as they sat down to lunch. His sympathy hypocritically covered a certain satisfaction that it should be his absence that had condemned her to dreariness.

"No, I met a friend," Pamela answered with a smile which the inward comparison of Guy with the author of *The Return of Eurydice* had tinged with a certain amused condescendingness.

"A friend?" He raised his eyebrows. "*Amico* or *amica*? Our English is so discreetly equivocal. With this key Bowdler locked up his heart. But I apologize. *Co* or *ca*?"

"*Co*. He's called Guy Browne and he's here learning Italian to get into the Foreign Office. He's a nice boy." Pamela might have been talking about a favorite, or even not quite favorite, retriever. "Nice; but nothing very special. I mean, not in the way of intelligence." She shook her head patronizingly over Guy's very creditable First in History as a guttersnipe capriciously favored by an archduke might learn in his protector's company to shake his head and patronizingly smile at the name of a marquis of only four or five centuries' standing. "He can dance, though," she admitted.

"So I suppose you danced with him?" said Fanning in a tone which, in spite of his amusement at the child's assumption of an aged superiority, he couldn't help making rather disobligingly sarcastic. It annoyed him to think that Pamela should have spent an evening, which he had pictured as dismally lonely, dancing with a young man.

"Yes, we danced," said Pamela, nodding.

"Where?"

"Don't ask me. We went to about six different places in the course of the evening."

"Of course you did," said Fanning almost bitterly. "Moving rapidly

from one place to another and doing exactly the same thing in each—
that seems to be the young's ideal of bliss."

Speaking as a young who had risen above such things, but who still had
to suffer from the folly of her unregenerate contemporaries, "It's quite
true," Pamela gravely confirmed.

"They go to Pekin to listen to the wireless and to Benares to dance the
fox trot. I've seen them at it. It's incomprehensible. And then the tooting
up and down in automobiles, and the roaring up and down in airplanes,
and the stinking up and down in motorboats. Up and down, up and down,
just for the sake of not sitting still, of having never time to think or feel.
No, I give them up, these young of yours." He shook his head. "But I'm
becoming a minor prophet," he added; his good humor was beginning to
return.

"But after all," said Pamela, "we're not all like that."

Her gravity made him laugh. "There's at least one who's ready to let
herself be bored by a tiresome survivor from another civilization. Thank
you, Pamela." Leaning across the table, he took her hand and kissed it.
"I've been horribly ungrateful," he went on, and his face as he looked at
her was suddenly transfigured by the bright enigmatic beauty of his
smile. "If you knew how charming you looked!" he said; and it was true.
That ingenuous face, those impertinent little breasts—charming. "And
how charming you were! But of course you do know," a little demon
prompted him to add: "no doubt Mr. Browne told you last night."

Pamela had blushed—a blush of pleasure, and embarrassed shyness,
and excitement. What he had just said and done was more significant,
she felt, even than the kiss he had given her when they met. Her cheeks
burned; but she managed, with an effort, to keep her eyes unwaveringly
on his. His last words made her frown. "He certainly didn't," she
answered. "He'd have got his face smacked."

"Is that a delicate hint?" he asked. "If so," and he leaned forward,
"here's the other cheek."

Her face went redder than ever. She felt suddenly miserable; he was
only laughing at her. "Why do you laugh at me?" she said aloud,
unhappily.

"But I wasn't," he protested. "I really did think you were annoyed."

"But why should I have been?"

"I can't imagine." He smiled. "But if you would have smacked Mr.
Browne's face . . ."

"But Guy's quite different."

It was Fanning's turn to wince. "You mean he's young, while I'm only
a poor old imbecile who needn't be taken seriously?"

"Why are you so stupid?" Pamela asked almost fiercely. "No, but I mean," she added in quick apology, "I mean . . . well, I don't care two pins about Guy. So you see, it would annoy me if he tried to push in, like that. Whereas with somebody who does mean something to me . . ." Pamela hesitated. "With you," she specified in a rather harsh, strained voice and with just that look of despairing determination, Fanning imagined, just that jumping-off-the-Eiffel-Tower expression, which her mother's face must have assumed in moments such as this, "it's quite different. I mean, with you of course I'm not annoyed. I'm pleased. Or at least I was pleased, till I saw you were just making a fool of me."

Touched and flattered, "But, my dear child," Fanning protested, "I wasn't doing anything of the kind. I meant what I said. And much more than I said," he added, in the teeth of the warning and reproachful outcry raised by his common sense. It was amusing to experiment, it was pleasant to be adored, exciting to be tempted (and how young she was, how perversely fresh!). There was even something quite agreeable in resisting temptation; it had the charms of a strenuous and difficult sport. Like mountain climbing. He smiled once more, consciously brilliant.

This time Pamela dropped her eyes. There was a silence which might have protracted itself uncomfortably, if the waiter had not broken it by bringing the *tagliatelle*. They began to eat. Pamela was all at once exuberantly gay.

After coffee they took a taxi and drove to the Villa Giulia. "For we mustn't," Fanning explained, "neglect your education."

"Mustn't we?" she asked. "I often wonder why we mustn't. Truthfully now, I mean without any hippoing and all that—why shouldn't I neglect it? Why should I go to this beastly museum?" She was preparing to play the cynical, boastfully unintellectual part which she had made her own. "Why?" she repeated truculently. Behind the rather vulgar low-brow mask she cultivated wistful yearnings and concealed the uneasy consciousness of inferiority. "A lot of beastly old Roman odds and ends!" she grumbled; that was one for Miss Figgis.

"Roman?" said Fanning. "God forbid! Etruscan."

"Well, Etruscan, then; it's all the same, anyhow. Why shouldn't I neglect the Etruscans? I mean, what have they got to do with me—*me*?" And she gave her chest two or three little taps with the tip of a crooked forefinger.

"Nothing, my child," he answered. "Thank goodness, they've got absolutely nothing to do with you, or me, or anybody else."

"Then why . . . ?"

"Precisely for that reason. That's the definition of culture—knowing and thinking about things that have absolutely nothing to do with us. About Etruscans, for example; or the mountains on the moon; or cat's cradle among the Chinese; or the Universe at large."

"All the same," she insisted, "I still don't see."

"Because you've never known people who weren't cultured. But make the acquaintance of a few practical businessmen—the kind who have no time to be anything but alternately efficient and tired. Or of a few workmen from the big towns. (Country people are different; they still have the remains of the old substitutes for culture—religion, folklore, tradition. The town fellows have lost the substitutes without acquiring the genuine article.) Get to know those people; they'll make you see the point of culture. Just as the Sahara'll make you see the point of water. And for the same reason: they're arid."

"That's all very well; but what about people like Professor Cobley?"

"Whom I've happily never met," he said, "but can reconstruct from the expression on your face. Well, all that can be said about those people is: just try to imagine them if they'd never been irrigated. Gobi or Shamo."

"Well, perhaps." She was dubious.

"And anyhow the biggest testimony to culture isn't the soulless philistines—it's the soulful ones. My sweet Pamela," he implored, laying a hand on her bare brown arm, "for heaven's sake don't run the risk of becoming a soulful philistine."

"But as I don't know what that is," she answered, trying to persuade herself, as she spoke, that the touch of his hand was giving her a tremendous frisson—but it really wasn't.

"It's what the name implies," he said. "A person without culture who goes in for having a soul. An illiterate idealist. A Higher Thinker with nothing to think about but his—or more often, I'm afraid, her—beastly little personal feelings and sensations. They spend their lives staring at their own navels and in the intervals trying to find other people who'll take an interest and come and stare too. Oh, figuratively," he added, noticing the expression of astonishment which had passed across her face. "En tout bien, tout honneur. At least, sometimes and to begin with. Though I've known cases . . ." But he decided it would be better not to speak about the lady from Rochester, N.Y. Pamela might be made to feel that the cap fitted. Which it did, except that her little head was such a charming one. "In the end," he said, "they go mad, these soulful philistines. Mad with self-consciousness and vanity and egotism and a kind of hopeless bewilderment; for when you're utterly without culture, every fact's an isolated, unconnected fact; every experience is unique and unprecedented. Your world's made up of a few bright points floating about inexplicably in the midst of an unfathomable darkness. Terrifying! It's enough to drive anyone mad. I've seen them, lots of them, gone utterly crazy. In the past they had organized religion, which meant that somebody had once been cultured for them, vicariously. But what with protestantism and the modernists, their philistinism's absolute now. They're alone with their own souls. Which is the worst companionship a human being can have. So bad that it sends you dotty. So beware, Pamela, beware! You'll go mad if you think only of what has something to do with you. The Etruscans will keep you sane."

"Let's hope so." She laughed. "But aren't we there?"

The cab drew up at the door of the villa; they got out.

"And remember that the things that start with having nothing to do with you," said Fanning, as he counted out the money for the entrance tickets, "turn out in the long run to have a great deal to do with you. Because they become a part of you and you of them. A soul can't know or fully become itself without knowing and therefore to some extent becoming what isn't itself. Which it does in various ways. By loving, for example."

"You mean . . . ?" The flame of interest brightened in her eyes.

But he went on remorselessly. "And by thinking of things that have nothing to do with you."

"Yes, I see." The flame had dimmed again.

"Hence my concern about your education." He beckoned her through the turnstile into the museum. "A purely selfish concern," he added, smiling down at her. "Because I don't want the most charming of my young friends to grow into a monster, whom I shall be compelled to flee from. So resign yourself to the Etruscans."

"I resign myself," said Pamela, laughing. His words had made her feel happy and excited. "You can begin." And in a theatrical voice, like that which used to make Ruth go off into such fits of laughter, "I am all ears," she added, "as they say in the Best Books." She pulled off her hat and shook out the imprisoned hair.

To Fanning, as he watched her, the gesture brought a sudden shock of pleasure. The impatient, exuberant youthfulness of it! And the little head, so beautifully shaped, so gracefully and proudly poised on its long neck! And her hair was drawn back smoothly from the face to explode in a thick tangle of curls on the nape of the neck. Ravishing!

"All ears," she repeated, delightedly conscious of the admiration she was receiving.

"All ears." And almost meditatively, "But do you know," he went on, "I've never even seen your ears. May I?" And without waiting for her permission, he lifted up the soft, goldy-brown hair that lay in a curve, drooping, along the side of her head.

Pamela's face violently reddened; but she managed nonetheless to laugh. "Are they as long and furry as you expected?" she asked.

He allowed the lifted hair to fall back into its place and, without answering her question, "I've always," he said, looking at her with a smile which she found disquietingly enigmatic and remote, "I've always had a certain fellow feeling for those savages who collect ears and thread them on strings as necklaces."

"But what a horror!" she cried out.

"You think so?" He raised his eyebrows.

But perhaps, Pamela was thinking, he was a sadist. In that book of Krafft-Ebbing's there had been a lot about sadists. It would be queer if he were . . .

"But what's certain," Fanning went on in another, businesslike voice, "what's only too certain is that ears aren't culture. They've got too much to do with us. With me, at any rate. Much too much." He smiled at her again. Pamela smiled back at him, fascinated and obscurely a little frightened; but the fright was an element in the fascination. She dropped her eyes. "So don't let's waste any more time," his voice went on. "Culture to right of us, culture to left of us. Let's begin with this culture on the left. With the vases. They really have absolutely nothing to do with us."

He began and Pamela listened. Not very attentively, however. She lifted her hand and, under the hair, touched her ear. "A fellow feeling for those savages." She remembered his words with a little shudder. He'd almost meant them. And "ears aren't culture. Too much to do with us. With me. Much too much." He'd meant that too, genuinely and whole-heartedly. And his smile had been a confirmation of the words; yes, and a comment, full of mysterious significance. What *had* he meant? But surely it was obvious what he had meant. Or wasn't it obvious?

The face she turned toward him wore an expression of grave attention. And when he pointed to a vase and said, "Look," she looked, with what an air of concentrated intelligence! But as for knowing what he was talking about! She went on confusedly thinking that he had a fellow feeling for those savages, and that her ears had too much to do with him, much too much, and that perhaps he was in love with her, perhaps also that he was like those people in Krafft-Ebbing, perhaps . . . ; and it seemed to her that her blood must have turned into a kind of hot, red soda water, all fizzy with little bubbles of fear and excitement.

She emerged, partially at least, out of this bubbly and agitated trance to hear him say, "Look at that now." A tall statue towered over her. "The

Apollo of Veii," he explained. "And really, you know, it is the most beautiful statue in the world. Each time I see it, I'm more firmly convinced of that."

Dutifully, Pamela stared. The God stood there on his pedestal, one foot advanced, erect in his draperies. He had lost his arms, but the head was intact and the strange Etruscan face was smiling, enigmatically smiling. Rather like him, it suddenly occurred to her.

"What's it made of?" she asked; for it was time to be intelligent.

"Terracotta. Originally colored."

"And what date?"

"Late sixth century."

"B.C.?" she queried, a little dubiously, and was relieved when he nodded. It really would have been rather awful if it had been A.D. "Who by?"

"By Vulca, they say. But as that's the only Etruscan sculptor they know the name of . . ." He shrugged his shoulders, and the gesture expressed a double doubt—doubt whether the archaeologists were right and doubt whether it was really much good talking about Etruscan art to someone who didn't feel quite certain whether the Apollo of Veii was made in the sixth century before or after Christ.

There was a long silence. Fanning looked at the statue. So did Pamela, who also, from time to time, looked at Fanning. She was on the point, more than once, of saying something; but his face was so meditatively glum that, on each occasion, she changed her mind. In the end, however, the silence became intolerable.

"I think it's extraordinarily fine," she announced in the rather religious voice that seemed appropriate. He only nodded. The silence prolonged itself, more oppressive and embarrassing than ever. She made another and despairing effort. "Do you know, I think he's really rather like you. I mean, the way he smiles. . . ."

Fanning's petrified immobility broke once more into life. He turned toward her, laughing. "You're irresistible, Pamela."

"Am I?" Her tone was cold; she was offended. To be told you were irresistible always meant that you'd behaved like an imbecile child. But her conscience was clear; it was a gratuitous insult—the more intolerable since it had been offered by the man who, a moment before, had been saying that he had a fellow feeling for those savages and that her ears had altogether too much to do with him.

Fanning noticed her sudden change of humor and obscurely divined the cause. "You've paid me the most irresistible compliment you could have invented," he said, doing his best to undo the effect of his words. For after all what did it matter, with little breasts like that and thin brown arms, if she did mix up the millenniums a bit? "You could hardly have pleased me more if you'd said I was another Rudolph Valentino."

Pamela had to laugh.

"But seriously," he said, "if you knew what this lovely God means to me, how much . . ."

Mollified by being once more spoken to seriously, "I think I can understand," she said in her most understanding voice.

"No, I doubt if you can." He shook his head. "It's a question of age, of the experience of a particular time that's not your time. I shall never forget when I came back to Rome for the first time after the War and found this marvelous creature standing here. They only dug him up in sixteen, you see. So there it was, a brand-new experience, a new and apocalyptic voice out of the past. Some day I shall try to get it on paper, all that this God has taught me." He gave a little sigh; she could see that he wasn't thinking about her any more; he was talking for himself. "Some day," he repeated. "But it's not ripe yet. You can't write a thing before it's ripe, before it wants to be written. But you can talk about it; you can take your mind for walks all round it and through it." He paused and, stretching out a hand, touched a fold of the God's sculptured garment, as though he were trying to establish a more intimate, more real connection with the beauty before him. "Not that what he taught me was fundamentally new," he went on slowly. "It's all in Homer, of course. It's even partially expressed in the archaic Greek sculpture. Partially. But Apollo here expresses it wholly. He's all Homer, all the ancient world, concentrated in a single lump of terracotta. That's his novelty. And then the circumstances gave him a special point. It was just after the War that I first saw him—just after the apotheosis and the logical conclusion of all the things Apollo didn't stand for. You can imagine how marvelously new he seemed by contrast. After that horrible enormity, he was a lovely symbol of the small, the local, the kindly. After all that extravagance of beastliness—yes, and all that extravagance of heroism and self-sacrifice—he seemed so beautifully sane. A God who doesn't admit the separate existence of either heroics or diabolics, but somehow includes them in his own nature and turns them into something else—like two gases combining to make a liquid. Look at him," Fanning insisted. "Look at his face, look at his body, see how he stands. It's obvious. He's neither the God of heroics, nor the God of diabolics. And yet it's equally obvious that he knows all about both, that he includes them, that he combines them into a third essence. It's the same with Homer. There's no tragedy in Homer. He's pessimistic, yes; but never tragic. His heroes aren't heroic in our sense of the word;

they're men." (Pamela took a very deep breath; if she had opened her mouth, it would have been a yawn.) "In fact, you can say there aren't any heroes in Homer. Nor devils, nor sins. And none of our aspiring spiritualities, and, of course, none of our horrible, nauseating disgusts— because they're the complement of being spiritual; they're the tails to its heads. You couldn't have had Homer writing 'the expense of spirit in a waste of shame.' Though, of course, with Shakespeare, it may have been physiological; the passion violent and brief, and then the most terrible reaction. It's the sort of thing that colors a whole life, a whole work. Only of course one's never allowed to say so. All that one isn't allowed to say!" He laughed. Pamela also laughed. "But physiology or no physiology," Fanning went on, "he couldn't have written like that if he'd lived before the great split—the great split that broke life into spirit and matter, heroics and diabolics, virtue and sin and all the other accursed antitheses. Homer lived before the split; life hadn't been broken when he wrote. They're complete, his men and women, complete and real; for he leaves nothing out, he shirks no issue, even though there is no tragedy. He knows all about it—*all*." He laid his hand again on the statue. "And this God's his portrait. He's Homer, but with the Etruscan smile. Homer smiling at the sad, mysterious, beautiful absurdity of the world. The Greeks didn't see that divine absurdity as clearly as Etruscans. Not even in Homer's day; and by the time you get to any sculptor who was anything like as accomplished as the man who made this, you'll find that they've lost it altogether. True, the earliest Greeks' God used to smile all right—or rather grin; for subtlety wasn't their strong point. But by the end of the sixth century they were already becoming a bit too heroic; they were developing those athlete's muscles and those tiresomely noble poses and damned superior faces. But our God here refused to be a prize fighter or an actor-manager. There's no *terribiltà* about him, no priggishness, no sentimentality. And yet without being in the least pretentious, he's beautiful, he's grand, he's authentically divine. The Greeks took the road that led to Michelangelo and Bernini and Thorwaldsen and Rodin. A rake's progress. These Etruscans were on a better track. If only people had had the sense to follow it! Or at least get back to it. But nobody has, except perhaps old Maillol. They've all allowed themselves to be lured away. Plato was the arch-seducer. It was he who first sent us whoring after spirituality and heroics, whoring after the complementary demons of disgust and sin. We needs must love—well, not the highest, except sometimes by accident—but always the most extravagant and exciting. Tragedy was much more exciting than Homer's luminous pessimism, than this God's smiling awareness of the divine absurdity. Being alternately a hero and a sinner is much more sensational than being an integrated man. So as men seem to have the Yellow Press in the blood, like syphilis, they went back on Homer and Apollo; they followed Plato and Euripides. And Plato and Euripides handed them over to the Stoics and the Neo-Platonists. And these in turn handed humanity over to the Christians. And the Christians have handed us over to Henry Ford and the machines. So here we are."

Pamela nodded intelligently. But what she was chiefly conscious of was the ache in her feet. If only she could sit down!

But, "How poetical and appropriate," Fanning began again, "that the God should have risen from the grave exactly when he did, in 1916! Rising up in the midst of the insanity, like a beautiful, smiling reproach from another world. It was dramatic. At least I felt it so, when I saw him for the first time just after the War. The resurrection of Apollo, the Etruscan Apollo. I've been his worshiper and self-appointed priest ever since. Or at any rate I've tried to be. But it's difficult." He shook his head. "Perhaps it's even impossible for us to recapture . . ." He left the sentence unfinished and, taking her arm, led her out into the great court-yard of the Villa. Under the arcades was a bench. Thank goodness, said Pamela inwardly. They sat down.

"You see," he went on, leaning forward, his elbows on his knees, his hands clasped, "you can't get away from the things that the God protests against. Because they've become a part of you. Tradition and education have driven them into your very bones. It's a case of what I was speaking about just now—of the things that have nothing to do with you coming by force of habit to have everything to do with you. Which is why I'd like you to get Apollo and his Etruscans into your system while you're still young. It may save you trouble. Or on the other hand," he added with a rueful little laugh, "it may not. Because I really don't know if he's everybody's God. He may do for me—and do, only because I've got Plato and Jesus in my bones. But does he do for you? *Chi lo sa?* The older one grows, the more often one asks that question. Until, of course, one's arteries begin to harden, and then one's opinions begin to harden too, harden till they fossilize into certainty. But meanwhile, *chi lo sa? chi lo sa?* And after all it's quite agreeable, not knowing. And knowing, and at the same time knowing that it's no practical use knowing—that's not disagree-able either. Knowing, for example, that it would be good to live according to this God's commandments, but knowing at the same time that one couldn't do it even if one tried, because one's very guts and skeleton are already pledged to other Gods."

"I should have thought that was awful," said Pamela.

"For you, perhaps. But I happen to have a certain natural affection for the accomplished fact. I like and respect it, even when it is a bit depressing. Thus, it's a fact that I'd like to think and live in the unsplit, Apollonian way. But it's also a fact—and the fact as such is lovable—that I can't help indulging in aspirations and disgusts; I can't help thinking in terms of heroics and diabolics. Because the division, the splitness, has been worked right into my bones. So has the microbe of sensationalism; I can't help wallowing in the excitements of mysticism and the tragic sense. Can't help it." He shook his head. "Though perhaps I've wallowed in them rather more than I was justified in wallowing—justified by my upbringing, I mean. There was a time when I was really quite perversely preoccupied with mystical experiences and ecstasies and private universes."

"Private universes?" she questioned.

"Yes, private, not shared. You create one, you live in it, each time you're in love, for example." (Brightly serious, Pamela nodded her understanding and agreement; yes, yes, she knew all about *that*.) "Each time you're spiritually exalted," he went on, "each time you're drunk, even. Everybody has his own favorite short cuts to the other world. Mine, in those days, was opium."

"Opium?" She opened her eyes very wide. "Do you mean to say you smoked opium?" She was thrilled. Opium was a vice of the first order.

"It's as good a way of becoming supernatural," he answered, "as looking at one's nose or one's navel, or not eating, or repeating a word over and over again till it loses its sense and you forget how to think. All roads lead to Rome. The only bother about opium is that it's rather an unwholesome road. I had to go to a nursing home in Cannes to get disintoxicated."

"All the same," said Pamela, doing her best to imitate the quiet casualness of his manner, "it must be rather delicious, isn't it? Awfully exciting, I mean," she added, forgetting not to be thrilled.

"Too exciting." He shook his head. "That's the trouble. We needs must love the excitingest when we see it. The supernatural *is* exciting. But I don't want to love the supernatural, I want to love the natural. Not that a little supernaturalness isn't, of course, perfectly natural and necessary. But you can overdo it. I overdid it then. I was all the time in t'other world, never here. I stopped smoking because I was ill. But even if I hadn't been, I'd have stopped sooner or later for esthetic reasons. The supernatural world is so terribly baroque—altogether too Counter-Reformation and Bernini. At its best it can be Greco. But you can have too much even of Greco. A big dose of him makes you begin to pine for Vulca and his Apollo."

"But doesn't it work the other way too?" she asked. "I mean, don't you sometimes long to start smoking again?" She was secretly hoping that he'd let her try a pipe or two.

Fanning shook his head. "One doesn't get tired of very good bread," he answered. "Apollo's like that. I don't pine for supernatural excitements. Which doesn't mean," he added, "that I don't in practice run after them. You can't disintoxicate yourself of your culture. That sticks deeper than a mere taste for opium. I'd like to be able to think and live in the spirit of the God. But the fact remains that I can't."

"Can't you?" said Pamela with a polite sympathy. She was more interested in the opium.

"No, no, you can't entirely disintoxicate yourself of mysticism and the tragic sense. You can't take a Turvey treatment for spirituality and disgust. You can't. Not nowadays. Acceptance is impossible in a split world like ours. You've got to recoil. In the circumstances it's right and proper. But absolutely it's wrong. If only one could accept as this God accepts, smiling like that . . ."

"But you do smile like that," she insisted.

He laughed and, unclasping his hands, straightened himself up in his seat. "But unhappily," he said, "a man can smile and smile and not be Apollo. Meanwhile, what's becoming of your education? Shouldn't we . . . ?"

"Well, if you like," she assented dubiously. "Only my feet are rather tired. I mean, there's something about sight-seeing . . ."

"There is indeed," said Fanning. "But I was prepared to be a martyr to culture. Still, I'm thankful you're not." He smiled at her, and Pamela was pleased to find herself once more at the focus of his attention. It had been very interesting to hear him talk about his philosophy and all that. But all the same . . .

"Twenty to four," said Fanning, looking at his watch. "I've an idea; shouldn't we drive out to Monte Cavo and spend the evening up there in the cool? There's a view. And a really very eatable dinner."

"I'd love to. But . . ." Pamela hesitated. "Well, you see I did tell Guy I'd go out with him this evening."

He was annoyed. "Well, if you prefer . . ."

"But I don't prefer," she answered hastily. "I mean, I'd much rather go with you. Only I wondered how I'd let Guy know I wasn't . . ."

"Don't let him know," Fanning answered, abusing his victory. "After all, what are young men there for, except to wait when young women don't keep their appointments? It's their function in life."

Pamela laughed. His words had given her a pleasing sense of importance and power. "Poor Guy!" she said through her laughter, and her eyes were insolently bright.

"You little hypocrite."

"I'm not," she protested. "I really *am* sorry for him."

"A little hypocrite *and* a little devil," was his verdict. He rose to his feet. "If you could see your own eyes now! But *andiamo*." He held out his hand to help her up. "I'm beginning to be rather afraid of you."

"What nonsense!" She was delighted. They walked together toward the door.

Fanning made the driver go out by the Appian Way. "For the sake of your education," he explained, pointing at the ruined tombs, "which we can continue, thank heaven, in comfort, and at twenty miles an hour."

Leaning back luxuriously in her corner, Pamela laughed. "But I must say," she had to admit, "it's really rather lovely."

From Albano the road mounted through the chestnut woods toward Rocca di Papa. A few miles brought them to a turning on the right; the car came to a halt.

"It's barred," said Pamela, looking out of the window. Fanning had taken out his pocketbook and was hunting among the banknotes and the old letters. "The road's private," he explained. "They ask for your card—heaven knows why. The only trouble being, of course, that I've never possessed such a thing as a visiting card in my life. Still, I generally have one or two belonging to other people. Ah, here we are! Good!" He produced two pieces of pasteboard. A gatekeeper had appeared and was waiting by the door of the car. "Shall we say we're Count Keyserling?" said Fanning, handing her the count's card. "Or alternatively," he read from the other, "that we're Herbert Watson, Funeral Furnisher, Funerals conducted with Efficiency and Reverence, Motor Hearses for use in every part of the Country." He shook his head. "The last relic of my poor old friend Tom Hatchard. Died last year. I had to bury him. Poor Tom! On the whole I think we'd better be Herbert Watson. *Ecco!*" He handed out the card; the man saluted and went to open the gate. "But give me back Count Keyserling." Fanning stretched out his hand. "He'll come in useful another time."

The car started and went roaring up the zigzag ascent. Lying back in her corner, Pamela laughed and laughed, inextinguishably.

"But what *is* the joke?" he asked.

She didn't know herself. Mr. Watson and the Count had only been a pretext; this enormous laughter, which they had released, sprang from some other, deeper source. And perhaps it was a mere accident that it should be laughter at all. Another pretext, a different finger on the trigger, and it might have been tears, or anger, or singing "Constantinople" at the top of her voice—anything.

She was limp when they reached the top. Fanning made her sit down where she could see the view and himself went off to order cold drinks at the bar of the little inn that had once been the monastery of Monte Cavo.

Pamela sat where he had left her. The wooded slopes fell steeply away beneath her, down, down to the blue shining of the Alban Lake; and that toy palace perched on the hill beyond was the Pope's, that tiny city in a picture book, Marino. Beyond a dark ridge on the left the round eye of Nemi looked up from its crater. Far off, behind Albano, an expanse of blue steel, burnished beneath the sun, was the Tyrrhenian, and flat like the sea, but golden with ripening corn and powdered goldenly with a haze of dust, the Campagna stretched away from the feet of the subsiding hills, away and up toward a fading horizon, on which the blue ghosts of mountains floated on a level with her eyes. In the midst of the expanse a half-seen golden chaos was Rome. Through the haze the dome of St. Peter's shone faintly in the sun with a glitter as of muted glass. There was an enormous silence, sad, sad but somehow consoling. A sacred silence. And yet when, coming up from behind her, Fanning broke it, his voice, for Pamela, committed no iconoclasm; for it seemed, in the world of her feelings, to belong to the silence, it was made, as it were, of the same intimate and friendly substance. He squatted down on his heels beside her, laying a hand on her shoulder to steady himself.

"What a panorama of space and time!" he said. "So many miles, such an expanse of centuries! You can still walk on the paved road that led to the temple here. The generals used to march up sometimes in triumph. With elephants."

The silence enveloped them again, bringing them together; and they were alone and as though conspiratorially isolated in an atmosphere of solemn amorousness.

"I signori son serviti," said a slightly ironic voice behind them.

"That's our drinks," said Fanning. "Perhaps we'd better . . ." He got up and, as he unbent them, his knees cracked stiffly. He stooped to rub them, for they ached; his joints were old. "Fool!" he said to himself, and decided that tomorrow he'd go to Venice. She was too young, too dangerously and perversely fresh.

They drank their lemonade in silence. Pamela's face wore an expression of grave serenity which it touched and flattered and moved him to see. Still, he was a fool to be touched and flattered and moved.

"Let's go for a bit of a stroll," he said, when they had slaked their thirst. She got up without a word, obediently, as though she had become his slave.

It was breathless under the trees and there was a smell of damp, hot greenness, a hum and flicker of insects in the probing slants of sunlight. But in the open spaces the air of the heights was quick and nimble, in spite of the sun; the broom flower blazed among the rocks; and round the bushes where the honeysuckle had clambered, there hung invisible islands of perfume, cool and fresh in the midst of the hot sea of bracken smell. Pamela moved here and there with little exclamations of delight, pulling at the tough sprays of honeysuckle. "Oh, look!" she called to him in her rapturous voice. "Come and look!"

"I'm looking," he shouted back across the intervening space. "With a telescope. With the eye of faith," he corrected; for she had moved out of sight. He sat down on a smooth rock and lighted a cigarette. Venice, he reflected, would be rather boring at this particular season. In a few minutes Pamela came back to him, flushed, with a great bunch of honeysuckle between her hands.

"You know, you ought to have come," she said reproachfully. "There were such *lovely* pieces I couldn't reach."

Fanning shook his head. "He also serves who only sits and smokes," he said, and made room for her on the stone beside him. "And what's more," he went on, " 'let Austin have his swink to him reserved.' Yes, let him. How wholeheartedly I've always agreed with Chaucer's Monk! Besides, you seem to forget, my child, that I'm an old, old gentleman." He was playing the safe, the prudent part. Perhaps if he played it hard enough, it wouldn't be necessary to go to Venice.

Pamela paid no attention to what he was saying. "Would you like this one for your buttonhole, Miles?" she asked, holding up a many-trumpeted flower. It was the first time she had called him by his Christian name, and the accomplishment of this much-meditated act of daring made her blush. "I'll stick it in," she added, leaning forward, so that he shouldn't see her reddened cheeks, till her face was almost touching his coat.

Near and thus offered (for it was an offer, he had no doubt of that, a deliberate offer) why shouldn't he take this lovely, this terribly and desperately tempting freshness? It was a matter of stretching out one's hands. But no; it would be too insane. She was near, this warm young flesh, this scent of her hair, near and offered—with what an innocent perversity, what a touchingly ingenuous and uncomprehending shameless-ness! But he sat woodenly still, feeling all of a sudden as he had felt when, a lanky boy, he had been too shy, too utterly terrified, in spite of his long-ings, to kiss that Jenny—what on earth was her name?—that Jenny Something-or-Other he had danced the polka with at Uncle Fred's one Christ-mas, how many centuries ago!—and yet only yesterday, only this instant.

"There!" said Pamela, and drew back. Her cheeks had had time to cool a little.

"Thank you." There was a silence.

"Do you know," she said at last, efficiently, "you've got a button loose on your coat."

He fingered the hanging button. "What a damning proof of celibacy!"

"If only I had a needle and thread . . ."

"Don't make your offer too lightly. If you knew what a quantity of unmended stuff I've got at home . . ."

"I'll come and do it all tomorrow," she promised, feeling delightfully protective and important.

"Beware," he said. "I'll take you at your word. It's sweated labor."

"I don't mind. I'll come."

"Punctually at ten-thirty, then." He had forgotten about Venice. "I shall be a ruthless taskmaster."

Nemi was already in shadow when they walked back; but the higher slopes were transfigured with the setting sunlight. Pamela halted at a twist of the path and turned back toward the western sky. Looking up, Fanning saw her standing there, goldenly flushed, the colors of her skin, her hair, her dress, the flowers in her hands, supernaturally heightened and intensi-fied in the almost level light.

"I think this is the most lovely place I've ever seen." Her voice was solemn with a natural piety. "But you're not looking," she added in a different tone, reproachfully.

"I'm looking at you," he answered. After all, if he stopped in time, it didn't matter his behaving like a fool—it didn't finally matter and, mean-while, was very agreeable.

An expression of impertinent mischief chased away the solemnity from her face. "Trying to see my ears again?" she asked; and, breaking off a honeysuckle blossom, she threw it down in his face, then turned and ran up the steep path.

"Don't imagine I'm going to pursue," he called after her. "The Pan and Syrinx business is a winter pastime. Like football."

Her laughter came down to him from among the trees; he followed the retreating sound. Pamela waited for him at the top of the hill and they walked back together toward the inn.

"Aren't there any ruins here?" she asked. "I mean, for my education."

He shook his head. "The Young Pretender's brother pulled them all down and built a monastery with them. For the Passionist Fathers," he added after a little pause. "I feel rather like a Passionist Father myself at the moment." They walked on without speaking, enveloped by the huge, the amorously significant silence.

But a few minutes later, at the dinner table, they were exuberantly gay. The food was well cooked, the wine an admirable Falernian. Fanning began to talk about his early loves. Vaguely at first, but later, under Pamela's questioning, with an ever-increasing wealth of specific detail. They were indiscreet, impudent questions, which at ordinary times she couldn't have uttered, or at least have only despairingly forced out, with a suicide's determination. But she was a little tipsy now, tipsy with the wine and her own laughing exultation; she rapped them out easily, without a tremor. "As though you were the immortal Sigmund himself," he assured her, laughing. Her impudence and that knowledgeable, scientific ingenuousness amused him, rather perversely; he told her everything she asked.

When she had finished with his early loves, she questioned him about the opium. Fanning described his private universes and that charming nurse who had looked after him while he was being disintoxicated. He went on to talk about the black poverty he'd been reduced to by the drug. "Because you can't do journalism or write novels in the other world," he explained. "At least I never could." And he told her of the debts he still owed and of his present arrangements with his publishers.

Almost suddenly the night was cold and Fanning became aware that the bottle had been empty for a long time. He threw away the stump of his cigar. "Let's go." They took their seats and the car set off, carrying with it the narrow world of form and color created by its head lamps. They were alone in the darkness of their padded box. An hour before Fanning had decided that he would take this opportunity to kiss her. But he was haunted suddenly by the memory of an Australian who had once complained to him of the sufferings of a young colonial in England. "In Sydney," he had said, "when I get into a taxi with a nice girl, I know exactly what to do. And I know exactly what to do when I'm in an American taxi. But when I apply my knowledge in London—God, isn't there a row!" How vulgar and stupid it all was! Not merely a fool, but a vulgar, stupid fool. He sat unmoving in his corner. When the lights of Rome were round them, he took her hand and kissed it.

"Good night."

She thanked him. "I've had the loveliest day." But her eyes were puzzled and unhappy. Meeting them, Fanning suddenly regretted his self-restraint, wished that he had been stupid and vulgar. And, after all, would it have been so stupid and vulgar? You could make any action seem anything you liked, from saintly to disgusting, by describing it in the appropriate words. But his regrets had come too late. Here was her hotel. He drove home to his solitude feeling exceedingly depressed.

VI

June 14th. Spent the morning with M., who lives in a house belonging to a friend of his who is a Catholic and lives in Rome, M. says, because he likes to get his popery straight from the horse's mouth. A nice house, old, standing just back from the Forum, which I said I thought was like a rubbish heap and he agreed with me, in spite of my education, and said he always preferred live dogs to dead lions and thinks it's awful the way the Fascists are pulling down nice ordinary houses and making holes to find more of these beastly pillars and things. I sewed on a lot of buttons, etc., as he's living in only two rooms on the ground floor and the servants are on their holiday, so he eats out and an old woman comes to clean up in the afternoons, but doesn't do any mending, which meant a lot for me, but I liked doing it, in spite of the darning, because he sat with me all the time, sometimes talking, sometimes just working. When he's writing or sitting with his pen in his hand thinking, his face is quite still and *terribly* serious and far, far away, as though he were a picture, or more like some sort of not human person, a sort of angel, if one can imagine them without nightdresses and long hair, really rather frightening, so that one longed to shout or throw a reel of cotton at him so as to change him back again into a man. He has very beautiful hands, rather long and bony, but strong. Sometimes, after he'd sat thinking for a long time, he'd get up and walk about the room, frowning and looking kind of angry, which was still more terrifying—sitting there while he walked up and down quite close to me, as though he were absolutely alone. But one time he suddenly stopped his walking up and down and said how profusely he apologized for his toes, because I was darning, and it was really very wonderful to see him suddenly changed back from that picture-angel sort of creature into a human being. Then he sat down by me and said he'd been spending the morning wrestling with the problem of speaking the truth in books; so I said, but haven't you always spoken it? because that always seemed to me the chief point of M.'s books. But he said, not much, because most of it was quite unspeakable in our world, as we found it too shocking and humiliating. So I said, all the same I didn't see why it shouldn't be spoken, and he said, nor did he in theory, but in practice he didn't want to be lynched. And he said, look for example at those advertisements in American magazines with the photos and life stories of people with unpleasant breath. So I said, yes, aren't they simply *too* awful. Because they really do make one shudder. And he said, precisely, there you are, and they're so successful because everyone thinks them so perfectly awful. They're outraged by them, he said, just as you're outraged, and they rush off and buy the stuff in sheer terror, because they're so terrified of being an outrage physically to other people. And he said, that's only one small sample of all the class of truths, pleasant and unpleasant, that you can't speak, except in scientific books, but that doesn't count, because you deliberately leave your feelings outside in the cloakroom when you're being scientific. And just because they're unspeakable, we pretend they're unimportant, but they aren't, on the contrary, they're terribly important, and he said, you've only got to examine your memory quite sincerely for five minutes to realize it, and of course he's quite right. When I think of Miss Poole giving me piano lessons—but no, really, one *can't* write these things, and yet one obviously ought to, because they are so important, the humiliating physical facts, both pleasant and unpleasant (though I must say, most of the ones I can think of seem to be unpleasant), so important in all human relation- ships, he says, even in love, which is really rather awful, but of course one must admit it. And M. said it would take a whole generation of being shocked and humiliated and lynching the shockers and humiliators before people could settle down to listening to that sort of truth calmly, which they did do, he says, at certain times in the past, at any rate much more so than now. And he says that when they can listen to it completely calmly, the world will be quite different from what it is now, so I asked, in what way? but he said he couldn't clearly imagine; only he knew it would be different. After that he went back to his table and wrote very quickly for about half an hour without stopping, and I longed to ask him if he'd been writing the truth, and if so, what about, but I didn't have the nerve, which was stupid.

We lunched at our usual place, which I really don't much like, as who wants to look at fat businessmen and farmers from the country simply *drinking* spaghetti? even if the spaghetti *is* good, but M. prefers it to the big places, because he says that in Rome one must do as the Romans do, not as the Americans. Still, I must say I do like looking at people who dress well and have good manners and nice jewels and things, which I told him, so he said all right, we'd go to Valadier tomorrow to see how the rich ate macaroni, which made me wretched, as it looked as though I'd been cadging, and of course that's the last thing in the world I meant to do, to make him waste a lot of money on me, particularly after what he told me yesterday about his debts and what he made on the average, which still seems to me shockingly little, considering who he is, so I said no, wouldn't he lunch with me at Valadier's, and he laughed and said it was the first time he'd heard of a gigolo of fifty being taken out by a woman of twenty. That rather upset me—the way it seemed to bring what we are to each other on to the wrong level, making it all a sort of joke and sniggery, like something in *Punch*. Which is hateful; I can't bear it. And I have the feeling that he does it on purpose, as a kind of protection, because he doesn't want to care too much, and that's why he's always saying he's so old, which is all nonsense, because you're only as old as you feel, and sometimes I even feel older than he does, like when he gets so amused and interested with little boys in the street playing that game of sticking out your fingers and calling a number, or when he talks about that awful old Dickens. Which I told him, but he only laughed and said age is a circle and you grow into a lot of the things you grew out of, because the whole world is a fried whiting with its tail in its mouth, which only confirms what I said about his saying he was old being all nonsense. Which I told him and he said, quite right, he only *said* he felt old when he *wished* that he felt old. Which made me see still more clearly that it was just a defense. A defense of *me*, I suppose, and all that sort of nonsense. What I'd have liked to say, only I didn't, was that I don't want to be defended, particularly if being defended means his defending himself against me and making stupid jokes about gigolos and old gentlemen. Because I think he really does rather care underneath—from the way he looks at me sometimes—and he'd like to say so and act so, but he won't on principle, which is really against all *his* principles, and some time I *shall* tell him so. I insisted he should lunch with me and in the end he said he would, and then he was suddenly very silent and, I thought, glum and unhappy, and after coffee he said he'd have to go home and write all the rest of the day. So I came back to the hotel and had a rest and wrote this, and now it's nearly seven and I feel terribly sad, almost like crying. *Next day.* Rang up Guy and had less difficulty than I expected getting him to forgive me for yesterday, in fact he almost apologized himself. Danced till 2.15.

June 15th. M. still sad and didn't kiss me when we met, *on purpose*, which made me angry, it's so humiliating to be defended. He was wearing an open shirt, like Byron, which suited him; but I told him, you look like the devil when you're sad (which is true, because his face ought to move, not be still), and he said that was what came of feeling and behaving like an angel; so of course I asked why he didn't behave like a devil, because in that case he'd look like an angel, and I preferred his looks to his morals, and then I blushed, like an idiot. But really it is too stupid that women aren't supposed to say what they think. Why can't we say, I like you, or whatever it is, without being thought a kind of monster, if we say it first, and even thinking ourselves monsters? Because one ought to say what one thinks and do what one likes or else one becomes like Aunt Edith, hippo-ish and dead inside. Which is after all what M.'s constantly saying in his books, so he oughtn't to humiliate me with his beastly defendings. Lunch at Valadier's was really rather a bore. Afterward we went and sat in a church, because it was so hot, a huge affair full of pink marble and frescoes and marble babies and gold. M. says that the modern equivalent is Lyons' Corner House, and that the Jesuits were so successful because they gave the poor a chance of feeling what it was like to live in a palace, or something better than a palace, because he says the chief difference between a Corner House and the state rooms at Buckingham Palace is that the Corner House is so much more sumptuous, almost as sumptuous as these Jesuit churches. I asked him if he believed in God and he said he believed in a great many gods; it depended on what he was doing, or being, or feeling at the moment. He said he believed in Apollo when he was working, and in Bacchus when he was drinking, and in Buddha when he felt depressed, and in Venus when he was making love, and in the Devil when he was afraid or angry, and in the Categorical Imperative when he had to do his duty. I asked him which he believed in now and he said he didn't quite know, but he thought it was the Categorical Imperative, which really made me furious, so I answered that I only believed in the Devil and Venus, which made him laugh, and he said I looked as though I were going to jump off the Eiffel Tower, and I was just going to say what I thought of his hippo-ishness, I mean I'd really made up my mind, when a most horrible old verger rushed up and said we must leave the church, because it seems the Pope doesn't allow you to be in a church with bare arms, which is really too indecent. But M. said that after all it wasn't surprising, because every god has to protect himself against hostile gods, and the gods of bare skin are hostile to the gods of souls and clothes, and he made me stop in front of a shop window where there were some mirrors and said, you can see for yourself, and I must say I really did look very nice in that pale-green linen which goes so awfully well with the skin, when one's a bit sun-burned. But he said, it's not merely a question of seeing; you must touch too, so I stroked my arms and said yes, they were nice and smooth, and he said, precisely, and then he stroked my arm very lightly, like a moth crawling, agonizingly creepy but delicious, once or twice, looking very serious and attentive, as though he were tuning a piano, which made me laugh, and I said I supposed he was experimenting to see if the Pope was in the right, and then he gave me the most horrible pinch and said, yes, the Pope was quite right and I ought to be muffled in Jaeger from top to toe. But I was so angry with the pain, because he pinched me really terribly, that I just rushed off without saying anything and jumped into a cab that was passing and drove straight to the hotel. But I was so wretched by the time I got there that I started crying in the lift and the lift man said he hoped I hadn't had any *dispiacere di famiglia*, which made me laugh and that made the crying much worse, and then I suddenly thought of Clare and felt such a horrible beast, so I lay on my bed and simply howled for about an hour, and then I got up and wrote a letter and sent one of the hotel boys with it to M.'s address, saying I was so sorry and would he come at once. But he didn't come, not for hours and hours, and it was simply too awful, because I thought he was offended, or despising, because I'd been such a fool, and I wondered whether he really did like me at all and whether this defending theory wasn't just my imagination. But at last, when I'd quite given him up and was so miserable I didn't know what I should do, he suddenly appeared—because he'd only that moment gone back to the house and found my note—and was too wonderfully sweet to me, and said he was so sorry, but he'd been on edge (though he didn't say why, but I know now that the defending theory wasn't just imagination) and I said I was so sorry and I cried, but I was happy, and then we laughed because it had all been so stupid and then M. quoted a bit of Homer which meant that after they'd eaten and drunk they wept for their friends and after they'd wept a little they went to sleep, so we went out and had dinner and after dinner we went and danced, and he dances really very well, but we stopped before midnight, because he said the noise of the jazz would drive him crazy. He was perfectly sweet, but though he didn't say anything sniggery, I could feel he was on the defensive all the time, sweetly and friendlily on the defensive, and when he said good night he only kissed my hand.

June 18th.   Stayed in bed till lunch rereading *The Return of Eurydice*. I understand Joan so well now, better and better, she's so like me in all she feels and thinks. M. went to Tivoli for the day to see some Italian friends who have a house there. What is he like with other people, I wonder? Got two tickets for the fireworks tomorrow night, the hotel porter says they'll be good, because it's the first Girandola since the War. Went to the Villa Borghese in the afternoon for my education, to give M. a surprise when he comes back, and I must say some of the pictures and statues were very lovely, but the most awful-looking fat man would follow me round all the time, and finally the old beast even had the

impertinence to speak to me, so I just said, *Lei è un porco,* which I must
say was very effective. But it's extraordinary how things do just depend
on looks and being *sympathique*, because if he hadn't looked such a pig,
I shouldn't have thought him so piggish, which shows again what rot
hippo-ism is. Went to bed early and finished *Eurydice.* This is the fifth
time I've read it.

VII

"Oh, it was marvelous before the War, the Girandola. Really marvelous."

"But then what wasn't *marvelous* before the War?" said Pamela
sarcastically. These references to a Golden Age in which she had had
no part always annoyed her.

Fanning laughed. "Another one in the eye for the aged gentleman!"

There, he had slipped back again behind his defenses! She did not
answer for fear of giving him some excuse to dig himself in, impregnably.
This hateful bantering with feelings! They walked on in silence. The
night was breathlessly warm; the sounds of brassy music came to them
faintly through the dim enormous noise of a crowd that thickened with
every step they took toward the Piazzo del Popolo. In the end they
had to shove their way by main force.

Sunk head over ears in this vast sea of animal contacts, animal smells
and noise, Pamela was afraid. "Isn't it awful?" she said, looking up at
him over her shoulder; and she shuddered. But at the same time she
rather liked her fear, because it seemed in some way to break down the
barriers that separated them, to bring him closer to her—close with a
physical closeness of protective contact that was also, increasingly, a
closeness of thought and feeling.

"You're all right," he reassured her through the tumult. He was standing behind her, encircling her with his arms. "I won't let you be
squashed"; and as he spoke he fended off the menacing lurch of a large
back. "*Ignorante!*" he shouted at it.

A terrific explosion interrupted the distant selections from *Rigoletto*
and the sky was suddenly full of colored lights; the Girandola had
begun. A wave of impatience ran through the advancing crowd; they were
violently pushed and jostled. But, "It's all right," Fanning kept repeating, "it's all right." They were squeezed together in a staggering embrace.
Pamela was terrified, but it was with a kind of swooning pleasure that
she shut her eyes and abandoned herself limply in his arms.

"Ma piano!" shouted Fanning at the nearest jostlers. "Piano!" and "'Sblood!" he said in English, for he had the affectation of using literary oaths. "Hell and Death!" But in the tumult his words were as though unspoken. He was silent; and suddenly, in the midst of that heaving chaos of noise and rough contacts, of movement and heat and smell, suddenly he became aware that his lips were almost touching her hair, and that under his right hand was the firm resilience of her breast. He hesitated for a moment on the threshold of his sensuality, then averted his face, shifted the position of his hand.

"At last!"

The haven to which their tickets admitted them was a little garden on the western side of the Piazza, opposite the Pincio and the source of the fireworks. The place was crowded, but not oppressively. Fanning was tall enough to overlook the interposed heads, and when Pamela had climbed on to a little parapet that separated one terrace of the garden from another, she too could see perfectly.

"But you'll let me lean on you," she said, laying a hand on his shoulder, "because there's a fat woman next me who's steadily squeezing me off. I think she's expanding with the heat."

"And she almost certainly understands English. So for heaven's sake . . ."

A fresh volley of explosions from the other side of the great square interrupted him and drowned the answering mockery of her laughter. "Ooh! ooh!" the crowd was moaning in a kind of amorous agony. Magical flowers in a delirium of growth, the rockets mounted on their slender stalks and, ah! high up above the Pincian hill, dazzlingly, deafeningly, in a bunch of stars and a thunderclap, they blossomed.

"Isn't it marvelous?" said Pamela, looking down at him with shining eyes. "Oh God!" she added, in another voice. "She's expanding again. Help!" And for a moment she was on the verge of falling. She leaned on him so heavily that he had to make an effort not to be pushed sideways. She managed to straighten herself up again into equilibrium.

"I've got you in case . . ." He put his arm round her knees to steady her.

"Shall I see if I can puncture the old beast with a pin?" And Fanning knew, by the tone of her voice, that she was genuinely prepared to make the experiment.

"If you do," he said, "I shall leave you to be lynched alone."

Pamela felt his arm tighten a little about her thighs. "Coward!" she mocked and pulled his hair.

"Martyrdom's not in my line," he laughed back. "Not even martyrdom for your sake." But her youth was a perversity, her freshness a kind of provocative vice. He had taken a step across that supernatural threshold. He had given—after all, why not?—a certain license to his desires. Amid their multitudinous uncoiling, his body seemed to be coming to a new and obscure life of its own. When the time came he would revoke the license, step back again into the daily world.

There was another bang, another, and the obelisk at the center of the Piazza leaped out sharp and black against apocalypse after apocalypse of jeweled light. And through the now flushed, now pearly-brilliant, now emerald-shining smoke clouds, a pine tree, a palm, a stretch of grass emerged, like strange unearthly visions of pine and palm and grass, from the darkness of the else invisible gardens.

There was an interval of mere lamplight—like sobriety, said Fanning, between two pipes of opium, like daily life after an ecstasy. And perhaps, he was thinking, the time to step back again had already come. "If only one could live without any lucid intervals," he concluded.

"I don't see why not." She spoke with a kind of provocative defiance, as though challenging him to contradict her. Her heart beat very fast, exultantly. "I mean, why shouldn't it be fireworks all the time?"

"Because it just isn't, that's all. Unhappily." It was time to step back again; but he didn't step back.

"Well, then, it's a case of damn the intervals and enjoy . . . Oh!" She started. That prodigious bang had sent a large red moon sailing almost slowly into the sky. It burst into a shower of meteors that whistled as they fell, expiringly.

Fanning imitated their plaintive noise. "Sad, sad," he commented. "Even the fireworks can be sad."

She turned on him fiercely. "Only because you want them to be sad. Yes, you want them to be. Why do you want them to be sad?"

Yes, why? It was a pertinent question. She felt his arm tighten again round her knees and was triumphant. He was defending himself no more; he was listening to those oracles. But at the root of his deliberate reckless-ness, its contradiction and its cause, his sadness obscurely persisted. "But I *don't* want them to be sad," he persisted.

Another garden of rockets began to blossom. Laughing, triumphant, Pamela laid her hand on his head.

"I feel so superior up here," she said.

"On a pedestal, what?" He laughed. " '*Guardami ben; ben son, ben son Beatrice!*' "

"Such a comfort you're not bald," she said, her fingers in his hair.

"That must be a great disadvantage of pedestals—I mean, seeing the baldness of the men down below."

"But the great advantage of pedestals, as I now suddenly see for the first time . . ." Another explosion covered his voice. ". . . make it possible . . ." Bang!

"Oh, look!" A bluish light was brightening, brightening.

". . . possible for even the baldest . . ." There was a continuous uninterrupted rattle of detonations. Fanning gave it up. What he had meant to say was that pedestals gave even the baldest men unrivaled opportunities for pinching the idol's legs.

"What were you saying?" she shouted through the battle.

"Nothing," he yelled back. He had meant, of course, to suit the action to the world, playfully. But the fates had decided otherwise and he wasn't really sorry. For he was tired; he had realized it almost suddenly. All this standing. He was no good at standing nowadays.

A cataract of silver fire was pouring down the slopes of the Pincian Hill, and the shining smoke clouds rolled away from it like the spray from a tumbling river. And suddenly, above it, the eagle of Savoy emerged from the darkness, enormous, perched on the lictor's ax and rods. There was applause and patriotic music. Then, gradually, the brightness of the cataract grew dim; the sources of its silver streaming were one by one dried up. The eagle moulted its shining plumage, the ax and rods faded, faded and at last were gone. Lit faintly by only the common lamplight, the smoke drifted slowly away toward the north. A spasm of motion ran through the huge crowd in the square below them. The show was over.

"But I feel," said Pamela, as they shoved their way back toward the open streets, "I feel as though the rockets were still popping off inside me." And she began to sing to herself as she walked.

Fanning made no comment. He was thinking of that Girandola he'd seen with Alice and Tony and Laurina Frescobaldi—was it in 1907 or 1908? Tony was an ambassador now, and Alice was dead, and one of Laurina's sons (he recalled the expression of despair on that worn, but still handsome face, when she had told him yesterday, at Tivoli) was already old enough to be getting housemaids into trouble.

"Not only rockets," Pamela went on, interrupting her singing, "but even Catherine wheels. I feel all Catherine wheely. You know, like when one's a little drunk." And she went on again with "Old Man River," tipsily happy and excited.

The crowd grew thinner round them and at last they were almost alone. Pamela's singing abruptly ceased. Here, in the open, in the cool of the dark night it had suddenly become inappropriate, a little shame-ful. She glanced anxiously at her companion; had he too remarked that inappropriateness, been shocked by it? But Fanning had noticed nothing; she wished he had. Head bent, his hands behind his back, he was walking at her side, but in another universe. When had his spirit gone away from her, and why? She didn't know, hadn't noticed. Those inward fireworks, that private festival of exultation, had occupied her whole attention. She had been too excitedly happy with being in love to be able to think of the object of that love. But now, abruptly sobered, she had become aware of him again, repentantly at first, and then, as she realized his new remoteness, with a sinking of the heart. What had hap-pened in these few moments? She was on the point of addressing him, then checked herself. Her apprehension grew and grew till it became a kind of terrified certainty that he'd never loved her at all, that he'd suddenly begun to hate her. But why, but why? They walked on.

"How lovely it is here!" she said at last. Her voice was timid and unnatural. "And so deliciously cool." They had emerged on to the em-bankment of the Tiber. Above the river, a second invisible river of air flowed softly through the hot night. "Shall we stop for a moment?" He nodded without speaking. "I mean, only if you want to," she added. He nodded again.

They stood, leaning on the parapet, looking down at the black water. There was a long, long silence. Pamela waited for him to say something, to make a gesture; but he did not stir, the word never came. It was as though he were at the other end of the world. She felt almost sick with unhappiness. Heart beat after heart beat, the silence prolonged itself.

Fanning was thinking of tomorrow's journey. How he hated the train! And in this heat. . . . But it was necessary. The wicked flee, and in this case fleeing would be an act of virtue—painful. Was it love? Or just an itch of desire, of the rather crazy, dirty desire of an aging man? "A cinquant' anni si diventa un po' pazzo." He heard his own voice speaking laughingly, mournfully, to Laurina. "Pazzo e porco. Si, anch' io di11ento un porco. Le minorenni—a cinquant' anni, sa, sono un ossessione. Pro-prio un' ossessione." Was that all—just an obsession of crazy desire? Or was it love? Or wasn't there any difference, was it just a question of names and approving or disapproving tones of voice? What was certain was that you could be as desperately unhappy when you were robbed of your crazy desire as when you were robbed of your love. A porco suffers as much as Dante. And perhaps Beatrice too was lovely, in Dante's memory, with the perversity of youth, the shamelessness of innocence, the vice of freshness. Still, the wicked flee; the wicked flee. If only he'd had the strength of mind to flee before! A touch made him start. Pamela had taken his hand.

"Miles!" Her voice was strained and abnormal. Fanning turned toward her and was almost frightened by the look of determined despair he saw on her face. The Eiffel Tower . . . "Miles!"

"What is it?"

"Why don't you speak to me?"

He shrugged his shoulders. "I didn't happen to be feeling very loquacious. For a change," he added, self-mockingly, in the hope (he knew it for a vain one) of being able to turn away her desperate attack with a counterattack of laughter.

She ignored his counterattack. "Why do you shut yourself away from me like this?" she asked. "Why do you hate me."

"But, my sweet child . . ."

"Yes, you hate me. You shut me away. Why are you so cruel, Miles?" Her voice broke; she was crying. Lifting his hand, she kissed it, passionately, despairingly. "I love you so much, Miles. I love you." His hand was wet with her tears when almost by force he managed to draw it away from her.

He put his arm round her, comfortingly. But he was annoyed as well as touched, annoyed by her despairing determination, by the way she had made up her mind to jump off the Eiffel Tower, screwed up her courage turn by turn. And now she was jumping—but how gracelessly! The way he had positively had to struggle for his hand! There was something forced and unnatural about the whole scene. She was being a character in fiction. But characters in fiction suffer. He patted her shoulder, he made consolatory murmurs. Consoling her for being in love with him! But the idea of explaining and protesting and being lucidly reasonable was appalling to him at the moment, absolutely appalling. He hoped that she'd just permit herself to be consoled and ask no further questions, just leave the whole situation comfortably inarticulate. But his hope was again disappointed.

"Why do you hate me, Miles?" she insisted.

"But, Pamela . . ."

"Because you did care a little; you did. I mean, I could see you cared. And now, suddenly . . . What have I done, Miles?"

"But nothing, my child, nothing." He could not keep a note of exasperation out of his voice. If only she'd allow him to be silent!

"Nothing? But I can hear from the way you speak that there's something." She returned to her old refrain. "Because you did care, Miles; a little, you did." She looked up at him, but he had moved away from her, he had averted his eyes toward the street. "You did, Miles."

Oh God! he was groaning to himself, God! And aloud (for she had made his silence untenable, she had driven him out into articulateness), "I cared too much," he said. "It would be so easy to do something stupid and irreparable, something mad, yes and bad, bad. I like you too much in other ways to want to run that risk. Perhaps, if I were twenty years younger . . . But I'm too old. It wouldn't do. And you're too young, you can't really understand; you . . . Oh, thank God, there's a taxi." And he darted forward, waving and shouting. Saved! But when they had shut themselves into the cab, he found that the new situation was even more perilous than the old.

"Miles!" A flash of lamplight through the window of the cab revealed her face to him. His words had consoled her; she was smiling, was trying to look happy; but under the attempted happiness her expression was more desperately determined than ever. She was not yet at the bottom of her Tower. "Miles!" And sliding across the seat toward him, she threw her arms round his neck and kissed him. "Take me, Miles," she said, speaking in quick abrupt little spurts, as though she were forcing the words out with violence against a resistance. He recognized the suicide's voice, despairing, strained, and at the same time, flat, lifeless. "Take me. If you want me . . ."

Fanning tried to protest, to disengage himself, gently, from her embrace.

"But I want you to take me, Miles," she insisted. "I want you . . ." She kissed him again; she pressed herself against his hard body. "I want you, Miles. Even if it is stupid and mad," she added in another little spurt of desperation, making answer to the expression on his face, to the words she wouldn't permit him to utter. "And it isn't. I mean, love isn't stupid or mad. And even if it were, I don't care. Yes, I want to be stupid and mad. Even if it were to kill me. So take me, Miles." She kissed him again. "Take me."

He turned away his mouth from those soft lips. She was forcing him back across the threshold. His body was uneasy with awakenings and supernatural dawn.

Held up by a tram at the corner of a narrow street, the cab was at a standstill. With quick strong gestures Fanning unclasped her arms from round his neck, and, taking her two hands in his, he kissed first one and then the other. "Good-by, Pamela," he whispered, and, throwing open the door, he was half out of the cab before she realized what he was doing.

"But what are you doing, Miles? Where . . ." The door slammed.

He thrust some money into the driver's hand and almost ran. Pamela rose to her feet to follow him, but the cab started with a sudden jerk that threw her off her balance, and she fell back onto the seat.

"Miles!" she called, and then, "Stop!"

But the driver either didn't hear or else paid no attention. She did not call again, but sat, covering her face with her hands, crying and feeling so agonizingly unhappy that she thought she would die of it.

VIII

By the time you receive this letter, I shall be—no, not dead, Pamela, though I know how thrilled and proud you'd be, through your temporary inconsolability, if I were to blow my brains out— not dead, but (what will be almost worse in these dog days) in the train, bound for some anonymous refuge. Yes, a refuge, as though you were my worst enemy. Which in fact you almost are at the moment, for the good reason that you're acting as your own enemy. If I were less fond of you, I'd stay and join forces with you against yourself. And, frankly, I wish I were less fond of you. Do you know how desirable you are? Not yet, I suppose, not consciously, in spite of Prof. Krafft-Ebbing and the novels of Miles F. You can't yet know what a terrible army with banners you are, you and your eyes and your laughter and your impertinent breasts, like La Maja's, and those anti-educational ears in ambush under the hair. You can't know. But I know. Only too well. Just *how* well you'll realize, per- haps, fifteen or twenty years from now. For a time will come when the freshness of young bodies, the ingenuousness of young minds will begin to strike you as a scandal of shining beauty and attractive- ness, and then finally as a kind of maddeningly alluring perversity, as the exhibition of a kind of irresistibly dangerous vice. The mad- ness of the desirer—for middle-aged desires are mostly more or less mad desires—comes off on the desired object, staining it, de- grading it. Which isn't agreeable if you happen to be fond of the object, as well as desiring. Dear object, let's be a little reasonable— oh, entirely against all my principles; I accept all the reproaches you made me the other day. But what are principles for but to be gone against in moments of crisis? And this *is* a moment of crisis. Con- sider: I'm thirty years older than you are; and even if one doesn't look one's age, one is one's age, somehow, somewhere; and even if one doesn't feel it, fifty's always fifty and twenty-one's twenty-one.

And when you've considered that, let me put a few questions. First: are you prepared to be a disreputable woman? To which, of course, you answer yes, because you don't care two pins about what the old cats say. But I put another question: Do you know, by experience, what it's like to be a disreputable woman? And you must answer, no. Whereupon I retort: If you can't answer yes to the second, you've got no right to answer to the first. And I don't intend to give you the opportunity of answering yes to the second question. Which is all pure Podsnapism. But there are certain circumstances in which Podsnap is quite right.

Sweet Pamela, believe me when I say it would be fatal. For when you say you love me, what do you mean? Who and what is it you love? I'll tell you. You love the author of *Eurydice* and of all those portraits of yourself he's filled his books with. You love the celebrated man, who was not only unsnubbing and attentive, but obviously admiring. Even before you saw him, you vaguely loved his reputation, and now you love his odd confidences. You love a kind of conversation you haven't heard before. You love a weakness in him which you think you can dominate and protect. You love—as I, of course, intended you to love—a certain fascinating manner. You even love a rather romantic and still youthful appearance. And when I say (which as yet, you know, I haven't said) that I love you, what do *I* mean? That I'm amused, and charmed, and flattered, and touched, and puzzled, and affectionate, in a word, a Passionist Father. But chiefly that I find you terribly desirable—an army with banners. Bring these two loves together and what's the result? A manifold disaster. To begin with, the nearer you come to me and the longer you remain with me, the more alien you'll find me, the more fundamentally remote. Inevitably. For you and I are foreigners to one another, foreigners in time. Which is a greater foreignness than the foreignness of space and language. You don't realize it now, because you don't know me—you're only in love, at first sight (like Joan in *Eurydice!*), and what's more, not really with me, with your imagination of me. When you come to know me better—well, you'll find that you know me much worse. And then one day you'll be attracted by a temporal compatriot. Perhaps, indeed, you're attracted already, only your imagination won't allow you to admit it. What about that long-suffering Guy of yours? Of whom I was, and am, so horribly jealous—jealous with the malignity of a weaker for a stronger rival; for though I seem to hold all the cards at the moment, the ace of trumps is his: he's young. And one day, when you're tired of

living at cross purposes with me, you'll suddenly realize it; you'll
perceive that he speaks your language, that he inhabits your world
of thought and feeling, that he belongs, in a word, to your nation—
that great and terrible nation, which I love and fear and hate, the
nation of Youth. In the end, of course, you'll leave the foreigner for
the compatriot. But not before you've inflicted a good deal of suffering on everyone concerned, including yourself. And meanwhile, what
about me? Shall I be still there for you to leave? Who knows? Not
I, at any rate. I can no more answer for my future desires than for
the Shah of Persia. For my future affection, yes. But it may last
(how often, alas, affections do last that way!) only on condition of its
object being absent. There are so many friends whom one's fond
of when they're not there. Will you be one of them? It's the more
possible since, after all, you're just as alien to me as I am to you.
My country's called Middle-Ageia and everyone who was out of the
egg of childhood before 1914 is my compatriot. Through all my
desires, shouldn't I also pine to hear my own language, to speak with
those who share the national traditions? Of course. But the tragedy
of middle-aged life is that its army with banners is hardly ever cap-
tained by a compatriot. Passion is divorced from understanding,
and the aging man's desire attaches itself with an almost insane
violence to precisely those outrageously fresh young bodies that
house the most alien souls. Conversely, for the body of an understood and understanding soul, he seldom feels desire. And now,
Pamela, suppose that my sentiment of your alienness should come
to be stronger (as some time it must) than my desire for the lovely
scandal of your young body. What then? This time I can answer;
for I am answering for a self that changes very little through every
change of circumstances—the self that doesn't intend to put up
with more discomfort than it can possibly avoid; the self that, as the
Freudians tell us, is homesick for that earthly paradise from which
we've all been banished, our mother's womb, the only place on earth
where man is genuinely omnipotent, where his every desire is satisfied, where he is perfectly at home and adapted to his surroundings,
and therefore perfectly happy. Out of the womb we're in an un-
friendly world, in which our wishes aren't anticipated, where we're
no longer magically omnipotent, where we don't fit, where we're
not snugly at home. What's to be done in this world? Either face
out the reality, fight with it, resignedly or heroically accept to suffer
or struggle. Or else flee. In practice even the strongest heroes do a
bit of fleeing—away from responsibility into deliberate ignorance,

away from uncomfortable fact into imagination. Even the strongest. And conversely even the weakest fleers can make themselves strong. No, not the weakest; that's a mistake. The weakest become daydreamers, masturbators, paranoiacs. The strong fleer is one who starts with considerable advantages. Take my case. I'm so endowed by nature that I can have a great many of the prizes of life for the asking—success, money in reasonable quantities, love. In other words I'm not entirely out of the womb; I can still, even in the extrauterine world, have at least some of my desires magically satisfied. To have my wishes fulfilled I don't have to rush off every time to some imaginary womb-substitute. I have the power to construct a womb for myself out of the materials of the real world. But of course it's not a completely perfect and watertight womb; no postnatal uterus can ever in the nature of things be that. It lets in a lot of unpleasantness and alienness and obstruction to wishes. Which I deal with by flight, systematic flight into unawareness, into deliberate ignorance, into irresponsibility. It's a weakness which is a source of strength. For when you can flee at will and with success (which is only possible if nature has granted you, as she has to me, the possibility of anarchic independence of society), what quantities of energy you save, what an enormous amount of emotional and mental wear and tear is spared you! I flee from business by leaving all my affairs in the hands of lawyers and agents, I flee from criticism (both from the humiliations of misplaced and wrongly motived praise and from the pain of even the most contemptible vermin's blame) by simply not reading what anybody writes of me. I flee from time by living as far as possible only in and for the present. I flee from cold weather by taking the train or ship to places where it's warm. And from women I don't love any more, I flee by just silently vanishing. For, like Palmerston, I never explain and never apologize. I just fade out. I decline to admit their existence. I consign their letters to the wastepaper basket, along with the press cuttings. Simple, crude even, but incredibly effective, if one's ready to be ruthless in one's weakness, as I am. Yes, quite ruthless, Pamela. If my desire grew weary or I felt homesick for the company of my compatriots, I'd just run away, determinedly, however painfully much you might still be in love with me, or your imagination, or your own hurt pride and humiliated self-love. And you, I fancy, would have as little mercy on my desires if they should happen to outlive what you imagine to be your passion for me. So that our love affair, if we were fools enough to embark on it, would be a race toward a series of successive goals—a race through boredom, misunderstanding, disillusion, toward the final winning post of cruelty and betrayal. Which of us is likely to win the race? The betting, I should say, is about even, with a slight tendency in favor of myself. But there's not going to be a winner or a loser, for the good reason that there's not going to be any race. I'm too fond of you, Pamela, to . . .

"Miles!"

Fanning started so violently that a drop of ink was jerked from his pen onto the paper. He felt as though his heart had fallen into an awful gulf of emptiness.

"Miles!"

He looked round. Two hands were clutching the bars of the unshuttered window and, as though desperately essaying to emerge from a subterranean captivity, the upper part of a face was peering in, over the high sill, with wide unhappy eyes.

"But Pamela!" There was reproach in his astonishment.

It was to the implied rebuke that she penitently answered. "I couldn't help it, Miles," she said; and, behind the bars, he saw her reddened eyes suddenly brighten and overflow with tears. "I simply had to come." Her voice trembled on the verge of breaking. "Had to."

The tears, her words and that unhappy voice were moving. But he didn't want to be moved, he was angry with himself for feeling the emotion, with her for inspiring it. "But, my dear child!" he began, and the reproach in his voice had shrilled to a kind of exasperation—the exasperation of one who feels himself hemmed in and helpless, increasingly helpless, against circumstances. "But I thought we'd settled," he began and broke off. He rose, and walked agitatedly toward the fireplace, agitatedly back again, like a beast in a cage; he was caught, hemmed in between those tearful eyes behind the bars and his own pity, with all those dangerous feelings that have their root in pity. "I thought," he began once more.

But, "Oh!" came her sharp cry, and looking again toward the window he saw that only the two small hands and a pair of straining wrists were visible. The tragical face had vanished.

"Pamela?"

"It's all right." Her voice came rather muffled and remote. "I slipped. I was standing on a little kind of ledge affair. The window's so high from the ground," she added plaintively.

"My poor child!" he said on a little laugh of amused commiseration. The reproach, the exasperation had gone out of his voice. He was conquered by the comic patheticness of her. Hanging onto the bars with those small, those rather red and childishly untended hands! And tumbling off the perch she had had to climb on, because the window was so high from the ground! A wave of sentimentality submerged him. "I'll come and open the door." He ran into the hall.

Waiting outside in the darkness, she heard the bolts being shot back, one by one. Clank, clank! and then "Damn!" came his voice from the other side of the door. "These things are so stiff. . . . I'm barricaded up as though I were in a safe." She stood there waiting. The door shook as he tugged at the recalcitrant bolt. The waiting seemed interminable. And all at once a huge, black weariness settled on her. The energy of wrought-up despair deserted her and she was left empty of everything but a tired misery. What was the good, what was the good of coming like this to be turned away again? For he *would* turn her away; he didn't want her. What was the good of renewing suffering, of once more dying?

"Hell and Death!" On the other side of the door Fanning was cursing like an Elizabethan.

Hell and Death. The words reverberated in Pamela's mind. The pains of Hell, the darkness and dissolution of Death. What was the good?

Clank! Another bolt had gone back. "Thank goodness. We're almost . . ." A chain rattled. At the sound Pamela turned and ran in a blind terror down the dimly lighted street.

"At last!" The door swung back and Fanning stepped out. But the sentimental tenderness of his outstretched hands wasted itself on an empty night. Twenty yards away a pair of pale legs twinkled in the darkness. "Pamela!" he called in astonishment. "What the devil . . . ?" The wasting on emptiness of his feelings had startled him into annoyance. He felt like one who has put forth all his strength to strike something, and, missing his aim, swipes the unresisting air, grotesquely. "Pamela!" he called again, yet louder.

She did not turn at the sound of his voice, but ran on. These wretched high-heeled shoes! "Pamela!" And then came the sound of his pursuing footsteps. She tried to run faster. But the pursuing footsteps came nearer and nearer. It was no good. Nothing was any good. She slackened her speed to a walk.

"But what on earth?" he asked from just behind her, almost angrily. Pursuing, he had called up within him the soul of a pursuer, angry and desirous. "What on earth?" And suddenly his hand was on her shoulder. She trembled a little at the touch. "But why?" he insisted. "Why do you suddenly run away?"

But Pamela only shook her averted head. She wouldn't speak, wouldn't meet his eyes. Fanning looked down at her intently, questioningly. Why? And as he looked at that weary hopeless face, he began to divine the reason. The anger of the pursuit subsided in him. Respecting her dumb, averted misery, he too was silent. He drew her comfortingly toward him. His arm round her shoulders, Pamela suffered herself to be led back toward the house.

Which would be best, he was wondering with the surface of his mind: to telephone for a taxi to take her back to the hotel, or to see if he could make up a bed for her in one of the upstairs rooms? But in the depths of his being he knew quite well that he would do neither of these things. He knew that he would be her lover. And yet, in spite of this deep knowledge, the surface mind still continued to discuss its little problem of cabs and bed linen. Discussed it sensibly, discussed it dutifully. Because it would be a madness, he told himself, a criminal madness if he didn't send for the taxi or prepare that upstairs room. But the dark certainty of the depths rose suddenly and exploded at the surface in a bubble of ironic laughter, in a brutal and cynical word. "Comedian!" he said to himself, to the self that agitatedly thought of telephones and taxis and pillow slips. "Seeing that it's obvious I'm going to have her." And, rising from the depths, her nakedness presented itself to him palpably in an integral and immediate contact with his whole being. But this was shameful, shameful. He pushed the naked Anadyomene back into the depths. Very well, then (his surface mind resumed its busy efficient rattle), seeing that it was perhaps rather late to start telephoning for taxis, he'd rig up one of the rooms on the first floor. But if he couldn't find any sheets . . . ? But here was the house, the open door.

Pamela stepped across the threshold. The hall was almost dark. Through a curtained doorway on the left issued a thin blade of yellow light. Passive in her tired misery, she waited. Behind her the chain rattled, as it had rattled only a few moments before, when she had fled from the ominous sound, and clank, clank! the bolts were thrust back into place.

"There," said Fanning's voice. "And now . . ." With a click, the darkness yielded suddenly to brilliant light.

Pamela uttered a little cry and covered her face with her hands. "Oh, please," she begged, "please." The light hurt her, was a sort of outrage. She didn't want to see, couldn't bear to be seen.

"I'm sorry," he said, and the comforting darkness returned. "This way." Taking her arm he led her toward the lighted doorway on the left. "Shut your eyes," he commanded, as they approached the curtain. "We've got to go into light again; but I'll turn it out the moment I can get to the switch. Now!" She shut her eyes and suddenly, as the curtain rings rattled, she saw, through her closed eyelids, the red shining of transparent blood. Still holding her arm, he led her forward into the room.

Pamela lifted her free hand to her face. "Please don't look at me," she whispered. "I don't want you to see me like this. I mean, I couldn't bear . . ." Her voice faded to silence.

"I won't look," he assured her. "And anyhow," he added, when they had taken two or three more steps across the room, "now I can't." And he turned the switch.

The pale translucent red went black again before her eyes. Pamela sighed. "I'm so tired," she whispered. Her eyes were still shut; she was too tired to open them.

"Take off your coat." A hand pulled at her sleeve. First one bare arm, then the other slipped out into the coolness.

Fanning threw the coat over a chair. Turning back, he could see her, by the tempered darkness that entered through the window, standing motionless before him, passive, wearily waiting, her face, her limp arms pale against the shadowy blackness.

"Poor Pamela," she heard him say, and then suddenly light finger tips were sliding in a moth-winged caress along her arm. "You'd better lie down and rest." The hand closed round her arm, she was pushed gently forward. That taxi, he was still thinking, the upstairs room . . . But his fingers preserved the silky memory of her skin; the flesh of her arm was warm and firm against his palm. In the darkness, the supernatural world was coming mysteriously, thrillingly into eixstence; he was once more standing upon its threshold.

"There, sit down," came his voice. She obeyed; a low divan received her. "Lean back." She let herself fall onto pillows. Her feet were lifted onto the couch. She lay quite still. "As though I were dead," she thought, "as though I were dead." She was aware, through the darkness of her closed eyes, of his warm breathing presence, impending and very near. "As though I were dead," she inwardly repeated with a kind of pleasure. For the pain of her misery had ebbed away into the warm darkness, and to be tired, she found, to be utterly tired and to lie there utterly still were pleasures. "As though I were dead." And the light reiterated touch of his finger tips along her arm—what were those caresses but another mode, a soothing and delicious mode, of gently dying?

In the morning, on his way to the kitchen to prepare their coffee, Fanning caught sight of his littered writing table. He halted to collect the scattered sheets. Waiting for the water to boil, he read. "By the time you receive this letter, I shall be—no, not dead, Pamela . . ." He crumbled up each page as he had finished reading it and threw it into the dustbin.

IX

The architectural background was like something out of Alma Tadema. But the figures that moved across the sunlit atrium, that lingered beneath the colonnades and in the colored shadow of the awnings, the figures were Hogarthian and Rowlandsonian, were the ferocious satires of Daumier and Rouveyre. Huge jellied females overflowed the chairs on which they sat. Sagging and with the gait of gorged bears, old men went slowly shambling down the porticoes. Like princes preceded by their outriders, the rich fat burgesses strutted with dignity behind their bellies. There was a hungry prowling of gaunt emaciated men and women, yellow-skinned and with tragical, bile-injected eyes. And, conspicuous by their trailing blackness, these bloated or cadaverous pencilings from an anti-clerical notebook were priests.

In the midst of so many monsters Pamela was a lovely miracle of health and beauty. These three months had subtly transformed her. The rather wavering and intermittent *savoir-vivre*, the child's forced easiness of manner, had given place to a woman's certainty, to that of repose even in action, that decision even in repose, which are the ordinary fruits of the intimate knowledge, the physical understanding of love.

"For it isn't only murder that will out," as Fanning had remarked some few days after the evening of the fireworks. "It isn't only murder. If you could see yourself, my child! It's almost indecent. Anyone could tell that you'd been in bed with your lover. Could tell in the dark, even; you're luminous, positively luminous. All shining and smooth and pearly with love making. It's really an embarrassment to walk about with you. I've a good mind to make you wear a veil."

She had laughed, delightedly. "But I don't mind them seeing. I want them to see. I mean, why should one be ashamed of being happy?"

That had been three months since. At present she had no happiness to be ashamed of. It was by no shining of eyes, no luminous soft pearliness of smoothed and rounded contour that she now betrayed herself. All that her manner, her pose, her gestures proclaimed was the fact that there *had* been such shinings and pearly smoothings, once. As for the present, her shut and sullen face announced only that she was discontented with it and with the man who, sitting beside her, was the symbol and the embodiment of that unsatisfactory present. A rather sickly embodiment at the moment, a thin and jaundiced symbol. For Fanning was hollow-cheeked, his eyes darkly ringed, his skin pale and sallow under the yellowed tan. He was on his way to becoming one of those pump-room monsters at whom they were now looking, almost incredulously. For, "Incredible!" was Fanning's comment. "Didn't I tell you that they simply weren't to be believed?"

Pamela shrugged her shoulders, almost imperceptibly, and did not answer. She did not feel like answering, she wanted to be uninterested, sullen, bored.

"How right old Butler was!" he went on, rousing himself by the stimulus of his own talk from the depression into which his liver and Pamela had plunged him. "Making the Erewhonians punish illness as a crime—how right! Because they are criminals, all these people. Criminally ugly and deformed, criminally incapable of enjoyment. Look at them. It's a caution. And when I think that I'm one of them . . ." He shook his head. "But let's hope this will make me a reformed character." And he emptied, with a grimace of disgust, his glass of tepid salt water. "Revolting! But I suppose it's right that Montecatini should be a place of punishment as well as cure. One can't be allowed to commit jaundice with impunity. I must go and get another glass of my punishment—my purgatory, in every sense of the word," he added, smiling at his own joke. He rose to his feet painfully (every moment was now a painful effort for him) and left her, threading his way through the crowd to where, behind their marble counters, the pump-room barmaids dispensed warm laxatives from rows of polished brass taps.

The animation had died out of Fanning's face as he turned away. No longer distracted and self-stimulated by talk, he relapsed at once into melancholy. Waiting his turn behind two bulging monsignori at the pump, he looked so gloomily wretched that a passing connoisseur of the waters pointed him out to his companion as a typical example of the hepatic pessimist. But bile, as a matter of fact, was not the only cause of Fanning's depression. There was also Pamela. And Pamela—he admitted it, though the fact belonged to that great class of humiliating phenomena whose existence we are always trying to ignore—Pamela, after all, was the cause of the bile. For if he had not been so extenuated by that crazy love making in the narrow cells of the Passionist Fathers at Monte Cavo, he would never have taken chill and the chill would never have settled on his liver and turned to jaundice. As it was, however, that night of the full moon had finished him. They had gone out, groping their way through the terrors of the nocturnal woods, to a little grassy terrace among the bushes, from which there was a view of Nemi. Deep sunk in its socket of impenetrable darkness and more than half eclipsed by shadow, the eye of water gleamed up at them secretly, as though through eyelids almost closed. Under the brightness of the moon, the hills, the woods seemed to be struggling out of ghostly grayness toward color, toward the warmth of life. They had sat there for a while, in silence, looking. Then, taking her in his arms, " '*Ceda al tatto la vista, al labro il lume*' " he had quoted with a kind of mockery—mocking her for the surrender to which he knew he could bring her, even against her will, even though, as he could see, she had made up her mind to sulk at him, mocking himself at the same time for the folly which drove him, weary and undesiring, to make the gesture. " '*Al labro il lume,*' " he repeated, with that undercurrent of derision in his voice, and leaned toward her. Desire returned to him as he touched her, and with it a kind of exultation, a renewal (temporary, he knew, and illusory) of all his energies.

"No, Miles. Don't. I don't want . . ." And she had averted her face, for she was angry, resentful, she wanted to sulk. Fanning knew it, mockingly, and mockingly he had turned back her face toward him—"*al labro il lume*"—and found her lips. She struggled a little in his arms, protested, and then was silent, lay still. His kisses had had the power to transform her. She was another person, different from the one who had sulked and been resentful. Or rather she was two people—the sulky and resentful one, with another person superimposed, a person who quiveringly sank and melted under his kisses, melted and sank down, down toward that mystical death, that apocalypse, that almost terrible transfiguration. But beneath, to one side, stood always the angry sulker, unappeased, unreconciled, ready to emerge again (full of new resentment for the way she had been undignifiedly hustled off the stage) the moment the other should have retired. His realization of this made Fanning all the more perversely ardent, quickened the folly of his passion with a kind of derisive hostility. He drew his lips across her cheek and suddenly their soft electrical touch on her ear made her shudder. "Don't!" she implored, dreading and yet desiring what was to come. Gently, inexorably his teeth closed, and the petal of cartilage was a firm elastic resistance between them. She shuddered yet more violently. Fanning relaxed the muscles of his jaws, then tightened them once more, gently, against that exquisite resistance. The felt beauty of rounded warmth and resilience was under his hand. In the darkness they were inhabitants of the supernatural world.

But at midnight they had found themselves, almost suddenly, on earth again, shiveringly cold under the moon. Cold, cold to the quick, Fanning had picked himself up. They stumbled homeward through the woods, in silence. It was in a kind of trance of chilled and sickened exhaustion that he had at last dropped down on his bed in the convent

cell. Next morning he was ill. The liver was always his weak point. That
had been nearly three weeks ago.

The second of the two monsignori moved away; Fanning stepped into
his place. The barmaid handed him his hot dilute sulphate of soda. He
deposited fifty centesimi as a largess and walked off, meditatively sipping.
But returning to the place from which he had come, he found their
chairs occupied by a pair of obese Milanese businessmen. Pamela had
gone. He explored the Alma Tadema background; but there was no sign
of her. She had evidently gone back to the hotel. Fanning, who still had
five more glasses of water to get through, took his place among the monsters round the bandstand.

In her room at the hotel Pamela was writing up her diary. "September
20th. Montecatini seems a beastly sort of hole, particularly if you come
to a wretched little hotel like this, which M. insisted on doing, because
he knows the proprietor, who is an old drunkard and also cooks the meals,
and M. has long talks with him and says he's like a character in Shakespeare, which is all very well, but I'd prefer food and a room with a bath,
not to mention the awfulness of the other people in the hotel, one of
whom is the chief undertaker in Florence, who's always boasting to the
other people at mealtimes about his business and what a fine motor
hearse with gilded angels he's got and the number of counts and dukes
he's buried. M. had a long conversation with him and the old drunkard
after dinner yesterday evening about how you preserve a corpse on ice
and the way to make money by buying up the best sites at the cemetery
and holding them till you could ask five times as much as you paid, and
it was the first time I'd seen him looking cheerful and amused since his
illness and even for some time before, but I was so horrified that I went
off to bed. This morning at eight to the pump room, where M. has to
drink eight glasses of different kinds of water before breakfast and there
are hundreds of hideous people all carrying mugs, and huge fountains
of purgatives, and a band playing the 'Geisha,' so I came away after half
an hour, leaving M. to his waters, because I really can't be expected to
watch him drinking, and it appears there are six hundred W.C.'s"

She laid down her pen and, turning round in her chair, sat for some
time pensively staring at her own reflection in the wardrobe mirror. "If
you look long enough" (she heard Clare's voice, she saw Clare, inwardly, sitting at her dressing table), "you begin to wonder if it isn't
somebody else. And perhaps, after all, one is somebody else, all the time."
Somebody else, Pamela repeated to herself, somebody else. But was that
a spot on her cheek, or a mosquito bite? A mosquito, thank goodness.
"Oh God," she said aloud, and in the looking glass somebody else moved

her lips, "if only I knew what to do! If only I were dead!" She touched
wood hastily. Stupid to say such things. But if only one knew, one were
certain! All at once she gave a little stiff sharp shudder of disgust, she
grimaced as though she had bitten on something sour. Oh, oh! she
groaned; for she had suddenly seen herself in the act of dressing, there,
in the moon-flecked darkness, among the bushes, that hateful night just
before Miles fell ill. Furious because he'd humiliated her, hating him;
she hadn't wanted to and he'd made her. Somebody else had enjoyed
beyond the limits of enjoyment, had suffered a pleasure transmuted into
its opposite. Or rather she had done the suffering. And then that further
humiliation of having to ask him to help her look for her suspender
belt! And there were leaves in her hair. And when she got back to the
hotel, she found a spider squashed against her skin under the chemise.
Yes, she had found the spider, not somebody else.

Between the brackish sips Fanning was reading in his pocket edition
of the Paradiso. "L' acqua che prendo giammai non si corse," he murmured;

> Minerva spira e conducemi Apollo,
> e nove Muse mi dimostran l'Orse.

He closed his eyes. "E nove Muse mi dimostran l'Orse." What a marvel!
"And the nine Muses point me to the Bears." Even translated the spell
did not entirely lose its potency. "How glad I shall be," he thought, "to
be able to do a little work again."

"Il caffè?" said a voice at his elbow. "Non lo bevo mai, mai. Per il
fegato, sa, è pessimo. Si dice anche che per gl'intestini . . ." The voice
receded out of hearing.

Fanning took another gulp of salt water and resumed his reading.

> Voi altri pochi che drizzante il collo
> per tempo al pan degli angeli, del quale
> vivesi qui ma non sen vien satollo . . .

The voice had returned. "Pesce bollito, carne ai ferri o arrostita, patate
lesse . . ."

He shut his ears and continued. But when he came to

> La concreata e perpetua sete
> del deiforme regno,

he had to stop again. This craning for angels' bread, this thirsting for
the godlike kingdom . . . The words reverberated questioningly in his

mind. After all, why not? Particularly when man's bread made you sick (he thought with horror of that dreadful vomiting of bile), when it was a case of *pesce bollito* and you weren't allowed to thirst for anything more palatable than this stuff. (He swigged again.) These were the circumstances when Christianity became appropriate. Christians, according to Pascal, ought to live like sick men; conversely, sick men can hardly escape being Christians. How pleased Colin Judd would be! But the thought of Colin was depressing; if only all Christians were like Dante! But in that case, what a frightful world it would be! Frightful.

> *La concreata e perpetua sete*
> *del deiforme regno cen portava*
> *Veloci, quasi come il ciel vedete.*
> *Beatrice in suso ed io in lei guardava. . . .*

He thought of Pamela at the fireworks. On that pedestal. *Ben son, ben son Beatrice* on that pedestal. He remembered what he had said beneath the blossoming of the rockets; and also what he had meant to say about those legs which the pedestal made it so easy for the worshiper to pinch. Those legs, how remote now, how utterly irrelevant! He finished off his third glass of Torretta and, rising, made his way to the bar for his first of Regina. Yes, how utterly irrelevant! he thought. A complete solution of continuity. You were on the leg level, then you vomited bile, and as soon as you were able to think of anything but vomiting, you found yourself on the Dante level. He handed his mug to the barmaid. She rolled black eyes at him as she filled it. Some liverish gentlemen, it seemed, could still feel amorous. Or perhaps it was only the obese ones. Fanning deposited his offering and retired. Irrelevant, irrelevant. It seemed, now, the unlikeliest story. And yet there it was, a fact. And Pamela was solid, too, too solid.

Phrases floated up, neat and ready-made, to the surface of his mind. "What does he see in her? What on earth can she see in him?"

"But it's not a question of sight, it's a question of touch."

And he remembered—*sentiments-centimètres*—that French pun about love, so appallingly cynical, so humiliatingly true. "But only humiliating," he assured himself, "because we choose to think it so, arbitrarily, only cynical because *Beatrice in suso ed io in lei guardava*; only appalling because we're creatures who sometimes vomit bile and because, even without vomiting, we sometimes feel ourselves naturally Christians." But in any case, *nove Muse mi dimostran l'Orse.* Meanwhile, however . . . He tilted another gill of water down his throat. And when he was well enough to work, wouldn't he also be well enough to thirst again for that other godlike kingdom, with its different ecstasies, its other peace beyond all understanding? But *tant mieux, tant mieux,* so long as the Bears remained unmoved and the Muses went on pointing.

Pamela was looking through her diary. "June 24th," she read. "Spent the evening with M. and afterward he said how lucky it was for me that I'd been seduced by him, which hurt my feelings (that word, I mean) and also rather annoyed me, so I said he certainly hadn't seduced me, and he said, all right, if I liked to say that I'd seduced him, he didn't mind, but anyhow it was lucky because almost anybody else wouldn't have been such a good psychologist as he, not to mention physiologist, and I should have hated it. But I said, how could he say such things? because it wasn't that at all and I was happy because I loved him, but M. laughed and said, you don't, and I said, I do, and he said, you don't, but if it gives you any pleasure to imagine you do, imagine, which upset me still more, his not believing, which is due to his not wanting to love himself, because I *do* love . . ."

Pamela quickly turned the page. She couldn't read that sort of thing now.

"June 25th. Went to the Vatican where M. . . ." She skipped nearly a page of Miles's remarks on classical art and the significance of orgies in the ancient religions; on the duty of being happy and having the sun inside you, like a bunch of ripe grapes; on making the world appear infinite and holy by an improvement of sensual enjoyment; on taking things untragically, unponderously.

"M. dined out and I spent the evening with Guy, the first time since the night of the fireworks, and he asked me what I'd been doing all this time, so I said, nothing in particular, but I felt myself blushing, and he said, anyhow you look extraordinarily well and happy and pretty, which also made me rather uncomfortable, because of what M. said the other day about murder will out, but then I laughed, because it was the only thing to do, and Guy asked what I was laughing about, so I said, nothing, but I could see by the way he looked at me that he was rather thrilled, which pleased me, and we had a very nice dinner and he told me about a girl he'd been in love with in Ireland and it seems they went camping together for a week, but he was never her lover because she had a kind of terror of being touched, but afterward she went to America and got married. Later on, in the taxi, he took my hand and even tried to kiss me, but I laughed, because it was somehow very funny, I don't know why, but afterward, when he persisted, I got angry with him.

"June 27th. Went to look at mosaics today, rather fine, but what a pity they're all in churches and always pictures of Jesus and sheep and apostles and so forth. On the way home we passed a wine shop and M. went in and ordered a dozen bottles of champagne, because he said that love can exist without passion, or understanding, or respect, but not without champagne. So I asked him if he really loved me, and he said, *Je t'adore*, in French, but I said, no, do you really *love* me? But he said, silence is golden and it's better to use one's mouth for kissing and drinking champagne and eating caviar, because he'd also bought some caviar; and if you start talking about love and thinking about love, you get everything wrong, because it's not *meant* to be talked about, but acted, and if people want to talk and think they'd better talk about mosaics and that sort of thing. But I still went on asking him if he loved me. . . ."

"Fool, fool!" said Pamela aloud. She was ashamed of herself. Dithering on like that! At any rate Miles had been honest; she had to admit that. He'd taken care to keep the thing on the champagne level. And he'd always told her that she was imagining it all. Which had been intolerable, of course; he'd been wrong to be so right. She remembered how she had cried when he refused to answer her insistent question; had cried and afterward allowed herself to be consoled. They went back to his house for supper; he opened a bottle of champagne, they ate the caviar. Next day he sent her that poem. It had arrived at the same time as some flowers from Guy. She reopened her notebook. Here it was.

> At the red fountain's core the thud of drums
> Quickens; for hairy-footed moths explore
> This aviary of nerves; the woken birds
> Flutter and cry in the branched blood; a bee
> Hums with his million-times-repeated stroke
> On lips your breast promotes geometers
> To measure curves, to take the height of mountains,
> The depth and silken slant of dells unseen.
> I read your youth, as the blind student spells
> With finger tips the song from *Cymbeline*.
> Caressing and caressed, my hands perceive
> (In lieu of eyes) old Titian's paradise
> With Eve unaproned; and the Maja dressed
> Whisks off her muslins, that my skin may know
> The blind night's beauty of brooding heat and cool,
> Of silk and fiber, of molten-moist and dry,
> Resistance and resilience.

But the drum
Throbs with yet faster beat, the wild birds go
Through their red liquid sky with wings yet more
Frantic and yet more desperate crying. Come!
The magical door its soft and breathing valves
Has set ajar. Beyond the threshold lie
Worlds after worlds receding into light,
As rare old wines on the ravished tongue renew
A miracle that deepens, that expands,
Blossoms, and changes hue, and chimes, and shines.
Birds in the blood and doubled drums incite
Us to the conquest of these new, strange lands
Beyond the threshold, where all common times,
Things, places, thoughts, events expire, and life
Enters eternity.

The darkness stirs, the trees are wet with rain;
Knock and it shall be opened, oh, again,
Again! The child is eager for its dam
And I the mother am of thirsty lips,
Oh, knock again!
Wild darkness wets this sound of strings.
How smooth it slides among the clarinets,
How easily slips through the trumpetings!
Sound glides through sound, and lo! the apocalypse,
The burst of wings above a sunlit sea.
Must this eternal music make an end?
Prolong, prolong these all but final chords!
Oh, wounded sevenths, breathlessly suspend
Our fear of dying, our desire to know
The song's last words!
Almost Bethesda sleeps, uneasily.
A bubble domes the flatness; gyre on gyre,
The waves expand, expire, as in the deeps
The woken spring subsides.
                              Play, music, play!
Reckless of death, a singing giant rides
His storm of music, rides; and suddenly
The tremulous mirror of the moon is broken;
On the farthest beaches of our soul, our flesh,
The tides of pleasure foaming into pain

Mount, hugely mount; break; and retire again.
The final word is sung, the last word spoken.

"Do I like it, or do I rather hate it? I don't know."

"June 28th. When I saw M. at lunch today, I told him I didn't really
know if I liked his poem, I mean apart from literature, and he said, yes,
perhaps the young are more romantic than they think, which rather annoyed me, because I believe he imagined I was shocked, which is too
ridiculous. All the same, I don't like it."

Pamela sighed and shut her eyes, so as to be able to think more
privately, without distractions. From this distance of time she could see
all that had happened in perspective, as it were, and as a whole. It was
her pride, she could see, her fear of looking ridiculously romantic that
had changed the quality of her feelings toward Miles—a pride and a fear
on which he had played, deliberately. She had given herself with passion
and desperately, tragically, as she imagined that Joan would have desperately given herself, at first sight, to a reluctant Walter. But the love
he had offered her in return was a thing of laughter and frank, admitted
sensuality, was a gay and easy companionship enriched, but uncompli-
cated, by pleasure. From the first he had refused to come up to her emotional level. From the first he had taken it for granted—and his taking
it for granted was in itself an act of moral compulsion—that she should
descend to his. And she had descended—reluctantly at first, but afterward without a struggle. For she came to realize, almost suddenly, that
after all she didn't really love him in the tragically passionate way she
had supposed she loved him. In a propitious emotional climate her belief
that she was a despairing Joan might perhaps have survived, at any rate
for a time. But it was a hothouse growth of the imagination; in the
cool dry air of his laughter and cheerfully cynical frankness it had withered. And all at once she had found herself, not satisfied, indeed, with
what he offered, but superficially content. She returned him what he
gave. Less even than he gave. For soon it became apparent to her that
their roles were being reversed, that the desperate one was no longer
herself, but Miles. For "desperate"—that was the only word to describe
the quality of his desires. From light and gay—and perhaps, she thought,
the lightness had been forced, the gaiety fabricated for the occasion as a
defense against the tragical vehemence of her attack and of his own
desires—his sensuality had become heavy, serious, intense. She had
found herself the object of a kind of focused rage. It had been frightening
sometimes, frightening and rather humiliating; for she had often felt

that, so far as he was concerned, she wasn't there at all; that the body between those strong, those ruthless and yet delicate, erudite, subtly intelligent hands of his, that were like a surgeon's or a sculptor's hands, was not her body, was no one's body, indeed, but a kind of abstraction, tangible, yes, desperately tangible, but still an abstraction. She would have liked to rebel; but the surgeon was a master of his craft, the sculptor's fingers were delicately learned and intelligent. He had the art to overcome her reluctances, to infect her with some of his strange, concentrated seriousness. Against her will. In the intervals he resumed his old manner; but the laughter was apt to be bitter and spiteful, there was a mocking brutality in the frankness.

Pamela squeezed her eyes more tightly shut and shook her head, frowning at her memories. For distraction she turned back to her diary.

"June 30th. Lunched with Guy, who was really rather tiresome, because what is more boring than somebody being in love with you when you're not in love with them? Which I told him quite frankly, and I could see he was dreadfully upset, but what was I to do?"

Poor Guy! she thought, and she was indignant, not with herself, but with Fanning. She turned over several pages. It was July now and they were at Ostia for the bathing. It was at Ostia that that desperate seriousness had come into his desire. The long hot hours of the siesta were propitious to his earnest madness. Propitious also to his talents, for he worked well in the heat. Behind her lowered eyelids Pamela had a vision of him sitting at his table, stripped to a pair of shorts, sitting there, pen in hand, in the next room and with an open door between them, but somehow at an infinite distance. Terrifyingly remote, a stranger more foreign for being known so well, the inhabitant of other worlds to which she had no access. They were worlds which she was already beginning to hate. His books were splendid, of course; still, it wasn't much fun being with a man who, for half the time, wasn't there at all. She saw him sitting there, a beautiful naked stranger, brown and wiry, with a face like brown marble, stonily focused on his paper. And then suddenly this stranger rose and came toward her through the door, across the room. "Well?" she heard herself saying. But the stranger did not answer. Sitting down on the edge of her bed, he took the sewing out of her hands and threw it aside onto the dressing table. She tried to protest, but he laid a hand on her mouth. Wordlessly he shook his head. Then, uncovering her mouth, he kissed her. Under his surgeon's, his sculptor's hands, her body was molded to a symbol of pleasure. His face was focused and intent, but not on her, on something else, and serious, serious, like a martyr's, like a mathematician's, like a criminal's. An hour later he was back at his table in the next room, in the next world, remote, a stranger once again —but he had never ceased to be a stranger.

Pamela turned over two or three more pages. On July 12th they went sailing and she had felt sick; Miles had been provokingly well all the time. The whole of the sixteenth had been spent in Rome. On the nineteenth they drove to Cerveteri to see the Etruscan tombs. She had been furious with him, because he had put out the lamp and made horrible noises in the cold sepulchral darkness, underground—furious with terror, for she hated the dark.

Impatiently Pamela went on turning the pages. There was no point in reading; none of the really important things were recorded. Of the earnest madness of his love making, of those hands, that reluctantly suffered pleasure, she hadn't been able to bring herself to write. And yet those were the things that mattered. She remembered how she had tried to imagine that she was like her namesake of *Pastures New*—the fatal woman whose cool detachment gives her such power over her lovers. But the facts had proved too stubborn; it was simply impossible for her to pretend that this handsome fancy-picture was her portrait. The days flicked past under her thumb.

"July 30th. On the beach this morning we met some friends of M.'s, a journalist called Pedder, who has just come to Rome as correspondent for some paper or other, and his wife; rather awful, I thought, both of them, but M. seemed to be extraordinarily pleased to see them, and they bathed with us and afterward came and had lunch at our hotel, which was rather boring so far as I was concerned, because they talked a lot about people I didn't know, and then there was a long discussion about politics and history and so forth, *too* highbrow, but what was intolerable was that the woman thought she ought to be kind and talk to me meanwhile about something I could understand, so she talked about shops in Rome and the best places for getting clothes, which was rather ridiculous, as she's obviously one of those absurd arty women, who appeared in M.'s novels as young girls just before and during the War, so advanced in those days, with extraordinary colored stockings and frocks like pictures by Augustus John. Anyhow, what she was wearing at lunch was really too fancy-dress, and really at her age one ought to have a little more sense of the decencies, because she must have been quite thirty-five. So that the idea of talking about smart shops in Rome was quite ludicrous to start with, and anyhow it was so insulting to me, because it implied that I was too young and half-witted to be able to take an interest in their beastly conversation. But afterward, apropos of some philosophical theory or other, M. began talking about his opium smoking, and he told them all the things he'd told me and a lot more besides, and it made me feel very uncomfortable and then miserable and rather angry, because I thought it was only me he talked to like that, so confidentially, but now I see he makes confidences to everybody and it's not a sign of his being particularly fond of a person, or in love with them, or anything like that. Which made me realize that I'm even less important to him than I thought, and I found I minded much more than I expected I should mind, because I thought I'd got past minding. But I do mind."

Pamela shut her eyes again. "I ought to have gone away then," she said to herself. "Gone straight away." But instead of retiring, she had tried to come closer. Her resentment—for oh, how bitterly she resented those Pedders and his confidential manner toward them!—had quickened her love. She wanted to insist on being more specially favored than a mere Pedder; and, loving him, she had the right to insist. By a process of imaginative incubation, she managed to revive some of the emotions she had felt before the night of the fireworks. Tragically, with a suicide's determination, she tried to force herself upon him. Fanning fought a retreating battle, ruthlessly. Oh, how cruel he could be, Pamela was thinking, how pitilessly cruel! The way he could shut himself up as though in an iron box of indifference! The way he could just fade out into absent silence, into another world! The way he could flutter out of an embarrassing emotional situation on the wings of some brilliant irrelevance! And the way he could flutter back again, the way he could compel you, with his charm, with the touch of his hands, to reopen the gates of your life to him, when you'd made up your mind to shut them against him forever! And not content with forcing you to yield, he would mock you for your surrender, mock himself, too, for having attacked—jeering, but without seeming to jeer, indirectly, in some terrible little generalization about the weakness of the human soul, the follies and insanities of the body. Yes, how cruel he could be! She reopened her eyes.

"August 10th. M. still very glum and depressed and silent, like a wall when I come near. I think he sometimes hates me for loving him. At lunch he said he'd got to go into Rome this afternoon, and he went and didn't come back till late, almost midnight. Waiting for him, I couldn't help crying."

"August 11th. Those Pedders came to lunch again today and all M.'s glumness vanished the moment he saw them and he was charming all through lunch and so amusing, that I couldn't help laughing, though I felt more like crying, because why should he be so much nicer and more *friendly* with them than with me? After lunch, when we went to rest, he came into my room and wanted to kiss me, but I wouldn't let him, because I said, I don't want to owe your fits of niceness to some-body else, and I asked him, why? why was he so much nicer to them than to me? And he said they were his people, they belonged to the same time as he did and meeting them was like meeting another English-man in the middle of a crowd of Kaffirs in Africa. So I said, I suppose I'm the Kaffirs, and he laughed and said, no, not quite Kaffirs, not more than a Rotary Club dinner in Kansas City, with the Pedders playing the part of a man one had known at Balliol in 'ninety-nine. Which made me cry, and he sat on the edge of the bed and took my hand and said he was very sorry, but that's what life was like, and it couldn't be helped, because time was always time, but people weren't always the same people, but sometimes one person and sometimes another, some-times Pedder-fanciers and sometimes Pamela-fanciers, and it wasn't my fault that I hadn't heard the first performance of *Pelléas* in 1902 and it wasn't Pedder's fault that he had, and therefore Pedder was his com-patriot and I wasn't. But I said, after all, Miles, you're my lover, doesn't that make any difference? But he said, it's a question of speech, and bodies don't speak, only minds, and when two minds are of different ages it's hard for them to understand each other when they speak, but bodies can understand each other, because they don't talk, thank God, he said, because it's such a comfort to stop talking sometimes, to stop thinking and just *be*, for a change. But I said that might be all right for him, but just *being* was my ordinary life and the change for me was talking, was being friends with somebody who knew how to talk and do all the other things talking implies, and I'd imagined I was that, besides just being somebody he went to bed with, and that was why I was so miserable, because I found I wasn't, and those beastly Pedders were. But he said, damn the Pedders, damn the Pedders for making you cry! and he was so *divinely* sweet and gentle that it was like gradually sinking, sinking and being drowned. But afterward he began laughing again in that rather hurting way, and he said, your body's so much more beautiful than their minds—that is, so long as one's a Pamela-fancier; which I am, he said, or rather was and shall be, but now I must go and work, and he got up and went to his room, and I was wretched again."

The entries of a few days later were dated from Monte Cavo. A superstitious belief in the genius of place had made Pamela insist on the change of quarters. They had been happy on Monte Cavo; perhaps they would be happy there again. And so, suddenly, the sea didn't suit her; she needed mountain air. But the genius of place is an unreliable deity. She had been as unhappy on the hilltop as by the sea. No, not quite so unhappy, perhaps. In the absence of the Pedders, the passion which their coming had renewed declined again. Perhaps it would have declined even if they had still been there. For the tissue of her imagination was, at the best of times, but a ragged curtain. Every now and then she came to a hole and through the hole she could see a fragment of reality, such as the bald and obvious fact that she didn't love Miles Fanning. True, after a peep through one of these indiscreet holes she felt it necessary to repent for having seen the facts, she would work herself up again into believing her fancies. But her faith was never entirely wholehearted. Under the superficial layer of imaginative suffering lay a fundamental and real indifference. Looking back now, from the further shore of his illness, Pamela felt astonished that she could have gone on obstinately imagining, in spite of those loopholes on reality, that she loved him. "Because I didn't," she said to herself, clear-sighted, weeks too late. "I didn't." But the belief that she did had continued, even on Monte Cavo, to envenom those genuinely painful wounds inflicted by him on her pride, her self-respect, inflicted with a strange malice that seemed to grow on him with the passage of the days.

"August 23rd." She had turned again to the notebook. "M. gave me this at lunch today.

> Sensual heat and sorrow cold
>   Are undivided twins;
> For there where sorrow ends, consoled,
>   Lubricity begins.

I told him I didn't exactly see what the point of it was, but I supposed it was meant to be hurting, because he's always trying to be hurting now, but he said, no, it was just a Great Thought for putting into Christmas crackers. But he did mean to hurt, and yet in one way he's crazy about me, he's . . ."

Yes, crazy was the right word. The more and the more crazily he had desired her, the more he had seemed to want to hurt her, to hurt himself too—for every wound he inflicted on her was inflicted at the same time on himself. "Why on earth didn't I leave him?" she wondered as she allowed a few more days to flick past.

"August 29th. A letter this morning from Guy in Scotland, so no wonder he took such an endless time to answer mine, which is a relief in one way, because I was beginning to wonder if he wasn't answering on purpose, but also rather depressing, as he says he isn't coming back to Rome till after the middle of September and goodness knows what will have happened by that time. So I felt very melancholy all the morning, sitting under the big tree in front of the monastery, such a marvelous huge old tree with very bright bits of sky between the leaves and bits of sun on the ground and moving across my frock, so that the sadness somehow got mixed up with the loveliness, which it often does do in a queer way, I find. M. came out unexpectedly and suggested going for a little walk before lunch, and he was very sweet for a change, but I dare say it was because he'd worked well. And I said, do you remember the first time we came up to Monte Cavo? and we talked about that afternoon and what fun it had been, even the museum, I said, even my education, because the Apollo was lovely. But he shook his head and said, *Apollo, Apollo, lama sabachthani,* and when I asked why he thought his Apollo had abandoned him he said it was because of Jesus and the Devil, and you're the Devil, I'm afraid, and he laughed and kissed my hand, but I ought to wring your neck, he said. For something that's *your* fault, I said, because it's you who make me a Devil for yourself. But he said it was me who made him make me into a Devil. So I asked how? And he said just by existing, just by having my particular shape, size, color, and consistency, because if I'd looked like a beetle and felt like wood, I'd have never made him make me into a Devil. So I asked him why he didn't just go away, seeing that what was wrong with me was that I was there at all. But that's easier said than done, he said, because a Devil's one of the very few things you can't run away from. And I asked why not? And he said because you can't run away from yourself and a Devil is at least half you. Besides, he said, the essence of a vice is that it *is* a vice—it holds you. Unless it unscrews itself, I said, because I'd made up my mind that minute that I'd go away, and it was such a relief having made up my mind that I wasn't furious or miserable any more, and when M. smiled and said, if it *can* unscrew itself, I just laughed."

A little too early, she reflected, as she read the words; she had laughed too early. That night had been the night of the full moon (oh, the humiliation of that lost suspender belt, the horror of that spider squashed against her skin!) and the next day he had begun to be ill. It had been impossible, morally impossible to leave him while he was ill. But how ghastly illness was! She shuddered with horror. Ghastly! "I'm sorry to be so repulsive," he had said to her one day, and from her place at his bedside she had protested, but hypocritically, hypocritically. As Aunt Edith might have protested. Still, one got to be hippo-ish, she excused herself, simply got to be sometimes. "But, thank goodness," she thought, "he's better now." In a day or two he'd be quite fit to look after himself. These waters were supposed to be miraculous.

She took a sheet of writing paper from the box on the table and uncorked the bottle of ink.

"Dear Guy," she began, "I wonder if you're back in Rome yet?"

III
POEMS

Mole

From *The Burning Wheel*

TUNNELED in solid blackness creeps
The old mole-soul, and wakes or sleeps,
He knows not which, but tunnels on
Through ages of oblivion;
Until at last the long constraint
Of each-hand wall is lost, and faint
Comes daylight creeping from afar,
And mole-work grows crepuscular.
Tunnel meets air and bursts; mole sees
Men hugely walking . . . or are they trees?
And far horizons smoking blue,
And chasing clouds forever new;
Green hills, like lighted lamps aglow
Or quenching 'neath the cloud-shadow;
Quenching and blazing turn by turn,
Spring's great green signals fitfully burn.
Mole travels on, but finds the steering
A harder task of pioneering
Than when he thridded through the strait
Blind catacombs that ancient fate
Had carved for him. Stupid and dumb
And blind and touchless he had come
A way without a turn; but here,
Under the sky, the passenger
Chooses his own best way; and mole
Distracted wanders, yet his hole
Regrets not much wherein he crept,
But runs, a joyous nympholept,
This way and that, by all made mad—
River nymph and oread,
Ocean's daughters and Lorelei,
Combing the silken mystery,

The glaucous gold of her rivery tresses—
Each haunts the traveler, each possesses
The drunken wavering soul awhile;
Then with a phantom's cock-crow smile
Mocks craving with sheer vanishment.
   Mole-eyes grow hawk's: knowledge is lent
In grudging driblets that pay high
Unconscionable usury
To unrelenting life. Mole learns
To travel more secure; the turns
Of his long way less puzzling seem,
And all those magic forms that gleam
In airy invitation cheat
Less often than they did of old.
   The earth slopes upward, fold by fold
Of quiet hills that meet the gold
Serenity of western skies.
Over the world's edge with clear eyes
Our mole transcendent sees his way
Tunneled in light: he must obey
Necessity again and thrid
Close catacombs as erst he did,
Fate's tunnelings, himself must bore
Through the sunset's inmost core.
The guiding walls to each-hand shine
Luminous and crystalline;
And mole shall tunnel on and on,
Till night let fall oblivion.

First Philosopher's Song

From *Leda*

A POOR degenerate from the ape,
Whose hands are four, whose tail's a limb,
I contemplate my flaccid shape
And know I may not rival him,

Save with my mind—a nimbler beast
Possessing a thousand sinewy tails,
A thousand hands, with which it scales,
Greedy of luscious truth, the greased

Poles and the coco palms of thought,
Thrids easily through the mangrove maze
Of metaphysics, walks the taut
Frail dangerous liana ways

That link across wide gulfs remote
Analogies between tree and tree;
Outruns the hare, outhops the goat;
Mind fabulous, mind sublime and free!

But oh, the sound of simian mirth!
Mind, issued from the monkey's womb,
Is still umbilical to earth,
Earth its home and earth its tomb.

Fifth Philosopher's Song

From *Leda*

A MILLION million spermatozoa,
    All of them alive:
Out of their cataclysm but one poor Noah
    Dare hope to survive.

And among that billion minus one
    Might have chanced to be
Shakespeare, another Newton, a new Donne—
    But the One was Me.

Shame to have ousted your betters thus,
    Taking ark while the others remained outside!
Better for all of us, froward Homunculus,
    If you'd quietly died!

Mediterranean

From *The Cicadas*

THIS tideless sapphire uniformly brims
Its jeweled circle of Tyrrhenian shore.
No vapors tarnish, not a cloud bedims,
And time descending only more and more
Makes rich, makes deep the unretiring gem.
And yet for me who look on it, how wide
The world of mud to which my thoughts condemn
This loathing vision of a sunken tide!
The ebb is mine. Life to its lowest neap
Withdrawn reveals that black and hideous shoal
Where I lie stranded. Oh deliver me
From this defiling death! Moon of the soul,
Call back the tide that ran so strong and deep,
Call back the shining jewel of the sea.

Carpe Noctem

From *The Cicadas*

THERE is no future, there is no more past,
No roots nor fruits, but momentary flowers.
Lie still, only lie still and night will last,
Silent and dark, not for a space of hours,
But everlastingly. Let me forget
All but your perfume, every night but this,
The shame, the fruitless weeping, the regret.
Only lie still: this faint and quiet bliss
Shall flower upon the brink of sleep and spread,
Till there is nothing else but you and I
Clasped in a timeless silence. But like one
Who, doomed to die, at morning will be dead,
I know, though night seem dateless, that the sky
Must brighten soon before tomorrow's sun.

Midsummer Day

From *The Cicadas*

THIS day was midsummer, the longest tarrying
Time makes between two sleeps. What have I done
With this longest of so few days, how spent,
Dear God, the golden, golden gift of sun?
Virginal, when I rose, the morning lay
Ready for beauty's rape, for wisdom's marrying.
I wrote: only an inky spider went,
Smear after smear, across the unsullied day.
If there were other places, if there were
But other days than this longest of few;
If one had courage, did one dare to do
That which alone might kill what now defaces
This the one place of all the countless places,
This only day when one will never dare!

The Cicadas

From *The Cicadas*

SIGHTLESS, I breathe and touch; this night of pines
Is needly, resinous and rough with bark.
Through every crevice in the tangible dark
The moonlessness above it all but shines.

Limp hangs the leafy sky; never a breeze
Stirs, nor a foot in all this sleeping ground;
And there is silence underneath the trees—
The living silence of continuous sound.

For like inveterate remorse, like shrill
Delirium throbbing in the fevered brain,
An unseen people of cicadas fill
Night with their one harsh note, again, again.

Again, again, with what insensate zest!
What fury of persistence, hour by hour!
Filled with what devil that denies them rest,
Drunk with what source of pleasure and of power!

Life is their madness, life that all night long
Bids them to sing and sing, they know not why;
Mad cause and senseless burden of their song;
For life commands, and Life! is all their cry.

I hear them sing, who in the double night
Of clouds and branches fancied that I went
Through my own spirit's dark discouragement,
Deprived of inward as of outward sight:

Who, seeking, even as here in the wild wood,
A lamp to beckon through my tangled fate,
Found only darkness and, disconsolate,
Mourned the lost purpose and the vanished good.

Now in my empty heart the crickets' shout
Re-echoing denies and still denies
With stubborn folly all my learned doubt,
In madness more than I in reason wise.

Life, life! The word is magical. They sing,
And in my darkened soul the great sun shines;
My fancy blossoms with remembered spring,
And all my autumns ripen on the vines.

Life! and each knuckle of the fig tree's pale
Dead skeleton breaks out with emerald fire.
Life! and the tulips blow, the nightingale
Calls back the rose, calls back the old desire:

And old desire that is forever new,
Desire, life's earliest and latest birth,
Life's instrument to suffer and to do,
Springs with the roses from the teeming earth;

Desire that from the world's bright body strips
Deforming time and makes each kiss the first;
That gives to hearts, to satiated lips
The endless bounty of tomorrow's thirst.

Time passes, and the watery moonrise peers
Between the tree trunks. But no outer light
Tempers the chances of our groping years,
No moon beyond our labyrinthine night.

Clueless we go; but I have heard thy voice,
Divine Unreason! harping in the leaves,
And grieve no more; for wisdom never grieves,
And thou hast taught me wisdom; I rejoice.

IV

ESSAYS

Jaipur

From *Jesting Pilate*

AT JAIPUR we were fortunate in having an introduction to one of the great *thakurs* of the State. He was a mighty landholder, the owner of twenty villages with populations ranging from five hundred to as many thousands, a feudal lord who paid for his fief (until, a year or two ago, a somewhat simpler and more modern system of tenure was introduced) by contributing to the State army one hundred and fifty armed and mounted men. This nobleman was kind enough to place his elephant at our disposal.

It was a superb and particularly lofty specimen, with gold-mounted tusks; ate two hundredweight of food a day and must have cost at least six hundred a year to keep. An expensive pet. But for a man in the *thakur's* position, we gathered, indispensable, a necessity. Pachyderms in Rajputana are what glass coaches were in Europe a century and a half ago—essential luxuries.

The *thakur* was a charming and cultured man, hospitably kind as only Indians can be. But at the risk of seeming ungrateful, I must confess that, of all the animals I have ever ridden, the elephant is the most uncomfortable mount. On the level, it is true, the motion is not too bad. One seems to be riding on a small chronic earthquake; that is all. The earthquake becomes more disquieting when the beast begins to climb. But when it goes downhill, it is like the end of the world. The animal descends very slowly and with an infinite caution, planting one huge foot deliberately before the other, and giving you time between each calculated step to anticipate the next convulsive spasm of movement —a spasm that seems to loosen from its place every organ in the rider's body, that twists the spine, that wrenches all the separate muscles of the loins and thorax. The hills round Jaipur are not very high. Fortunately; for by the end of the three or four hundred feet of our climbing and descending, we had almost reached the limits of our endurance. I returned full of admiration for Hannibal. He crossed the Alps on an elephant.

We made two expeditions with the pachyderm; one—over a rocky pass entailing, there and back, two climbs and two sickening descents —to the tanks and ruined temples of Galta, and one to the deserted palaces of Amber. Emerging from the palace precincts—I record the trivial and all too homely incident, because it set me mournfully reflecting about the cosmos—our monster halted and, with its usual deliberation, relieved nature, portentously. Hardly, the operation over, had it resumed its march when an old woman who had been standing at the door of a hovel among the ruins, expectantly waiting—we had wondered for what—darted forward and fairly threw herself on the mound of steaming excrement. There was fuel here, I suppose, for a week's cooking. "Salaam, Maharaj," she called up to us, bestowing in her gratitude the most opulent title she could lay her tongue to. Our passage had been to her like a sudden and unexpected fall of manna. She thanked us; she blessed the great and charitable Jumbo for his Gargantuan bounty.

Our earthquake lurched on. I thought of the scores of millions of human beings to whom the passage of an unconstipated elephant seems a godsend, a stroke of enormous good luck. The thought depressed me. Why are we here, men and women, eighteen hundred millions of us, on this remarkable and perhaps unique planet? To what end? Is it to go about looking for dung—cow dung, horse dung, the enormous and princely excrement of elephants? Evidently it is—for a good many of us, at any rate. It seemed an inadequate reason, I thought, for our being here—immortal souls, first cousins of the angels, own brothers of Buddha and Mozart and Sir Isaac Newton.

But a little while later I saw that I was wrong to let the consideration depress me. If it depressed me, that was only because I looked at the whole matter from the wrong end, so to speak. In painting my mental picture of the dung-searchers I had filled my foreground with the figures of Sir Isaac Newton and the rest of them. These, I perceived, should have been relegated to the remote background and the foreground should have been filled with cows and elephants. The picture so arranged, I should have been able to form a more philosophical and proportionable estimate of the dung-searchers. For I should have seen at a glance how vastly superior were their activities to those of the animal producers of dung in the foreground. The philosophical Martian would admire the dung-searchers for having discovered a use for dung; no other animal, he would point out, has had the wit to do more than manufacture it.

We are not Martians and our training makes us reluctant to think of ourselves as animals. Nobody inquires why cows and elephants inhabit the world. There is as little reason why we should be here, eating, drinking, sleeping and in the intervals reading metaphysics, saying prayers, or collecting dung. We are here, that is all; and like other animals we do what our native capacities and our environment permit of our doing. Our achievement, when we compare it with that of cows and elephants, is remarkable. They automatically make dung; we collect it and turn it into fuel. It is not something to be depressed about; it is something to be proud of. Still, in spite of the consolations of philosophy, I remained pensive.

Cawnpore

From *Jesting Pilate*

FROM its advertisements much may be learned of a nation's character and habits of thought. The following brief anthology of Indian advertisements is compiled from newspapers, magazines, medical catalogues, and the like. Several of the most characteristic specimens are taken from the *Cawnpore Congress Guide*, an official publication intended for the use of delegates and interested visitors. It is with one of these appeals to India's most enlightened public that I make a beginning.

Beget a son and Be Happy by using the SON BIRTH PILLS, my special secret Hindu Shastrick preparation, according to directions. Ladies who have given birth to daughters only WILL SURELY HAVE SONS NEXT, and those who have sons MUST HAVE MALE ISSUES ONCE AGAIN by the Grace of God. Fortunate persons desirous of begetting sons are bringing this marvelous Something into use for brightening their dark homes and making their lives worth their living. It is very efficacious and knows no failure. Self-praise is no recommendation. Try and be convinced. But if you apply, mentioning this publication, with full history of your case, along with a consultation fee of Rupees Ten (Foreign one guinea) only giving your "Word of Honor" to give me a SUITABLE REWARD (naming the amount) according to your means and position in life, just on the accomplishment of your desire in due course of time, you can have the same Free, ABSOLUTELY FREE. Act immediately, for this FREE OFFER may not remain open indefinitely.

Here are some pleasing Hair-oil advertisements from various sources:

Dr.——'s Scented Almond Oil. Best preparation to be used as hair oil for men who do mental work. The effects of almond oil on brain are known to everybody.

Jabukusum is a pure vegetable oil, to which medicinal ingredients and the perfume have been added to prevent all affectations (sic) of the hair and the brain.

There are several panaceas on the Indian market. There is, for example, Sidda Kalpa Makaradhwaja which "is a sure and infallible specific for all Diseases, and it never fails to effect a satisfactory cure in the patient, be his ailment whatever it may. Among the various diseases amenable to its administration, to state a few, are the following: Debility, general or nervous, including Nervous Prostration, due to whatever cause, Loss of Memory, Giddiness and Insanity . . . Asthma and Consumption, all stomach troubles . . . Cholera . . . all Kidney and Bladder Troubles . . . all Acute and Chronic Venereal Diseases . . . Leprosy of all kinds, White, Black, Red, etc. . . . Rheumatism, Paralysis, Epilepsy . . . Hysteria, Sterility . . . and all Fevers, including Malaria, Pneumonia, Influenza, and such other poisonous ones."

Not a bad medicine, but I prefer the "Infallible Cure for Incurable Diseases, Habits, and Defects" advertised in the *Cawnpore Guide*. The announcement runs as follows:

I have discovered the natural system of cure for all diseases, habits, defects, failings, etc., without the use of deleterious and pernicious drugs or medicines. Being Scientific, it is absolutely safe, simple, painless, pleasant, rapid, and infallible. Diseases like hysteria, epilepsy, rheumatism, loss of memory, paralysis, insanity and mania; addiction to smoking, opium, drink etc.; impotence, sterility, adultery, and the like can be radically cured duly by My System. Come to me after everyone else has failed to do you good. I guarantee a cure in every case undertaken. Every case needs to be treated on its special merits, and so applicants should furnish me with the complete history of the health of the patient and general occupation from birth, height, measurement over chest or bust, waist and hips, and a photograph with as little dress on as possible, along with a consultation fee of Rupees Five, without which no replies can be sent.

If the buying of a postal order were not so insuperable a nuisance, I should send five rupees to get the details of the adultery cure. So much cheaper than divorce.

The following are characteristic of a large class of Indian advertisements:

WONDERFUL WORK! ! !

Works wonders in the earthly pleasure.

MARAD MITRA LAPE

Will make you a man in one day

MARAD MITRA YAKUTI

Renews all your lost vigor and enables you to enjoy the pleasure with increased delights. Try once. 1 Bottle Rs. 10. ½ Bottle Rs. 5.

FREE! FREE! !

Do you want "Secret of Happiness from Conjugal Encounter" and "Good Luck"? If so, apply for the illustrated literature to ——.

The enormous number of such advertisements testifies to the disastrous effect on Indian manhood of the system of child marriages. The effects, as Gandhi has pointed out in his autobiography, would probably be still worse if it were not for the fact that Hindu girl wives generally spend at least half the year with their own parents, away from their schoolboy husbands.

The testimonials of Indian sufferers relieved by patent medicines are generally of a most lyrical character, and the oddity of the English in which they are written gives them an added charm. Here is one from an Indian Christian:

I can say really the medicine —— is sent by Lord Jesus Christ to the sinful world to save the poor victims from their dreadful diseases. In my 8 years' experience in medical line I have come across many preparations of medicine, but I have not seen such a wonderful medicine as ——. Please send 10 phials more.

Another pious gentleman writes:

I am living to see that I am what I am by the wonderful cure these pills wrought in me by the Grace of God, who I think has put the wisdom of preparing such pills into the head of our Venerable Pundit ——.

Another has "no hesitation in recommending it to the suffering humanity."

Yet another writes as follows:

> Several of my friends and myself have been using your ——— for over four months for Influenza, Lumbago, Dyspepsia, Syphilis, Rheumatism and Nervous Debility with complete success. There has not been a case in which it failed. I will call it an Ambrosia.

The classical allusion is elegant and apt. One is not surprised to find that the author of the testimonial is a Bachelor of Arts.

Fashions in Love

From *Do What You Will*

HUMAN nature does not change, or, at any rate, history is too short for any changes to be perceptible. The earliest known specimens of art and literature are still comprehensible. The fact that we can understand them all and can recognize in some of them an unsurpassed artistic excellence is proof enough that not only men's feelings and instincts but also their intellectual and imaginative powers, were in the remotest times precisely what they are now. In the fine arts it is only the convention, the form, the incidentals that change: the fundamentals of passion, of intellect and imagination remain unaltered.

It is the same with the arts of life as with the fine arts. Conventions and traditions, prejudices and ideals and religious beliefs, moral systems and codes of good manners, varying according to the geographical and historical circumstances, mold into different forms the unchanging material of human instinct, passion, and desire. It is a stiff, intractable material— Egyptian granite, rather than Hindu bronze. The artists who carved the colossal statues of Rameses II may have wished to represent the Pharaoh standing on one leg and waving two or three pairs of arms over his head, as the Indians still represent the dancing Krishna. But with the best will in the world they could not have imposed such a form upon the granite. Similarly, those artists in social life whom we call statesmen, moralists, founders of religions, have often wished to mold human nature into forms of superhuman elegance; but the material has proved too stubborn for them, and they have had to be content with only a relatively small alteration in the form which their predecessors had given it. At any given historical moment human behavior is a compromise (enforced from without by law and custom, from within by belief in religious or philosophical myths) between the raw instinct on the one hand and the unattainable ideal on the other—a compromise, in our sculptural metaphor, between the unshaped block of stone and the many-armed dancing Krishna.

Like all the other great human activities, love is the product of unchanging passions, instincts, and desires (unchanging, that is to say, in the mass of humanity; for, of course, they vary greatly in quantity and quality from individual to individual), and of laws and conventions, beliefs and ideals, which the circumstances of time and place, or the arbitrary fiats of great personalities, have imposed on a more or less willing society. The history of love, if it were ever written (and doubtless some learned German, unread, alas, by me, *has* written it, and in several volumes), would be like the current histories of art—a record of succeeding "styles" and "schools," of "influences," "revolutions," "technical discoveries." Love's psychological and physiological material remains the same; but every epoch treats it in a different manner, just as every epoch cuts its unvarying cloth and silk and linen into garments of the most diverse fashion. By way of illustration, I may mention that vogue of homosexuality which seems, from all accounts, to have been universal in the Hellenic world. Plutarch attributes the inception of this mode to the custom (novel in the fifth century, according to Thucydides) of exercising naked in the palestra.* But whatever may have been its origin, there can be no doubt that this particular fashion in love spread widely among people who were not in the least congenitally disposed to homosexuality. Convention and public opinion molded the material of love into forms which a later age has chosen to call "unnatural." A recrudescence of this amorous mode was very noticeable in Europe during the years immediately following the war. Among the determining causes of this recrudescence a future Plutarch will undoubtedly number the writings of Proust and André Gide.

The present fashions in love are not so definite and universal as those in clothes. It is as though our age were dubiously hesitating between crinolines and hobble skirts, trunk hose and Oxford trousers. Two distinct and hostile conceptions of love coexist in the minds of men and women, two sets of ideals, of conventions, of public opinions, struggle for the right to mold the psychological and physiological material of love. One is the conception evolved by the nineteenth century out of the ideals of Christianity on the one hand and romanticism on the other. The other is that still rather inchoate and negative conception which contemporary

---

* Plutarch, who wrote some five hundred years after the event, is by no means an unquestionable authority. The habit of which he and Thucydides speak may have facilitated the spread of the homosexual fashion. But that the fashion existed before the fifth century is made sufficiently clear by Homer, not to mention Sappho. Like many modern oriental peoples, the ancient Greeks were evidently, in Sir Richard Burton's expressive phrase, "omnifutuent."

youth is in process of forming out of the materials provided by modern psychology. The public opinion, the conventions, ideals, and prejudices which gave active force to the first convention and enabled it, to some extent at least, to modify the actual practice of love, had already lost much of their strength when they were rudely shattered, at any rate in the minds of the young, by the shock of the war. As usually happens, practice preceded theory, and the new conception of love was called in to justify existing postwar manners. Having gained a footing, the new conception is now a cause of new behavior, instead of being, as it was for the generation of the first world war, an explanation of wartime behavior made after the fact.

Let us try to analyze these two coexisting and conflicting conceptions of love. The older conception was, as I have said, the product of Christianity and romanticism—a curious mixture of contradictions, of the ascetic dread of passion and the romantic worship of passion. Its ideal was a strict monogamy, such as St. Paul grudgingly conceded to amorous humanity, sanctified and made eternal by one of those terrific exclusive passions which are the favorite theme of poetry and drama. It is an ideal which finds its most characteristic expression in the poetry of that infinitely respectable rebel, that profoundly anglican worshiper of passion, Robert Browning. It was Rousseau who first started the cult of passion for passion's sake. Before his time the great passions, such as that of Paris for Helen, of Dido for Aeneas, of Paolo and Francesca for one another, had been regarded rather as disastrous maladies than as enviable states of soul. Rousseau, followed by all the romantic poets of France and England, transformed the grand passion from what it had been in the Middle Ages— a demoniac possession—into a divine ecstasy, and promoted it from the rank of a disease to that of the only true and natural form of love. The nineteenth-century conception of love was thus doubly mystical, with the mysticism of Christian asceticism and sacramentalism, and with the romantic mysticism of Nature. It claimed an absolute rightness on the grounds of its divinity and of its naturalness.

Now, if there is one thing that the study of history and psychology makes abundantly clear, it is that there are no such things as either "divine" or "natural" forms of love. Innumerable gods have sanctioned and forbidden innumerable kinds of sexual behavior, and innumerable philosophers and poets have advocated the return to the most diverse kinds of "nature." Every form of amorous behavior, from chastity and monogamy to promiscuity and the most fantastic "perversions," is found both among animals and men. In any given human society, at any given moment, love, as we have seen, is the result of the interaction of the unchanging instinctive and physiological material of sex with the local conventions of morality and religion, the local laws, prejudices, and ideals. The degree of permanence of these conventions, religious myths, and ideals is proportional to their social utility in the given circumstances of time and place.

The new twentieth-century conception of love is realistic. It recognizes the diversity of love, not merely in the social mass from age to age, but from individual to contemporary individual, according to the dosage of the different instincts with which each is born, and the upbringing he has received. The new generation knows that there is no such thing as Love with a large L, and that what the Christian romantics of the last century regarded as the uniquely natural form of love is, in fact, only one of the indefinite number of possible amorous fashions, produced by specific circumstances at that particular time. Psychoanalysis has taught it that all the forms of sexual behavior previously regarded as wicked, perverse, unnatural, are statistically normal (and normality is solely a question of statistics), and that what is commonly called amorous normality is far from being a spontaneous, instinctive form of behavior, but must be acquired by a process of education. Having contracted the habit of talking freely and more or less scientifically about sexual matters, the young no longer regard love with that feeling of rather guilty excitement and thrilling shame which was for an earlier generation the normal reaction to the subject. Moreover, the practice of birth control has robbed amorous indulgence of most of the sinfulness traditionally supposed to be inherent in it by robbing it of its socially disastrous effects. The tree shall be known by its fruits: where there are no fruits, there is obviously no tree. Love has ceased to be the rather fearful, mysterious thing it was, and become a perfectly normal, almost commonplace, activity—an activity, for many young people, especially in America, of the same nature as dancing or tennis, a sport, a recreation, a pastime.

Such, then, are the two conceptions of love which oppose one another today. Which is the better? Without presuming to pass judgment, I will content myself with pointing out the defects of each. The older conception was bad, in so far as it inflicted unnecessary and undeserved sufferings on the many human beings whose congenital and acquired modes of love-making did not conform to the fashionable Christian-romantic pattern which was regarded as being uniquely entitled to call itself Love. The new conception is bad, it seems to me, in so far as it takes love too easily and lightly. On love regarded as an amusement the last word is surely this of Robert Burns:

> I waive the quantum of the sin,
> The hazard of concealing;
> But oh! it hardens all within
> And petrifies the feeling.

Nothing is more dreadful than a cold, unimpassioned indulgence. And love infallibly becomes cold and unimpassioned when it is too lightly made. It is not good, as Pascal remarked, to have too much liberty. Love is the product of two opposed forces—of an instinctive impulsion and a social resistance acting on the individual by means of ethical imperatives justified by philosophical or religious myths. When, with the destruction of the myths, resistance is removed, the impulse wastes itself on emptiness; and love, which is only the product of conflicting forces, is not born. The twentieth century is reproducing in a new form the error of the early nineteenth-century romantics. Following Rousseau, the romantics imagined that exclusive passion was the "natural" mode of love, just as virtue and reasonableness were the "natural" forms of men's social behavior. Get rid of priests and kings, and men will be forever good and happy; poor Shelley's faith in this palpable nonsense remained unshaken to the end. He believed also in the complementary paralogism that you had only to get rid of social restraints and erroneous mythology to make the Grand Passion universally chronic. Like the Mussets and Sands, he failed to see that the Grand Passion was produced by the restraints that opposed themselves to the sexual impulse, just as the deep lake is produced by the dam that bars the passage of the stream, and the flight of the airplane by the air which resists the impulsion given to it by the motor. There would be no air-resistance in a vacuum; but precisely for that reason the machine would not leave the ground, or even move at all. Where there are no psychological or external restraints, the Grand Passion does not come into existence and must be artificially cultivated, as George Sand and Musset cultivated it—with what painful and grotesque results the episode of Venice made only too ludicrously manifest.

"*J'aime et je veux pâlir; j'aime et je veux souffrir,*" says Musset, with his usual hysterically masochistic emphasis. Our young contemporaries do not wish to suffer or grow pale; on the contrary, they have a most determined desire to grow pink and enjoy themselves. But too much enjoyment "blunts the fine point of seldom pleasure." Unrestrained indulgence kills not merely passion, but, in the end, even amusement. Too much liberty is as life-destroying as too much restraint. The present fashion in love-making is likely to be short, because love that is psychologically too easy is not interesting. Such, at any rate, was evidently the opinion of the French, who, bored by the sexual license produced by the Napoleonic upheavals, reverted (so far, at any rate, as the upper and middle classes were concerned) to an almost anglican strictness under Louis Philippe. We may anticipate an analogous reaction in the not distant future. What new or what revived mythology will serve to create those internal restraints without which sexual impulse cannot be transformed into love? Christian morality and ascetic ideals will doubtless continue to play their part, but there will no less certainly be other moralities and ideals. For example, Mr. D. H. Lawrence's mythology of nature (new in its expression, but reassuringly old in substance) is a doctrine that seems to me fruitful in possibilities. The "natural love" which he sets up as a norm is a passion less self-conscious and highfalutin, less obviously and precariously artificial, than that "natural love" of the romantics, in which Platonic and Christian notions were essential ingredients. The restraints which Mr. Lawrence would impose on sexual impulse, so as to transform it into love, are not the restraints of religious spirituality. They are restraints of a more fundamental, less artificial nature—emotional, not intellectual. The impulse is to be restrained from promiscuous manifestations because, if it were not, promiscuity would "harden all within and petrify the feeling." The restraint is of the same personal nature as the impulse. The conflict is between a part of the personality and the personality as an organized whole. It does not pretend, as the romantic and Christian conflict pretends, to be a battle between a diabolical Lower Self and certain transcendental Absolutes, of which the only thing that philosophy can tell us is that they are absolutely unknowable, and therefore, for our purposes, nonexistent. It only claims to be, what in fact it is, a psychological conflict taking place in the more or less known and finite world of human interests. This doctrine has several great advantages over previous systems of inward restraint. It does not postulate the existence of any transcendental, nonhuman entity. This is a merit which will be increasingly appreciated as the significance of Kant's and Nietzsche's destructive criticism is more widely realized. People will cease to be interested in unknowable absolutes; but they will never lose interest in their own personalities. True, that "personality as a whole," in whose interests the sexual impulse is to be restrained and turned into love, is, strictly speaking, a mythological figure. Consisting, as we do, of a vast colony of souls—souls of individual cells, of organs, of groups of organs, hunger-souls, sex-souls, power-souls, herd-souls, of whose multifarious activities our consciousness (the Soul with a large S) is only very imperfectly and indirectly aware—we are not in a position to know the real nature of our personality as a whole. The only thing we can do is to hazard a hypothesis, to create a mythological figure, call it Human Personality, and hope that circumstances will not, by destroying us, prove our imaginative guesswork too hopelessly wrong. But myth for myth, Human Personality is preferable to God. We do at least know something of Human Personality, whereas of God we know nothing and, knowing nothing, are at liberty to invent as freely as we like. If men had always tried to deal with the problem of love in terms of known human rather than of grotesquely imagined divine interests, there would have been less "making of eunuchs for the kingdom of heaven's sake," less persecution of "sinners," less burning and imprisoning of the heretics of "unnatural" love, less Grundyism, less Comstockery, and, at the same time, less dirty Don Juanism, less of that curiously malignant and vengeful love-making so characteristic of the debauchee under a Christian dispensation. Reacting against the absurdities of the old mythology, the young have run into absurdities no less inordinate at the other end of the scale. A sordid and ignoble realism offers no resistance to the sexual impulse, which now spends itself purposelessly, without producing love, or even, in the long run, amusement, without enhancing vitality or quickening and deepening the rhythms of living. Only a new mythology of nature, such as, in modern times, Blake, Robert Burns, and Lawrence have defined it, an untranscendental and (relatively speaking) realistic mythology of Energy, Life, and Human Personality, will provide, it seems to me, the inward resistances necessary to turn sexual impulse into love, and provide them in a form which the critical intelligence of Post-Nietzschean youth can respect. By means of such a conception a new fashion in love may be created, a mode more beautiful and convenient, more healthful and elegant, than any seen among men since the days of remote and pagan antiquity.

Meditation on El Greco

From *Music at Night*

THE pleasures of ignorance are as great, in their way, as the pleasures of knowledge. For though the light is good, though it is satisfying to be able to place the things that surround one in the categories of an ordered and comprehensible system, it is also good to find oneself sometimes in the dark; it is pleasant now and then to have to speculate with vague bewilderment about a world which ignorance has reduced to a quantity f mutually irrelevant happenings dotted, like so many unexplored and antastic islands, on the face of a vast ocean of incomprehension. For ne, one of the greatest charms of travel consists in the fact that it offers nique opportunities for indulging in the luxury of ignorance. I am not ne of those conscientious travelers who, before they visit a new country, pend weeks mugging up its geology, its economics, its art history, its iterature. I prefer, at any rate during my first few visits, to be a thoroughly nintelligent tourist. It is only later, when my ignorance has lost its irgin freshness, that I begin to read what the intelligent tourist would ave known by heart before he bought his tickets. I read—and forthwith, n a series of apocalypses, my isolated and mysteriously odd impressions egin to assume significance, my jumbled memories fall harmoniously nto patterns. The pleasures of ignorance have given place to the pleasures f knowledge.

I have only twice visited Spain—not often enough, that is to say, o have grown tired of ignorance. I still enjoy bewilderedly knowing s little as possible about all I see between the Pyrenees and Cape Trafalgar. Another two or three visits, and the time will be ripe for me o go to the London Library and look up "Spain" in the subject index. n one of the numerous, the all too numerous, books there catalogued shall find, no doubt, the explanation of a little mystery that has mildly nd intermittently puzzled me for quite a number of years—ever since, t one of those admirable Loan Exhibitions in Burlington House, I saw or the first time a version of El Greco's *Dream of Philip II*.

This curious composition, familiar to every visitor to the Escorial, represents the king, dressed and gloved like an undertaker in inky black, neeling on a well-stuffed cushion in the center foreground; beyond him, n the left, a crowd of pious kneelers, some lay, some clerical, but all manifestly saintly, are looking upward into a heaven full of waltzing ngels, cardinal virtues and biblical personages, grouped in a circle ound the Cross and the luminous monogram of the Saviour. On the ight a very large whale gigantically yawns, and a vast concourse, presumably of the damned, is hurrying (in spite of all that we learned in hildhood about the anatomy of whales) down its crimson throat. A urious picture, I repeat, and, as a work of art, not remarkably good; here are many much better Grecos belonging even to the same youthful eriod. Nevertheless, in spite of its mediocrity, it is a picture for which have a special weakness. I like it for the now sadly unorthodox reason hat the subject interests me. And the subject interests me because I do ot know what the subject is. For this dream of King Philip—what was t? Was it a visionary anticipation of the Last Judgment? A mystical

peep into Heaven? An encouraging glimpse of the Almighty's short way
with heretics? I do not know—do not at present even desire to know
In the face of so extravagant a fantasy as this of Greco's, the pleasures
of ignorance are peculiarly intense. Confronted by the mysterious whale
the undertaker king, the swarming aerial saints and scurrying sinners
I give my fancy license and fairly wallow in the pleasure of bewilderedly
not knowing.

The fancy I like best of all that have occurred to me is the one which
affirms that this queer picture was painted as a prophetic and symbolic
autobiography, that it was meant to summarize hieroglyphically the whole
of Greco's future development. For that whale in the right foreground
—that great-grandfather of Moby Dick, with his huge yawn, his crimson
gullet and the crowd of the damned descending, like bank clerks at six
o'clock into the underground—that whale, I say, is the most significantly
autobiographical object in all El Greco's early pictures. For whither
are they bound, those hastening damned? "Down the red lane," as our
nurses used to say when they were encouraging us to swallow the uneat
able viands of childhood. Down the red lane into a dim inferno of
tripes. Down, in a word, into that strange and rather frightful universe
which Greco's spirit seems to have come more and more exclusively, as
he grew older, to inhabit. For in the Cretan's later painting every
personage is a Jonah. Yes, every personage. Which is where The Dream
of Philip II reveals itself as being imperfectly prophetic, a mutilated
symbol. It is for the damned alone that the whale opens his mouth
If El Greco had wanted to tell the whole truth about his future develop
ment, he would have sent the blessed to join them, or at least have pro
vided his saints and angels with another monster of their own, a superna
whale floating head downward among the clouds, with a second red lane
ascending, strait and narrow, toward a swallowed Heaven. Paradise and
Purgatory, Hell, and even the common Earth—for El Greco in his artistic
maturity, every department of the universe, was situated in the belly of
a whale. His Annunciations and Assumptions, his Agonies and Transfig
urations and Crucifixions, his Martyrdoms and Stigmatizations are all
without exception, visceral events. Heaven is no larger than the Black
Hole of Calcutta, and God Himself is whale-engulfed.

Critics have tried to explain El Greco's pictorial agoraphobia in terms
of his early, Cretan education. There is no space in his pictures, they
assure us, because the typical art of that Byzantium, which was El Greco's
spiritual home, was the mosaic, and the mosaic is innocent of depth. A
specious explanation, whose only defect is that it happens to be almost
entirely beside the point. To begin with, the Byzantine mosaic was not

invariably without depth. Those extraordinary eighth-century mosaics in the Omeyyid mosque at Damascus, for example, are as spacious and airy as impressionist landscapes. They are, it is true, somewhat exceptional specimens of the art. But even the commoner shut-in mosaics have really nothing to do with El Greco's painting, for the Byzantine saints and kings are enclosed, or, to be more accurate, are flatly inlaid in a kind of two-dimensional abstraction—in a pure Euclidean, plane-geometrical heaven of gold or blue. Their universe never bears the smallest resemblance to that whale's belly in which every one of El Greco's personages has his or her mysterious and appalling being. El Greco's world is no Flatland; there is depth in it—just a little depth. It is precisely this that makes it seem such a disquieting world. In their two-dimensional abstraction the personages of the Byzantine mosaists are perfectly at home; they are adapted to their environment. But, solid and three-dimensional, made to be the inhabitants of a spacious universe, El Greco's people are shut up in a world where there is perhaps just room enough to swing a cat, but no more. They are in prison and, which makes it worse, in a visceral prison. For all that surrounds them is organic, animal. Clouds, rock, drapery have all been mysteriously transformed into mucus and skinned muscle and peritoneum. The Heaven into which Count Orgaz ascends is like some cosmic operation for appendicitis. The Madrid *Resurrection* is a resurrection in a digestive tube. And from the later pictures we receive the gruesome impression that all the personages, both human and divine, have begun to suffer a process of digestion, are being gradually assimilated to their visceral surroundings. Even in the Madrid *Resurrection* the forms and texture of the naked flesh have assumed a strangely tripelike aspect. In the case of the nudes in *Laocoon* and *The Opening of the Seventh Seal* (both of them works of El Greco's last years) this process of assimilation has been carried a good deal further. After seeing their draperies and the surrounding landscape gradually peptonized and transformed, the unhappy Jonahs of Toledo discover, to their horror, that they themselves are being digested. Their bodies, their arms and legs, their faces, fingers, toes are ceasing to be humanly their own; they are becoming—the process is slow but inexorably sure—part of the universal Whale's internal workings. It is lucky for them that El Greco died when he did. Twenty years more, and the Trinity, the Communion of Saints and all the human race would have found themselves reduced to hardly distinguishable excrescences on the surface of a cosmic gut. The most favored might perhaps have aspired to be taenias and trematodes.

For myself, I am very sorry that El Greco did not live to be as old as Titian. At eighty or ninety he would have been producing an almost abstract art—a cubism without cubes, organic, purely visceral. What pictures he would then have painted! Beautiful, thrilling, profoundly appalling. For appalling are even the pictures he painted in middle age, dreadful in spite of their extraordinary power and beauty. This swallowed universe into which he introduces us is one of the most disquieting creations of the human mind. One of the most puzzling too. For what were El Greco's reasons for driving mankind down the red lane? What induced him to take God out of His boundless Heaven and shut Him up in a fish's gut? One can only obscurely speculate. All that I am quite certain of is that there were profounder and more important reasons for the whale than the memory of the mosaics—the wholly unvisceral mosaics —which he may have seen in the course of a Cretan childhood, a Venetian and Roman youth. Nor will a disease of the eye account, as some have claimed, for his strange artistic development. Diseases must be very grave indeed before they become completely coextensive with their victims. That men are affected by their illnesses is obvious; but it is no less obvious that, except when they are almost *in extremis*, they are something more than the sum of their morbid symptoms. Dostoevski was not merely personified epilepsy, Keats was other things besides a simple lump of pulmonary tuberculosis. Men make use of their illnesses at least as much as they are made use of by them. It is likely enough that El Greco had something wrong with his eyes. But other people have had the same disease without for that reason painting pictures like the *Laocoon* and *The Opening of the Seventh Seal*. To say that El Greco was just a defective eyesight is absurd; he was a man who used a defective eyesight.

Used it for what purpose? to express what strange feeling about the world, what mysterious philosophy? It is hard indeed to answer. For El Greco belongs as a metaphysician (every significant artist is a metaphysician, a propounder of beauty-truths and form-theories) to no known school. The most one can say, by way of classification, is that, like most of the great artists of the baroque, he believed in the validity of ecstasy, of the nonrational, "numinous" experiences out of which, as a raw material, the reason fashions the gods or the various attributes of God. But the kind of ecstatic experience artistically rendered and meditated on by El Greco was quite different from the kind of experience which is described and symbolically "rationalized" in the painting, sculpture and architecture of the great Baroque artists of the *seicento*. Those mass producers of spirituality, the Jesuits, had perfected a simple technique for the fabrication of orthodox ecstasies. They had cheapened an experience, hitherto accessible only to the spiritually wealthy, and so placed it within the reach of all. What the Italian *seicento* artists so brilliantly and copiously rendered was this cheapened experience and the metaphysic in terms of which it could be rationalized. "St. Teresa for All." "A John of the Cross in Every Home." Such were, or might have been, their slogans. Was it to be wondered at if their sublimities were a trifle theatrical, their tendernesses treacly, their spiritual intuitions rather commonplace and vulgar? Even the greatest of the Baroque artists were not remarkable for subtlety and spiritual refinement.

With these rather facile ecstasies and the orthodox Counter-Reformation theology in terms of which they could be interpreted, El Greco has nothing to do. The bright reassuring Heaven, the smiling or lachrymose, but always all too human divinities, the stage immensities and stage mysteries, all the stock-in-trade of the *seincentisti*, are absent from his pictures. There is ecstasy and flamy aspiration; but always ecstasy and aspiration, as we have seen, within the belly of a whale. El Greco seems to be talking all the time about the physiological root of ecstasy, not the spiritual flower; about the primary corporeal facts of numinous experience, not the mental derivatives from them. However vulgarly, the artists of the Baroque were concerned with the flower, not the root, with the derivatives and theological interpretations, not the brute facts of immediate physical experience. Not that they were ignorant of the physiological nature of these primary facts. Bernini's astonishing *St. Teresa* proclaims it in the most unequivocal fashion; and it is interesting to note that in this statue (as well as in the very similar and equally astonishing *Ludovica Albertoni* in San Francesco a Ripa) he gives to the draperies a kind of organic and, I might say, intestinal lusciousness of form. A little softened, smoothed and simplified, the robe of the great mystic would be indistinguishable from the rest of the swallowed landscape inside El Greco's whale. Bernini saves the situation (from the Counter-Reformer's point of view) by introducing into his composition the figure of the dart-brandishing angel. This aerial young creature is the inhabitant of an unswallowed Heaven. He carries with him the implication of infinite spaces. Charmingly and a little preposterously (the hand which holds the fiery dart has a delicately crook'd little finger, like the hand of some too refined young person in the act of raising her teacup), the angel symbolizes the spiritual flower of ecstasy, whose physiological root is the swooning Teresa in her peritoneal robe. Bernini is, spiritually speaking, a *plein-airiste*.

Not so El Greco. So far as he is concerned, there is nothing outside the whale. The primary physiological fact of religious experience is also for him, the final fact. He remains consistently on the plane of that visceral consciousness which we so largely ignore, but with which our ancestors (as their language proves) did so much of their feeling and thinking. "Where is thy zeal and thy strength, the sounding of the bowels and of thy mercies toward me?" "My heart is turned within me, my repentings are kindled together." "I will bless the Lord who hath given me counsel; my reins also instruct me in the night season." "For God is my record, how greatly I long after you all in the bowels of Jesus Christ." "For Thou hast possessed my reins." "Is Ephraim my dear son? . . . Therefore my bowels are troubled for him." The Bible abounds in such phrases—phrases which strike the modern reader as queer, a bit indelicate, even repellent. We are accustomed to thinking of ourselves as thinking entirely with our heads. Wrongly, as the physiologists have shown. For what we think and feel and are is to a great extent determined by the state of our ductless glands and our viscera. The Psalmist drawing instruction from his reins, the Apostle with his yearning bowels, are thoroughly in the modern physiological movement.

El Greco lived at a time when the reality of the primary visceral consciousness was still recognized—when the heart and the liver, the spleen and reins did all a man's feeling for him, and the four humors of blood, phlegm, choler and melancholy determined his character and imposed his passing moods. Even the loftiest experiences were admitted to be primarily physiological. Teresa knew God in terms of an exquisite pain in her heart, her side, her bowels. But while Teresa, and along with her the generality of human beings, found it natural to pass from the realm of physiology into that of the spirit—from the belly of the whale out into the wide open sky—El Greco obstinately insisted on remaining swallowed. His meditations were all of religious experience and ecstasy—but always of religious experience in its raw physiological state, always of primary, immediate, visceral ecstasy. He expressed these meditations in terms of Christian symbols—of symbols, that is to say, habitually employed to describe experiences quite different from the primary physiological states on which he was accustomed to dwell. It is the contrast between these symbols, with their currently accepted significance, and the special private use to which El Greco puts them—it is this strange contrast which gives to El Greco's pictures their peculiarly disquieting quality. For the Christian symbols remind us of all the spiritual open spaces—the open spaces of altruistic feeling, the open spaces of abstract thought, the open spaces of free-floating spiritual ecstasy. El Greco imprisons them, claps them up in a fish's gut. The symbols of the spiritual open spaces are compelled by him to serve as a language in terms of which he talks about the close immediacies of visceral awareness, about the ecstasy that annihilates the personal soul, not by dissolving it out into universal infinity, but by drawing it down and drowning it in the warm, pulsating, tremulous darkness of the body.

Well, I have wandered far and fancifully from the undertaker king and his enigmatic nightmare of whales and Jonahs. But imaginative wandering is the privilege of the ignorant. When one doesn't know one is free to invent. I have seized the opportunity while it presented itself. One of these days I may discover what the picture is about, and when that has happened I shall no longer be at liberty to impose my own interpretations. Imaginative criticism is essentially an art of ignorance. It is only because we don't know what a writer or artist meant to say that we are free to concoct meanings of our own. If El Greco had some-where specifically told us what he meant to convey by painting in terms of Black Holes and mucus, I should not now be in a position to speculate. But luckily he never told us; I am justified in letting my fancy loose to wander.

Sermons in Cats

From *Music at Night*

I met, not long ago, a young man who aspired to become a novelist. Knowing that I was in the profession, he asked me to tell him how he should set to work to realize his ambition. I did my best to explain. "The first thing," I said, "is to buy quite a lot of paper, a bottle of ink, and a pen. After that you merely have to write." But this was not enough for my young friend. He seemed to have a notion that there was some sort of esoteric cookery book, full of literary recipes, which you had only to follow attentively to become a Dickens, a Henry James, a Flaubert—"according to taste," as the authors of recipes say, when they come to the question of seasoning and sweetening. Wouldn't I let him have a glimpse of this cookery book? I said that I was sorry, but that (unhappily—for what an endless amount of time and trouble it would save!) I had never even seen such a work. He seemed sadly disappointed; so, to console the poor lad, I advised him to apply to the professors of dramaturgy and short-story writing at some reputable university; if anyone possessed a trust-worthy cookery book of literature, it should surely be they. But even this was not enough to satisfy the young man. Disappointed in his hope that I would give him the fictional equivalent of "One Hundred Ways of

Cooking Eggs" or the "Carnet de la Ménagère," he began to cross-examine me about my methods of "collecting material." Did I keep a notebook or a daily journal? Did I jot down thoughts and phrases in a card index? Did I systematically frequent the drawing rooms of the rich and fashionable? Or did I, on the contrary, inhabit the Sussex downs? or spend my evenings looking for "copy" in East End gin palaces? Did I think it was wise to frequent the company of intellectuals? Was it a good thing for a writer of novels to try to be well educated, or should he confine his reading exclusively to other novels? And so on. I did my best to reply to these questions —as noncommittally, of course, as I could. And as the young man still looked rather disappointed, I volunteered a final piece of advice, gratuitously. "My young friend," I said, "if you want to be a psychological novelist and write about human beings, the best thing you can do is to keep a pair of cats." And with that I left him.

I hope, for his own sake, that he took my advice. For it was good advice—the fruit of much experience and many meditations. But I am afraid that, being a rather foolish young man, he merely laughed at what he must have supposed was only a silly joke: laughed, as I myself foolishly laughed when, years ago, that charming and talented and extraordinary man, Ronald Firbank, once told me that he wanted to write a novel about life in Mayfair and so was just off to the West Indies to look for copy among the Negroes. I laughed at the time; but I see now that he was quite right. Primitive people, like children and animals, are simply civilized people with the lid off, so to speak—the heavy elaborate lid of manners, conventions, traditions of thought and feeling beneath which each one of us passes his or her existence. This lid can be very conveniently studied in Mayfair, shall we say, or Passy, or Park Avenue. But what goes on underneath the lid in these polished and elegant districts? Direct observation (unless we happen to be endowed with a very penetrating intuition) tells us but little; and, if we cannot infer what is going on under other lids from what we see, introspectively, by peeping under our own, then the best thing we can do is to take the next boat for the West Indies, or else, less expensively, pass a few mornings in the nursery, or alternatively, as I suggested to my literary young friend, buy a pair of cats.

Yes, a pair of cats. Siamese by preference; for they are certainly the most "human" of all the race of cats. Also the strangest, and, if not the most beautiful, certainly the most striking and fantastic. For what disquieting pale-blue eyes stare out from the black-velvet mask of their faces! Snow white at birth, their bodies gradually darken to a rich mulatto color. Their forepaws are gloved almost to the shoulder like the long black kid arms of Yvette Guilbert; over their hind legs are tightly drawn the black-silk stockings with which Félicien Rops so perversely and indecently clothed his pearly nudes. Their tails, when they have tails—and I would always recommend the budding novelist to buy the tailed variety; for the tail, in cats, is the principal organ of emotional expression and a Manx cat is the equivalent of a dumb man—their tails are tapering black serpents endowed, even when the body lies in Sphinxlike repose, with a spasmodic and uneasy life of their own. And what strange voices they have! Sometimes like the complaining of small children; sometimes like the noise of lambs; sometimes like the agonized and furious howling of lost souls. Compared with these fantastic creatures, other cats, however beautiful and engaging, are apt to seem a little insipid.

Well, having bought his cats, nothing remains for the would-be novelist but to watch them living from day to day; to mark, learn, and inwardly digest the lessons about human nature which they teach; and finally—for, alas, this arduous and unpleasant necessity always arises—finally write his book about Mayfair, Passy, or Park Avenue, whichever the case may be.

Let us consider some of these instructive sermons in cats, from which the student of human psychology can learn so much. We will begin—as every good novel should begin, instead of absurdly ending—with marriage. The marriage of Siamese cats, at any rate as I have observed it, is an extraordinarily dramatic event. To begin with, the introduction of the bridegroom to his bride (I am assuming that, as usually happens in the world of cats, they have not met before their wedding day) is the signal for a battle of unparalleled ferocity. The young wife's first reaction to the advances of her would-be husband is to fly at his throat. One is thankful, as one watches the fur flying and listens to the piercing yells of rage and hatred, that a kindly providence has not allowed these devils to grow any larger. Waged between creatures as big as men, such battles would bring death and destruction to everything within a radius of hundreds of yards. As things are, one is able, at the risk of a few scratches, to grab the combatants by the scruffs of their necks and drag them, still writhing and spitting, apart. What would happen if the newly wedded pair were allowed to go on fighting to the bitter end, I do not know and have never had the scientific curiosity or the strength of mind to try to find out. I suspect that, contrary to what happened in Hamlet's family, the wedding baked meats would soon be serving for a funeral. I have always prevented this tragical consummation by simply shutting up the bride in a room by herself and leaving the bridegroom for a few hours to languish outside the door. He does not languish dumbly; but for a long time there is no answer, save an occasional hiss or growl, to his melancholy cries of love. When, finally, the bride begins replying in tones as soft and yearning as his own, the door may be opened. The bridegroom darts in and is received, not with tooth and claw as on the former occasion, but with every demonstration of affection.

At first sight there would seem, in this specimen of feline behavior, no special "message" for humanity. But appearances are deceptive; the lids under which civilized people live are so thick and so profusely sculptured with mythological ornaments that it is difficult to recognize the fact, so much insisted upon by D. H. Lawrence in his novels and stories, that there is almost always a mingling of hate with the passion of love and that young girls very often feel (in spite of their sentiments and even their desires) a real abhorrence of the fact of physical love. Unlidded, the cats make manifest this ordinarily obscure mystery of human nature. After witnessing a cats' wedding no young novelist can rest content with the falsehood and banalities which pass, in current fiction, for descriptions of love.

Time passes and, their honeymoon over, the cats begin to tell us things about humanity which even the lid of civilization cannot conceal in the world of men. They tell us—what, alas, we already know—that husbands soon tire of their wives, particularly when they are expecting or nursing families; that the essence of maleness is the love of adventure and infidelity; that guilty consciences and good resolutions are the psychological symptoms of that disease which spasmodically affects practically every male between the ages of eighteen and sixty—the disease called "the morning after"; and that with the disappearance of the disease the psychological symptoms also disappear, so that when temptation comes again, conscience is dumb and good resolutions count for nothing. All these unhappily too familiar truths are illustrated by the cats with a most comical absence of disguise. No man has ever dared to manifest his boredom so insolently as does a Siamese tomcat when he yawns in the face of his amorously importunate wife. No man has ever dared to proclaim his illicit amors so frankly as this same tom caterwauling on the tiles. And how slinkingly—no man was ever so abject—he returns next day to the conjugal basket by the fire! You can measure the guiltiness of his conscience by the angle of his back-pressed ears, the droop of his tail. And when, having sniffed him and so discovered his infidelity, his wife, as she always does on these occasions, begins to scratch his face (already scarred, like a German student's, with the traces of a hundred duels), he makes no attempt to resist; for, self-convicted of sin, he knows that he deserves all he is getting.

It is impossible for me in the space at my disposal to enumerate all the human truths which a pair of cats can reveal or confirm. I will cite only one more of the innumerable sermons in cats which my memory holds—an acted sermon which, by its ludicrous pantomime, vividly brought home to me the most saddening peculiarity of our human nature, its irreducible solitariness. The circumstances were these. My she-cat, by now a wife of long standing and several times a mother, was passing through one of her occasional phases of amorousness. Her husband, now in the prime of life and parading that sleepy arrogance which is the characteristic of the mature and conquering male (he was now the feline equivalent of some herculean young Alcibiades of the Guards), refused to have anything to do with her. It was in vain that she uttered her lovesick mewing, in vain that she walked up and down in front of him, rubbing herself voluptuously against doors and chair legs as she passed, it was in vain that she came and licked his face. He shut his eyes, he yawned, he averted his head, or, if she became too importunate, got up and slowly, with an insulting air of dignity and detachment, stalked away. When the opportunity presented itself, he escaped and spent the next twenty-four hours upon the tiles. Left to herself, the wife went wandering disconsolately about the house, as though in search of a vanished happiness, faintly and plaintively mewing to herself in a voice and with a manner that reminded one irresistibly of Mélisande in Debussy's opera. "*Je ne suis pas heureuse ici,*" she seemed to be saying. And, poor little beast, she wasn't. But, like her big sisters and brothers of the human world, she had to bear her unhappiness in solitude, uncomprehended, unconsoled. For in spite of language, in spite of intelligence and intuition and sympathy, one can never really communicate anything to anybody. The essential substance of every thought and feeling remains incommunicable, locked up in the impenetrable strong room of the individual soul and body. Our life is a sentence of perpetual solitary confinement. This mournful truth was overwhelmingly borne in on me as I watched the abandoned and lovesick cat as she walked unhappily round my room. "*Je ne suis pas heureuse ici,*" she kept mewing, "*je ne suis pas heureuse ici.*" And her expressive black tail would lash the air in a tragical gesture of despair. But each time it twitched, hop-la! from under the armchair, from behind the bookcase, wherever he happened to be hiding at the moment, out jumped her only son (the only one, that is, we had not given away), jumped like a ludicrous toy tiger, all claws out, onto the moving tail. Sometimes he would miss, sometimes he caught it, and getting the tip between his teeth would pretend to worry it, absurdly ferocious. His mother would have to jerk it violently to get it out of his mouth. Then, he would go back under his armchair again and, crouching down, his hindquarters trembling, would prepare once more to spring. The tail, the tragical, despairingly gesticulating tail, was for him the most irresistible of playthings. The patience of the mother was angelical. There was never a rebuke or a punitive reprisal; when the child became too intolerable, she just moved away; that was all. And meanwhile, all the time, she went on mewing, plaintively, despairingly. "*Je ne suis pas heureuse ici, je ne suis pas heureuse ici.*" It was heartbreaking. The more so as the antics of the kitten were so extraordinarily ludicrous. It was as though a slapstick comedian had broken in on the lamentations of Mélisande—not mischievously, for there was not the smallest intention to hurt in the little cat's performance, but simply from lack of comprehension. Each was alone, serving his life sentence of solitary confinement. There was no communication from cell to cell. Absolutely no communication. These sermons in cats can be exceedingly depressing.

Vulgarity in Literature

Extracts

From *Music at Night*

I

VULGARITY in literature must be distinguished from the vulgarity inherent in the profession of letters. Every man is born with his share of Original Sin, to which every writer adds a pinch of Original Vulgarity. Necessarily and quite inevitably. For exhibitionism is always vulgar, even if what you exhibit is the most exquisitely refined of souls.

Some writers are more squeamishly conscious than others of the essential vulgarity of their trade—so much so that, like Flaubert, they have found it hard to commit that initial offense against good breeding: the putting of pen to paper.

It is just possible, of course, that the greatest writers have never written, that the world is full of Monsieur Testes and mute inglorious Miltons, too delicate to come before the public. I should like to believe it; but I find it hard. Your great writer is possessed by a devil, over which he has very little control. If the devil wants to come out (and, in practice, devils always do want to come out), it will do so, however loud the protests of the aristocratic consciousness, with which it uneasily cohabits. The profession of literature may be "fatally marred by a secret absurdity"; the devil simply doesn't care. *Scribo quia absurdum.*

II

To be pale, to have no appetite, to swoon at the slightest provocation—these, not so long ago, were the signs of maidenly good breeding. In other words, when a girl was marked with the stigmata of anemia and chronic constipation, you knew she was a lady. Virtues are generally fashioned (more or less elegantly, according to the skill of the moral *couturier*) out of necessities. Rich girls had no need to work; the aristocratic tradition discouraged them from voluntarily working; and the Christian tradition discouraged them from compromising their maiden modesty by taking anything like violent exercise. Good carriage roads and, finally, railways spared them the healthy fatigues of riding. The virtues of Fresh Air had not yet been discovered and the Draft was still the commonest, as it was almost the most dangerous, manifestation of the Diabolic Principle. More perverse than Chinese foot-squeezers, the topiarists of European fashion had decreed that the elegant should have all her viscera constricted and displaced by tight lacing. In a word, the rich girl lived a life scientifically calculated to make her unhealthy. A virtue was made of humiliating necessity, and the pale, ethereal swooner of romantic literature remained for years the type and mirror of refined young womanhood.

Something of the same kind happens from time to time in the realm of literature. Moments come when too conspicuous a show of vigor, too frank an interest in common things are signs of literary vulgarity. To be really ladylike, the Muses, like their mortal sisters, must be anemic and constipated. On the more sensitive writers of certain epochs circumstances impose an artistic wasting away, a literary consumption. This distressing fatality is at once transformed into a virtue, which it becomes a duty for all to cultivate.

"Vivre? Nos valets le feront pour nous." For, oh, the vulgarity of it! The vulgarity of this having to walk and talk; to open and close the eyes; to think and drink and every day, yes, every day, to eat, eat and excrete. And then this having to pursue the female of one's species, or the male, whichever the case may be; this having to cerebrate, to calculate, to copulate, to propagate . . . No, no—too gross, too stupidly low. Such things, as Villiers de l'Isle-Adam says, are all very well for footmen. But for a descendant of how many generations of Templars, of Knights of Rhodes and of Malta, Knights of the Garter and the Holy Ghost and all the variously colored Eagles—obviously, it was out of the question; it simply wasn't done. *Vivre? Nos valets le feront pour nous.*

At the same point, but on another plane, of the great spiral of history, Prince Gotama, more than two thousand years before, had also discovered the vulgarity of living. The sight of a corpse rotting by the roadside had set him thinking. It was his first introduction to death. Now, a corpse, poor thing, is an untouchable and the process of decay is, of all pieces of bad manners, the vulgarest imaginable. For a corpse is, by definition, a person absolutely devoid of *savoir vivre*. Even your sweeper knows better. But in every greatest king, in every loveliest flowery princess, in every poet most refined, every best-dressed dandy, every holiest and most spiritual teacher, there lurks, waiting, waiting for the moment to emerge, an out-caste of the outcastes, a dung carrier, a dog, lower than the lowest, bottom-lessly vulgar.

What with making their way and enjoying what they have won, heroes have no time to think. But the sons of heroes—ah, they have all the necessary leisure. The future Buddha belonged to the generation which has time. He saw the corpse, he smelled it vulgarly stinking, he thought. The echoes of his meditations still reverberate, rich with an accumulated wealth of harmonics, like the memory of the organ's final chord pulsing back and forth under the vaulting of a cathedral.

No less than that of war or statecraft, the history of economics has its heroic ages. Economically, the nineteenth century was the equivalent of those brave times about which we read in Beowulf and the Iliad. Its heroes struggled, conquered or were conquered, and had no time to think. Its bards, the romantics, sang rapturously, not of the heroes, but of higher things (for they were Homers who detested Achilles), sang with all the vehemence which one of the contemporary heroes would have put into grinding the faces of the poor. It was only in the second and third genera-tion that men began to have leisure and the necessary detachment to find the whole business—economic heroism and romantic bardism—rather vulgar. Villiers, like Gotama, was one who had time. That he was the descendant of all those Templars and Knights of this and that was, to a great extent, irrelevant. The significant fact was this: he was, or at any rate chronologically might have been, the son and grandson of economic heroes and romantic bards—a man of the decadence. Sons have always a rebellious wish to be disillusioned by that which charmed their fathers; and, wish or no wish, it was difficult for a sensitive man to see and smell the already putrefying corpse of industrial civilization and not be shocked by it into distressful thought. Villiers was duly shocked; and he expressed his shockedness in terms of an aristocratic disdain that was almost

Brahminical in its intensity. But his feudal terminology was hardly more than an accident. Born without any of Villiers' perhaps legendary advantages of breeding, other sensitives of the same postheroic generation were just as profoundly shocked. The scion of Templars had a more striking vocabulary than the others—that was all. For the most self-conscious and intelligent artists of the last decades of the nineteenth century, too frank an acceptance of the obvious actualities of life, too hearty a manner and (to put it grossly) too many "guts" were rather vulgar. Vivre? Nos valets le feront pour nous. (Incidentally, the suicide rate took a sharp upward turn during the sixties. In some countries it is nearly five times what it was seventy years ago.) Zola was the master footman of the age. That vulgar interest in actual life! And all those guts of his—was the man preparing to set up as a tripe-dresser?

A few aging ninetyites survive; a few young neoninetyites, who judge of art and all other human activities in terms of the Amusing and the Tiresome, play kittenishly around with their wax flowers and stuffed owls and Early Victorian beadwork. But, old and young, they are insignificant. Guts and an acceptance of the actual are no longer vulgar. Why not? What has happened? Three things: the usual reaction of sons against fathers, another industrial revolution and a rediscovery of mystery. We have entered (indeed, we have perhaps already passed through) a second heroic age of economics. Its Homers, it is true, are almost without exception sceptical, ironic, denunciatory. But this scepticism, this irony, this denunciation are as lively and vehement as that which is doubted and denounced. Babbitt infects even his detractors with some of his bouncing vitality. The Romantics, in the same way, possessed an energy proportionate to that of their enemies, the economic heroes who were creating modern industrialism. Life begets life even in opposition to itself.

Vivre? Nos valets le feront pour nous. But the physicists and psychologists have revealed the universe as a place, in spite of everything, so fantastically queer that to hand it over to be enjoyed by footmen would be a piece of gratuitous humanitarianism. Servants must not be spoiled. The most refined spirits need not be ashamed in taking a hearty interest in the rediscovered mystery of the actual world. True, it is a sinister as well as a fascinating and mysterious world. And what a mess, with all our good intentions, we have made and are busily making of our particular corner of it! The same old industrial corpse—to some extent disinfected and galvanically stimulated at the moment into a twitching semblance of healthy life—still rots by the wayside, as it rotted in Villiers' time. And as for Gotama's carrion—that of course is always with us. There are, as ever, excellent reasons for personal despair; while the reasons for despairing about society are actually a good deal more cogent than at most times. A Mallarméan shrinking away into pure poetry, a delicate Henry Jamesian avoidance of all the painful issues would seem to be justified. But the spirit of the time—the industrially heroic time in which we live—is opposed to these retirements, these handings over of life to footmen. It demands that we should "press with strenuous tongue against our palate," not only joy's grape, but every Dead Sea fruit. Even dust and ashes must be relished with gusto. Thus, modern American fiction, like the modern American fact which it so accurately renders, is ample and lively. And yet, "Dust and ashes, dust and ashes" is the fundamental theme and final moral of practically every modern American novel of any distinction. High spirits and a heroic vitality are put into the expression of despair. The hopelessness is almost Rabelaisian.

III

It was vulgar at the beginning of the nineteenth century to mention the word "handkerchief" on the French tragic stage. An arbitrary convention had decreed that tragic personages must inhabit a world in which noses exist only to distinguish the noble Romans from the Greeks and Hebrews, never to be blown. Arbitrary conventions of one sort or another are essential to art. But as the sort of convention constantly varies, so does the corresponding vulgarity. We are back among the relativities.

In the case of the handkerchief we have a particular and rather absurd application of a very widely accepted artistic convention. This convention is justified by the ancient metaphysical doctrine which distinguishes in the universe two principles, mind and matter, and which attributes to mind an immeasurable superiority. In the name of this principle many religions have demanded the sacrifice of the body; their devotees have responded by mortifying the flesh and, in extreme cases, by committing self-castration and even suicide. Literature has its Manichaeans as well as religion: men who on principle would exile the body and its functions from the world of their art, who condemn as vulgar all too particular and detailed accounts of physical actuality, as vulgar any attempt to relate mental or spiritual events to happenings in the body. The inhabitants of their universe are not human beings but the tragical heroes and heroines who never blow their noses.

Artistically, the abolition of handkerchiefs and all that handkerchiefs directly or indirectly stand for has certain advantages. The handkerchiefless world of pure mind and spirit is, for an adult, the nearest approach to that infinitely comfortable Freudian womb toward which, as toward a lost paradise, we are always nostalgically yearning. In the handkerchiefless mental world we are at liberty to work things out to their logical conclusions, we can guarantee the triumph of justice, we can control the weather and (in the words of those yearning popular songs which are the national anthems of Wombland) make our Dreams come True by living under Skies of Blue with You. Nature in the mental world is not that collection of tiresomely opaque and recalcitrant objects, so bewildering to the man of science, so malignantly hostile to the man of action; it is the luminously rational substance of a Hegelian nature-philosophy, a symbolic manifestation of the principles of dialectic. Artistically, such a nature is much more satisfactory (because so much more easy to deal with) than the queer, rather sinister and finally quite incomprehensible monster by which, when we venture out of our ivory towers, we are instantly swallowed. And man, than whom, as Sophocles long since remarked, nothing is more monstrous, more marvelous, more terrifyingly strange (it is hard to find a single word to render his *deinoteron*)—man, too, is a very unsatisfactory subject for literature. For this creature of inconsistencies can live on too many planes of existence. He is the inhabitant of a kind of psychological Woolworth Building; you never know—he never knows himself—which floor he'll step out at tomorrow, nor even whether, a minute from now, he won't take it into his head to jump into the elevator and shoot up a dozen or down perhaps twenty stories into some totally different mode of being. The effect of the Manichaean condemnation of the body is at once to reduce this impossible skyscraper to less than half its original height. Confined henceforward to the mental floors of his being, man becomes an almost easily manageable subject for the writer. In the French tragedies (the most completely Manichaean works of art ever created) lust itself has ceased to be corporeal and takes its place among the other abstract symbols, with which the authors write their strange algebraical equations of passion and conflict. The beauty of algebraical symbols lies in their universality; they stand not for one particular case but for all cases. Manichaeans, the classical writers confined themselves exclusively to the study of man as a creature of pure reason and discarnate passions. Now the body particularizes and separates, the mind unites. By the very act of imposing limitations the classicists were enabled to achieve a certain universality of statement impossible to those who attempt to reproduce the particularities and incompletenesses of actual corporeal life. But what they gained in universality, they lost in vivacity and immediate truth. You cannot get something for nothing. Some people think that universality can be paid for too highly.

To enforce their ascetic code the classicists had to devise a system of critical sanctions. Chief among these was the stigma of vulgarity attached to all those who insisted too minutely on the physical side of man's existence. Speak of handkerchiefs in a tragedy? The solecism was as monstrous as picking teeth with a fork.

At a dinner party in Paris not long ago I found myself sitting next to a French Professor of English, who assured me in the course of an otherwise very agreeable conversation that I was a leading member of the Neo-Classic school and that it was as a leading member of the Neo-Classic school that I was lectured about to the advanced students of contemporary English literature under his tutelage. The news depressed me. Classified, like a museum specimen, and lectured about, I felt most dismally posthumous. But that was not all. The thought that I was a Neo-Classic preyed upon my mind—a Neo-Classic without knowing it, a Neo-Classic against all my desires and intentions. For I have never had the smallest ambition to be a Classic of any kind, whether Neo, Palaeo, Proto or Eo. Not at any price. For, to begin with, I have a taste for the lively, the mixed and the incomplete in art, preferring it to the universal and the chemically pure. In the second place, I regard the classical discipline, with its insistence on elimination, concentration, simplification, as being, for all the formal difficulties it imposes on the writer, essentially an escape from, a getting out of, the greatest difficulty—which is to render adequately, in terms of literature, that infinitely complex and mysterious thing, actual reality. The world of mind is a comfortable Wombland, a place to which we flee from the bewildering queerness and multiplicity of the actual world. Matter is incomparably subtler and more intricate than mind. Or, to put it a little more philosophically, the consciousness of events which we have immediately, through our senses and intuitions and feelings, is incomparably subtler than any idea we can subsequently form of that immediate consciousness. Our most refined theories, our most elaborate descriptions are but crude and barbarous simplifications of a reality that is, in every smallest sample, infinitely complex. Now, simplifications must, of course, be made; if they were not, it would be quite impossible to deal artistically (or, for that matter, scientifically) with reality at all. What is the smallest amount of simplification compatible with comprehensibility, compatible with the expression of a humanly significant meaning? It is the business of the nonclassical naturalistic writer to discover. His ambition is to render, in literary terms, the quality of immediate experience—in other words, to express the finally inexpressible. To come anywhere near achieving this impossibility is much more difficult, it seems to me, than, by eliminating and simplifying, to achieve the perfectly realizable classical ideal. The cutting out of all the complex particularities of a situation (which means, as we have seen, the cutting out of all that is corporeal in it) strikes me as mere artistic shirking. But I disapprove of the shirking of artistic difficulties. Therefore I find myself disapproving of classicism.

Literature is also philosophy, is also science. In terms of beauty it enunciates truths. The beauty-truths of the best classical works possess, as we have seen, a certain algebraic universality of significance. Naturalistic works contain the more detailed beauty-truths of particular observation. These beauty-truths of art are truly scientific. All that modern psychologists, for example, have done is to systematize and debeautify the vast treasures of knowledge about the human soul contained in novel, play, poem and essay. Writers like Blake and Shakespeare, like Stendhal and Dostoevski, still have plenty to teach the modern scientific professional. There is a rich scientific harvest to be reaped in the works even of minor writers. By nature a natural historian, I am ambitious to add my quota to the sum of particularized beauty-truths about man and his relations with the world about him. (Incidentally, this world of relationships, this borderland between "subjective" and "objective" is one which literature is peculiarly, perhaps uniquely, well fitted to explore.) I do not want to be a Classical, or even a Neo-Classical, eliminator and generalizer.

This means, among other things, that I cannot accept the Classicists' excommunication of the body. I think it not only permissible but necessary that literature should take cognizance of physiology and should investigate the still obscure relations between the mind and its body. True, many people find the reports of such investigations, when not concealed in scientific textbooks and couched in the decent obscurity of a Greco-Latin jargon, extremely and inexcusably vulgar; and many more find them downright wicked. I myself have frequently been accused, by reviewers in public and by unprofessional readers in private correspondence, both of vulgarity and of wickedness—on the grounds, so far as I have ever been able to discover, that I reported my investigations into certain phenomena in plain English and in a novel. The fact that many people should be shocked by what he writes practically imposes it as a duty upon the writer to go on shocking them. For those who are shocked by truth are not only stupid but morally reprehensible as well; the stupid should be educated, the wicked punished and reformed. All these praiseworthy ends can be attained by a course of shocking: retributive pain will be inflicted on the truth-haters by the first shocking truths, whose repetition will gradually build up in those who read them an immunity to pain and will end by reforming and educating the stupid criminals out of their truth-hating. For a familiar truth ceases to shock. To render it familiar is therefore a duty. It is also a pleasure. For, as Baudelaire says, "ce qu'il y a d'enivrant dans le mauvais goût, c'est le plaisir aristocratique de déplaire."

V

THE WORLD OF ALDOUS HUXLEY

Of Time and The Ego

From *After Many a Summer Dies the Swan*

"WHAT precisely are we supposed to be talking about?" Jeremy Pordage asked acidulously. "The New Jerusalem?"

Mr. Propter smiled at him good-humoredly. "It's all right," he said. "I won't say a word about harps or wings."

"Well, that's something," said Jeremy.

"I never could get much satisfaction out of meaningless discourse," Mr. Propter continued. "I like the words I use to bear some relation to facts. That's why I'm interested in eternity—psychological eternity. Because it's a fact."

"For you, perhaps," said Jeremy in a tone which implied that more civilized people didn't suffer from these hallucinations.

"For anyone who chooses to fulfill the conditions under which it can be experienced."

"And why should anyone choose to fulfill them?"

"Why should anyone choose to go to Athens to see the Parthenon? Because it's worth the bother. And the same is true of eternity. The experience of timeless good is worth all the trouble it involves."

"Timeless good," Jeremy repeated with distaste. "I don't know what the words mean."

"Why should you?" said Mr. Propter. "One doesn't know the full meaning of the word 'Parthenon' until one has actually seen the thing."

"Yes, but at least I've seen photographs of the Parthenon; I've read descriptions."

"You've read descriptions of timeless good," Mr. Propter answered. "Dozens of them. In all the literatures of philosophy and religion. You've read them; but you've never bought your ticket for Athens."

In a resentful silence, Jeremy had to admit to himself that this was true. The fact that it was true made him disapprove of the conversation even more profoundly than he had done before.

"Time and craving," said Mr. Propter, "craving and time—two aspects of the same thing; and that thing is the raw material of evil. So you see, Pete," he added, turning to the young scientist, "you see what a queer sort of present you'll be making us, if you're successful in your work. Another century or so of time and craving. A couple of extra lifetimes of potential evil."

"And potential good," the young man insisted with a note of protest in his voice.

"And potential good," Mr. Propter agreed. "But only at a far remove from that extra time you're giving us."

"Why do you say that?" Pete asked.

"Because potential evil is *in* time; potential good isn't. The longer you live, the more evil you automatically come into contact with. Nobody comes automatically into contact with good. Men don't find more good by merely existing longer. It's curious," he went on reflectively, "that people should always have concentrated on the problem of evil. Exclusively. As though the nature of good were something self-evident. But it isn't self-evident. There's a problem of good at least as difficult as the problem of evil."

"And what's the solution?" Pete asked.

"The solution is very simple and profoundly unacceptable. Actual good is outside time."

"Outside time? But then how . . ."

"I told you it was unacceptable," said Mr. Propter.

"But if it's outside time, then . . ."

". . . then nothing within time can be actual good. Time is potential evil, and craving converts the potentiality into actual evil. Whereas a temporal act can never be more than potentially good, with a potentiality, what's more, that can't be actualized except out of time."

"But inside time, here—you know, just doing the ordinary things— hell! we do sometimes do right. What acts *are* good?"

"Strictly speaking, none," Mr. Propter answered. "But in practice, I think one's justified in applying the word to certain acts. Any act that contributes toward the liberation of those concerned in it—I'd call it a good act."

"Liberation?" the young man repeated dubiously. The words, in his mind, carried only economic and revolutionary connotations. But it was evident that Mr. Propter wasn't talking about the necessity for getting rid of capitalism. "Liberation from what?"

"Liberation from time," said Mr. Propter. "Liberation from craving and revulsion. Liberation from personality."

"But, heck," said Pete, "you're always talking about democracy. Doesn't that mean respecting personality?"

"Of course," Mr. Propter agreed. "Respecting it in order that it may be able to transcend itself. Slavery and fanaticism intensify the obsession with time and evil and the self. Hence the value of democratic institutions and a sceptical attitude of mind. The more you respect a personality, the better its chance of discovering that all personality is a prison. Potential good is anything that helps you to get out of prison. Actualized good lies outside the prison, in timelessness, in the state of pure, disinterested consciousness."

"I'm not much good at abstractions," said the young man. "Let's take some concrete examples. What about science, for instance? Is that good?"

"Good, bad and indifferent, according to how it's pursued and what it's used for. Good, bad and indifferent, first of all, for the scientists themselves—just as art and scholarship may be good, bad or indifferent for artists and scholars. Good if it facilitates liberation; indifferent if it neither helps nor hinders; bad if it makes liberation more difficult by intensifying the obsession with personality. And, remember, the apparent selflessness of the scientist, or the artist, is not necessarily a genuine freedom from the bondage of personality. Scientists and artists are men devoted to what we vaguely call an ideal. But what is an ideal? An ideal is merely the projection, on an enormously enlarged scale, of some aspect of personality."

"Say that again," Pete requested, while even Jeremy so far forgot his pose of superior detachment to lend his most careful attention.

Mr. Propter said it again. "And that's true," he went on, "of every ideal except the highest, which is the ideal of liberation—liberation from personality, liberation from time and craving, liberation into union with God, if you don't object to the word, Mr. Pordage. Many people do," he added. "It's one of the words that the Mrs. Grundys of the intellect find peculiarly shocking. I always try to spare their sensibilities, if I can. Well, to return to our idealist," he continued, glad to see that Jeremy had been constrained, in spite of himself, to smile. "If he serves any ideal except the highest—whether it's the artist's ideal of beauty, or the scientist's ideal of truth, or the humanitarian's ideal of what currently passes for goodness—he's not serving God; he's serving a magnified aspect of himself. He may be completely devoted; but, in the last analysis, his devotion turns out to be directed toward an aspect of his own personality. His apparent selflessness is really not a liberation from his ego, but merely another form of bondage. This means that science may be bad for scientists even when it appears to be a deliverer. And the same holds good of art, of scholarship, of humanitarianism."

"But you can't call self-sacrifice an intensification of the ego," said Pete.

"I can and I do," Mr. Propter insisted. "For the good reason that it generally is. Self-sacrifice to any but the highest cause is sacrifice to an ideal, which is simply a projection of the ego. What is commonly called self-sacrifice is the sacrifice of one part of the ego to another part, one set of personal feelings and passions for another set—as when the feelings connected with money or sex are sacrificed in order that the ego may have the feelings of superiority, solidarity and hatred which are associated with patriotism, or any kind of political or religious fanaticism."

Pete shook his head. "Sometimes," he said, with a smile of rueful perplexity, "sometimes you almost talk cynically."

Mr. Propter laughed. "It's good to be cynical," he said. "That is, if you know when to stop. Most of the things that we're all taught to respect and reverence—they don't deserve anything but cynicism. Take your own case. You've been taught to worship ideals like patriotism, social justice, science, romantic love. You've been told that such virtues as loyalty, temperance, courage and prudence are good in themselves, in any circumstances. You've been assured that self-sacrifice is always splendid and fine feelings invariably good. And it's all nonsense, all a pack of lies that people have made up in order to justify themselves in continuing to deny God and wallow in their own egotism. Unless you're steadily and unflaggingly cynical about the solemn twaddle that's talked by bishops and bankers and professors and politicians and all the rest of them, you're lost. Utterly lost. Doomed to perpetual imprisonment in your ego—doomed to be a personality in a world of personalities; and a world of personalities is this world, the world of greed and fear and hatred, of war and capitalism and dictatorship and slavery. Yes, you've got to be cynical, Pete. Specially cynical about all the actions and feelings you've been taught to suppose were good. Most of them are not good. They're merely evils which happen to be regarded as creditable. But unfortunately, creditable evil is just as bad as discreditable evil. Scribes and Pharisees aren't any better, in the last analysis, than publicans and sinners. Indeed, they're often much worse. For several reasons. Being well thought of by others, they think well of themselves; and nothing so confirms an egotism as thinking well of oneself. In the next place, publicans and sinners are generally just human animals, without enough energy or self-control to do much harm. Whereas the scribes and Pharisees have all the virtues, except the only two which count, and enough intelligence to understand everything except the real nature of the world. Publicans and sinners merely fornicate and overeat and get drunk. The people who make wars, the people who reduce their fellows to slavery, the people who kill and torture and tell lies in the name of their sacred causes,

OF TIME AND THE EGO

the really evil people in a word—these are never the publicans and the sinners. No, they're the virtuous, respectable men, who have the finest feelings, the best brains, the noblest ideals."

"So what it all boils down to," Pete concluded in a tone of angry despair, "is that there just isn't anything you can do. Is that it?"

"Yes and no," said Mr. Propter, in his quiet judicial way. "On a strictly human level, the level of time and craving, I should say that it's quite true: in the last resort, there isn't anything you can do."

"But that's just defeatism!" Pete protested.

"Why is it defeatism to be realistic?"

"There must be something to do!"

"I see no 'must' about it."

"Then what about the reformers and all those people? If you're right, they're just wasting their time."

"It depends on what they think they're doing," said Mr. Propter. "If they think they're just temporarily palliating particular distresses, if they see themselves as people engaged in laboriously deflecting evil from old channels into new and slightly different channels, then they can justifiably claim to be successful. But if they think they're making good appear where evil was before, why then all history clearly shows that they are wasting their time."

"But why can't they make good appear where evil was before?"

"Why do we fall when we jump out of a tenth-story window? Because the nature of things happens to be such that we do fall. And the nature of things is such that, on the strictly human level of time and craving, you can't achieve anything but evil. If you choose to work exclusively on that level and exclusively for the ideals and causes that are character- istic of it, then you're insane if you expect to transform evil into good. You're insane, because experience should have shown you that, on that level, there doesn't happen to be any good. There are only different de- grees and different kinds of evil."

"Then what do you want people to do?"

"Don't talk as though it were all my fault," said Mr. Propter. "I didn't invent the universe."

"What ought they to do, then?"

"Well, if they want fresh varieties of evil, let them go on with what they're doing now. But if they want good, they'll have to change their tactics. And the encouraging thing," Mr. Propter added, in another tone, "the encouraging thing is that there are tactics which will produce good. We've seen that there's nothing to be done on the strictly human level —or rather there are millions of things to be done, only none of them.

will achieve any good. But there is something effective to be done on the levels where good actually exists. So you see, Pete, I'm not a defeatist. I'm a strategist. I believe that if a battle is to be fought it had better be fought under conditions in which there's at least some chance of winning. I believe that if you want the golden fleece it's more sensible to go to the place where it exists than to rush round performing prodigies of valor in a country where all the fleeces happen to be coal black."

"Then where ought we to fight for good?"

"Where good is."

"But where is it?"

"On the level below the human and on the level above. On the animal level and on the level . . . well, you can take your choice of names: the level of eternity; the level, if you don't object, of God; the level of the spirit—only that happens to be about the most ambiguous word in the language. On the lower level, good exists as the proper functioning of the organism in accordance with the laws of its own being. On the higher level, it exists in the form of a knowledge of the world without desire or aversion; it exists as the experience of eternity, as the transcendence of personality, the extension of consciousness beyond the limits imposed by the ego. Strictly human activities are activities that prevent the manifestation of good on the other two levels. For, insofar as we're human, we're obsessed with time; we're passionately concerned with our personalities and with those magnified projections of our personalities which we call our policies, our ideals, our religions. And what are the results? Being obsessed with time and our egos, we are forever craving and worrying. But nothing impairs the normal functioning of the organism like craving and revulsion, like greed and fear and worry. Directly or indirectly, most of our physical ailments and disabilities are due to worry and craving. We worry and crave ourselves into high blood pressure, heart disease, tuberculosis, peptic ulcer, low resistance to infection, neurasthenia, sexual aberrations, insanity, suicide. Not to mention all the rest." Mr. Propter waved his hand comprehensively. "Craving even prevents us from seeing properly," he went on. "The harder we try to see, the graver our error of accommodation. And it's the same with bodily posture: the more we worry about doing the thing immediately ahead of us in time, the more we interfere with our correct body posture and the worse, in consequence, becomes the functioning of the entire organism. In a word, insofar as we're human beings, we prevent ourselves from realizing the physiological and instinctive good that we're capable of as animals. And, mutatis mutandis, the same thing is true in regard to the sphere above. Insofar as we're human beings, we prevent ourselves from realizing the spiritual and timeless good that we're capable of as potential inhabitants of eternity, as potential enjoyers of the beatific vision. We worry and crave ourselves out of the very possibility of transcending personality and knowing, intellectually at first and then by direct experience, the true nature of the world."

Mr. Propter was silent for a moment; then, with a sudden smile, "Luckily," he went on, "most of us don't manage to behave like human beings all the time. We forget our wretched little egos and those horrible great projections of our egos in the ideal world—forget them and relapse for a while into harmless animality. The organism gets a chance to function according to its own laws; in other words, it gets a chance to realize such good as it's capable of. That's why we're as healthy and sane as we are. Even in great cities, as many as four persons out of five manage to go through life without having to be treated in a lunatic asylum. If we were consistently human, the percentage of mental cases would rise from twenty to a hundred. But fortunately most of us are incapable of consistency. The animal is always trying to resume its rights. And to some people fairly frequently, perhaps occasionally to all, there come little flashes of illumination—momentary glimpses into the nature of the world as it is for a consciousness liberated from appetite and time, of the world as it might be if we didn't choose to deny God by being our personal selves. Those flashes come to us when we're off our guard; then craving and worry come rushing back and the light is eclipsed once more by our personality and its lunatic ideals, its criminal policies and plans."

"Minimum Working Hypothesis"

From *Time Must Have A Stop*

THE difference between metaphysics now and metaphysics in the past is the difference between word-spinning which makes no difference to anybody and a system of thought associated with a transforming discipline. "Short of the Absolute, God cannot rest, and having reached that goal He is lost and religion with Him." That is Bradley's view, the modern view. Sankara was as strenuously an Absolutist as Bradley—but with what an enormous difference! For him, there is not only discursive knowledge about the Absolute, but the possibility (and the final necessity) of a direct intellectual intuition, leading the liberated spirit to identification with the object of its knowledge. "Among all means of liberation, bhakti or devotion is supreme. To seek earnestly to know one's real nature—this is said to be devotion. In other words, devotion can be defined as the search for the reality of one's own atman," and the atman, of course, is the spiritual principle in us, which is identical with the Absolute. The older metaphysicians did not lose religion; they found it in the highest and purest of all possible forms.

To the surprise of Humanists and Liberal Churchmen, the abolition of God left a perceptible void. But Nature abhors vacuums. Nation, Class and Party, Culture and Art have rushed in to fill the empty niche. For politicians and for those of us who happen to have been born with a talent, the new pseudo-religions have been, still are and (until they destroy the entire social structure) will continue to be extremely profitable superstitions. But regard them dispassionately, *sub specie aeternitatis*. How unutterably odd, silly and satanic!

Research by means of controlled sense-intuitions into material reality —research motivated and guided by a working hypothesis, leading up through logical inference to the formulation of a rational theory, and resulting in appropriate technological action. That is natural science.

No working hypothesis means no motive for starting the research, no reason for making one experiment rather than another, no rational theory for bringing sense or order to the observed facts.

Contrariwise, too much working hypothesis means finding only what you know, dogmatically, to be there and ignoring all the rest.

Among other things, religion is also research. Research by means of pure intellectual intuition into nonsensuous, nonpsychic, purely spiritual reality, descending to rational theories about its results and to appropriate moral action in the light of such theories.

To motivate and (in its preliminary stages) guide this research, what sort and how much of a working hypothesis do we need?

None, say the sentimental humanists; just a little bit of Wordsworth, say the blue-dome-of-nature boys. Result: they have no motive impelling them to make the more strenuous investigations; they are unable to explain nonsensuous facts as come their way; they make very little progress in Charity.

At the other end of the scale are the Papists, the Jews, the Moslems, all with historical, one-hundred-per-cent revealed religions. These people have a working hypothesis about nonsensuous reality—which means that they have a motive for doing something to get to know about it. But because their working hypotheses are too elaborately dogmatic, most of them discover only what they were taught to believe. But what they believe is a hotchpotch of good, less good and even bad. Records of the infallible intuitions of great saints into the highest spiritual reality are mixed up with records of the less reliable and infinitely less valuable intuitions of psychics into lower levels of nonsensuous existence; and to these are added mere fancies, discursive reasonings and sentimentalisms, projected into a kind of secondary objectivity and worshiped as though they were divine facts. But at all times and in spite of the handicap imposed by these excessive working hypotheses, a passionately persistent few continue the research to the point where they become aware of the Intelligible Light and are united with the divine Ground.

For those of us who are not congenitally the members of any organized church, who have found that humanism and blue-domeism are not enough, who are not content to remain in the darkness of spiritual ignorance, the squalor of vice or that other squalor of mere respectability, the minimum working hypothesis would seem to be about as follows:

That there is a Godhead or Ground, which is the unmanifested principle of all manifestation.

That the Ground is transcendent and immanent.

That it is possible for human beings to love, know and, from virtually, to become actually identified with the Ground.

That to achieve this unitive knowledge, to realize this supreme identity, is the final end and purpose of human existence.

That there is a Law or Dharma, which must be obeyed, a Tao or Way, which must be followed, if men are to achieve their final end.

That the more there is of I, me, mine, the less there is of the Ground; and that consequently the Tao is a Way of humility and compassion, the Dharma a Law of mortification and self-transcending awareness. Which accounts, of course, for the facts of human history. People love their egos and don't wish to mortify them, don't wish to see why they shouldn't "express their personalities" and "have a good time." They get their good times; but also and inevitably they get wars and syphilis and revolution and alcoholism, tyranny and, in default of an adequate religious hypothesis, the choice between some lunatic idolatry, like nationalism, and a sense of complete futility and despair. Unutterable miseries! But throughout recorded history most men and women have preferred the risks, the positive certainty, of such disasters to the laborious whole-time job of trying to get to know the divine Ground of all being. In the long run we get exactly what we ask for.

Decentralization and Self-Government

From *Ends and Means*

BY WHAT means can the principle of self-government be applied to the daily lives of men and women? To what extent is the self-government of the component parts of a society compatible with its efficiency as a whole?

The technique for self-government all round, self-government for ordinary people in their ordinary avocations, is a matter which we cannot profitably discuss unless we have a clear idea of what may be called the natural history and psychology of groups. Quantitatively, a group differs from a crowd in size; qualitatively, in the kind and intensity of the mental life of the constituent individuals. A crowd is a lot of people; a group is a few. A crowd has a mental life inferior in intellectual quality and emotionally less under voluntary control than the mental life of each of its members in isolation. The mental life of a group is not inferior, either intellectually or emotionally, to the mental life of the individuals composing it and may, in favorable circumstances, actually be superior.

The significant psychological facts about the crowd are as follows. The tone of crowd emotion is essentially orgiastic and dionysiac. In virtue of his membership of the crowd, the individual is released from the limitations of his personality, made free of the subpersonal, subhuman world of unrestrained feeling and uncriticized belief. To be a member of a crowd is an experience closely akin to alcoholic intoxication. Most human beings feel a craving to escape from the cramping limitations of their ego, to take periodical holidays from their all too familiar, all too squalid little self. As they do not know how to travel upward from personality into a region of superpersonality and as they are unwilling, even if they do know, to fulfill the ethical, psychological and physiological conditions of self-transcendence, they turn naturally to the descending road, the road that leads down from personality to the darkness of subhuman emotionalism and panic animality. Hence the persistent craving for narcotics and stimulants, hence the never-failing attraction of the crowd. The success of the dictators was due in large measure to their extremely skillful exploitation of the universal human need for escape from the limitations of personality. Perceiving that people wished to take holidays from themselves in subhuman emotionality, they systematically provided their subjects with the occasions for doing so. The Communists denounce religion as the opium of the people; but all they have done is to replace this old drug by a new one of similar composition. For the crowd round the relic of the saint they have substituted the crowd at the political meeting; for religious procession, military reviews and May Day parades. It is the same with the surviving Fascist dictators. In all the totalitarian states the masses are persuaded, and even compelled, to take periodical holidays from themselves in the subhuman world of crowd emotion. It is significant that while they encourage and actually command the descent into subhumanity the dictators do all they can to prevent men from taking the upward road from personal limitation, the road that leads toward nonattachment to the "things of this world" and attachment to that which is superpersonal. The higher manifestations of religion are far more suspect to the tyrants than the lower—and with reason. For the man who escapes from egotism into superpersonality has transcended his old idolatrous loyalty, not only to himself, but also to the local divinities—nation, party, class, deified boss. Self-transcendence, escape from the prison of the ego into union with what is above personality, is generally accomplished in solitude. That is why the tyrants like to herd their subjects into those vast crowds, in which the individual is reduced to a state of intoxicated subhumanity.

It is time now to consider the group. The first question we must ask ourselves is this: when does a group become a crowd? This is not a problem in verbal definition; it is a matter of observation and experience. It is found empirically that group activities and characteristic group feeling become increasingly difficult when more than about twenty or less than about five individuals are involved. Groups which come together for the purpose of carrying out a specific job of manual work can afford to be larger than groups which meet for the purpose of pooling information and elaborating a common policy, or which meet for religious exercises, or for mutual comfort, or merely for the sake of convivially "getting together." Twenty or even as many as thirty people can work together and still remain a group. But these numbers would be much too high in a group that had assembled for the other purposes I have mentioned. It is significant that Jesus had only twelve apostles; that the Benedictines were divided into groups of ten under a dean (Latin *decanus*, from Greek δέκα, ten); that ten is the number of individuals constituting a Communist cell. Committees of more than a dozen members are found to be unmanageably large. Eight is the perfect number for a dinner party.

The most successful Quaker meetings are generally meetings at which few people are present. Educationists agree that the most satisfactory size for a class is between eight and fifteen. In armies, the smallest unit is about ten. The witches' "coven" was a group of thirteen. And so on. All evidence points clearly to the fact that there is an optimum size for groups and that this optimum is round about ten for groups meeting for social, religious or intellectual purposes, and from ten to thirty for groups engaged in manual work. This being so, it is clear that the units of self-government should be groups of the optimum size. If they are smaller than the optimum, they will fail to develop that emotional field which gives to group activity its characteristic quality, while the available quantity of pooled information and experience will be inadequate. If they are larger than the optimum, they will tend to split into subgroups of the optimum size or, if the constituent individuals remain together in a crowd, there will be a danger of their relapsing into the crowd's sub-human stupidity and emotionality.

The technique of industrial self-government has been discussed with a wealth of concrete examples in a remarkable book by the French economist, Hyacinthe Dubreuil, entitled *A Chacun sa Chance*. Dubreuil points out that even the largest industries can be organized so as to consist of a series of self-governing, yet co-ordinated, groups of, at the outside, thirty members. Within the industry each one of such groups can act as a kind of subcontractor, undertaking to perform so much of such and such a kind of work for such and such a sum. The equitable division of this sum among the constituent members is left to the group itself, as is also the preservation of discipline, the election of representatives and leaders. The examples which Dubreuil quotes from the annals of industrial history and from his own experience as a workman tend to show that this form of organization is appreciated by the workers, to whom it gives a measure of independence even within the largest manufacturing concern, and that in most cases it results in increased efficiency of working. It possesses, as he points out, the further merit of being a form of organization that educates those who belong to it in the practice of co-operation and mutual responsibility.

Under the present dispensation, the great majority of factories are little despotisms, benevolent in some cases, malevolent in others. Even where benevolence prevails, passive obedience is demanded of the workers, who are ruled by overseers, not of their own election, but appointed from above. In theory, they may be the subjects of a democratic state; but in practice they spend the whole of their working lives as the subjects of a petty tyrant. Dubreuil's scheme, if it were generally acted upon, would introduce genuine democracy into the factory. And if some such scheme is not acted upon, it is of small moment to the individual whether the industry in which he is working is owned by the state, by a co-operative society, by a joint-stock company or by a private individual. Passive obedience to officers appointed from above is always passive obedience, whoever the general in ultimate control may be.

Of modern wage slaves, Lenin writes that they "remain to such an extent crushed by want and poverty that they 'can't be bothered with democracy,' have 'no time for politics,' and in the ordinary peaceful course of events, the majority of the population is debarred from participating in public political life." This statement is only partially true. Not all those who can't be bothered with democracy are debarred from political life by want and poverty. Plenty of well-paid workmen and, for that matter, plenty of the wealthiest beneficiaries of the capitalistic system find that they can't be bothered with politics. The reason is not economic, but psychological; has its source, not in environment, but in heredity. People belong to different psychophysiological types and are endowed with different degrees of general intelligence. The will and ability to take an effective interest in large-size politics do not belong to all, or even a majority of, men and women. Preoccupation with general ideas, with things and people distant in space, with contingent events remote in future time, is something which it is given to only a few to feel. "What's Hecuba to him or he to Hecuba?" The answer in most cases is: Nothing whatsoever. An improvement in the standard of living might perceptibly increase the number of those for whom Hecuba meant something. But even if all were rich, there would still be many congenitally incapable of being bothered with anything so far removed from the warm, tangible facts of everyday experience. As things are at present, millions of men and women come into the world disfranchised by nature. They have the privilege of voting on long-range, large-scale political issues; but they are congenitally incapable of taking an intelligent interest in any but short-range, small-scale problems. Too often the framers of democratic constitutions have acted as though man were made for democracy, not democracy for man. The vote has been a kind of bed of Procrustes upon which, however long their views, however short their ability, all human beings were expected to stretch themselves. Not unnaturally, the results of this kind of democracy have proved disappointing. Nevertheless, it remains true that democratic freedom is good for those who enjoy it, and that practice in self-government is an almost indispensable element in the curriculum of man's moral and psychological education. Human beings belong to different types; it is therefore necessary to create different types of democratic and self-governing institutions, suitable for the various kinds of men and women. Thus, people with short-range, small-scale interests can find scope for their kind of political abilities in self-governing groups within an industry, within a consumer or producer co-operative, within the administrative machinery of the parish, borough or county. By means of comparatively small changes in the existing systems of local and professional organization it would be possible to make almost every individual a member of some self-governing group. In this way the curse of merely passive obedience could be got rid of, the vice of political indolence cured and the advantages of responsible and active freedom brought to all. In this context it is worth remarking on a very significant change which has recently taken place in our social habits. Materially, this change may be summed up as the decline of the community; psychologically, as the decline of the community sense. The reasons for this double change are many and of various kinds. Here are a few of the more important.

Birth control has reduced the size of the average family and, for various reasons which will be apparent later, the old habits of patriarchal living have practically disappeared. It is very rare nowadays to find parents, married children and grandchildren living together in the same house or in close association. Large families and patriarchal groups were communities in which children and adults had to learn (often by very painful means) the art of co-operation and the need to accept responsibility for others. These admittedly rather crude schools of community sense have now disappeared.

New methods of transport have profoundly modified the life in the village and small town. Up to only a generation ago most villages were to a great extent self-sufficing communities. Every trade was represented by its local technician; the local produce was consumed or exchanged in the neighborhood; the inhabitants worked on the spot. If they desired instruction or entertainment or religion, they had to mobilize the local talent and produce it themselves. Today all this is changed. Thanks to improved transport, the village is now closely bound up with the rest of the economic world. Supplies and technical services are obtained from a distance. Large numbers of the inhabitants go out to work in factories and offices in far-off cities. Music and the drama are provided, not by local talent, but over the ether and in the picture theater. Once all the members of the community were always on the spot; now, thanks to cars, motorcycles and buses the villagers are rarely in their village. Community fun, community worship, community efforts to secure culture have tended to decline, for the simple reason that, in leisure hours, a large part of the community's membership is always somewhere else. Nor is this all. The older inhabitants of Middletown, as readers of the Lynds' classical study of American small-town life will remember, complained that the internal-combustion engine had led to a decline of neighborliness. Neighbors have Fords and Chevrolets, consequently are no longer there to be neighborly; or if by chance they should be at home, they content themselves with calling up on the telephone. Technological progress has reduced the number of physical contacts, impoverished the spiritual relations between the members of a community.

Centralized professionalism has not only affected local entertainment; it has also affected the manifestations of local charity and mutual aid. State-provided hospitals, state-provided medical and nursing services are certainly much more efficient than the ministrations of the neighbors. But this increased efficiency is purchased at the price of a certain tendency on the part of neighbors to disclaim liability for one another and throw their responsibilities entirely upon the central authority. Under a perfectly organized system of state socialism charity would be, not merely superfluous, but actually criminal. Good Samaritans would be prosecuted for daring to interfere in their bungling amateurish way with what was obviously a case for state-paid professionals.

The last three generations have witnessed a vast increase in the size and number of large cities. Life is more exciting and more money can be earned in the cities than in villages and small towns. Hence the migration from country to city. In the van of this migrating host have marched the ambitious, the talented, the adventurous. For more than a century there has been a tendency for the most gifted members of small rural communities to leave home and seek their fortunes in the towns. Consequently what remains in the villages and country towns of the industrialized countries is in the nature of a residual population, dysgenically selected for its lack of spirit and intellectual gifts. Why is it so hard to induce peasants and small farmers to adopt new scientific methods? Among other reasons, because almost every exceptionally intelligent child born into a rural family for a century past has taken the earliest opportunity of deserting the land for the city. Community life in the country is thus impoverished; but (and this is the important point) the community life of the great urban centers is not correspondingly enriched. It is not enriched for the good reason that, in growing enormous, cities have also grown chaotic. A metropolitan "wen," as Cobbett was already calling the relatively tiny London of his day, is no longer an organic whole, no longer exists as a community, in whose life individuals can fruitfully participate. Men and women rub shoulders with other men and women; but the contact is external and mechanical. Each one of them can say, in the words of the Jolly Miller of the song: "I care for nobody, no, not I, and nobody cares for me." Metropolitan life is atomistic. The city, as a city, does nothing to correlate its human particles into a pattern of responsible, communal living. What the country loses on the swings, the city loses all over again on the roundabouts.

In the light of this statement of the principal reasons for the recent decline of the community and of the community sense in individuals, we can suggest certain remedies. For example, schools and colleges can be transformed into organic communities and used to offset, during a short period of the individual's career, the decay in family and village life. (A very interesting experiment in this direction is being made at Black Mountain College in North Carolina.) To some extent, no doubt, the old "natural" life of villages and small towns, the life that the economic, technological and religious circumstances of the past conspired to impose upon them, can be replaced by a consciously designed synthetic product —a life of associations organized for local government, for sport, for cultural activities and the like. Such associations already exist, and there should be no great difficulty in opening them to larger numbers and, at the same time, in making their activities so interesting that people will wish to join them instead of taking the line of least resistance, as they do now, and living unconnected, atomistic lives, passively obeying during their working hours and passively allowing themselves to be entertained by machinery during their hours of leisure. The existence of associations of this kind would serve to make country life less dull and so do something to arrest the flight toward the city. At the same time, the decentralization of industry and its association with agriculture should make it possible for the countryman to earn as much as the city dweller. In spite of the ease with which electric power can now be distributed, the movement toward the decentralization of industry is not yet a very powerful one. Great centers of population, like London and Paris, possess an enormous power of attraction to industries. The greater the population, the greater the market; and the greater the market, the stronger the gravitational pull exercised upon the manufacturer. New industries establish themselves on the outskirts of large cities and make them become still larger. For the sake of slightly increased profits, due to lower distributing costs, the manufacturers are busily engaged in making London chaotically large, hopelessly congested, desperately hard to enter or leave, and vulnerable to air attacks as no other city of Europe is vulnerable. To compel a rational and planned decentralization of industry is one of the legitimate, the urgently necessary functions of the state.

Life in the great city is atomistic. How shall it be given a communal pattern? How shall the individual be incorporated in a responsible, self-governing group? In a modern city, the problem of organizing responsible community life on a local basis is not easily solved. Modern cities have been created and are preserved by the labors of highly specialized technicians. The massacre of a few thousands of engineers, administrators and doctors would be sufficient to reduce any of the great metropolitan centers to a state of plague-stricken, starving chaos. Accordingly, in most of its branches, the local government of a great city has become a highly technical affair, a business of the kind that must be centrally planned and carried out by experts. The only department in which there would seem to be a possibility of profitably extending the existing institutions of local self-government is the department concerned with police work and the observance of laws. I have read that in Japan the cities were, and perhaps still are, divided into wards of about a hundred inhabitants apiece. The people in each ward accepted a measure of liability for one another and were to some extent responsible for good behavior and the observance of law within their own small unit. That such a system lends itself to the most monstrous abuses is obvious. But there is no governmental institution that cannot be abused. Elected parliaments have been used as instruments of oppression; plebiscites have served to confirm and strengthen tyranny; courts of justice have been transformed into Star Chambers and military tribunals. Like all the rest, the ward system may be a course of good in a desirable context and a source of unmitigated evil in an undesirable context. It remains in any case a device worth considering by those who aspire to impose a communal pattern upon the atomistic, irresponsible life of modern city dwellers. For the rest, it looks as though the townsman's main experience of democratic institutions and responsible self-government would have to be obtained, not in local administration, but in the fields of industry and economics, of religious and cultural activity, of athletics and entertainment.

In the preceding paragraphs I have tried to answer the first of our questions and have described the methods by which the principle of self-government can be applied to the daily lives of ordinary men and women. Our second question concerns the compatibility of self-government all round with the efficiency of industry in particular and society as a whole. In Russia self-government in industry was tried in the early years of the revolution and was abandoned in favor of authoritarian management. Within the factory discipline is no longer enforced by elected representatives of the Soviet or workers' committee, but by appointees of the Communist Party. The new conception of management current in

Soviet Russia was summed up by Kaganovitch in a speech before the seventeenth congress of the Communist Party. "Management," he said, "means the power to distribute material things, to appoint and discharge subordinates, in a word, to be master of the particular enterprise." This is a definition of management to which every industrial dictator in the capitalist countries would unhesitatingly subscribe.

By supporters of the present Russian government it is said that the change-over from self-government to authoritarian management had to be made in the interests of efficiency. That extremely inexperienced and ill-educated workers should have been unable to govern themselves and keep up industrial efficiency seems likely enough. But in Western Europe and the United States such a situation is not likely to arise. Indeed, Dubreuil has pointed out that, as a matter of historical fact, self-government within factories has often led to increased efficiency. It would seem, then, that in countries where all men and women are relatively well educated and have been accustomed for some time to the working of democratic institutions there is no danger that self-government will lead to a breakdown of discipline within the factory or a decline in output. But, like "liberty," the word "efficiency" covers a multitude of sins. Even if it should be irrefragably demonstrated that self-government in industry invariably led to greater contentment and increased output, even if it could be proved experimentally that the best features of individualism and collectivism could be combined if the state were to co-ordinate the activities of self-governing industries, there would still be complainers of "inefficiency." And by their own lights, the complaints would be quite right. For to the ruling classes, not only in the totalitarian, but also in the democratic countries, "efficiency" means primarily "military efficiency." Now, a society in which the principle of self-government has been applied to the ordinary activities of all its members is a society which, for purely military purposes, is probably decidedly inefficient. A militarily efficient society is one whose members have been brought up in habits of passive obedience and at the head of which there is an individual exercising absolute authority through a perfectly trained hierarchy of administrators. In time of war, such a society can be manipulated as a single unit and with extraordinary rapidity and precision. So long as nations persist in using war as an instrument of policy, military efficiency will be prized above all else. Therefore schemes for extending the principle of self-government will either not be tried at all or, if tried, as in Russia, will be speedily abandoned. Inevitably, we find ourselves confronted, yet once more, by the central evil of our time: the overpowering and increasing evil of war.

I must try now to answer our question concerning the efficiency (as distinct from military efficiency) of a society made up of co-ordinated self-governing units. Dubreuil has shown that even the largest industrial undertakings can be organized so as to consist of a number of co-ordinated but self-governing groups; and he has produced reasons for supposing that such an organization would not reduce the efficiency of the businesses concerned and might even increase it. This small-scale industrial democracy is theoretically compatible with any kind of large-scale control of the industries concerned. It can be (and in certain cases actually has been applied to industries working under the capitalist system; to businesses under direct state control; to co-operative enterprises; to mixed concerns, like the Port of London Authority, which are under state supervision, but have their own autonomous, functional management. In practice this small-scale industrial democracy, this self-government for all, is intrinsically most compatible with business organizations of the last two kinds—co-operative and mixed. It is almost equally incompatible with capitalism and state Socialism. Capitalism tends to produce a multiplicity of petty dictators, each in command of his own little business kingdom. State Socialism tends to produce a single, centralized, totalitarian dictatorship, wielding absolute authority over all its subjects through a hierarchy of bureaucratic agents.

Co-operatives and mixed concerns already exist and work extremely well. To increase their numbers and to extend their scope would not seem a revolutionary act, in the sense that it would probably not provoke the violent opposition which men feel toward projects involving an entirely new principle. In its effects, however, the act would be revolutionary; for it would result in a profound modification of the existing system. This alone is a sufficient reason for preferring these forms of ultimate industrial control to all others. The intrinsic compatibility of the co-operative enterprise and mixed concern with small-scale democracy and self-government all round constitutes yet another reason for the preference.

Politics and Religion

From *Grey Eminence*

I

About politics one can make only one completely unquestionable generalization, which is that it is quite impossible for statesmen to foresee, for more than a very short time, the results of any course of large-scale political action. Many of them, it is true, justify their actions by pretending to themselves and others that they can see a long way ahead; but the fact remains that they can't. If they were completely honest they would say, with Father Joseph,

> J'ignore où mon dessein, qui surpasse ma vue,
>   Si vite me conduit;
> Mais comme un astre ardent qui brille dans la nue,
>   Il me guide en la nuit.

If hell is paved with good intentions, it is, among other reasons, because of the impossibility of calculating consequences.

But though it is impossible to foresee the remoter consequences of any given course of action, it is by no means impossible to foresee, in the light of past historical experience, the sort of consequences that are likely, in a general way, to follow certain sorts of acts. Thus, from the records of past experience, it seems sufficiently clear that the consequences attendant on a course of action involving such things as large-scale war, violent revolution, unrestrained tyranny and persecution are likely to be bad. Consequently, any politician who embarks on such courses of action cannot plead ignorance as an excuse. Father Joseph, for example, had read enough history to know that policies like that which Richelieu and he were pursuing are seldom, even when nominally successful, productive of lasting good to the parties by whom they were framed. But his passionate ambition for the Bourbons made him cling to a voluntary ignorance, which he proceeded to justify by speculations about the will of God.

Here it seems worth while to comment briefly on the curious time sense of those who think in political terms. Courses of action are recommended on the ground that, if carried out, they cannot fail to result in a solution to all outstanding problems—a solution either definitive and everlasting, like that which Marx foresaw as the result of the setting up of a classless society, or else of very long duration, like the thousand-year futures foretold for their regimes by Mussolini and Hitler, or like the more modest five-hundred-year Pax Americana of which Miss Dorothy Thompson has spoken. Richelieu's admirers envisaged a Bourbon golden age longer than the hypothetical Nazi or Fascist era, but shorter (since it had a limit) than the final, classless stage of Communism. In a contemporary defense of the Cardinal's policy against the Huguenots, Voiture justifies the great expenditures involved by saying that "the capture of La Rochelle alone has economized millions; for La Rochelle would have raised rebellion at every royal minority, every revolt of the nobles during the next two thousand years." Such are the illusions cherished by the politically minded when they reflect on the consequences of a policy immediately before or immediately after it has been put in action. But when the policy has begun to show its fruits, their time sense undergoes a radical change. Gone are the calculations in terms of centuries or millennia. A single victory is now held to justify a *Te Deum*, and if the policy yields apparently successful results for only a few years, the statesman feels satisfied and his sycophants are lavish in their praise of his genius. Even sober historians writing long after the event tend to express themselves in the same vein. Thus, Richelieu is praised by modern writers as a very great and farsighted statesman, even though it is perfectly clear that the actions he undertook for the aggrandizement of the Bourbon dynasty created the social and economic and political conditions, which led to the downfall of that dynasty, the rise of Prussia and the catastrophes of the nineteenth and twentieth centuries. His policy is praised as if it had been eminently successful, and those who objected to it are blamed for their shortsighted views.

Such extraordinary inconsistency can only be explained by the fact that, when people come to talk of their nation's successes, they think in terms of the very briefest periods of time. A triumph is to be hymned and gloated over, even if it lasts no more than a day. Retrospectively, men like Richelieu and Louis XIV and Napoleon are more admired for the brief glory they achieved than hated for the long-drawn miseries which were the price of that glory.

Among the sixteen hundred-odd ladies whose names were set down in the catalogue of Don Giovanni's conquests, there were doubtless not a few whose favors made it necessary for the hero to consult his physician. But pox or no pox, the mere fact that the favors had been given was a thing to feel proud of, a victory worth recording in Leporello's chronicle of successes. The history of the nations is written in the same spirit.

II

Most people at the present time probably take for granted the validity of the pragmatists' contention, that the end of thought is action. In the philosophy which Father Joseph had studied and made his own, this position is reversed. Here contemplation is the end and action (in which is included discursive thought) is valuable only as a means to the beatific vision of God. In the words of St. Thomas Aquinas, "action should be something added to the life of prayer, not something taken away from it." To the man of the world, this statement is almost totally devoid of meaning. To the contemplative, whose concern is with spiritual religion, with the kingdom of God rather than the kingdom of selves, it seems axiomatic. Starting from this fundamental principle of theocentric religion, the practical mystics have critically examined the whole idea of action and have laid down, in regard to it, a set of rules for the guidance of those desiring to follow the mystical path toward the beatific vision. One of the best formulations of the traditional mystical doctrine in regard to action was made by Father Joseph's contemporary, Louis Lallemant. Lallemant was a Jesuit, who, in spite of the prevailing anti-mystical tendencies of his order, was permitted to teach a very advanced (but entirely orthodox) kind of spirituality to the men entrusted to his care.

Whenever we undertake any action, Father Lallemant insists, we must model ourselves upon God himself, who creates and sustains the world without in any way modifying his essential existence. But we cannot do this unless we learn to practice formal contemplation and a constant awareness of God's presence. Both are difficult, especially the latter which is possible only to those very far advanced along the way of perfection. So far as beginners are concerned, even the doing of good works may distract the soul from God. Action is not safe, except for proficients in the art of mental prayer. "If we have gone far in orison," says Lallemant, "we shall give much to action; if we are but middlingly advanced in the inward life, we shall give ourselves only moderately to outward life; if we have only a very little inwardness, we shall give nothing at all to what is external, unless our vow of obedience commands the contrary." To the reasons already given for this injunction we may add others of a strictly utilitarian nature. It is a matter of experience and observation that actions undertaken by ordinary unregenerate people, sunk in their

selfhood and without spiritual insight, seldom do much good. A generation before Lallemant, St. John of the Cross had put the whole matter
in a single question and answer. Those who rush headlong into good
works without having acquired through contemplation the power to act
well—what do they accomplish? "Poco mas que nada, y a veces nada, y
aun a veces dano." (Little more than nothing, and sometimes nothing
at all, and sometimes even harm.) One reason for hell being paved with
good intentions has already been mentioned, and to this, the impossibility
of foreseeing the consequences of actions, we must now add another,
the intrinsically unsatisfactory nature of actions performed by the ordinary
run of average unregenerate men and women. This being so, Lallemant
recommends the least possible external activity until such time as, by
contemplation and the unremitting practice of the presence, the soul
has been trained to give itself completely to God. Those who have
traveled only a little way along the road to union, "should not go out
of themselves for the service of their neighbors, except by way of trial
and experiment. We must be like those hunting dogs that are still half
held upon the leash. When we shall have come by contemplation to
possess God, we shall be able to give greater freedom to our zeal." External activity causes no interruption in the orison of the proficient; on the
contrary it is a means for bringing them nearer to reality. Those for
whom it is not such a means should as far as possible refrain from action.
Once again Father Lallemant justifies himself by the appeal to experience
and a purely utilitarian consideration of consequences. In all that concerns
the saving of souls and the improving of the quality of people's thoughts
and feelings and behavior, "a man of orison will accomplish more in one
year than another man in all his life."

What is true of good works is true, a fortiori, of merely worldly activity,
particularly when it is activity on a large scale, involving the collaboration
of great numbers of individuals in every stage of unenlightenment. Good
is a product of the ethical and spiritual artistry of individuals; it cannot
be mass-produced. All Catholic theologians were well aware of this truth,
and the church has acted upon it since its earliest days. The monastic
orders—and pre-eminently that to which Father Joseph himself belonged
—were living demonstrations of the traditional doctrine of action. This
doctrine affirmed that goodness of more than average quantity and quality
could be practically realized only on a small scale, by self-dedicated and
specially trained individuals.

III

This brings us to the heart of that great paradox of politics—the fact that political action is necessary and at the same time incapable of satisfying the needs which called it into existence.

Only static and isolated societies, whose way of life is determined by an unquestioned tradition, can dispense with politics. In unstable, unisolated, technologically progressive societies, such as ours, large-scale political action is unavoidable. But even when it is well intentioned (which it very often is not) political action is always foredoomed to a partial, sometimes even a complete, self-stultification. The intrinsic nature of the human instruments with which, and the human materials upon which, political action must be carried out is a positive guarantee against the possibility that such action shall yield the results that were expected from it. This generalization could be illustrated by an indefinite number of instances drawn from history. Consider, for example, the results actually achieved by two reforms upon which well-intentioned people have placed the most enormous hopes—universal education and public ownership of the means of production. Universal education has proved to be the state's most effective instrument of universal regimentation and militarization, and has exposed millions, hitherto immune, to the influence of organized lying and the allurements of incessant, imbecile and debasing distractions. Public ownership of the means of production has been put into effect on a large scale only in Russia, where the results of the reform have been, not the elimination of oppression, but the replacement of one kind of oppression by another—of money power by political and bureaucratic power, of the tyranny of rich men by a tyranny of the police and the party.

For several thousands of years now men have been experimenting with different methods for improving the quality of human instruments and human material. It has been found that a good deal can be done by such strictly humanistic methods as the improvement of the social and economic environment, and the various techniques of character training. Among men and women of a certain type, startling results can be obtained by means of conversion and catharsis. But though these methods are somewhat more effective than those of the purely humanistic variety, they work only erratically and they do not produce the radical and permanent transformation of personality, which must take place, and take place on a very large scale, if political action is ever to produce the beneficial results expected from it. For the radical and permanent trans-

formation of personality only one effective method has been discovered
—that of the mystics. It is a difficult method, demanding from those
who undertake it a great deal more patience, resolution, self-abnegation
and awareness than most people are prepared to give, except perhaps in
times of crisis, when they are ready for a short while to make the most
enormous sacrifices. But unfortunately the amelioration of the world
cannot be achieved by sacrifices in moments of crisis; it depends on the
efforts made and constantly repeated during the humdrum, uninspiring
periods, which separate one crisis from another, and of which normal
lives mainly consist. Because of the general reluctance to make such
efforts during uncritical times, very few people are prepared, at any given
moment of history, to undertake the method of the mystics. This being
so, we shall be foolish if we expect any political action, however well
intentioned and however nicely planned, to produce more than a fraction
of the general betterment anticipated. Moreover, should the amount of
mystical, theocentric leaven in the lump of humanity suffer a significant
decrease, politicians may find it impossible to raise the societies they rule
even to the very moderate heights realized in the past.

Meanwhile, politicians can do something to create a social environment
favorable to contemplatives. Or perhaps it is better to put the matter
negatively and say that they can refrain from doing certain things and
making certain arrangements which are specially unfavorable.

The political activity that seems to be least compatible with theocentric
religion is that which aims at increasing a certain special type of social
efficiency—the efficiency required for waging or threatening large-scale
war. To achieve this kind of efficiency, politicians always aim at some
kind of totalitarianism. Acting like the man of science who can only deal
with the complex problems of real life by arbitrarily simplifying them
for experimental purposes, the politician in search of military efficiency
arbitrarily simplifies the society with which he has to deal. But whereas
the scientist simplifies by a process of analysis and isolation, the politician
can only simplify by compulsion, by a Procrustean process of chopping
and stretching designed to make the living social organism conform to a
certain easily understood and readily manipulated mechanical pattern.
Planning a new kind of national, military efficiency Richelieu set himself
to simplify the complexity of French society. That complexity was largely
chaotic, and a policy of simplification judiciously carried out by desirable
means would have been fully justified. But Richelieu's policy was not
judicious and, when continued after his death, resulted in the totalitarianism of Louis XIV—a totalitarianism which was intended to be as
complete as anything we see in the modern world, and which only failed

to be so by reason of the wretched systems of communication and organization available to the Grand Monarque's secret police. The tyrannical spirit was very willing, but, fortunately for the French, the technological flesh was weak. In an era of telephones, fingerprinting, tanks and machine guns, the task of a totalitarian government is easier than it was.

Totalitarian politicians demand obedience and conformity in every sphere of life, including, of course, the religious. Here, their aim is to use religion as an instrument of social consolidation, an increaser of the country's military efficiency. For this reason, the only kind of religion they favor is strictly anthropocentric, exclusive and nationalistic. Theocentric religion, involving the worship of God for his own sake, is inadmissible in a totalitarian state. All the contemporary dictators, Russian, Turkish, Italian and German, have either discouraged or actively persecuted any religious organization whose members advocated the worship of God, rather than the worship of the deified state or the local political boss.

Technological progress, nationalism and war seem to guarantee that the immediate future of the world shall belong to various forms of totalitarianism. But a world made safe for totalitarianism is a world, in all probability, made very unsafe for mysticism and theocentric religion. And a world made unsafe for mysticism and theocentric religion is a world where the only proved method of transforming personality will be less and less practiced, and where fewer and fewer people will possess any direct, experimental knowledge of reality to set up against the false doctrine of totalitarian anthropocentrism and the pernicious ideas and practices of nationalistic pseudo-mysticism. In such a world there seems little prospect that any political reform, however well intentioned, will produce the results expected of it.

The quality of moral behavior varies in inverse ratio to the number of human beings involved. Individuals and small groups do not always and automatically behave well. But at least they can be moral and rational to a degree unattainable by large groups. For, as numbers increase, personal relations between members of the group, and between its members and those of other groups, become more difficult and finally, for the vast majority of the individuals concerned, impossible. Imagination has to take the place of direct acquaintance, behavior motivated by a reasoned and impersonal benevolence, the place of behavior motivated by personal affection and a spontaneous and unreflecting compassion. But in most men and women reason, sympathetic imagination and the impersonal view of things are very slightly developed. That is why, among other reasons, the ethical standards prevailing within large groups, between large groups, and between the rulers and the ruled in a large group are generally lower than those prevailing within and among small groups. The art of what may be called "goodness politics," as opposed to power politics, is the art of organizing on a large scale without sacrificing the ethical values which emerge only among individuals and small groups. More specifically, it is the art of combining decentralization of government and industry, local and functional autonomy and smallness of administrative units with enough over-all efficiency to guarantee the smooth running of the federated whole. Goodness politics have never been attempted in any large society, and it may be doubted whether such an attempt, if made, could achieve more than a partial success, so long as the majority of individuals concerned remain unable or unwilling to transform their personalities by the only method known to be effective. But though the attempt to substitute goodness politics for power politics may never be completely successful, it still remains true that the methods of goodness politics combined with individual training in theocentric theory and contemplative practice alone provide the means whereby human societies can become a little less unsatisfactory than they have been up to the present. So long as they are not adopted, we must expect to see an indefinite continuance of the dismally familiar alternations between extreme evil and a very imperfect, self-stultifying good, alternations which constitute the history of all civilized societies. In a world inhabited by what the theologians call unregenerate, or natural men, church and state can probably never become appreciably better than the best of the states and churches, of which the past has left us the record. Society can never be greatly improved until such time as most of its members choose to become theocentric saints. Meanwhile, the few theocentric saints who exist at any given moment are able in some slight measure to qualify and mitigate the poisons which society generates within itself by its political and economic activities. In the gospel phrase, theocentric saints are the salt which preserves the social world from breaking down into irremediable decay.

IV

To be a seer is not the same thing as to be a mere spectator. Once the contemplative has fitted himself to become, in Lallemant's phrase, "a man of much orison," he can undertake work in the world with no risk of being thereby distracted from his vision of reality, and with fair hope of achieving an appreciable amount of good. As a matter of historical fact, many of the great theocentrics have been men and women of enormous and beneficent activity.

The work of the theocentrics is always marginal, is always started on the smallest scale and, when it expands, the resulting organization is always subdivided into units sufficiently small to be capable of a shared spiritual experience and of moral and rational conduct.

The first aim of the theocentrics is to make it possible for anyone who desires it to share their own experience of ultimate reality. The groups they create are organized primarily for the worship of God for God's sake. They exist in order to disseminate various methods (not all of equal value) for transforming the "natural man," and for learning to know the more-than-personal reality immanent within the leathery casing of selfhood. At this point, many theocentrics are content to stop. They have their experience of reality and they proceed to impart the secret to a few immediate disciples, or commit it to writing in a book that will be read by a wider circle removed from them by great stretches of space and time. Or else, more systematically, they establish small organized groups, a self-perpetuating order of contemplatives living under a rule. Insofar as they may be expected to maintain or possibly increase the number of seers and theocentrics in a given community, these proceedings have a considerable social importance. Many theocentrics, however, are not content with this, but go on to employ their organizations to make a direct attack upon the thorniest social problems. Such attacks are always launched from the margin, not the center, always (at any rate in their earlier phases) with the sanction of a purely spiritual authority, not with the coercive power of the state. Sometimes the attack is directed against economic evils, as when the Benedictines addressed themselves to the revival of agriculture and the draining of swamps. Sometimes, the evils are those of ignorance and the attack is through various kinds of education. Here again the Benedictines were pioneers. (It is worth remarking that the Benedictine order owed its existence to the apparent folly of a young man who, instead of doing the proper, sensible thing, which was to go through the Roman schools and become an administrator under the Gothic emperors, went away and, for three years, lived alone in a hole in the mountains. When he had become "a man of much orison," he emerged, founded monasteries and composed a rule to fit the needs to a self-perpetuating order of hard-working contemplatives. In the succeeding centuries, the order civilized northwestern Europe, introduced or re-established the best agricultural practice of the time, provided the only educational facilities then available, and preserved and disseminated the treasures of ancient literature. For generations Benedictinism was the principal antidote to barbarism. Europe owes an incalculable debt to the young man who, because he was more interested in knowing God than in getting on, or even "doing good," in the world, left Rome for that burrow in the hillside above Subiaco.)

Work in the educational field has been undertaken by many theocentric organizations other than the Benedictine order—all too often, unhappily, under the restrictive influence of the political, state-supported and state-supporting church. More recently the state has everywhere assumed the role of universal educator—a position that exposes governments to peculiar temptations to which sooner or later they all succumb, as we see at the present time, when the school system is used in almost every country as an instrument of regimentation, militarization and nationalistic propaganda. In any state that pursued goodness politics rather than power politics, education would remain a public charge, paid for out of the taxes, but would be returned, subject to the fulfillment of certain conditions, to private hands. Under such an arrangement, most schools would probably be little or no better than they are at present; but at least their badness would be variegated, while educators of exceptional originality or possessed of the gift of seership would be given opportunities for teaching at present denied them.

Philanthropy is a field in which many men and women of the margin have labored to the great advantage of their fellows. We may mention the truly astounding work accomplished by Father Joseph's contemporary, St. Vincent de Paul, a great theocentric, and a great benefactor to the people of seventeenth-century France. Small and insignificant in its beginnings, and carried on, as it expanded, under spiritual authority alone and upon the margin of society, Vincent's work among the poor did something to mitigate the sufferings imposed by the war and by the ruinous fiscal policy which the war made necessary. Having at their disposal all the powers and resources of the state, Richelieu and Father Joseph were able, of course, to do much more harm than St. Vincent and his little band of theocentrics could do good. The antidote was sufficient to offset only a part of the poison.

It was the same with another great seventeenth-century figure, George Fox. Born at the very moment when Richelieu was made president of the council and Father Joseph finally committed himself to the political life, Fox began his ministry the year before the Peace of Westphalia was signed. In the course of the next twenty years the Society of Friends gradually crystallized into its definitive form. Fanatically marginal—for when invited, he refused even to dine at Cromwell's table, for fear of being compromised—Fox was never corrupted by success, but remained to the end the apostle of the inner light. The society he founded has had its ups and downs, its long seasons of spiritual torpor and stagnation, as well as its times of spiritual life; but always the Quakers have clung to Fox's intransigent theocentrism and, along with it, to his conviction that, if it is to remain at all pure and unmixed, good must be worked for upon the margin of society, by individuals and by organizations small enough to be capable of moral, rational and spiritual life. That is why, in the two hundred and seventy-five years of its existence, the Society of Friends has been able to accomplish a sum of useful and beneficent work entirely out of proportion to its numbers. Here again the antidote has always been insufficient to offset more than a part of the poison injected into the body politic by the statesmen, financiers, industrialists, ecclesiastics and all the undistinguished millions who fill the lower ranks of the social hierarchy. But though not enough to counteract more than some of the effects of the poison, the leaven of theocentrism is the one thing which, hitherto, has saved the civilized world from total self-destruction. Father Joseph's hope of leading a whole national community along a political short cut into the kingdom of heaven on earth is illusory so long as the human instruments and material of political action remain untransformed. His place was with the antidote makers, not with those who brew the poisons.

What Can the Scientist Do?

From *Science, Liberty and Peace*

"Science" is an abstract word, and when we are trying to think about concrete political and economic problems, it is best to talk concretely, not of science but of the people who work in the various scientific fields, from the fields of uncontaminated theory and disinterested research into basic problems to those of applied science and technology. Assuming that the abolition of war is desirable, we proceed to ask ourselves how scientific workers can help to achieve this end.

1. As individuals or in organized groups, scientific workers can take three kinds of action against war. There is, first, the possibility of negative action in the form of a refusal, on conscientious grounds, to collaborate in any project whose purpose is the destruction or enslavement of human beings.

2. Negative action is good so far as it goes, but it needs to be supplemented by action of a positive and constructive kind. Such positive action may be classified under two heads: (a) action which takes its start in politics, to end in the field of science, and (b) action which takes its start in science, to end in politics.

a) In recent months several suggestions have been made for the political control, in the interests of humanity, of the activities of scientists and technologists. Thus, in the course of an interesting two-day debate in the House of Lords, Lord Vansittart urged the necessity of subjecting all German laboratories, whether attached to universities or supported by the state or by private industrialists, to strict supervision over a long term of years. Only in this way, he claimed, could the danger of a war of revenge, waged with new "secret weapons," be avoided. More realistically, Lord Brabazon proposed that this supervision of scientific developments should not be confined exclusively to the defeated nations—nations whose opportunities for the large-scale manufacture of new weapons would, for many years at least, be small. His suggestion was that, under the final peace treaties, an international committee of inspection should be constituted, having authority to enter laboratories and factories in any part of the world. In Lord Brabazon's view, the only alternative to such a scheme of international inspection would be an armament race between Britain and the United States on the one hand and the rest of the world on the other. By intensive research the Anglo-Saxon group might hope to obtain the lead in such a race, and so discourage attack by other powers. Lord Brabazon's speech was made before the dropping of the first atomic bomb. As things now stand, the United States and Britain already possess an enormous lead in the postwar armament race. For a few years they may keep that lead. Then other nations (unless, of course, they are previously blown to bits by the present possessors of the bomb, or unless reason, surrender of absolute sovereignty and world government come to replace nationalism) will be supplied by their scientists with the same or even better methods for manufacturing atomic missiles. Meanwhile the desirability of an international inspectorate charged with preserving humanity from the triumphs of science is even greater now than it was before Hiroshima. The existence of an international inspectorate would involve the adoption of another security measure, advocated in the course of the same debate by Lord Strabolgi—namely, the pooling of all scientific discoveries considered by competent experts to be actually or potentially a danger to mankind.

Similar suggestions have been made on the other side of the Atlantic, and it remains to be seen whether, and to what extent, the United Nations will act upon them. Meanwhile Messrs. Truman, Attlee and King have decided to keep such secrets as their scientists and engineers still possess until "enforcible safeguards" against their use for destructive purposes can be devised. What is to be the nature of those "enforcible safeguards"? As yet, it would seem, nobody has any very clear idea. In principle, the proposals for a pooling of dangerous knowledge and for an international inspectorate are excellent; and, to some, the theory of an "international police force" seems attractive and even workable. But, alas, from principle to application and from theory to practice the road is long and hard. Two disturbing questions inevitably propound themselves. First, will the various national governments concerned agree to act upon these suggestions? Second, if they do agree, will they and the men of science they employ consent to play the game according to the internationally imposed rules? In attempting to answer these questions one must weigh the power of enlightened self-interest against the power of nationalistic passions and prejudices. Enlightened self-interest will unquestioningly vote for world government, international inspection and the pooling of information. But unfortunately, in some of the most important issues of life, human beings do not act from considerations of enlightened self-interest. If they did, we should now be living in something very like paradise. In the field of international politics, as we have seen, the gravest decisions are always taken, not by reasonable adults but by boy gangsters. Despite the lessons of Hiroshima and Nagasaki, it is quite possible that some national governments will refuse to allow their laboratories and factories to be inspected—and, of course, the refusal of even one government will entail the general abandonment of the scheme. Alternatively, the principle of international inspection will be accepted; but at first some and then (when suspicion has been aroused) all the governments concerned will conspire with the scientists in their employ to carry on research in caves or forests or mountain fastnesses, where no prying eye can see what they are up to. It may perhaps seem unlikely that workers trained in the methods of science should support their political bosses in machinations so manifestly senseless, as well as immoral. But it is not because men have learned to behave rationally in the laboratory that they can be trusted to behave rationally toward foreigners and unpopular minorities, or even toward their own wives and children. Until a very few years ago the best scientific and technological education available was given in Germany; but most of the persons who received that education not only worked for the Nazi bosses, but believed in their doctrines and were swayed by the nationalistic passions which they so skillfully exploited. The case of Germany is not unique. In all countries nationalistic passions (of the same kind as were manifested in Germany, but at a somewhat lower level of intensity) are almost as common among scientists and technicians as in other classes of society. In spite of their training (perhaps, indeed, owing to the narrowly specialized character of that training, because of it), scientists and technicians are perfectly capable of the most dangerously irrational prejudice, nor are they immune to deceitful propaganda. The same men who reject as superstitious the belief in a transcendent and immanent spiritual Reality beyond and within phenomena prove by their actions that they find no difficulty in worshiping as a supreme god whichever one of the world's fifty-odd nations they happen to belong to, and in accepting the infallibility of the local Foreign Office and the quasi-divinity of the local political boss. In view of all this we need not be surprised if the plans for an international inspectorate and the pooling of scientific knowledge should fail in practice to produce the good results expected of them.

b) We must now consider the specifically scientific action which might be taken by men of science and technicians with a view to diminishing the probability of war and so to increasing the sum of human liberty. Such action can only be taken on the plane of applied science. Basic research is essentially disinterested. Men undertake it because, in the words used by the boy Clerk Maxwell, they want to find out "what's the go" of things—to discover how nature works and how its parts are related within a causal system. What is subsequently done with the results of disinterested research is something which the researcher cannot foresee, and for which he is not responsible. Thus, Clerk Maxwell's own adult curiosity to find out the go of such things as light and magnetism led him to certain conclusions, and these conclusions have since been utilized by technicians for the development of instruments, which are now used, in the main, for the dissemination of maudlin drama, cigarette advertising, bad music and government-sponsored or capitalist-sponsored propaganda. Clerk Maxwell would probably have been horrified by all these uses of the radio, and he is, of course, in no way to blame for them. In practice, it would seem, basic research cannot be planned, except perhaps to the extent of subsidizing inquiry into branches of knowledge which, for whatever reason, appear to have been unduly neglected. If the facilities for research are supplied, men and women with an overpowering desire to find out the go of things will always be forthcoming to make use of them. The planning of scientific activity with a view to achieving certain predetermined political, social and economic ends must begin at the point where the results of disinterested research are applied to the solution of practical problems. Individually and through their professional organizations, scientists and technicians could do a great deal to direct that planning toward humane and reasonable ends.

In theory everyone agrees that applied science was made for man and not man for applied science. In practice great masses of human beings have again and again been sacrificed to applied science. The conflict between science, as it has been applied up to the present, and human interests was clearly stated by Thorstein Veblen in his *Science in the Modern World*. In this essay Veblen distinguishes between what he calls the pragmatic and the scientific point of view. Pragmatically human beings know pretty well what is good for them, and have developed myths and fairly tales, proverbs and popular philosophies, behavior patterns and moralities, in order to illustrate and embody their findings about life. The findings of science—especially of science as applied for the benefit of the holders of centralized economic and political power—are frequently in conflict with humanity's pragmatic values, and this conflict has been and still is the source of much unhappiness, frustration and bitterness.

When science is applied in such a way as to create a form of production, which cannot be run efficiently without coming into sharp conflict with fundamental human values, and which therefore continually calls for the intervention of a governmental authority having power to "integrate" the conflicting persons and points of view, it may be fairly presumed that the application of the results of disinterested research has been, humanly speaking, misguided and undesirable. Up to the present time applied science has not been used mainly or primarily for the benefit of humanity at large, or (to put the matter less abstractly) for the benefit of individual men and women, considered as personalities each one of which is capable, given suitable material and social conditions, of a moral and spiritual development amounting, in some cases, to a total transfiguration; rather man has been used for applied science, for the technicians who enjoy designing more and more complicated gadgets, and for the financial and governmental interests which profit by the centralization of power. If applied science is henceforward to be used for man, technicians and scientists will have to adopt a professional policy, consciously and deliberately designed to serve fundamental human needs and to forward the causes of peace and personal liberty. Such a policy could not be worked out in detail except by an international organization of scientific workers, highly trained in their respective fields, so that each could contribute his or her share of skill or information toward the realization of the common end—namely, the welfare, liberty and peace of the individuals composing the human race. It would be absurd for me to try to anticipate the findings of this hypothetical group of experts; but it is possible, without too much presumption, to indicate in a general way a few of the lines which their discussion would have to follow.

Humanity's primary requirement is a sufficiency of food; but it is primarily by considerations of power that the policies of national governments are at present dictated. The ruling minorities of the world invariably contrive to have enough, and (to judge by the disgusting descriptions of recent diplomatic banquets) more than enough, to eat; consequently they tend to take food for granted and to think first, and at times almost exclusively, in terms of the questions: Who shall bully whom? But the great majority of the men, women and children on this planet are in no position to take food for granted. Their first and often their exclusive concern is the next meal. The question as to who shall bully whom is of hardly more than academic interest to them. They would like, of course, to be left in peace to go their own way; but they know by bitter experience that, under the present dispensation, there will always be a ruling minority to order them about, to bully and badger them in the name of the divine Nation, the omniscient Party, the sacred Principles of this or that political doctrine. They are therefore unable to take much interest in the national and international policies, which are the prime concern of the well-fed power lovers at the top of the social lovers at the top of the social pyramid.

At the San Francisco Conference the only problems discussed were problems of power. The basic problem of mankind—the problem of getting enough to eat—was relegated to an obscure international committee on agriculture. And yet it is surely obvious that if genuine international agreement is ever to be reached and preserved it must be an agreement with regard to problems which, first, are of vital interest to the great masses of humanity and which, second, are capable of solution without resort to war or the threat of war. The problems of power are primarily the concern of the ruling few, and the nature of power is essentially expansive, so that there is not the least prospect of power problems being solved, when one expanding system collides with another expanding system, except by means of organized, scientific violence or war. But war on the modern scale shatters the thin, precarious crust of civilization and precipitates vast numbers of human beings into an abyss of misery and slow death of moral apathy or positive and frenzied diabolism. If politicians were sincere in their loudly expressed desire for peace, they would do all they could to by-pass the absolutedly insoluble problems of power by concentrating all their attention, during international conferences and diplomatic discussions, on the one great problem which every member of the human race is concerned to solve—the one great problem which not only does not require military violence for its solution, but which, for the world at large, is wholly insoluble so long as the old games of militarism and power politics continue to be played. The first item on the agenda of every meeting between the representatives of the various nations should be: *How are all men, women and children to get enough to eat?*

It is fashionable nowadays to say that Malthus was wrong, because he did not foresee that improved methods of transportation can now guarantee that food surpluses produced in one area shall be quickly and cheaply transferred to another, where there is a shortage. But first of all, modern transportation methods break down whenever the power politicians resort to modern war, and even when the fighting stops they are apt to remain disrupted long enough to guarantee the starvation of millions of persons. And, secondly, no country in which population has outstripped the local food supply can, under present conditions, establish a claim on the surpluses of other countries without paying for them in cash or exports. Great Britain and the other countries in western Europe, which cannot feed their dense populations, have been able, in times of peace, to pay for the food they imported by means of the export of manufactured goods. But industrially backward India and China—countries in which Malthus' nightmare has come true with a vengeance and on the largest scale—produce few manufactured goods, consequently lack the means to buy from underpopulated areas the food they need. But when and if they develop mass-producing industries to the point at which they are able to export enough to pay for the food their rapidly expanding populations require, what will be the effect upon world trade and international politics? Japan had to export manufactured goods in order to pay for the food that could not be produced on the overcrowded home islands. Goods produced by workers with a low standard of living came into competition with goods produced by the better-paid workers of the West, and undersold them. The West's retort was political and consisted of the imposition of high tariffs, quotas and embargoes. To these restrictions on her trade Japan's answer was the plan for creating a vast Asiatic empire at the expense of China and of the Western imperialist powers. The result was war. What will happen when India and China are as highly industrialized as prewar Japan and seek to exchange their low-priced manufactured goods for food, in competition with Western powers, whose standard of living is a great deal higher than theirs? Nobody can foretell the future; but undoubtedly the rapid industrialization of Asia (with equipment, let it be remembered, of the very latest and best postwar design) is pregnant with the most dangerous possibilities.

It is at this point that internationally organized scientists and technicians might contribute greatly to the cause of peace by planning a world-wide campaign, not merely for greater food production, but also (and this is the really important point) for regional self-sufficiency in food production. Greater food production can be obtained relatively easily by the opening up of the earth's vast subarctic regions at present almost completely sterile. Spectacular progress has recently been made in this direction by the agricultural scientists of the Soviet Union; and presumably what can be done in Siberia can also be done in northern Canada.

The opening up of the Arctic will be undoubtedly a great good. But it will also be a great temptation for the power politicians—a temptation to exploit a natural monopoly in order to gain influence and finally control over hitherto independent countries, in which population has outstripped the food supply.

It would seem, then, that any scientific and technological campaign aimed at the fostering of international peace and political and personal liberty must, if it is to succeed, increase the total planetary food supply by increasing the various regional supplies to the point of self-sufficiency.

Recent history makes it abundantly clear that nations, as at present constituted, are quite unfit to have extensive commercial dealings with one another. International trade has always, hitherto, gone hand in hand with war, imperialism and the ruthless exploitation of industrially backward peoples by the highly industrialized powers. Hence the desirability of reducing international trade to a minimum, until such time as nationalist passions lose their intensity and it becomes possible to establish some form of world government. As a first step in this direction, scientific and technical means must be found for making it possible for even the most densely populated countries to feed their inhabitants. The improvement of existing food plants and domestic animals; the acclimatization in hitherto inhospitable regions of plants that have proved useful elsewhere; the reduction of the present enormous wastes of food by the improvement of insect controls and the multiplication of refrigerating units; the more systematic exploitation of seas and lakes as sources of food; the development of entirely new foods, such as edible yeasts; the synthesizing of sugars as a food for such edible yeasts; the synthesizing of chlorophyll so as to make direct use of solar energy in food production —these are a few of the lines along which important advances might be made in a relatively short time.

Hardly less important than regional self-sufficiency in food is self-sufficiency in power for industry, agriculture and transportation. One of the contributing causes of recent wars has been international competition for the world's strictly localized sources of petroleum, and the current jockeying for position in the Middle East, where all the surviving great powers have staked out claims to Persian, Mesopotamian and Arabian oil, bodes ill for the future. Organized science could diminish these temptations to armed conflict by finding means for providing all countries, whatever their natural resources, with a sufficiency of power. Water power has already been pretty well exploited. Besides, over large areas of the earth's surface there are no mountains and therefore no sources of hydroelectric power. But across the plains where water stands almost still, the air often moves in strong and regular currents. Small windmills have been turning for centuries; but the use of large-scale wind turbines is still, strangely enough, only in the experimental stage. Until recently the direct use of solar power has been impracticable, owing to the technical difficulty of constructing suitable reflectors. A few months ago, however, it was announced that Russian engineers had developed a cheap and simple method for constructing paraboloid mirrors of large size, capable of producing superheated steam and even of melting iron. This discovery could be made to contribute very greatly to the decentralization of production and population and the creation of a new type of agrarian society making use of cheap and inexhaustible power for the benefit of individual small holders or self-governing, co-operative groups. For the peoples of such tropical countries as India and Africa the new device for directly harnessing solar power should be of enormous and enduring benefit—unless, of course, those at present possessing economic and political power should choose to build mass-producing factories around enormous mirrors, thus perverting the invention to their own centralistic purposes, instead of encouraging its small-scale use for the benefit of individuals and village communities. The technicians of solar power will be confronted with a clear-cut choice. They can work either for the completer enslavement of the industrially backward peoples of the tropics, or for their progressive liberation from the twin curses of poverty and servitude to political and economic bosses.

The storage of the potentialities of power is almost as important as the production of power. One of the most urgent tasks before applied science is the development of some portable source of power to replace petroleum—a most undesirable fuel from the political point of view, since deposits of it are rare and unevenly distributed over the earth's surface, thus constituting natural monopolies which, when in the hands of strong nations, are used to increase their strength at the expense of their neighbors and, when possessed by weak ones, are coveted by the strong and constitute almost irresistible temptations to imperialism and war. From the political and human point of view, the most desirable substitute for petroleum would be an efficient battery for storing the electric power produced by water, wind or the sun. Further research into atomic structure may perhaps suggest new methods for the construction of such a battery.

Meanwhile it is possible that means may be devised, within the next few years, for applying atomic energy to the purposes of peace, as it is now being applied to those of war. Would not this technological development solve the whole problem of power for industry and transportation? The answer to this question may turn out to be simultaneously affirmative and negative. The problems of power may indeed be solved —but solved in the wrong way, by which I mean in a way favorable to centralization and the ruling minority, not for the benefit of individuals and co-operative, self-governing groups. If the raw material of atomic energy must be sought in radioactive deposits, occurring sporadically, here and there, over the earth's surface, then we have natural monopoly with all its undesirable political consequences, all its temptations to power politics, war, imperialistic aggression and exploitation. But of course it is always possible that other methods of releasing atomic energy may be discovered—methods that will not involve the use of uranium. In this case there will be no natural monopoly. But the process of releasing atomic energy will always be a very difficult and complicated affair, to be accomplished only on the largest scale and in the most elaborately equipped factories. Furthermore, whatever political agreements may be made, the fact that atomic energy possesses unique destructive potentialities will always constitute a temptation to the boy gangster who lurks within every patriotic nationalist. And even if a world government should be set up within a fairly short space of time, this will not necessarily guarantee peace. The Pax Romana was a very uneasy affair, troubled at almost every imperial death by civil strife over the question of succession. So long as the lust for power persists as a human trait—and in persons of a certain kind of physique and temperament this lust is overmasteringly strong—no political arrangement, however well contrived, can guarantee peace. For such men the instruments of violence are as fearfully tempting as are, to others, the bodies of women. Of all instruments of violence, those powered by atomic energy are the most decisively destructive; and for power lovers, even under a system of world government, the temptation to resort to these all too simple and effective means for gratifying their lust will be great indeed. In view of all this, we must conclude that atomic energy is, and for a long time is likely to remain, a source of industrial power that is, politically and humanly speaking, in the highest degree undesirable.

It is not necessary in this place, nor am I competent, to enter any further into the hypothetical policy of internationally organized science. If that policy is to make a real contribution toward the maintenance of peace and the spread of political and personal liberty, it must be patterned throughout along the decentralist lines laid down in the preceding discussion of the two basic problems of food and power. Will scientists and technicians collaborate to formulate and pursue some such policy as that which has been adumbrated here? Or will they permit themselves, as they have done only too often in the past, to become the conscious or unconscious instruments of militarists, imperialists and a ruling oligarchy of capitalistic or governmental bosses? Time alone will show. Meanwhile, it is to be hoped that all concerned will carefully consider a suggestion made by Dr. Gene Weltfish in the September, 1945, issue of the Scientific Monthly. Before embarking upon practice, all physicians swear a professional oath—the oath of Hippocrates—that they will not take improper advantage of their position, but always remember their responsibilities toward suffering humanity. Technicans and scientists, proposes

Dr. Weltfish, should take a similar oath in some such words as the following: "I pledge myself that I will use my knowledge for the good of humanity and against the destructive forces of the world and the ruthless intent of men; and that I will work together with my fellow scientists of whatever nation, creed or color for these our common ends."